George Tyler

Freshman

Class of '65

CHEMISTRY

Michell J. Sienko *Professor of Chemistry, Cornell University*

Robert A. Plane *Associate Professor of Chemistry, Cornell University*

NEW YORK   TORONTO   LONDON

CHEMISTRY SECOND EDITION

McGRAW-HILL BOOK COMPANY, INC.   1961

This book has been set
in Fotosetter Bodoni Book, a type face
derived from the designs
of the early-nineteenth-century
Parmese type founder, Giambattista Bodoni.
Heads are in italic Bodoni Bold and Futura Bold.
Felix Cooper made the illustrations.

Preface to the Second Edition

MODERN EMPHASIS ON THE STUDY OF PHYSICAL SCIENCES, particularly as presented in the years of preparatory schooling, has multiplied rather than diminished the problems encountered in the first-year college chemistry course. Perhaps the most serious of these problems is the increased divergence in student backgrounds. At the top, the class seems improved; at the bottom, weakened. Even among the average students, there appears a greater store of factual material but, paradoxically, less ability to understand and use it. The greater knowingness probably comes from more widespread exposure to the trappings of modern science; the greater helplessness, from a universal acceptance of smatterings at the expense of intellectual depth. In any case, many students do not want to think if they can get by with memorizing key words.

In writing this book we used a "principles" approach, an approach which encourages students to understand ideas instead of memorizing definitions. We also posed hundreds of problems that call for comprehension in their solution. In the revised edition, we have continued the emphasis on principles and problems. We believe that it is the best way to overcome the difficulty of increasingly divergent backgrounds.

In recognition of the disparate student preparation, we have introduced material to extend even the better student. In order to encourage less developed students to master essentials before getting involved, the more abstruse subjects are differentiated typographically by printing them in smaller type. As a further aid to these students, the discussions of difficult topics have been amplified.

The primary revision has been in the direction of extending the material in depth rather than scope. The sections on atomic and molecular structure now contain discussions of orbitals and molecular geometry. The material on changes of state and solution processes now includes some elementary ideas about the concept of entropy. Sections on aqueous solutions now include a consideration of buffers and an extended treatment of acids and bases. Chapters on descriptive chemistry now have separate sections reviewing the pertinent chemical reactions of qualitative analysis.

All the numerical problems have been changed (partly in order to neutralize the effect of solutions accumulated in fraternity files and partly in order to make available to teachers a bigger store of problems). Many stoichiometry and equilibrium calculations have been added as problems to the second half of the book in order to help make quantitative some of the descriptive chemistry.

It is a pleasure to record here our appreciation of the many kind and useful comments we have received from colleagues in the profession.

Michell J. Sienko
Robert A. Plane

Preface to the First Edition

THIS BOOK IS BASED ON THE LECTURES given in the large introductory chemistry course at Cornell University. Though offered in the College of Arts and Sciences, the course draws students about equally from the Colleges of Agriculture, Arts and Sciences, and Engineering. Some of the students have had no previous training in chemistry, while others have had extensive high-school preparation in the field. Our approach assumes no previous knowledge of the subject. Most of the students go on to take one or more additional chemistry courses; a few become chemistry majors; some get no further formal training in the field. To meet the needs of these diverse groups, we place great emphasis on the principles of chemistry, sometimes at the expense of descriptive details usually included in a first course. We feel this is justified since the student who has learned sufficient principles to use intelligently his textbook, a chemical handbook, or other reference work, is well equipped to apply his chemistry no matter what his future endeavor.

The book consists of two main sections. The first part is devoted to establishing the fundamental principles of chemistry at their present stage of development; the second part, to applying these principles to a discussion of the descriptive chemistry of the elements. Frequent cross references between sections, especially in the second half of the book, tie the parts together and encourage the student to review specific material pertinent to the discussion.

In Part I, the order is that of increasing complexity. We start with the isolated atom, discuss the nature of the chemical bond and of the states of matter, and culminate with chemical kinetics and chemical equilibrium. Most students come to chemistry with a rather hazy notion of the distinction between observed experimental fact and interpretation of that fact. To clarify the distinction, we present at the very beginning of Chap. 1 sufficient descriptive material on water, hydrogen, and oxygen to establish a basis for an atomic model of matter. Then, as the atomic model is developed, more descriptive material is woven in so that during the elaboration of principles, the student is frequently reminded of the fact that he is accounting for experimental observations.

In Part II, hydrogen, oxygen, and water are again discussed, but now in a framework based on the principles of Part I. Similar treatment is then given other elements, which are taken up as groups. Because the fundamental principles have been collected in Part I, it is possible for the instructor to make the discussion of any group as intensive as desired. (Material for extended discussion can be found in references listed in Appendix 9.) The order in which the groups are studied can be modified at the discretion of individual instructors. We have chosen to proceed from left to right through the periodic table because the chemistry of the alkali metals is relatively the simplest and because group similarities are the most pronounced. Also, in thus considering typical metallic behavior from the start, we avoid the necessity of interrupting discussion of a later group to introduce a description of metals. Such an interruption may encourage belief that there is a sharp break between nonmetallic and metallic behavior. Finally, we have found that an unbroken progression across the periodic table aids the student in learning the positions of elements in the table.

The growth of chemical knowledge has placed considerable pressure on the time available for descriptive chemistry in a first course. However, by making full use of the principles from Part I, such as oxidation potentials and equilibrium constants, we have been able to draw together a large body of descriptive material. The emphasis is on those topics which are most characteristic of a particular element. Considerable attention is given to its behavior in aqueous solutions. It is our conviction that, no matter what the student's future contact with chemistry, it will most probably concern aqueous solutions.

Throughout the book, the approach is quantitative. It is somewhat more rigorous than usual, since our basic philosophy is that the student should not be required to unlearn his freshman chemistry in later courses. Concepts of physics such as magnetism, spectra, and electrical conduction through matter are introduced at an elementary level, where they overlap the concepts of chemistry and where they are needed for an understanding of observed behavior. Topics which are known to be difficult, e.g., stoichiometry, hydrolysis, and oxidation-reduction, are given extended treatment. Many illustrative problems with detailed solutions are included in the text but set apart for easy reference. At the end of each chapter, there is given a large selection of study questions arranged approximately in order of increasing difficulty. Since in most cases numerical answers do not indicate the method of solution but rather serve as final checks for the student, answers have been supplied to many of the quantitative problems.

So far as specific points are concerned, it might be noted that we have postponed consideration of moles until Chap. 5. We do this because in our classes we have found that the student has less difficulty with the concept of gram-atoms than with the concept of moles. After thorough drill on the relation between atoms and gram-atoms, the step to moles is easily made. Furthermore, we have postponed consideration of the states of matter until after individual particles have been discussed. This order is one of increasing complexity and has the advantage of making possible for the states of matter immediate interpretation of their observed properties, including nonideal behavior, in terms of atoms and molecules. Such consideration of observation and theory aids the student in remembering the experimentally observed behavior of the solid, liquid, and gaseous states.

In our treatment of the important subjects of chemical kinetics (Chap. 12) and chemical equilibrium (Chap. 13), we have tried to be most careful in avoiding dangerous oversimplification. The topics have been clearly separated to point up the distinction between these two aspects of chemical reaction. In both cases, observations have been presented first and then their interpretation.

The fraction of time devoted to organic chemistry in different general-chemistry courses varies widely. In order to permit flexibility in extent of coverage, two separate organic sections are presented. Some instructors may choose to discuss only the section found in Chap. 24. The section is complete in itself and considers organic chemistry as a unique aspect of the group IV element carbon. Other instructors may choose a more extended treatment, which is made possible by the use of the additional material in Chap. 28. In our treatment of organic chemistry, we have kept to a minimum introduction of nomenclature but instead have emphasized those aspects which will give the student a feeling for the subject.

In writing this book, we have been guided by the observation that students respond to an intellectual challenge in proportion to the magnitude of the challenge. Furthermore, we have noted that student interest is greatest when the subject is most fundamental. Therefore, this book goes deeply into the fundamentals of chemistry and covers certain topics not normally discussed in elementary texts. We believe that this approach does not make the subject more difficult but actually makes it clearer.

We should like to acknowledge here the debt we owe to our teachers, especially Profs. W. C. Bray and Henry Taube, who stirred our interest in chemical research and in teaching others. We are indebted also to Profs. J. P. Hunt, Ogden Baine, J. F. Baxter, and M. L. Branin and to Mary Ann Allan for suggestions and to Carol Sienko for assistance in preparation of the manuscript.

Michell J. Sienko
Robert A. Plane

Contents

Acquisition of knowledge is simplified by seeking basic principles. In chemistry, the principles include generalizing statements that summarize observed phenomena and theories, or explanations, proposed to account for the observations. Recognition of the principles of chemistry increases the depth of understanding and serves as a convenient framework for remembering a large body of information and also as a firm basis from which to make predictions about the unknown.

I   *Principles of Chemistry*

1   *Methods of Chemistry*

THE WORD "SCIENTIST" evokes for most people one of two images. In one, a figure in white at a lab desk of impressive complexities stands ready to save humanity from nameless sufferings and to make the world a better place to live in; in the other, a muttering genius hunches over dimly seen instruments of doom. Neither of these is a correct portrait. Missing is the essential characteristic of all scientists—curiosity which cannot be confined by predetermined limits of prejudice.

Chemistry is the branch of science which seeks to answer the questions, What are substances composed of, how are their properties related to their composition, how does one substance interact with another? The answers to these questions are of interest to the chemist, not just because he is called on to make new plastics, alloys, and antibiotics, but because he wants to understand the world around him. In other professions, problems concerning chemistry occur repeatedly. The physician, for example, needs to be familiar with numerous chemical reactions that govern human life, as well as to know how they can be altered by chemical means. The engineer, whether he specializes in the civil, mechanical, or electrical aspects of his profession, deals with materials. He must know their properties and their behavior under varying conditions. For example, why does steel cor-

3

rode, and under what conditions does it corrode least rapidly? The agriculturist is faced with all these problems and more. Besides the chemistry of life processes and the chemical behavior of structural materials, he needs to understand the complex chemical make-up of soils and its influence on growing plants.

For anyone, the study of chemistry provides an understanding of the thought processes used in science. Like other scientists, the chemist seeks to understand a large number of observed facts in terms of a few broad principles. The uncovering of these principles is the ultimate aim of scientific research. Once the principles have been established, they not only account for experimental observations, but also make possible the systematic organization of knowledge and the prediction of behavior in new situations. However, these principles can be only as good as the experimental observations on which they are based.

In this chapter we shall first describe some of the observed facts of chemistry and then discuss the general methods used in the systematic investigation of chemical behavior. Because the substance water is so familiar, it is used to begin our discussion.

1.1   WATER

Water is one of the most plentiful and readily available of all chemicals; almost three-fourths of the earth's surface is covered with it. It is essential to life; two-thirds of the human body is water. It has special importance to the chemist because of its ability to dissolve so many other substances. As a result, water serves as a medium in which a great variety of chemical changes occur.

Liquid water can be poured from one container to another without change of volume, even though its shape changes in the process. *Retention of volume but not of shape* is characteristic of all liquids, and this property serves as a convenient criterion of the liquid state. In addition to having the general properties observed for all liquids, water has certain characteristic properties. For example, unlike most other liquids, it is colorless, odorless, and tasteless.* Its *density*, or *mass per unit volume*, is 1.0 g. per ml. (see Appendix 5 for an explanation of units). In contrast to this, the density of liquid mercury is 13.6 g. per ml. Further, water is characterized by the extent to which it conducts electric current. Compared with water, liquid mercury is a much better conductor, whereas alcohol is poorer.

The behavior of water just mentioned can be described *without refer-*

---

* It is possible that creatures from another planet might not have water as their body fluid, and they might find water to have an objectionable odor or taste.

ence to any other specific chemical substance. Such properties are usually called *physical properties.* Density, for example, is a physical property because it can be measured by using only devices for determining mass and volume. In contrast to physical properties are *chemical properties,* which describe the *reactions of a substance with other chemicals.* For example, when a piece of sodium is dropped into water, there is an immediate, vigorous interaction, and the sodium soon disappears. When a piece of iron is dropped into water, there is no reaction apparent until perhaps days later, when the iron is found to be corroded and covered with a reddish slime. These reactions of water with other chemicals represent chemical properties.

Less spectacular than the reaction of sodium with water is the reaction of table salt with water. When table salt and water are mixed, the salt disappears and is said to go into solution. The resulting solution looks very much like water, in that it is clear and colorless; however, it now has a salty taste, has a slightly higher density than the original water, and conducts electric current much better than pure water does. How much the properties are changed depends on how much salt is dissolved in the water. It is also observed that the water can be boiled off from the solution so as to restore the original salt. Apparently, the reaction of water with table salt is different from that with sodium, for, in the latter case, boiling off the water from the reacted mixture leaves a white powder quite unlike the original piece of sodium.

The properties just mentioned are those of water in the liquid state. If liquid water is allowed to stand in an open container, it slowly *evaporates,* i.e., passes into the gaseous state. If the evaporation is accompanied by bubbling, as when liquid water is heated, then the process is called *boiling.* In the gaseous state, water vapor behaves like all gases. It expands to fill the entire container in which it is held. When transferred to a different container, it *retains neither shape nor volume.* This behavior is unlike that of liquids and can be used to define gases.

When water vapor is cooled, it *condenses,* or *liquefies,* to form liquid water. Further cooling causes *freezing,* which produces ice. The change of state from liquid to solid is also called *solidification,* or *crystallization.* In general, the solid state is characterized by *retention of volume and shape.* No matter what container a piece of ice is placed in, it will have a fixed size and shape. In addition to having the general properties of solids, ice has its own characteristic properties. It is a very poor conductor of heat and electricity, even worse than liquid water. Its density is about 10 per cent less than that of liquid water, or 0.9 g. per ml. Under appropriate conditions, e.g., when a piece of ice has been partially melted, it is possible to have solid and liquid coexisting. The temperature at which this occurs is called the *melting point,* or *freezing point.*

In a mixture of ice and liquid water, there are some portions with the properties of ice and others with the properties of liquid water. Such a mixture is said to be *heterogeneous.* It consists of more than one phase where the term *phase* is used to represent *any region with a uniform set of properties.* A water-ice mixture is a two-phase system, no matter how many pieces of ice are present. All the pieces of ice have properties characteristic of ice and so constitute the ice phase. Similarly, all the liquid water constitutes one phase; it has one set of properties, or is *homogeneous.*

Although liquid water is homogeneous, it can be decomposed into simpler substances. Hence we say that water is composed of simpler substances, or that its composition is complex. Water can be decomposed by using the apparatus shown in Fig. 1.1. The battery is connected by means of wires to two platinum plates (electrodes), which dip into the water. (It helps to have some sulfuric acid in the water, but the acid remains unchanged at the end of the experiment and may be disregarded.) As the experiment proceeds, bubbles of gas form on the electrodes. The gas that forms on one electrode is different from that on the other, as may be shown by the fact that one burns in air while the other does not. If the two gases are mixed and ignited, water is re-formed. The conclusion is that each of the two gases is of simpler composition than the water. Since these gases *cannot be decomposed by chemical reaction into substances of simpler composition,* they are considered to be elementary substances, or *elements.* One of the gases is the elementary substance hydrogen, and the other, oxygen.

At the present time there are only a few more than 100 elements. Each of these can be isolated, at least in principle, as a pure substance with a characteristic set of properties. All other substances are combinations of two or more such elements. Elements are often represented by *symbols.* For example, H is the symbol for the element hydrogen and O for the element oxygen. In many cases, the symbol is just the first letter of the name of the

Fig. 1.1   *Decomposition of water.*

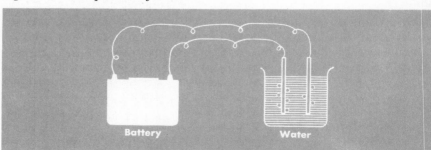

Battery   Water

element. In other cases, two letters are required, as in He for helium. Sometimes, the symbols come from Latin names of the elements. As an example, the symbol Na for the element sodium comes from the Latin name *natrium*. A list of all the elements and their symbols is given inside the back cover of the book.

Complex substances such as water can be decomposed into their constituent elements. When this is done for water, it is always found that 11.19 per cent of the weight shows up as hydrogen and 88.81 per cent as oxygen. In other words, the composition of water is fixed—11.19 per cent hydrogen and 88.81 per cent oxygen—no matter where the sample comes from. Furthermore, the same result is obtained if part of the sample is frozen and only the liquid water is analyzed. Complex substances showing this constancy of composition are called *compounds*. They have a fixed composition which is the same for all samples and which does not vary when part of the sample undergoes a change of state as from liquid to solid. At the present time there are recognized over half a million distinct compounds. They are frequently represented by *formulas*, which are combinations of the symbols of the constituent elements. The formula for the compound water is H_2O; for table salt or sodium chloride, NaCl; for sulfuric acid, H_2SO_4.* The full significance of chemical formulas will be discussed in Chap. 5.

Solutions, such as NaCl dissolved in H_2O, are also complex substances which can be decomposed into their constituent elements. However, solutions differ from compounds in that their composition is variable, not only from sample to sample, but also when part of a sample undergoes a change in state. For example, practically an infinite number of different solutions can be obtained from NaCl and H_2O by changing the relative amounts of NaCl and H_2O used to make up the solution. Each of these solutions has its own composition, which, however, can change when part of the solution is put through a change of state. Specifically, if some salt water is partially frozen, the solid formed is pure H_2O. Consequently, the composition of the remaining solution has changed; it is now richer in NaCl. Of course, if a sample of salt water is *completely* frozen, the composition of the sample does not change, because all the salt and water present in the initial solution are now found in the solid state as a mixture of ice and salt crystals. The composition of solutions can be specified by indicating what percentage of the total weight is contributed by each component. For example, a certain solution may be designated as 1 per cent NaCl and 99 per cent H_2O.

---

* Although it may not seem true, there is a somewhat systematic way of naming compounds, which is outlined in Appendix 1. To help establish familiarity with some common chemicals, their names and formulas are given when they are first met.

1.2 HYDROGEN AND OXYGEN

In addition to their presence in water, the elements hydrogen and oxygen each occur in many other compounds. For example, hydrogen is found in *acids,* compounds which in water solution have a *sour taste* and cause the purple dye *litmus to turn red.* Hydrogen also occurs combined with the element carbon in a great variety of compounds called hydrocarbons. These hydrocarbons occur in nature as coal and petroleum. Compounds related to the hydrocarbons make up all living matter.

Oxygen is the most abundant element on the surface of the earth. About 15 per cent of this oxygen occurs as water. The rest is found in rocks, in living organisms, and in the atmosphere. Most rocks are complex substances consisting mainly of combinations of oxygen with the elements silicon and aluminum. There are some minerals which are simple *oxides, i.e., compounds of oxygen and one other element.* Examples of such minerals are sand, which is silicon dioxide (SiO_2), and the red oxide of iron (Fe_2O_3).

When a small amount of hydrogen is desired, as for laboratory use, it is conveniently prepared from an acid. If a metal such as zinc is dropped into a solution of acid, hydrogen gas bubbles off. Another convenient method of preparation is the liberation of hydrogen from water by sodium, but the reaction is dangerous because the hydrogen evolved frequently catches fire. In large amounts, it is cheaper to prepare hydrogen by decomposing water with an electric current. The process, called *electrolysis* of water, is similar to that described in Fig. 1.1.

In the laboratory, oxygen is usually made from potassium chlorate ($KClO_3$). When heated, this white solid decomposes to give oxygen gas and leaves behind a new white solid, which is potassium chloride (KCl). It is found experimentally that, when a small amount of finely powdered manganese dioxide (MnO_2) is added to $KClO_3$, the formation of oxygen is speeded up. When the reaction is finished, the black manganese dioxide remains. Substances which *accelerate chemical reaction without being used up themselves* are called *catalysts.* Commercially, oxygen is obtained from water by electrolysis or from the atmosphere by partial evaporation of liquid air. In the latter process, air is first liquefied by cooling and compression. The liquid air so obtained is a solution consisting mainly of nitrogen and oxygen. As evaporation proceeds, the nitrogen tends to evaporate first, and the liquid phase becomes richer in oxygen. Oxygen of 99 per cent purity can be made in this way.

At room temperature, hydrogen and oxygen are both colorless and odorless gases. They can be bubbled through water without loss, because neither dissolves in water to any appreciable extent. Hydrogen gas is about one-fourteenth as dense as air; oxygen gas is very slightly more dense than air. At very low temperatures, both elements can exist as liquids or even as solids. Chemically, hydrogen and oxygen are quite different from each other. For example, a feebly burning match thrust into a bottle of hydrogen causes the hydrogen to catch fire at the mouth of the bottle; in a bottle of oxygen, the match itself flares brightly. In the first experiment, water is formed by combination of the hydrogen in the bottle with oxygen from the air; in the second, carbon and hydrogen from the match stick combine with the oxygen in the bottle to form carbon dioxide (CO_2) and water. Mixtures of hydrogen and oxygen gas can be exploded, sometimes with dangerous violence.

Hydrogen combines chemically with practically all the other elements. With chlorine, it forms the gas hydrogen chloride (HCl), which in water solution is called hydrochloric acid. With nitrogen, hydrogen forms ammonia (NH_3), a gas at room temperature. Ammonia dissolves in water to give a solution which, as we shall see later, does not have acid properties despite the presence of hydrogen in NH_3. With carbon, hydrogen is combined in a whole series of hydrocarbons. Probably most familiar of these is methane (CH_4), the principal component of natural gas. With metals such as sodium, hydrogen forms brittle, saltlike compounds called hydrides. Sodium hydride, NaH, for example, is a white, crystalline solid which reacts with water to liberate hydrogen gas.

Oxygen also combines chemically with practically all the other elements. In the simplest of its compounds, the oxides, oxygen is associated with only one other element. One such oxide is carbon dioxide, the solid form of which is familiar as dry ice. Another is calcium oxide (CaO), commonly called lime. The properties of one oxide may be quite different from those of another. For example, CO_2 is a gas at room temperature which dissolves in water to give an acid solution; CaO is a white solid of very high melting point which also dissolves in water, but the solution (called limewater) is not acidic. Instead of turning litmus red and having a sour taste, limewater turns litmus blue and has a bitter taste and a characteristic slippery feel. Furthermore, when limewater is added to an acidic solution, the acid properties are destroyed; it is said that the acid is *neutralized*. Solutions which, like limewater, *turn litmus blue* and have the ability to *neutralize acids* are said to be *alkaline*, or *basic*. When a basic solution is mixed with an acidic solution in proper proportion, the alkaline properties and the acid properties disappear. If the resulting solution is evaporated, a solid is left. Such *compounds which result from acid-base neutralization* are called *salts*. Calcium sulfate ($CaSO_4$), for instance, is a salt that can be formed by neutralizing sulfuric acid with limewater.

In addition to the oxides, oxygen forms compounds in which it is combined with two or more other elements. Such compounds are called *oxy compounds*. Both sulfuric acid (H_2SO_4) and calcium sulfate ($CaSO_4$) are examples. An important class of oxycompounds are the *hydroxy compounds*, which contain hydrogen, oxygen, and at least one other element. They can often be made by the reaction of an oxide with water. For example, when calcium oxide is treated with a limited amount of water, the product is solid calcium hydroxide [$Ca(OH)_2$], sometimes called slaked lime. Although a solution of calcium hydroxide is alkaline, not all hydroxy compounds give alkaline solutions. Solutions of lye, i.e., sodium hydroxide ($NaOH$), are basic, but solutions of the hydroxy compounds ethyl alcohol (C_2H_5OH) and sulfuric acid (H_2SO_4) are not. For convenience, the term *hydroxide* is applied to hydroxy compounds which give basic solutions.

Oxygen's abundance in the atmosphere and its ability to combine with other elements account for its role in the important processes of combustion, corrosion, and respiration. In *combustion*, oxygen reacts with other substances to liberate heat and light. Most common fuels such as coal, petroleum, and wood are hydrocarbons or their derivatives. When they burn, oxygen from the air combines with the hydrogen and carbon to form water and oxides of carbon. In rusting, perhaps the most important case of *corrosion*, oxygen from the air attacks iron in the presence of water to form a complicated oxide of iron. In *respiration*, oxygen is taken in by a living organism and used in chemical reactions with food to produce heat necessary for the life process. In many respects, the utilization of food is like a combustion (e.g., the final products are water and carbon dioxide), but apparently it is more complex, because it occurs slowly and at temperatures much below those of ordinary burning. Before we can hope to understand complicated processes such as these, we must first study simple chemical change in a thorough, systematic manner.

1.3   MEASUREMENT

In the preceding discussion, the descriptions were in almost every case *qualitative*, i.e., *specified as to kind but not to amount*. As opposed to qualitative properties, which are described without the use of numbers, there are also *quantitative* properties, which give a *description in terms of numbers*. Since properties of substances frequently differ only in degree, their systematic comparison demands quantitative measurement.

In order to measure properties, it is necessary to set up *units*, or standards of comparison. In the English system, a familiar unit of length is the inch; of volume, the quart; and of mass, the pound. In the metric system, commonly used in chemistry, corresponding units are the centimeter (cm.), the liter (1.), and the gram (g.). It is convenient to remember that 1 in. is about 2.5 cm., 1 qt. is about 1 liter, and 1 lb. is about 500 g. More precise conversion factors are given in Appendix 5.

In any quantitative description it is desirable to give the maximum amount of information. This implies specification of the magnitude of the quantity and an indication of the limits of uncertainty of the measurement. Thus, for example, the weight of a sample may be given as 136.2 ± 0.1 g. Such notation indicates that the reported value 136.2 g. has been measured to the nearest tenth of a gram. For convenience, the $\pm\ 0.1$ is often omitted with the understanding that there is uncertainty in the last digit. *Numbers which express the result of a measurement such that only the last digit is in doubt* are called *significant figures.*

The number of significant figures used to express a measured result depends on how precisely the measuring instrument is calibrated. This is illustrated by the example in Fig. 1.2. What can be determined, by measurement, about the length of line *AB?* The upper ruler gives 4.6 cm.; the line is certainly between 4 and 5 cm. and appears to be about six-tenths of the way from 4 to 5. The lower ruler gives 4.63 cm.; the line is certainly between 4.6 and 4.7 cm. and appears to be about three-tenths of the way from 4.6 to 4.7. The first measurement (4.6 cm.) has two significant figures; the second measurement (4.63 cm.) has three significant figures. Because of the difference in the two measuring instruments, there are two ways of ex-

Fig. 1.2   Accuracy of line measurement to illustrate significant figures.

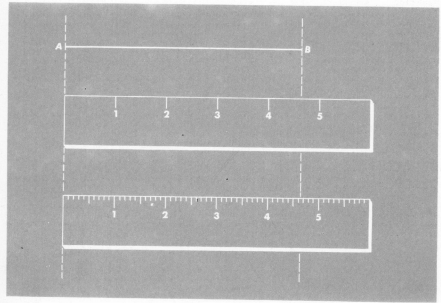

pressing the length of the same line. These represent different degrees of precision. The first measurement, 4.6 cm., is precise to 1 part in 46, or approximately 2 per cent. The second, 4.63 cm., is precise to 1 part in 463, or about 0.2 per cent.*

Understanding significant figures is important in calculations involving measured quantities. For example, adding a 0.101-cm. line to a 4.63-cm. line does not give one 4.731 cm. long, but rather 4.73 cm. long. This is true because the measurement 4.63 cm. specifies nothing about the third decimal place. The measurement is not precise enough to distinguish between 4.630 cm. and 4.633 cm., for instance. When 0.101 cm. is added, the total length might be 4.731 cm. or 4.734 cm. To keep from giving any misinformation, the total length should be stated as 4.73 cm. Similarly, in calculating the area of a square measured to be 1.2 cm. on edge, the result should be specified not as 1.44 sq. cm. but as 1.4 sq. cm. Since the edge is known only to 1 part in 12, or about 8 per cent, the area cannot possibly be calculated to 1 part in 144, or 0.7 per cent. A simple rule that usually holds is that the number of significant figures resulting from multiplication or division of measured quantities is the same as the number of significant figures in the least precisely known quantity. In rounding off answers to get the proper number of significant figures, the usual convention is to increase the last significant digit if the following discarded digit is five or greater. For example, to two significant figures the number 0.011863 is 0.012. Zeros used only to show the position of a decimal point are not counted as significant figures.

There is a somewhat special problem associated with exact numbers that are not the result of measurement. For example, by definition of the centigrade scale of temperature the freezing point of water is taken to be exactly zero degrees. This zero is an exact number to as many decimal places as desired and can be written 0.00000 *ad infinitum.* Similarly, there are exactly 12 in. in a foot by definition. The number 12 has complete certainty and so may be followed by as many zeros beyond the decimal point as wished. Occasionally, exact numbers arise even from measurement, as in counting discrete objects. For example, the number of men on a football team is 11 and not 11.26 or some other fractional number.

The numbers obtained in chemical measurements vary from extremely large to extremely small. To save writing many zeros, it is convenient to express such numbers as powers of 10. For example, 10,000,000 can be written as 1×10^7 and 36,000,000 as 3.6×10^7. Similarly, 0.000036 can

---

* The somewhat risky assumption has been made here that both the measuring devices are accurately, or correctly, ruled. If they are not, the measurements made may be quite inaccurate. It should be emphasized that the word precision connotes nothing about accuracy and merely raises the question of the degree of detail—that is, the $\pm$ uncertainty—involved in the measurements.

be written as 3.6×10^{-5}. In forming 3.6×10^{-5} from 0.000036, the decimal point has been moved five places to the right as indicated by the exponent -5. Rules for arithmetic manipulation of exponential numbers are given in Appendix 2. Since zeros used to indicate the position of a decimal point may or may not be significant, powers of 10 can be used to remove ambiguity. Thus, 100 may have one, two, or three significant figures. If 100 is known to three significant figures, it is better written as 1.00×10^2. The only excuse for writing the two zeros in 1.00×10^2 is to indicate that these digits are known to be zero. If 100 has two significant figures, it is written 1.0×10^2.

1.4   METHODS OF SCIENCE

Science starts with observation. *Observed facts,* be they qualitative or quantitative, are called *data,* and the descriptions given previously of the behavior of water, hydrogen, and oxygen are examples of data. Over the years the data accumulated has reached staggering proportions, but still a chemist must have a working knowledge of a good share of these. To remember data as isolated facts is practically impossible. Fortunately, most data can be ordered in terms of simple summarizing statements. Such *statements describing the general behavior of nature* are called *laws.*

Natural laws, which may be qualitative statements or mathematical formulas, describe observed phenomena. This is in contrast to man-made laws which require or prohibit. A familiar example of a natural law is the law of gravity, which states that the force of attraction between two bodies is directly proportional to the product of their masses and inversely proportional to the square of the distance between them. (Mathematical methods of expressing proportionality are given in Appendix 3.1.) Less familiar examples of laws are those which describe the behavior of gases. For example, all gases can be compressed, and Boyle's law states that their volume is inversely proportional to the pressure exerted on them. It should be noted that neither the law of gravity nor Boyle's law gives reasons for natural behavior but simply states what the behavior is.

An essential quality of man is his curiosity, and once he has learned facts, he wants to know why they are so. Why, for example, are all gases compressible? At this point, the scientist departs from observations and begins to make guesses. In accounting for the compressibility of gases, he assumes that all gases consist of submicroscopic particles (called molecules) with relatively large spaces between them. When a gas is compressed, the molecules are pushed closer together. Such a model for a gas is an example of a *theory*. In general, any theory is an *explanation of observed behavior in terms of a simple model which has familiar properties.* The observed facts are thus "explained," but only in the sense that they are made plausible by being related to simpler or more familiar phenomena. Since it is a product of the mind, theory is not infallible. It may have to be modified or even completely discarded in the light of further experiments.

Once a model has been proposed to account for some observations, it may be possible to predict from the model behavior which has not been previously investigated. New experiments can be performed which test the validity of the model and incidentally uncover new facts. Thus, theories serve as a stimulus for the growth of science.

In the previous discussion of hydrogen and oxygen (Sec. 1.2), full use was not made of the powerful methods of science. Only isolated facts were presented with no mention of the basic laws of chemistry, and no theories were presented to explain them. However, even the few facts presented raise many broad questions. For example, which elements react with each other? Why does reaction occur? When reaction occurs, how fast does it proceed and to what extent? What is the fundamental nature of matter? In later sections we investigate these questions in terms of the laws and theories which constitute the principles of chemistry.

1.5   MATTER AND ENERGY

The physical universe is composed entirely of matter and energy, which together are the basis of all objective phenomena. *Matter* is usually defined as anything that *has mass and occupies space.* The term *mass* describes the tendency of an object to remain at rest if it is stationary or to continue in motion if it is already moving. The mass of an object can be determined by measuring the force with which it is attracted to the earth, i.e., by measuring its *weight.* Because the force of gravity is not the same at every point of the earth's surface, the weight of an object is not constant.* However, the *mass* of an object is constant and can be determined by comparing its weight with that of a known mass; this may be done, for example, by means of a chemical balance (Fig. 1.3).

Energy is usually defined as the *capacity to do work,* where *work* means the moving of matter against an opposing force. Anything which has the capacity to push matter from one place to another has energy. This energy may be either kinetic or potential. The term *kinetic* is derived from the Greek word for motion, and *kinetic energy* is that energy *intrinsic in an object which has motion.* A moving truck, for example, has the capacity to

---

* For example, an object weighing 1.00000 lb. in Panama weighs 1.00412 lb. in Reykjavik, Iceland.

Fig 1.3   Chemical balance with unknown mass on left pan and known mass on right.

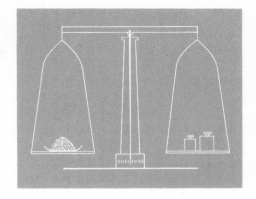

push over a telephone pole just because the truck is moving. The amount of kinetic energy a body possesses is equal to one-half its mass times the square of its speed, or $(\frac{1}{2})ms^2$. *Potential energy* is "stored" energy intrinsic in an object not because of its motion but because of its *position with respect to other objects.*

The choice of arrangement that corresponds to zero potential energy is arbitrary. For example, consider a book held above the floor. When the book is dropped to the floor, work is done. We say that the initial system (book above the floor) has higher potential energy than the final system (book on the floor), because it has more capacity to do work. If we arbitrarily label the final system as having zero potential energy, then the initial system has a positive value of the potential energy. In so doing, we must appreciate that we have set an arbitrary zero. We can get more work out of the book by dropping it through a hole cut in the floor. It will reach a position of lower potential energy, a position of negative potential energy on the scale that assigns the zero point to the book-on-the-floor position.

In any system, the total energy present is distributed partly as kinetic energy and partly as potential energy. Some familiar forms of both kinetic and potential energy are mechanical energy (e.g., a falling rock), heat, light, sound, electric energy, and chemical energy. These may be transformed one into another, and it is usually these transformations which are observed. For example, the energy of a falling rock may be converted partially into sound when the rock is stopped. The explosions and fireballs that accompany certain chemical reactions represent transformations in which part of the chemical energy is converted into other forms of energy, such as heat, light, and sound. In any energy transformation the total energy remains the same. This is consistent with the *law of conservation of energy*, which states that the *total energy of the universe is constant.*

Chemical reaction is a transformation in which substances are converted into other substances, i.e., one form of matter is changed to another. For example, the element zinc (Zn) reacts with the element sulfur (S) to form the compound zinc sulfide (ZnS). In shorthand form, this can be written

$$Zn + S \rightarrow ZnS$$

where the arrow is read "reacts to give." Associated with this transformation of matter is a transformation of energy. The chemical energy of the zinc and the sulfur when uncombined is greater than the chemical energy of the zinc sulfide. Most of this difference in energy shows up in the form of heat liberated as the reaction proceeds. Chemical reactions in which heat is liberated are said to be *exothermic.* There are some chemical reactions in which the final state is higher in chemical energy than the initial state. In such cases, when reaction occurs, energy must be supplied. This is usually in the form of heat absorbed from the surroundings. Reactions which use up heat are called *endothermic.*

In addition to transformations from one form of energy to another and transformations from one form of matter to another, it is possible to transform matter into energy and vice versa. It is believed that the sun's energy comes from a conversion of hydrogen into other elements with a net loss of mass. Apparently, in the sun, mass is changed into energy, just as it is in the hydrogen bomb. However, these transformations occur to an appreciable extent only under drastic conditions, e.g., at extremely high temperature. In ordinary chemical reactions change of mass is so slight as to be undetectable. According to the theory developed by Einstein, mass is another manifestation of energy, and the equivalence is expressed by the relation $E = mc^2$, where E is the energy change in ergs (see Appendix 4.3) associated with the mass change m in grams and c is the speed of light, 3×10^{10} cm. per sec. In its broadest sense, the law of conservation of energy includes mass as a form of energy.

1.6   HEAT AND TEMPERATURE

Frequently, there is confusion of the concepts of heat and temperature. *Heat* is measured as a *quantity of energy,* whereas *temperature* describes the *intensity of heat,* or hotness. The distinction may be made clear by considering that a burning match and a bonfire can be at the same temperature, but there is certainly much more heat in a bonfire. The difference can also be illustrated by noting that a given quantity of heat will raise the temperature of a small amount of water more than it will raise the temperature of a large amount of water.

Temperature can also be defined as the property which fixes the direction of heat flow, in the sense that heat always flows from a body at high temperature to a body at low temperature. Qualitatively, a hot body has a high temperature, and a colder body has a lower temperature. Quantitatively, temperature is frequently measured by taking advantage of the fact that most substances expand as they get hot. The mercury thermometer is

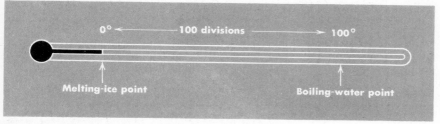

Fig 1.4 *Centigrade scale on mercury thermometer.*

a temperature-measuring device which works because the volume occupied by mercury increases as its temperature increases. As shown in Fig. 1.4, the sensing bulb contains a large volume of mercury which on expansion can move into a capillary. The volume of the capillary is much less than the volume of the bulb, so that a small expansion of the mercury causes a large movement of the mercury thread. The centigrade scale of temperature is defined by placing the thermometer in melting ice and marking the point at which the mercury thread stops as 0°C. When the thermometer is placed in boiling water, the mercury expands and the thread moves to a new position, which is marked as 100°C. The space between is divided into 100 equal parts. The Fahrenheit scale differs in that the ice point is marked 32° and the boiling point 212°, with 180 equal divisions between them. To convert from Fahrenheit temperature to centigrade temperature, we subtract 32 from the Fahrenheit reading and multiply the result by $\frac{5}{9}$.

To measure heat quantitatively, we use the *calorie*. This unit is the amount of heat required to change the temperature of 1 g. of water 1° on the centigrade scale.* The burning of a match liberates approximately 500 cal. It is sometimes more convenient to use the *kilocalorie*, which, as the name implies, is equal to 1000 cal. The kilocalorie is often abbreviated as kcal. The so-called "big calorie," or Calorie, used in nutrition is actually the kilocalorie.

QUESTIONS

In working through these questions, bear in mind that the final answer is not so important as the reasoning used to obtain it. It is a good idea in the solution of any numerical problem to write out the steps followed in logically arriving at the result.

1.1 *States of matter.* How could you demonstrate experimentally that a gas differs

---

* Actually the amount of heat required to change the temperature of a gram of water by one degree depends slightly on what the temperature of the water is. One generally uses the "15° calorie" defined in the interval 14.5 to 15.5°C.

from the other states of matter in that it retains neither shape nor volume? Be specific.

1.2   Compound. (*a*) What evidence is there that hydrogen and oxygen are of simpler composition than water? (*b*) Discuss whether your answer to (*a*) proves that hydrogen and oxygen are elements.

1.3   Phase. Tell what are the phases in each of the following: (*a*) a balloon half-filled with salt solution; (*b*) a bowl of punch containing 14 cherries, 2 slices of pineapple, and a cake of ice; (*c*) two pieces of Swiss cheese; (*d*) contents of the beaker in Fig. 1.1.

1.4   Solution. Given two liquid samples: One is a pure compound, the other a solution. How could you experimentally distinguish between them?

1.5   Significant figures. Calculate to the proper number of significant figures: (*a*) the altitude of a mountain peak which is 6,742.3 ft. above a lake which has an elevation of 913 ft.; (*b*) the area of a circle of radius 2.40 cm.; (*c*) the volume of a cube with edge 2.4 cm.   *Ans.* 7,655 ft.; 18.1 sq. cm.; 14 cu. cm.

1.6   Exponential numbers. Express as powers of 10: (*a*) 96,501; (*b*) 0.000000-00749; (*c*) 22,400; (*d*) 206 million millions.

1.7   Terms. Tell what is meant by each of the following: acid, base, salt, hydroxide, hydroxy compound, electrolysis, catalyst, endothermic, density, temperature.

1.8   Energy. How does the experiment illustrated in Fig. 1.1 represent the interconversion of various forms of energy?

1.9   Hydrogen and oxygen. Compare and contrast hydrogen and oxygen with respect to occurrence, preparation, properties, and compounds formed.

1.10   Significant figures and exponential numbers. To the proper number of significant figures, carry out the following operations: (*a*) $2.06 \times 10^{32} + 2.06 \times 10^{33}$; (*b*) $2.73 \times 10^{-8} - 3.20 \times 10^{-9}$; (*c*) $8.04 \times 10^{-9} \div 2.00 \times 10^{-23}$.

1.11   Scientific method. (*a*) What is the difference between "theory" and "law" as used in chemistry? (*b*) Discuss critically the following: "When a theory has been tested repeatedly and found to be true, it becomes a law."

1.12   Heat. How much heat is required to warm (*a*) 934 g. of water from 9 to 21°C? (*b*) 49 g. of water from 2 to 49°C?   *Ans.* 11 kcal.; 2.3 kcal.

1.13   Energy. Describe the interconversion of potential and kinetic energy in the following: (*a*) bouncing ball; (*b*) burning candle; (*c*) electric water pump.

1.14   Density and significant figures. Show how significant figures are important in calculating the density of a liquid from the following data:

Weight of container	102.6 g.
Weight of container and liquid	126.598 g.
Volume of liquid	30.00 ml.

1.15 *Heat.* Devise an experiment to determine the number of calories liberated by the burning of a match. Indicate quantities measured and method of calculation.

1.16 *Density.* A tank contains: (*a*) an iron ball of radius 2.00 cm. and density 7.86 g. per cc.; (*b*) an aluminum rod 28.0 cm. long and 3.00 cm. in radius with density 2.70 g. per cc.; (*c*) 6.05 liters (1 liter is 1,000 cc.) of water of density 0.998 g. per cc. Calculate the average density of matter in the tank.

Ans. 1.23 g./cc.

2   *Nature of Matter*

IN ORDER TO UNDERSTAND THE NATURE OF MATTER, it is necessary to have an acceptable theory—a theory that accounts for both qualitative and quantitative observations of matter and its behavior. Historically, observations of chemical reaction were most significant in the development of a satisfactory theory of the nature of matter. These observations of chemical reaction are summarized in certain broad statements known as the laws of chemical change. In this chapter we consider three such laws and show how they are accounted for by assuming that matter is made up of atoms.

2.1   CONSERVATION OF MASS

In the preceding chapter it was mentioned that in ordinary chemical reactions there is no appreciable conversion of mass into energy. This means that the *products* resulting from a chemical reaction have the same mass as the starting materials, or *reactants*. Experimentally, the constancy of mass during a reaction can be investigated by carrying out the reaction in a closed container and weighing the system both before and after the chemical change. As was first shown by the classic investigation of Lavoisier in 1774 on the reaction of tin with oxygen, it is necessary to have reaction occur in a system isolated from the surroundings, so that nothing is lost or gained. A modern example of such a reaction is the flashing of a magnesium photographic flash bulb. The flash bulb represents an isolated system containing two elements, magnesium wire and oxygen gas, sealed in a closed container. When electric current passes through the bulb, the bulb flashes as chemical reaction occurs. Magnesium disappears, oxygen disappears, and a white compound, magnesium oxide, is formed. Comparison of the final mass with the initial mass shows that after reaction the total mass is the same as before.

Some of the most careful experiments designed to determine whether mass is conserved in a chemical reaction were carried out by the German chemist Landolt at the end of the nineteenth century. Among the many reactions he studied was that between silver sulfate (Ag_2SO_4) and ferrous sulfate ($FeSO_4$) to give solid silver (Ag) and ferric sulfate [$Fe_2(SO_4)_3$]. He enclosed solutions of the starting materials in separate arms of a sealed tube shaped like an inverted V. The tube with contents was weighed, inverted so that reaction could occur, and then reweighed. In a typical experiment the observed weight change was a loss of 1.30×10^{-4} g. for a total weight of over 170 g. of starting solutions. This minute change of less than one part in a million was noted to be smaller than the error in weighing. Similar careful work by other experimenters has substantiated the *law of conservation of mass*, which states that in a chemical change *mass is neither created nor destroyed* to any appreciable extent.

2.2   DEFINITE COMPOSITION

In the formation of a compound it is observed that *the quantity of one element needed to combine with a fixed weight of another is the same.* In other words, given a definite weight of sodium, for example, the weight of chlorine required to combine with it to form sodium chloride is always the same, no matter how much chlorine is available in the reaction mixture. Specifically, 1.00 g. of sodium uses up only 1.54 g. of chlorine even though 10 g. of chlorine might be available. This is an illustration of the law of definite composition, also called the law of definite proportions.

The fact that elements combine in fixed proportions means also that compounds have characteristic compositions. Thus, for example, analysis of sodium chloride, as by electrolysis of the melted salt, always leads to the composition 39 per cent sodium and 61 per cent chlorine by weight. Compounds containing more than two elements also have definite composition. Calcium carbonate, for instance, found in nature as the mineral limestone, is composed of 40 per cent calcium, 12 per cent carbon, and 48 per cent oxygen. Deviation from this percentage composition indicates impurities are present.

Because the law of definite composition is well established, it forms the basis of quantitative predictions, as illustrated in the following examples:

Example 1

When magnesium burns in oxygen, 1.52 g. of Mg combines with 1.00 g. of O. How many grams of oxygen are required to combine with 12.2 g. of Mg?
    1.52 g. of Mg requires 1.00 g. of O
    1.00 g. of Mg requires (1.00/1.52) g. of O
    12.2 g. of Mg requires (12.2) (1.00/1.52), or 8.03 g. of O

Example 2

How much ammonia can be made from 12 g. of nitrogen and 12 g. of hydrogen? Ammonia is 82% nitrogen and 18% hydrogen. (Percentage composition can be conveniently converted to weight by assuming 100 g. of compound.)
    82 g. of N requires 18 g. of H
    1.0 g. of N requires (18/82) g. of H
    12 g. of N requires (12) (18/82), or 2.6 g. of H
    Therefore, the weight of product is 12 g. of N plus 2.6 g. of H, or (to the proper number of significant figures) 15 g. of ammonia.

2.3   MULTIPLE PROPORTIONS

Under different conditions the same two elements may react to give different compounds. It is found experimentally that there is a simple relation between the weights of these elements; this relation is expressed by the law of multiple proportions. Before stating the law, we look at some typical data. The elements lead and oxygen under one set of conditions form the compound litharge, an orange-yellow solid used in glazing pottery; under a different set of conditions they form the compound called red lead, used in making paint for protecting structural steel. It is observed that the weight of oxygen combined per unit weight of lead in litharge is a simple multiple of the weight of oxygen combined per unit weight of lead in red lead. (By simple multiple we mean a multiple expressible by the ratio of small whole numbers.) Specifically, in litharge 0.0772 g. of oxygen is combined with 1.00 g. of lead; in red lead, 0.103 g. of oxygen is combined with 1.00 g. of lead. The weight of oxygen per unit weight of lead in litharge, 0.0772, is a simple multiple of the weight of oxygen per unit weight of lead in red lead, 0.103. The multiple, 0.0772/0.103, is 0.750, or three-fourths.

The *law of multiple proportions* states that, in a series of compounds

between the same elements *A* and *B, the weight of element A per unit weight
of element B in one compound is a simple multiple of the weight of A per
unit weight of B in another.* It should be noted that the law of multiple proportions, like the other two laws of chemical change, is concerned only
with weights and therefore is demonstrated by easily measured quantities.

Example 3

*The elements hydrogen and oxygen react normally to form water, but in the presence of
a high-energy electric discharge they also form the compound hydrogen peroxide. Water
is 11.2% hydrogen and 88.8% oxygen; hydrogen peroxide is 5.93% hydrogen and
94.07% oxygen. Show how these data illustrate the law of multiple proportions.*

In water,

        11.2 g. of H is combined with 88.8 g. of O

        1.00 g. of H is combined with (88.8/11.2), or 7.93 g. of O

In hydrogen peroxide,

        5.93 g. of H is combined with 94.07 g. of O

        1.00 g. of H is combined with (94.07/5.93), or 15.9 g. of O

In hydrogen peroxide, the weight of oxygen per unit weight of hydrogen, 15.9, is
twice the weight of oxygen per unit weight of hydrogen in water, 7.93.

2.4   ATOMIC THEORY

The laws of chemical change summarize a large number of experimental
facts concerning the quantitative aspects of chemical reactions. How can
these laws be explained? To be satisfactory, not only must the explanation or theory account for the laws; but there must be no known facts in
contradiction to the theory, and all predictions made from it should be
borne out by experiment. Of necessity, any theory which accounts for a
great many observations must deal with the ultimate nature of matter.
Logically, there are only two points of view: either matter is continuous or
it is discontinuous, i.e., either the process of progressive subdivision of a
substance can be continued without limit or else progressive subdivision
leads to an ultimate indivisible particle. The two alternatives can be visualized by imagining that on a submicroscopic scale a piece of iron must
appear either continuous like a jelly or discontinuous like an array of buck-
shot.

Speculation that matter is ultimately discontinuous dates back at least
to the time of the early Greek philosophers. One school of thought reasoned
that matter is composed of tiny, indestructible particles which were called
atoms (from the Greek word *atomos,* meaning uncut). However, this was
only a philosophical doctrine, and there was not enough experimental evidence to encourage its universal acceptance. In about 1803, an English

schoolteacher, John Dalton, developed the model sufficiently so that it could explain the experimental observations made up to his time. These included the laws of conservation of mass and of definite composition. It is a tribute to Dalton that he was able to predict from atomic theory the law of multiple proportions, which had not yet been discovered. Actually the law of multiple proportions is one of the strongest supports of atomic theory.

In his theory, Dalton assumed that all matter is ultimately composed of atoms, that these atoms can be neither subdivided nor changed one into another, and that atoms can neither be created nor destroyed. Furthermore, he assumed that atoms of a particular element are identical in size, shape, mass, and all other properties and differ from atoms of other elements in these properties. Finally, he proposed that chemical change is the union or separation of atoms.

A test of any theory lies in how well it accounts for the observed facts. Does the Dalton atomic model account for the conservation of mass in chemical reactions? If chemical change is merely the union or separation of undivided atoms, mass must be conserved. No new atoms are created, and no old ones are destroyed. For example, in the reaction of hydrogen with oxygen to form water, hydrogen atoms unite with oxygen atoms, but all the atoms initially present, and no others, remain after reaction is complete. The contribution to the total mass by the hydrogen atoms and by the oxygen atoms is the same whether they are present as the original elements or are combined in the compound water.

Does the Dalton atomic theory account for the law of definite composition? One way of stating this law is to say that the weight of product formed from reaction of two elements is fixed by the weight of one element. Suppose we consider the reaction of weighed amounts of carbon and oxygen to form carbon monoxide. The weighed amount of carbon corresponds to a definite number of carbon atoms, and the weighed amount of oxygen to a definite number of oxygen atoms. We assume that, in the formation of carbon monoxide, only one carbon atom unites with each oxygen atom. If,

Fig. 2.1   Limitation of product by one reactant.

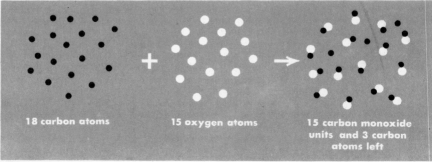

18 carbon atoms   15 oxygen atoms   15 carbon monoxide
                                                      units and 3 carbon
                                                      atoms left

Fig. 2.2 Different products from reaction of carbon and oxygen atoms.

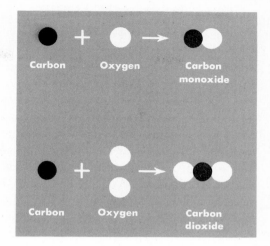

as shown in Fig. 2.1, there are 18 carbon atoms and 15 oxygen atoms available, there will be 3 carbon atoms left after reaction. There are not enough oxygen atoms to satisfy all the carbon atoms; hence the amount of product is limited only by the oxygen, not by the carbon. Another way of stating the law of definite composition is to say that compounds have characteristic compositions. The explanation can be seen by considering pure carbon monoxide, which is composed of complex units, or *molecules;** each containing one carbon atom and one oxygen atom. In each carbon monoxide molecule, the fraction of the weight contributed by carbon is the weight of the carbon atom divided by the weight of the molecule. Since according to Dalton's theory all carbon monoxide molecules are alike, any sample containing many such molecules has the same percentage of carbon by weight as the single molecule.

Does the Dalton atomic theory account for the law of multiple proportions? Suppose there are two or more different reactions possible between the same two elements, as shown in Fig. 2.2. Carbon monoxide is formed when one atom of carbon unites with one atom of oxygen. Under different conditions, one atom of carbon unites with two atoms of oxygen to form carbon dioxide. If atoms are indivisible, either one atom of oxygen or two atoms of oxygen unite with a single carbon atom; there cannot be a fractional number of oxygen atoms combined with one carbon atom. Thus, the ratio of oxygen atoms per carbon atom in the two compounds is exactly $1:2$, a ratio expressible by small whole numbers. Likewise, the *weight* of oxygen per unit *weight* of carbon in the two compounds is in the ratio of $1:2$.

---

* In his original works, Dalton did not use the term molecule, which in its modern sense usually denotes a characteristic aggregate of two or more atoms. Instead, he referred to compound atoms such as atoms of water, atoms of sugar, atoms of "sulphuretted hydrogen," etc. An atom of sulphuretted hydrogen, according to Dalton, was composed of one atom of sulfur and three atoms of hydrogen!

2.5 ATOMIC WEIGHT

One of the most important concepts to come from Dalton's work is that of atomic weight. How does the weight of one atom compare with the weight of another atom? Because atoms are so tiny, their *absolute* weights are difficult to measure. However, the *relative* weights of different atoms can be obtained by measuring the weight of one element combined with another, provided that the relative number of atoms in the compound is known. For example, analysis of water shows that it is 11.19 per cent hydrogen and 88.81 per cent oxygen. This means that in water 88.81/11.19, or 7.937, times as much weight is contributed by the oxygen atoms as by the hydrogen atoms. If there is one oxygen atom for each hydrogen atom, then the oxygen atom is 7.937 times as heavy as the hydrogen atom. If, however, there is one oxygen atom for every two hydrogen atoms, then the oxygen atom is 7.937 times as heavy as two hydrogen atoms, or 15.87 times as heavy as one hydrogen atom. Since the second formulation turns out to be correct, the oxygen atom is 15.87 times as heavy as the hydrogen atom.*

In setting up a relative scale of atomic weights, one element is chosen as a standard and all other elements are referred to it. The choice of standard is arbitrary. At the present time oxygen is chosen, partly because it combines with most other elements. Although hydrogen also combines with most other elements, it is not chosen as standard because it is so light that, when its weight is added to that of another element, the change of weight is difficult to determine precisely. At one time oxygen was assigned a numerical value of 100, but at present the atomic weight assigned to it is exactly 16 atomic mass units. (There is, however, a complication which is discussed in Sec. 3.4.) By definition, then, 1 atomic mass unit (abbreviated a.m.u.) is one-sixteenth the mass of an oxygen atom. The choice of 16 for oxygen makes most of the other elements come out to have approximately whole-number atomic weights. For example, the atomic weight of hydrogen is 1.008 a.m.u., sodium is 22.991 a.m.u., and sulfur is 32.066 a.m.u. Chlorine, however, has an atomic weight of 35.457 a.m.u. A complete list of the latest internationally accepted atomic weights is given inside the back cover of the book. Only small changes in these values now occur from year to year. Although no units are specified in the table, all values are given in atomic mass units.

---

* In Dalton's early attempt to set up a scale of relative atomic weights, he made the mistake of assuming that water contains one oxygen atom for each hydrogen atom. Consequently, his oxygen atom was underweight by a factor of 2. Furthermore, the weight composition of water was poorly determined, so that he believed the oxygen atom was only seven times as heavy as the hydrogen atom.

Table 2.1   Specific Heats and Atomic Weights

Element	Specific heat, cal./g.-deg.	Atomic weight	Product, spec. heat × at. wt.
Aluminum	0.216	26.98	5.8
Calcium	0.157	40.08	6.3
Copper	0.0922	63.54	5.9
Gold	0.0306	197.0	6.0
Iodine	0.0518	126.91	6.6
Iron	0.108	55.85	6.0
Lead	0.0308	207.21	6.4
Magnesium	0.235	24.32	5.7
Nickel	0.105	58.71	6.2
Potassium	0.178	39.100	7.0
Silver	0.0565	107.880	6.1
Sulfur	0.169	32.066	5.4
Tin	0.0531	118.70	6.3
Zinc	0.0928	65.38	6.1

In the experimental determination of atomic weights, there is a problem of deciding how many atoms of one element combine with one atom of another. An important way of solving this problem makes use of the *law of Dulong and Petit*. This law states that for many solid elements the *product of the atomic weight and the specific heat is approximately equal to* 6.3. The *specific heat*, defined as the amount of heat needed to change the temperature of 1 g. of a substance by 1°C., can be determined experimentally for a given element. Some sample values of specific heats are shown in Table 2.1. For example, the specific heat of silver is 0.0565 cal. per deg. per g., and so its atomic weight is approximately 6.3/0.0565, or about 110. The use of this approximate atomic weight of silver is illustrated in Example 4.

Example 4

In the formation of silver oxide, it is observed that 1.074156 g. of compound is formed from 1.000000 g. of silver. From the specific heat, the approximate atomic weight is 110. What is the atomic weight of silver?

0.074156 g. of O combines with 1.000000 g. of Ag

16.000 g. of O combines with (16.000)(1.000000/0.074156), or 215.76 g. of Ag

This means that 16.000 a.m.u. of oxygen is combined with 215.76 a.m.u. of silver. If one oxygen atom is combined with one silver atom, then the atomic weight of silver is 215.76 a.m.u. If one oxygen atom is combined with two silver atoms, then the atomic weight of silver is half as much, or 107.88 a.m.u. The approximate value of 110 from the law of Dulong and Petit indicates that the second value, 107.88, is correct.

2.6   GRAM-ATOMS

Since atoms are extremely small, any laboratory experiment dealing with weighable amounts of chemicals must, of necessity, involve tremendous numbers of atoms. For example, in making carbon monoxide, it is not possible to weigh out one carbon and one oxygen atom, because any weighable amount of carbon or oxygen contains an enormous number of atoms. However, it is possible to get equal numbers of carbon and of oxygen atoms by using the relative weights of these atoms. From the atomic weights (12.011 for C and 16.000 for O), we know that a carbon atom is 12.011/16.000 times as heavy as an oxygen atom. Suppose we take any definite number of carbon atoms and an equal number of oxygen atoms. The weight of the entire collection of carbon atoms is 12.011/16.000 times as great as the weight of the collection of oxygen atoms. Conversely, any weight of carbon that is 12.011/16.000 times as great as a weight of oxygen must contain just as many carbon atoms as there are oxygen atoms. For example, 12.011 g. of carbon contains the same number of atoms as does 16.000 g. of oxygen. In general, when we take weights equal to the relative atomic weights of different elements, we always have the same number of atoms. We can take these weights in grams, pounds, or any other convenient units of weight. In other words, 16.000 lb. of oxygen contains the same number of atoms as 12.011 lb. of carbon.

The *gram-atom* is defined as a collection of atoms whose total weight is the number of grams numerically equal to the atomic weight. Since sulfur has an atomic weight of 32.066 a.m.u., a collection of sulfur atoms weighing 32.066 g. is 1 gram-atom of sulfur. Since the atomic weight of iron is 55.85 a.m.u., a collection of iron atoms weighing 55.85 g. is 1 gram-atom of iron. The collections have different weights, but each has the same number of atoms.

The concept of the gram-atom enables us to choose the proper number of atoms for reaction. Suppose we wish to make a compound in which there is one atom of iron for each atom of sulfur. If we take 1 gram-atom of iron and 1 gram-atom of sulfur, there are just exactly enough iron atoms to match the sulfur atoms. Furthermore, the weights taken are of a size that can be handled with usual laboratory apparatus. Because equal numbers of gram-atoms of different elements contain equal numbers of atoms, it is convenient to refer to amounts of elements in terms of numbers of gram-atoms. For instance, 3.2 g. of sulfur is 3.2/32.066, or 0.10, gram-atom.

Example 5

How many grams of sulfur are required to react with 336 g. of iron in a reaction in which one atom of iron unites with one atom of sulfur? (The atomic weight of iron is 55.85 a.m.u., and that of sulfur is 32.066 a.m.u.)

55.85 g. of iron is 1 gram-atom of iron

336 g. of iron is 336/55.85, or 6.02, gram-atoms of iron

1 atom of iron requires 1 atom of sulfur

1 gram-atom of iron requires 1 gram-atom of sulfur

6.02 gram-atoms of iron require 6.02 gram-atoms of sulfur

6.02 gram-atoms of sulfur is (6.02)(32.066), or 193, g. of sulfur

Example 6

How many grams of aluminum are required to react with 10.0 g. of oxygen to form a compound which contains 2 atoms of aluminum for every 3 atoms of oxygen? How many grams of product will be formed? (The atomic weight of aluminum is 26.98 a.m.u.)

10.0 g. of O is 10.0/16.0, or 0.625, gram-atom of O

3 atoms of O require 2 atoms of Al

3 gram-atoms of O require 2 gram-atoms of Al

1 gram-atom of O requires ⅔ gram-atom of Al

0.625 gram-atom of O requires (⅔)(0.625), or 0.417, gram-atom of Al

0.417 gram-atom of Al is (0.417)(26.98), or 11.3, g. of Al

The product weighs 11.3 plus 10.0, or 21.3 g.

2.7 AVOGADRO NUMBER

With modern techniques, it has been possible to determine the *number of atoms in 1 gram-atom*. The value of this number is 6.0235×10^{23}, or 602,350,000,000,000,000,000,000. This number is referred to as the *Avogadro number* and should be remembered, to at least three significant figures: 6.02×10^{23}. Detailed consideration of the methods used to determine the Avogadro number must be postponed until further principles have been discussed. For the present, we simply mention methods used.

Probably the most accurate determination of the Avogadro number is based on the study of solids. From the measured weight per unit volume (density) of the solid, the volume of 1 gram-atom can be calculated. As discussed in Chap. 8, the spacing of atoms in a solid can be found by using X rays. This enables a precise determination of the number of atoms in the volume which contains 1 gram-atom. The method is illustrated in detail by Question 8.11. Another method based on radioactivity is illustrated in Question 6.18.

A knowledge of the number of atoms in a gram-atom enables calculation of the weights of individual atoms as well as the number of atoms in any given weight of an element.

Example 7

What is the weight in grams of a single uranium atom? The atomic weight of uranium is 238.07 a.m.u.

      1 gram-atom of uranium weighs 238.07 g.

      1 gram-atom of any element contains the Avogadro number of atoms

      6.02×10^{23} atoms of uranium weigh 238.07 g.

      1 atom of uranium weighs $238.07/(6.02 \times 10^{23})$ g., or 3.95×10^{-22} g.

Example 8

How many atoms of iron are there in 363 g. of iron filings? The atomic weight of iron is 55.85 a.m.u.

      363 g. of iron is 363/55.85, or 6.50, gram-atoms

      1 gram-atom contains 6.02×10^{23} atoms

      6.50 gram-atoms contain $(6.50)(6.02 \times 10^{23})$, or 3.91×10^{24}, atoms

QUESTIONS

For needed atomic weights, see table inside back cover.

2.1   *Terms.* What is the distinction between a gram, a gram-atom, and an atom?

2.2   *Gram-atoms.* (*a*) A gross of oranges weighs 69 lb.; a gross of cherries weighs 2.7 lb. What weight of cherries must you buy in order to get the same number of cherries as there are oranges in 23 lb.? (*b*) A gram-atom of sodium weighs 23.0 g.; a gram-atom of chlorine weighs 35.5 g. What weight of chlorine must you buy in order to get the same number of chlorine atoms as there are sodium atoms in 4.60 g.?

2.3   *Gram-atoms.* Which of the following weighs most: (*a*) 50 g. of iron; (*b*) 5 gram-atoms of nitrogen; (*c*) 0.10 gram-atom of silver; (*d*) 1×10^{23} atoms of radium?

2.4   *Atomic theory.* Show how atomic theory accounts for each of the following observations: (*a*) The weight of carbon per gram of hydrogen in the compound ethane is exactly four-thirds the weight of carbon per gram of hydrogen in the compound methane; (*b*) 39.3 g. of sodium reacts with 68.0 g. of chlorine to give 100.0 g. of sodium chloride and 7.3 g. of chlorine.

2.5   *Pound-atoms.* (*a*) What is a pound-atom? (*b*) Are there more or less atoms in a pound-atom than in a gram-atom? Explain.

2.6   *Ton-atoms.* How many atoms are there in a ton-atom?

                                                  Ans. 5.47×10^{29} atoms

2.7 *Gram-atoms.* Calcium has atomic weight 40.08 a.m.u. (*a*) What is the weight in grams of one calcium atom? (*b*) How many atoms and how many gram-atoms are there in 10.0 g. of Ca?

Ans. 6.66×10^{-23} g.; 1.51×10^{22} atoms; 0.250 gram-atom

2.8 *Law of Dulong and Petit.* The element chromium has a specific heat of 0.122 cal. per deg. per g. If 3.121 g. of chromium combines with oxygen to form 4.561 g. of oxide, what is the atomic weight of chromium?

2.9 *Multiple proportions.* Elements *A* and *B* form two different compounds. In one, 0.579 g. of *A* is combined with 0.422 g. of *B*; in the other, 0.179 g. of *A* is combined with 0.261 g. of *B*. Show that these data illustrate the law of multiple proportions.

2.10 *Atomic weights.* Suppose atom *X* weighs 2.97×10^{-22} g. (*a*) What is the relative atomic weight of *X* on the usual scale of O = 16? (*b*) How many gram-atoms of *X* in 3.58 g. of *X*? (*c*) How many grams of *X* are required to combine with 0.36 gram-atom of *Y* in a reaction requiring 3 atoms of *Y* for every 2 atoms of *X*?

2.11 *Atomic volume.* (*a*) Lead has an atomic weight of 207.21 and a density of 11.4 g. per cc. What is the volume occupied by 1 gram-atom of lead? (*b*) Compute the average volume occupied by a single lead atom. (*c*) If a lead atom is spherical in shape and has the volume computed in (*b*), what is its diameter?

Ans. 18.2 cc.; 3.02×10^{-23} cc.; 1.93×10^{-8} cm.

2.12 *Multiple proportions.* Suppose element *X* combines with *Z* to give two different compounds. In compound I there is 8.0 g. of *X* combined with 18.0 g. of *Z*; compound II is 25% *X* and 75% *Z* by weight. Show how these data illustrate the law of multiple proportions.

2.13 *Laws of chemical change.* Element *A* reacts with element *B* at 100° to form compound *C*. At 1000°, *A* and *B* react to form compound *D*. Describe the experiment or series of experiments (indicate what substance should be weighed) which could be performed with *A* and *B* to verify: (*a*) the law of conservation of mass; (*b*) the law of definite composition; (*c*) the law of multiple proportions.

2.14 *Gram-atoms.* (*a*) In a chemical reaction requiring 3 atoms of Mg for 2 atoms of N, how many gram-atoms of nitrogen are required by 4.86 g. of magnesium? (*b*) How many grams of N are required in (*a*)?

Ans. 0.133 gram-atom; 1.87 g.

2.15 *Definite composition.* (*a*) Silver chloride (AgCl) consists of 75.3% by weight of Ag and 24.7% Cl. If 17.80 g. of Ag is allowed to react with 5.47 g. of Cl, what weight of AgCl is formed? (*b*) Show how this problem illustrates the law of definite composition. *Ans.* 22.1 g.

2.16 *Gram-atoms.* Calculate the weight in grams of each of the following: (*a*) 4.0 gram-atoms of oxygen; (*b*) just enough sulfur to react with 4.0 gram-atoms of oxygen to form a compound which has 2 oxygen atoms for each sulfur atom; (*c*) 1 atomic mass unit.

2.17 *Gram-atoms and weight relations.* You are given 1.2×10^{24} atoms of hydrogen, 1.0 gram-atom of sulfur, and 88 grams of oxygen. (*a*) What is the total weight in grams of the collection of all three elements? (*b*) How many gram-atoms (all kinds) are there in the collection? (*c*) If the three elements are allowed to react to form a compound having 2 H atoms and 4 O atoms for each S atom, how many grams of material will remain unreacted?

2.18 *Definite composition.* As we shall see in Sec. 3.4, all the atoms of a given element are not identical in mass. Even so, the law of definite composition holds. Explain.

2.19 *Gram-atoms.* In a chemical reaction requiring 1 atom of Ca for 2 atoms of F, how many grams of compound can be formed from 1.26 g. of Ca and 1.14 g. of F? *Ans.* 2.34 g.

2.20 *Multiple proportions.* Ammonia contains 17.76% hydrogen and 82.24% nitrogen. When 3.77 g. of H completely reacts with 26.23 g. of N, 30.00 g. of hydrazine is formed. Show how these data illustrate the law of multiple proportions.

2.21 *Avogadro number.* An average signature written in pencil weighs about 1 mg. Assuming that the black stuff is carbon, calculate the approximate number of atoms required to write such a signature. *Ans.* 5×10^{19} atoms

2.22 *Gram-atoms.* A given compound contains atoms *A*, *B*, and *C* in the ratio $2:2:7$, respectively. Your task is to make the maximum weight of compound from 0.175 gram-atom of *A*, 9.03×10^{22} atoms of *B*, and 9.63 g. of *C*. The atomic weights are 23.0, 31.0, and 16.0, respectively, for *A*, *B*, and *C*. How much compound can you make?

2.23 *Definite composition.* White vinegar is a solution of acetic acid in water. Acetic acid contains C, H, and O atoms in the ratio $1:2:1$, respectively. If a sample of vinegar shows on analysis 2.0% carbon by weight, what percentage of the weight of the vinegar is actually acetic acid? *Ans.* 5.0%

2.24 *Gram-atoms.* Compound *Q* contains for every atom of *K*, 3 atoms of *L*, and 2 atoms of *M*. In a given reaction starting with 0.36×10^{23} atoms of *K* and 0.12 gram-atom of *L*, 3.6 g. of *M* is required. What is the atomic weight of *M*?

2.25 *Avogadro number.* An ancient theological question asks, How many angels can stand on the point of a pin? We can set an upper limit to this number by assuming that each angel requires at least one atom to stand on. A fairly sharp pin will have a point diameter of about 0.0010 cm. Gold has an atomic weight of 197.0 and a density of 19.3 g. per cc. Make any simplifying assumptions you wish. How many angels can stand on the point of the pin?

2.26 *Nature of matter.* Assume that matter is not atomistic but rather is continuous. Try to account for the three laws of chemical change with this model.

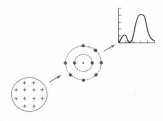

3   *Atoms*

THE LAWS OF CHEMICAL CHANGE can be accounted for by assuming that matter is atomic. In this chapter we examine ideas about the nature of atoms and consider some of the experiments on which these ideas are based.

3.1   FARADAY'S EXPERIMENTS ON ELECTROLYSIS

When electricity is passed through liquids, evidences of chemical change can be observed at the electrodes. In many cases, compounds can be thus decomposed into their constituent elements. For example, as described in Sec. 1.1, water on electrolysis yields hydrogen and oxygen. Similarly, when molten sodium chloride is electrolyzed, the elements sodium and chlorine are formed. The quantitative aspects of electrolysis were first studied by Michael Faraday shortly after Dalton enunciated his atomic theory.

Faraday found that the weight of an element formed at an electrode is *directly proportional to the amount of electricity* passed through the liquid. He also noted that the weight of element formed is *directly proportional to the atomic weight of the element divided by a small whole number,* e.g., 1, 2, 3, etc. These statements are called Faraday's laws of electrolysis.

33

The following experiments are specific illustrations of Faraday's laws: A steady flow of electricity through molten sodium chloride produces twice as much sodium and twice as much chlorine in 2 hr. as in 1 hr. If enough electricity flows to produce 23 g. (i.e., 1 gram-atom) of sodium at one electrode, 35.5 g. (i.e., 1 gram-atom) of chlorine is produced at the other. If an *identical* amount of electricity is used to electrolyze water, 1 g. (1 gram-atom) of hydrogen is formed at one electrode and 8 g. (½ gram-atom) of oxygen at the other. These numbers illustrate Faraday's law, since the weights of sodium, chlorine, and hydrogen formed are the respective atomic weights divided by 1, and the weight of oxygen is its atomic weight divided by 2.

The fact that chemical change can be produced by electricity indicates a relationship between electricity and matter. Since matter is assumed to consist of atoms, the phenomenon of electrolysis hints that atoms might be partly electrical in structure. Furthermore, the appearance of whole numbers in one of Faraday's laws suggests that an electrical structure of atoms must involve discrete particles of electricity.

3.2   DISCHARGE-TUBE EXPERIMENTS

Further indications that atoms can be subdivided into electrically charged fragments come from observations of the behavior of discharge tubes. A typical discharge tube is shown in Fig. 3.1. It consists of a glass tube with two metal plates, or electrodes, sealed in at either end. The electrodes are connected to the positive and negative sides of a high-voltage source and are called anode and cathode, respectively. When the tube is full of air at normal pressure, nothing is observed even if 10,000 volts are applied across the electrodes. However, as air is pumped out of the tube, electricity starts to flow, and the air remaining in the tube begins to glow. Certain minerals, such as zinc sulfide, placed between the electrodes, give off an intense light

Fig. 3.1   Simple discharge tube.

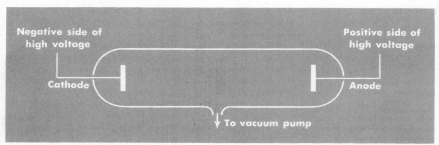

Negative side of high voltage

Positive side of high voltage

Cathode

Anode

To vacuum pump

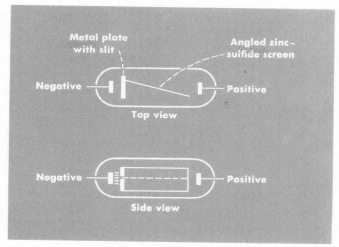

Fig. 3.2   Discharge tube with screen to observe path of cathode particles.

which can be shown to be emitted in flashes. The fact that the emitted light is intermittent hints that the electricity flows through the tube as a beam of discrete particles.

More detailed information about the nature of the beams observed in electric discharge tubes can be obtained with the tube shown in Fig. 3.2. This tube is fitted with a detecting screen covered with zinc sulfide and has a slotted metal plate near the cathode. When we observe the tube from the side, we see a line of light across the screen. We can explain this observation by assuming that electrical beams, or rays, emanate from the cathode and move toward the anode. Most of these are stopped by the metal plate, but the slit lets through a narrow sheaf of them, which hits the screen and produces a line of light. Because the beams seem to come from the cathode, they are called *cathode rays*. When the north pole of a magnet is brought up to the side of the tube, the line of light curves downward; when the south pole of the magnet is brought up, the line curves upward. The direction of the deflection indicates that the cathode rays are *negatively charged*. The same conclusion can be reached by noting that, if electrically charged plates are placed above and below the screen, the line curves toward the positive plate. Opposite charges attract each other; hence apparently cathode rays are negatively charged.

As described in the following sections, the quantitative determination of the electric charge and mass of the particles believed to make up cathode rays shows that these particles are identical, no matter what material the cathode is made of and no matter what gas is present in the tube. These particles are called *electrons* and are considered to be constituents of all matter. In the operation of the discharge tube, it is thought that electrons come from the cathode material.

Experiments first performed by Goldstein in 1886 suggested that *positive particles* are also formed in discharge tubes. The Goldstein tube is shown in Fig. 3.3. The electrode on the right is positive; the electrode toward the left is negative and consists of a piece of metal with a hole bored in it. A detecting screen similar to that used in Fig. 3.2 can be placed to the left of the cathode. A line of light appears on it and is deflected by a magnet in the direction opposite to the deflection in the experiment with cathode rays. The inference is that a positive beam exists to the left of the cathode. Its origin can be explained as follows: Electrons emitted from the cathode are attracted to the anode. Since there is gas in the tube, these electrons collide with neutral atoms of the gas. If the electrons have enough energy, they can knock other electrons off the neutral atoms. This subtraction of negative electrons leaves residual positive particles, which are accelerated toward the negative electrode. Here most of them pick up electrons and are neutralized. Occasionally, a positive particle coasts through the hole, giving a beam of positive particles directed toward the left end of the tube. Using the techniques to be discussed in the next section, it is found that these particles are always more massive than electrons, with the mass dependent on the kind of gas which is in the tube.

3.3 DETERMINATION OF MASS AND CHARGE

Information about the particles that constitute the beams in discharge tubes comes from the quantitative study of the deflection of these beams by electric and magnetic fields. The first measurements of this kind were made by J. J. Thomson in 1897. Figure 3.4 shows an arrangement which could be

Fig. 3.3   Discharge tube for studying positive particles.

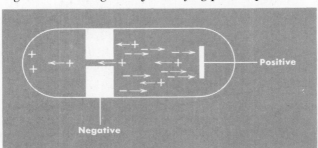

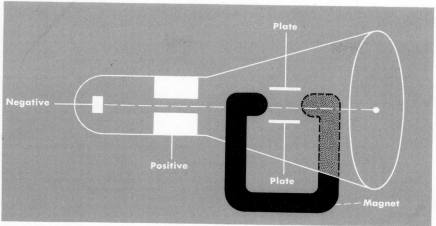

Fig. 3.4   *Deflection of cathode rays by electric and magnetic fields.*

used for such a study. The negative electrode emits electrons, which are accelerated to the right. Some pass through the hole in the anode to give a narrow beam, which falls on the detecting screen at the face of the tube. The presence of the magnet causes the beam to be deflected. By suitably charging the plates above and below the beam, the deflection of the beam caused by the magnet can be counteracted by the deflection caused by the charged plates. Quantitative measurements are made of the strength of the magnet and of the voltage on the plates required to produce no net deflection. This information, when combined with a measurement of the deflection observed when the magnet is removed or when the plates are uncharged, allows a calculation of the ratio of charge to mass for the particles. (The detailed calculation can be found in most books on atomic physics.) The deflection depends on the charge of the particles, because the bigger the charge of a particle, the more it is attracted to (or repelled by) a charged plate. The deflection depends inversely on the mass of the particles, because the greater the mass of a moving particle, the more difficult it is to deflect the particle from its straight-line path.

Experiments such as that just described indicate that for an electron the ratio of charge to mass is equal to -1.76×10^8 coulombs per g. (The coulomb, a unit for measuring electric charge, is described in Appendix 4.4.) This ratio is observed to be the same no matter what material the cathode is made of. The minus sign of the ratio indicates the negative nature of the charge of the electron.

Beams of positive particles can also be studied by the above method, using a slightly modified apparatus. The mass spectrometer shown in Fig. 3.5 is an example of such an instrument. It measures the charge-to-mass

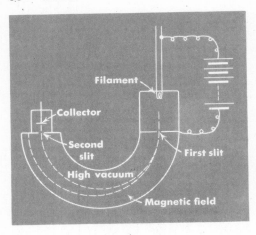

Fig. 3.5 Mass spectrometer. Positive ions are produced by electron bombardment of neutral molecules near the filament. The positive ions are accelerated through the first slit and bent in a circular path by a magnetic field. Particles of different charge-to-mass ratio follow different paths, shown by the dotted lines.

ratio of positive particles. When positive particles are produced from different gases, it is observed that the charge-to-mass ratio varies from one gas to another. Also, it is observed in all cases that the charge-to-mass ratio (about 10^5 coulombs per g., or less) is considerably smaller than that for electrons.

A measurement of the charge-to-mass ratio of a particle tells nothing about the actual charge or the actual mass of the particle. However, once either of these quantities has been determined, the other can be calculated from the ratio. The experiment of Thomson gave a value for the charge-to-mass ratio of the electron. The charge of the electron was measured in a classic experiment by R. A. Millikan in 1909. Figure 3.6 shows the essential features of the experiment. An atomizer is used to spray oil droplets between two charged plates. Because of gravity, the droplets settle. However, if the droplets can be given a negative charge, they can be made to rise because of attraction to the positive plate. (The negative charge can be imparted to the droplets by irradiation with X rays. The X rays presumably knock electrons off atoms in the air, just as the cathode rays do in the Goldstein tube. One or more of these electrons can be picked up by an oil droplet and thus make it negative.) The rate of rise of a charged oil droplet is measured by observing it with a telescope. From the rate of rise, the amount of charge on an individual droplet can be calculated. It is found that, although the charge on different droplets varies, the total charge on any one droplet is always a small whole-number multiple of -1.60×10^{-19} coulomb. Apparently, the smallest possible charge that any one oil droplet can pick up is -1.60×10^{-19} coulomb and this is assumed to be the charge of an individual electron. Combining the charge of the electron (-1.60×10^{-19} coulomb) with its charge-to-mass ratio (-1.76×10^8 coulombs per g.) gives the mass of the electron as 9.1×10^{-28} g.

The mass of positive particles can similarly be deduced from knowledge of their charge-to-mass ratio and their actual charge. Positive particles presumably result when electrons are pulled off neutral atoms. If a single electron is removed from a neutral atom, the positive particle left must have a charge exactly equal to but opposite in sign to the charge of the electron. For example, if an electron is pulled off a neutral hydrogen atom, the resulting positive particle (called the *proton*) has a charge of $+1.60 \times 10^{-19}$ coulomb. Its mass is found to be 1.67×10^{-24} g., which is about 1,840 times the mass of the electron. If two electrons are removed from a neutral helium atom, the resulting particle (called the *alpha particle*) has a charge of $+3.20 \times 10^{-19}$ coulomb and a mass of 6.6×10^{-24} g.

3.4   ISOTOPES

The study of positive particles by means of the mass spectrometer (Fig. 3.5) indicates that all atoms of a particular element do not have the same mass. For example, when the charge-to-mass ratio is measured for the positive particles formed from a sample of neon gas, several values of the ratio, rather than only one, are obtained. Some of these values are $+4.81 \times 10^3$, $+9.62 \times 10^3$, and $+4.33 \times 10^3$ coulombs per g. The second of these values is exactly twice the first. Apparently, some of the atoms have lost two electrons instead of one and hence have twice as large a charge-to-mass ratio. The third value, $+4.33 \times 10^3$, bears no simple relation to the other two and cannot be explained by assuming a loss of a different number

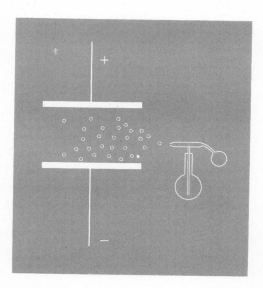

Fig. 3.6   Oil-drop method for determining electronic charge.

of electrons. The fact that the charge-to-mass ratio differs by something other than a whole-number multiple indicates that particles of different mass must be present. In other words, the sample of the element neon contains nonidentical atoms. These *atoms of a single element which differ from each other in mass* are called *isotopes.* For every element, two or more isotopes are known.*

3.5   RADIOACTIVITY

A significant feature of the experiments discussed in the preceding sections is the indication that atoms can be broken down into charged particles. The idea that atoms are not indivisible is also supported by studies on *radioactivity*, the spontaneous emission of radiation by certain elements such as radium. There are at least four kinds of radiation which have been detected: alpha (α), positive beta (β^+), negative beta (β^-), and gamma (γ). Investigation of these types of radiation can be made with the same techniques used for cathode rays. The experiments indicate that alpha radiation consists of positive particles having a charge of $+3.20 \times 10^{-19}$ coulomb and a mass of 6.6×10^{-24} g.; i.e., they are identical with the particles produced by stripping two electrons off helium atoms. Negative beta rays consist of particles having a charge of -1.60×10^{-19} coulomb and a mass of 9.1×10^{-28} g.; i.e., they are identical with electrons. Positive beta rays have a charge of $+1.60 \times 10^{-19}$ coulomb and a mass of 9.1×10^{-28} g.; they are sometimes called positive electrons or *positrons.* Gamma rays have no electrical charge and no detectable mass. They are like X rays and can be considered to be a very energetic form of light.

The emission of radiation by a radioactive element is frequently accompanied by the gradual disappearance of the radioactive element and the appearance of a new element. Apparently, atoms of one element may spontaneously change into atoms of another element. This process, the change of one element into another, is called *transmutation.* A specific

* The existence of isotopes complicates the setting up of atomic-weight scales, because oxygen, which is the standard for atomic weights, exists in nature as three different isotopes. On the physicist's scale of atomic weights, the lightest and most abundant of these isotopes is selected as standard and assigned an atomic weight of exactly 16 a.m.u. The other two isotopes have, on this scale, atomic weights of 17.005 a.m.u. and 18.005 a.m.u. In any natural mixture of oxygen atoms, 99.76 per cent of the atoms are of the lightest variety; 0.039 per cent, of the intermediate; and 0.20 per cent, of the heaviest. On the physicist's scale, naturally occurring oxygen has an atomic weight of 16.00436 a.m.u. In setting up the chemist's scale of atomic weights, the naturally occurring mixture of oxygen isotopes is taken as standard and assigned an atomic weight of exactly 16 a.m.u. As a result of these two different ways of defining a standard, the atomic weights given on the chemist's scale are somewhat smaller than corresponding values on the physicist's scale. To convert from the "chemical" atomic weight to the "physical" atomic weight, it is necessary to multiply the chemist's values by 1.000272.

example of transmutation is the radioactive decay of uranium. With no external cause, uranium atoms divide to form atoms of thorium and alpha particles. The inference is that atoms are complex and in some cases break up into simpler fragments.

3.6   NUCLEAR ATOM

If, as indicated in the preceding sections, atoms are complex, the question arises as to what their detailed structure is. J. J. Thomson in 1898 proposed that the atom be considered a sphere of positive electricity in which negative electrons are embedded like jelly beans in a ball of cotton. Most of the mass of the atom would have to be associated with the positive electricity, a conclusion drawn from the observation that the positive fragments of atoms are much heavier than the electrons. In 1911 Lord Rutherford performed a classic experiment which tested the Thomson model. He was investigating the scattering of alpha particles by thin sheets of metal. According to the Thomson model, a metal consists of atoms which are spheres of positive electricity containing negative electrons; i.e., the metal is essentially a sea of positive electricity containing negative charges. Since alpha particles are very energetic, it was thought that they would go right through metal foils. If the positive charge and the mass are distributed uniformly throughout the metal, the alpha particle has little reason to swerve off its original path and should plow right through.

Figure 3.7 shows details of the Rutherford experiment. The alpha

Fig. 3.7   Rutherford's experiment for studying the scattering of alpha particles by metal foil.

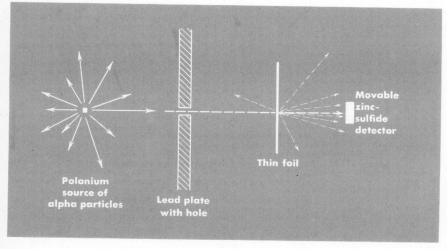

Movable zinc-sulfide detector

Thin foil

Polonium source of alpha particles

Lead plate with hole

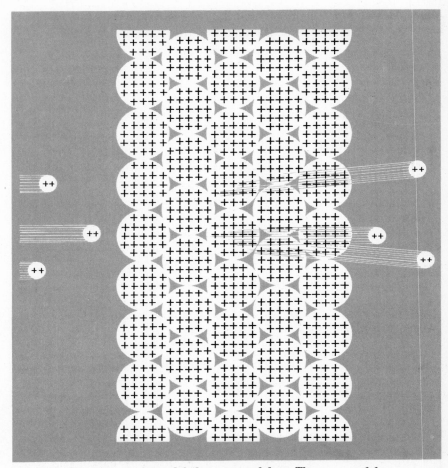

Fig. 3.8   Penetration of metal foil as expected from Thomson model.

particles come from the radioactive element polonium. A thick lead plate, with a hole cut in it, serves to give a beam of alpha particles. In the path of the beam is a metal foil. The alpha particles may be detected with a screen coated with zinc sulfide.

As expected, 99 per cent of the alpha particles go through. However, some are deflected at fairly large angles. A few are actually reflected back along their path. To Rutherford this was absolutely unbelievable. In his own words, "it was almost as incredible as if you fired a 15-inch shell at a piece of tissue paper and it came back and hit you." The Thomson model could not account for such large deflections. If mass and positive charge are uniformly spread throughout the metal, a positively charged alpha particle would not encounter a large repulsion or major obstacle anywhere in its path. This is shown in Fig. 3.8. According to Rutherford, the only way to account for the large deflection is to say that the positive electricity and mass in the metal foil are concentrated in very small regions. Although, as shown in Fig. 3.9, most of the alpha particles can go through without any deflection, occasionally one comes very close to the high concentration of positive charge. This high concentration of positive charge is essentially immovable because of its high mass. As the like charges get closer together, they repel each other, and the repulsion may be big enough to cause the alpha particle to swerve considerably from its original path. So, Rutherford suggested that an atom has a *nucleus,* or *center, in which its positive charge and mass are concentrated.*

The quantitative results of scattering experiments such as Rutherford's

Fig. 3.9   *Rutherford model to account for deflection of alpha particles.*

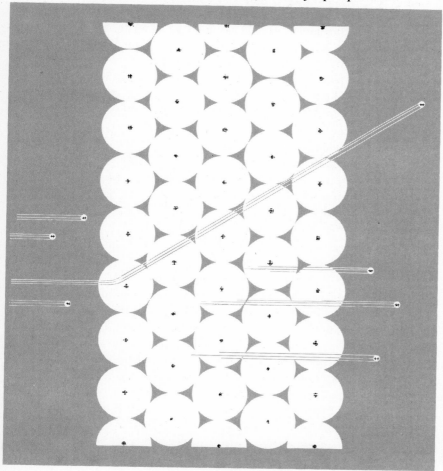

Table 3.1 Fundamental Particles

Particle	Mass, a.m.u.	Charge
Electron	0.00055	−1
Proton	1.00732	+1
Neutron	1.00866	0

indicate that the nucleus of an atom has a diameter of approximately 10^{-13} cm. Calculations of the type used in Question 2.11 suggest that atoms have diameters about 100,000 times as great. In other words, the nucleus occupies an extremely tiny portion of the volume of the entire atom; practically all the volume of the atom is occupied by electrons. As an analogy, if an atom were magnified so that the nucleus were the size of the period at the end of this sentence, then the whole atom would be bigger than a house.

In a neutral atom, the negative charge contributed by the electrons is exactly balanced by the positive charge of the nucleus. Just as the negative charge is thought to come from electrons (discrete units of negative charge), the positive charge of the nucleus is thought to come from protons (discrete units of positive charge). In addition, the nucleus is considered to contain *neutrons*, which, as the name implies, are fundamental particles having no charge at all.* The properties of the fundamental particles—electrons, protons, and neutrons—are summarized in Table 3.1. For simplicity, the charge is given in electronic charge units, where the electron (actual charge -1.60×10^{-19} coulomb) is assigned a charge of -1.

In summary, the atom is considered to be composed of electrons, neutrons, and protons. The extranuclear region, which comprises practically the whole volume of the atom, contains only the negatively charged electrons. The nucleus, which comprises practically the whole mass of the atom, contains protons and neutrons. Since each proton carries a charge of $+1$, the charge on a nucleus is equal to the number of protons in that nucleus. For example, if there are 8 protons in a nucleus (as in the nucleus of an oxygen atom), the charge on that nucleus is $+8$, no matter how many neutrons there are. The number of protons in a nucleus is referred to as the

---

* In 1920 Rutherford proposed that a nucleus contained, besides protons, pairs of protons and electrons, which he called neutrons. However, in 1932 Chadwick discovered the neutron as a separate entity, and at present it is believed that there are no electrons in the nucleus.

atomic number. This number is unique for a given element (e.g., oxygen, and only oxygen, has atomic number 8) and is usually designated by the letter Z. (Z can be any number from one to a hundred or so.) In any neutral atom, the number of electrons is also given by Z, since the number of negative electrons must equal the number of positive protons if the atom is to be electrically neutral.

The number of protons plus the number of neutrons is referred to as the *mass number A.* To designate a specific nucleus, it is convenient to use a symbol such as $_{11}Na^{23}$. The subscript 11 is Z, the number of protons; the superscript 23 is A, the number of protons plus neutrons. A minus Z gives the number of neutrons, which in this case is 12. Because the mass of both the proton and the neutron is approximately 1 a.m.u., the mass of a nucleus (in atomic mass units) is approximately equal to its mass number A.*

The existence of isotopes results from differences in the nucleus. All the atoms of a given element have the same number of electrons and, likewise, the same number of protons. However, they may differ in the number of neutrons. In fact, isotopes may be defined as atoms of the same atomic number but of different numbers of neutrons. Some elements have as many as 20 isotopes. Chlorine, however, has only two naturally occurring isotopes, $_{17}Cl^{35}$ and $_{17}Cl^{37}$. The first isotope has 17 protons and 18 neutrons; the second has 17 protons and 20 neutrons. The two isotopes have nearly identical chemical properties. Apparently, chemical properties are essentially unaffected by the number of neutrons in the nucleus. The mean atomic weight determined by experiment is a weighted average of the masses of the different isotopes. In the case of chlorine, the natural isotope abundance is 75.40 per cent of the light variety and 24.60 per cent of the heavy variety. Of 1,000 chlorine atoms selected at random, 754 have a mass number of 35 (mass 34.97 a.m.u.), and 246 atoms have a mass number of 37 (mass 36.97 a.m.u.). The observed atomic weight of chlorine is 754×34.97 plus 246×36.97 divided by 1,000, or 35.46 a.m.u.

For the light elements, the number of protons and neutrons in the nucleus is approximately the same, but for the heavy elements the number of neutrons is larger (sometimes by 50 per cent) than the number of protons. Since the mean atomic weight of elements generally increases as the atomic number increases, if the elements are arranged in order of increasing atomic number, they are also arranged according to increasing atomic weight. The only exceptions observed are the elements potassium, nickel,

---

* However, it is not exactly equal. Apparently, in the formation of a nucleus from protons and neutrons, some of the mass of the protons and neutrons is converted to energy, so that the nuclear mass does not exactly equal the sum of the initial masses of the protons and neutrons. A quantitative discussion of mass-energy conversion is given in Sec. 29.5.

and iodine (atomic numbers 19, 28, and 53), for each of which the mean atomic weight is less than for the element of next lower Z.

3.7   PERIODIC LAW

Important deductions about the more detailed structure of atoms can be made from studies of the chemical behavior of the different elements. For example, it is found that most elements react with some other elements, but there are some, like helium and neon, which are inert and have no tendency to react with any of the other elements. When all the elements are arranged in order of increasing atomic number, the inert elements are not bunched together but occur periodically throughout the sequence. This is shown in Fig. 3.10. The observation that various *properties* (of which inertness is but one example) *recur periodically* throughout the sequence of elements is called the *periodic law.* The law was discovered independently by Lothar Meyer in Germany and Mendeleev in Russia in about 1868 to 1870.

The inert elements—helium, neon, argon, krypton, xenon, and radon, with atomic numbers 2, 10, 18, 36, 54, and 86, respectively—are all gases under usual conditions. For this reason, they are frequently called the *inert gases.* The elements which directly follow the inert gases—lithium, sodium, potassium, rubidium, cesium, and francium, with atomic numbers 3, 11, 19, 37, 55, and 87, respectively—are *metals;* i.e., they have a *shiny luster* and are *good conductors of heat and electricity.* As a group they are called the *alkali metals.* In their chemical properties, the alkali metals bear strong resemblance to each other. For example, they all react vigorously with water to liberate hydrogen and form basic solutions. If these basic solutions are neutralized with hydrochloric acid and the water evaporated, a white salt is formed in each case. These salts, e.g., sodium chloride (NaCl) or potassium chloride (KCl), are quite similar to each other; for

Fig. 3.10   Periodic occurrence of inertness in the elements.

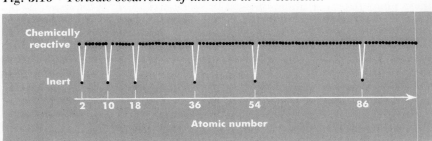

instance, all dissolve readily in water to give electrically conducting solutions. The salts can also be made by direct reaction between the alkali metals and chlorine gas. All the alkali metals form hydroxy compounds (e.g., NaOH) which are basic.

The elements which directly precede the inert gases—fluorine, chlorine, bromine, iodine, and astatine, with atomic numbers 9, 17, 35, 53, and 85, respectively—also resemble each other. As a group, they are called the *halogens.* (The element hydrogen, which directly precedes helium, is not included in this group. As the first of all elements, hydrogen has unique properties, which do not resemble those of the halogens.) Unlike the alkali elements, the halogens are *nonmetals;* i.e., they are *poor conductors of heat and electricity.* Under usual conditions, fluorine and chlorine are gases; bromine is a liquid; and iodine and astatine are solids. The halogens resemble each other in that all react with hydrogen to form compounds, e.g., hydrogen fluoride (HF) or hydrogen chloride (HCl), which dissolve in water to give acid solutions. Neutralization of these acid solutions with sodium hydroxide, followed by evaporation of the water, leads to the formation of white sodium salts. These salts, e.g., sodium fluoride (NaF) or sodium iodide (NaI), can also be prepared by the direct reaction of the halogens with sodium. With the exception of fluorine, halogens form hydroxy compounds which are all acidic. An example is HOCl (hypochlorous acid).

The elements that fall between an alkali metal and the next following halogen show a progressive gradation of properties between the two extremes. For example, the elements magnesium (atomic number 12), aluminum (13), silicon (14), phosphorus (15), and sulfur (16), which lie between sodium (11) and chlorine (17), represent such a gradation. In this sequence, there is a decrease in metallic character. Magnesium and aluminum are metals; phosphorus and sulfur are nonmetals; silicon is intermediate. Concurrently, there is a progressive change from basic to acidic character of the hydroxy compounds. The hydroxy compound of magnesium, $Mg(OH)_2$, or magnesium hydroxide, is basic; the hydroxy compounds of sulfur and phosphorus, e.g., H_2SO_4 or $(HO)_2SO_2$, sulfuric acid, and H_3PO_4 or $(HO)_3PO$, phosphoric acid, are acidic; the hydroxy compounds of aluminum and silicon are intermediate.

In order to emphasize the periodic reappearance of properties, it is customary to lay out the elements, not in a long straight line as in Fig. 3.10, but in what is known as a *periodic table.* There are many forms of the periodic table, one of which is shown in Table 3.2. The number beneath the symbol of each element is the atomic number. The asterisk and the dagger represent the elements listed at the bottom.

The basic feature of the periodic table is the arrangement of the elements in order of increasing atomic number, with elements that are similar in properties placed under each other in a vertical column called a *group*. There are eight main groups, designated in Table 3.2 as I, II, III, IV, V, VI, VII, and 0. Group I includes hydrogen plus the alkali metals; group VII, the halogens; and group 0, the inert gases. The elements intervening between groups II and III are called the *transition elements*. Each short vertical column of transition elements is called a *subgroup* and is named after the head element. Thus, Zn, Cd, and Hg make up the zinc subgroup.

A horizontal sequence of the periodic table is called a *period.* These are numbered from the top down. The first period contains two elements (H and He); the second and third, eight elements; the fourth and fifth, eighteen elements. The elements denoted by the single asterisk are part of the sixth period; those by the dagger, the seventh period.

The periodic table is a useful device for organizing the chemistry of

Table 3.2   Periodic Table

Group	I	II												III	IV	V	VI	VII	0
Period																			
1	H 1																		He 2
2	Li 3	Be 4												B 5	C 6	N 7	O 8	F 9	Ne 10
3	Na 11	Mg 12		Transition elements										Al 13	Si 14	P 15	S 16	Cl 17	Ar 18
4	K 19	Ca 20	Sc 21	Ti 22	V 23	Cr 24	Mn 25	Fe 26	Co 27	Ni 28	Cu 29	Zn 30		Ga 31	Ge 32	As 33	Se 34	Br 35	Kr 36
5	Rb 37	Sr 38	Y 39	Zr 40	Nb 41	Mo 42	Tc 43	Ru 44	Rh 45	Pd 46	Ag 47	Cd 48		In 49	Sn 50	Sb 51	Te 52	I 53	Xe 54
6	Cs 55	Ba 56	* 57–71	Hf 72	Ta 73	W 74	Re 75	Os 76	Ir 77	Pt 78	Au 79	Hg 80		Tl 81	Pb 82	Bi 83	Po 84	At 85	Rn 86
7	Fr 87	Ra 88	† 89–																

	*	La 57	Ce 58	Pr 59	Nd 60	Pm 61	Sm 62	Eu 63	Gd 64	Tb 65	Dy 66	Ho 67	Er 68	Tm 69	Yb 70	Lu 71
	†	Ac 89	Th 90	Pa 91	U 92	Np 93	Pu 94	Am 95	Cm 96	Bk 97	Cf 98	Es 99	Fm 100	Md 101	(?) 102	

the elements. Furthermore, the fact that the elements can be arranged systematically in such a table indicates a periodic recurrence of detailed structure of individual atoms. We shall consider the periodic table in greater detail in Sec. 3.9.

3.8   ELECTRONIC ENERGY LEVELS

The picture of an atom as consisting of a positive nucleus with surrounding negative electrons presents a problem. Because of the opposite charges, electrons are attracted to the nucleus. They would be pulled into the nucleus if they were stationary, so we must assume that the electrons are in some sort of motion which counteracts the pull of the nucleus. However, if they are in motion, they should radiate energy, since it is observed in all other cases that electric charges moving under the influence of attractive forces give off energy. Such a loss of energy would result in a slowing down of the electron, making it less able to withstand the attraction of the nucleus. Consequently, the electron would spiral down into the nucleus, and the atom should collapse. Since atoms do not collapse, there must be an inconsistency in the above argument.

A clue to solving the problem comes from the study of light emitted from substances when they are heated. It is a familiar fact that white light consists of different colors and is separated into its constituent colors when passed through a prism. Suppose that white light from a glowing solid, as, for example, the filament of a lamp, is passed through a prism, as diagrammed in Fig. 3.11. The film shows a *continuous spectrum* of colors, a gradual blending from one color to the next. The colors correspond to light of different energies. On passing through the prism, the light of highest energy (violet) is bent most; the light of lowest energy (red) is bent least.

If the above experiment is repeated using as the light source a flame to which a vaporizable salt is added, the spectrum obtained is not continuous. As represented in Fig. 3.12, the film shows a *line spectrum*, narrow lines of colors. Since each of the lines corresponds to light of a definite energy,

Fig. 3.11   *Continuous spectrum.*

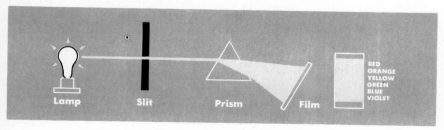

Lamp   Slit   Prism   Film

RED
ORANGE
YELLOW
GREEN
BLUE
VIOLET

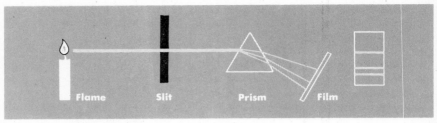

Fig. 3.12   Line spectrum.

the existence of a line spectrum implies that atoms can radiate only certain energies. In other words, not just any energy is emitted from atoms but only definite, discrete values.

When compounds of the different elements are used as the light source and the spectra investigated as above, it is observed that each element contributes its own characteristic line spectrum. Furthermore, it is noted that there is a pattern of regularity in the lines of a given element. Also, it is found that the spectrum of one element is related to that of another.

Niels Bohr, the Danish physicist, in 1913 proposed a theory which not only accounted for the existence of line spectra but also suggested why atoms do not collapse. He made the revolutionary suggestion that the total energy (kinetic plus potential) of an electron in an atom is *quantized,* i.e., *restricted to having only certain values.* This amounts to assuming that in an atom an electron cannot have just any energy but only certain specific values. The only way an electron can change its energy is to shift from one discrete energy level to another. The transition cannot be gradual but must occur all at once. If no lower energy level is available, the electron cannot emit energy. For this reason, atoms do not collapse. If a lower energy level is available, the electron can radiate energy, but only a definite amount. This amount of energy has to be exactly equal to the difference between one energy level and another. In the production of line spectra, electrons are presumably raised to higher energy levels by the heat energy of the flame. When the electrons drop back to lower energy levels, light of characteristic energy is emitted.

Bohr's assumption established the foundation for *quantum mechanics,* the study of the laws of motion that govern the behavior of small particles.* Particles of small mass, such as electrons, apparently do not follow Newton's laws of motion and the classical laws of electrodynamics which describe the interactions of moving charges. New principles are required. The basic principle is that only specified energy levels are possible for elec-

---

* Although the laws of quantum mechanics are necessary for describing how small bodies move, they also apply to large bodies. In the latter case, the results from quantum mechanics are identical with those obtained more simply from Newton's laws of motion.

OPTICAL SPECTRA

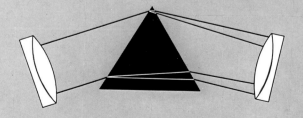

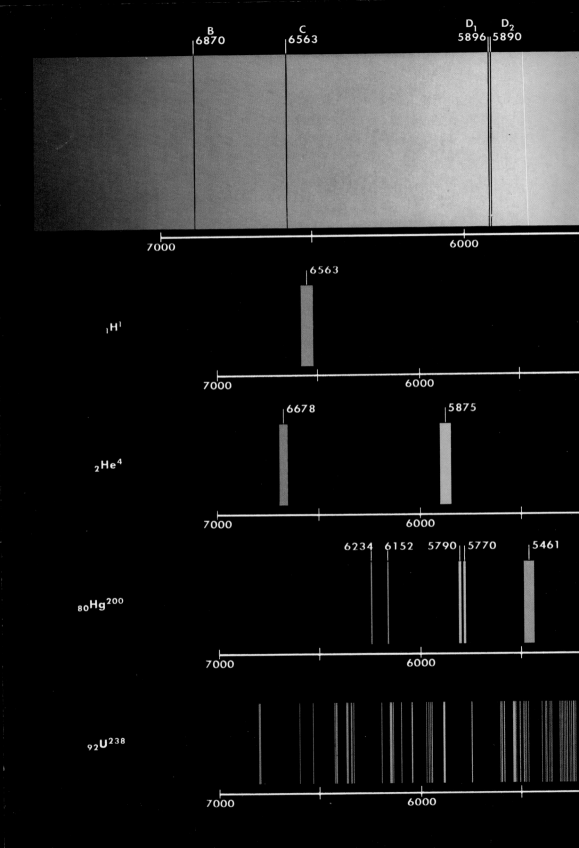

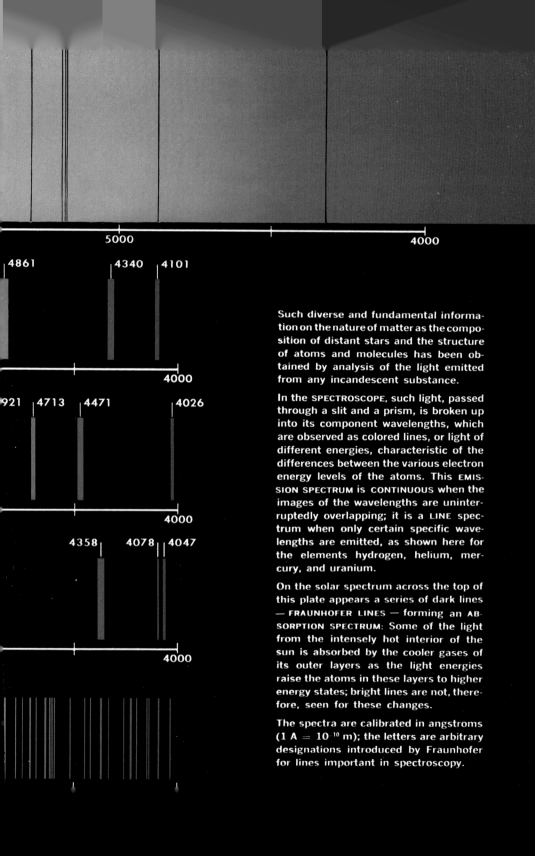

5000

4000

4861

4340

4101

4000

921

4713

4471

4026

4000

4358

4078

4047

4000

Such diverse and fundamental information on the nature of matter as the composition of distant stars and the structure of atoms and molecules has been obtained by analysis of the light emitted from any incandescent substance.

In the SPECTROSCOPE, such light, passed through a slit and a prism, is broken up into its component wavelengths, which are observed as colored lines, or light of different energies, characteristic of the differences between the various electron energy levels of the atoms. This EMISSION SPECTRUM is CONTINUOUS when the images of the wavelengths are uninterruptedly overlapping; it is a LINE spectrum when only certain specific wavelengths are emitted, as shown here for the elements hydrogen, helium, mercury, and uranium.

On the solar spectrum across the top of this plate appears a series of dark lines — FRAUNHOFER LINES — forming an ABSORPTION SPECTRUM: Some of the light from the intensely hot interior of the sun is absorbed by the cooler gases of its outer layers as the light energies raise the atoms in these layers to higher energy states; bright lines are not, therefore, seen for these changes.

The spectra are calibrated in angstroms ($1 A = 10^{-10}$ m); the letters are arbitrary designations introduced by Fraunhofer for lines important in spectroscopy.

trons in atoms. These energy levels are numbered, starting with the lowest as 1, the next higher as 2, the next higher as 3, etc. The number of the energy level, usually designated by n, is referred to as the principal quantum number. A second principle of quantum mechanics is that the electron population of any energy level in an atom is limited to $2n^2$. This means that for the lowest energy level ($n = 1$) the maximum population is $2(1)^2$, or 2. For the second level ($n = 2$), the maximum population is $2(2)^2$, or 8.

We can now draw what is known as an energy-level diagram. Figure 3.13 is such a diagram. The bottom line represents the lowest energy level —the level for which it requires the addition of the greatest energy in order to expel the electron from the atom. Other lines represent levels of higher energy. In principle, there are an infinite number of energy levels, but usually only the lowest seven or eight need to be considered. As shown in Fig. 3.13, the energy difference between low energy levels is observed to be greater than that between high levels.

The first principle of quantum mechanics states that electrons are in energy levels, and no electrons have energies that lie between levels. The second principle requires that the maximum population in the first energy level be 2; in the second level, 8; in the third level, 18; in the fourth level, 32; in the fifth level, 50; etc. Electrons in the lowest energy level ($n = 1$) are referred to as being in the K shell, in the K orbit, or in the innermost orbit.* These electrons are the ones most tightly bound. Those in the second energy level ($n = 2$) are

---

* The terms "shell" and "orbit" come from early models of the atom. Originally, Bohr suggested that the electrons in atoms move in curved orbits about the nucleus. This motion was not limited to a single plane but occurred in three dimensions, so that the path traced out by an electron described a spherical shell. All the electrons in a given shell were identified with one energy level. The shell closest to the nucleus corresponded to the lowest energy level; shells farther from the nucleus corresponded to higher energy levels. As we shall see later, this picture of the atom is no longer acceptable. However, the terms "shell" and "orbit" are still sometimes used to refer to energy levels.

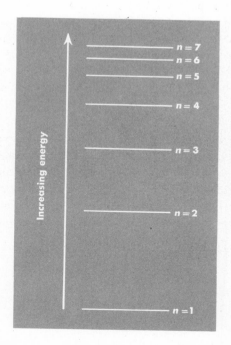

Fig. 3.13   *Energy levels of electrons in an atom.*

referred to as being in the L shell, or L orbit. The higher energy levels are numbered ($n = 3, 4, 5, \ldots$) or lettered ($M, N, O, \ldots$) consecutively from there on. Higher energy levels are referred to as outer energy levels.

3.9 ENERGY LEVELS AND THE PERIODIC TABLE

The limitation of the number of electrons in a given energy level can be used to account for the periodic recurrence of properties in the elements, if it is assumed that the properties of atoms depend significantly on the number of electrons in the outermost energy level. Imagine the building up of an atom by addition of electrons to a nucleus of the proper atomic number. Each electron enters the lowest energy level available. In the case of hydrogen ($Z = 1$), the lone electron goes into the K shell. In helium, the nucleus contains 2 protons, and both electrons enter the K shell. For lithium, with $Z = 3$, the third electron has to go into the L shell, since the maximum population in the K shell is 2. Table 3.3 lists the first 18 elements in order of increasing atomic number and shows the number of electrons in the various energy levels. Since the K shell can accommodate only 2 electrons, it becomes completely populated in the inert gas helium. Proceeding from helium, the L-shell population increases from 1 in lithium to 8 in neon. In neon, the situation is like that of helium. With 2 electrons in the K shell and 8 electrons in the L shell, the shells which are occupied are completely filled, and the shells which are empty are completely empty. Neon is inert. In other words, after a period or a cycle of 8 atoms, a repetition of the property of inertness appears. With the next 8 elements, electrons add to the third, or M, shell, building it up gradually from 1 to 8

Table 3.3 *Electronic Configurations*

Atomic no.	1	2	3	4	5	6	7	8	9	10	11	12	13	14	15	16	17	18
Element	H	He	Li	Be	B	C	N	O	F	Ne	Na	Mg	Al	Si	P	S	Cl	Ar
Electron Population																		
K level	1	2	2	2	2	2	2	2	2	2	2	2	2	2	2	2	2	2
L level			1	2	3	4	5	6	7	8	8	8	8	8	8	8	8	8
M level											1	2	3	4	5	6	7	8
		↑								↑								↑
		in-ert								in-ert								in-ert

electrons. The element argon, number 18, might not be expected to be inert, because, according to the energy-level diagram, 10 more, or a total of 18, electrons can be put into the M shell. However, argon is observed to be inert. It must be that 8 electrons in the third shell behave like a full shell. This point will be considered in greater detail later in this section.

That the properties of atoms are closely tied to the number of electrons in the outermost energy level can be seen further from the following examples. In the case of lithium, there is 1 electron in the outermost energy level (the L shell). Sodium also has 1 electron in its outermost energy level (the M shell). The properties of lithium and sodium are close to being identical, as already noted in Sec. 3.7. Likewise, beryllium ($Z = 4$) and magnesium ($Z = 12$) are similar. Each has 2 electrons in its outermost shell. In the periodic table, elements with similar properties are placed under each other. This corresponds to grouping together atoms which have the same number of electrons in the outermost energy level.

In the periodic table (see Table 3.2 or the back cover), the first period contains but two elements (H and He), a fact that is consistent with limiting the population of the K energy level to 2 electrons. The second period contains eight elements (lithium, beryllium, boron, carbon, nitrogen, oxygen, fluorine, and neon), a grouping consistent with the gradual filling of the L energy level to a maximum population of 8 electrons. Since the L energy level is the outermost level occupied in these particular atoms, significant changes in properties are observed within the period.

The third period, covering sodium through argon, is more difficult to account for. Based on observed properties, it contains only 8 elements, whereas the energy-level picture suggests 18. (The reason for this apparent discrepancy is associated with the fact that, after 8 electrons have been added to the third shell, the next 2 electrons go into the fourth shell, even though the third shell is not yet filled.) In the periodic table the element sodium, which has 1 electron in its outermost shell, is placed under lithium in group I; magnesium is placed under beryllium in group II; aluminum under boron in group III; silicon under carbon in group IV; phosphorus under nitrogen in group V; sulfur under oxygen in group VI; chlorine under fluorine in group VII; and argon under neon in group 0. Because they have the same number of electrons in the outermost shell, the elements of each pair just mentioned have chemical similarity.

The fourth period, potassium through krypton, is even more complicated than the third period. As can be seen from the periodic table, there are 18 elements in the fourth period, ranging from atomic number 19 through atomic number 36. Of these 18 elements, the first two—K and Ca—and the last six—Ga, Ge, As, Se, Br, and Kr—correspond to addition of elec-

Table 3.4 **Electronic Configurations**

Element	Z	K level	L level	M level	N level
Potassium	19	$2e^-$	$8e^-$	$8e^-$	$1e^-$
Copper	29	$2e^-$	$8e^-$	$18e^-$	$1e^-$

trons to the outermost (fourth) shell. The 10 intervening elements—Sc, Ti, V, Cr, Mn, Fe, Co, Ni, Cu, and Zn—have no more than 2 electrons in the outermost shell. The build-up of the outermost shell is interrupted to allow for the belated filling of the next-to-outermost shell. Similar delayed filling of a next-to-outermost shell also occurs in the fifth and sixth periods.

The filling of shells in the fourth period occurs so that there are two fourth-period elements, potassium ($Z = 19$) and copper ($Z = 29$), both of which have 1 electron in the outermost, or fourth, energy level. Similarly, calcium ($Z = 20$) and zinc ($Z = 30$) have 2 electrons in the fourth energy level. Potassium and copper are similar in some properties, presumably because each has the same number of electrons in its outermost shell. However, K and Cu show differences in other properties, apparently because there are different numbers of electrons in the second-outermost shell (Table 3.4). The second shell from the outside also seems to have an influence, sometimes quite large, on the chemical properties of an atom.

In succeeding periods, the electronic configuration expansion proceeds in a similar but somewhat more complicated fashion. Before going on, we need to clear up one question raised previously. In the third period we found 8 elements. From the energy-level diagram, we expected 18. Apparently the energy diagram as given is not satisfactory without some correction.

We have implied that all the electrons in a given shell are of the same energy. This is not quite true. Studies of the spectra of the different elements indicate that each energy level in Fig. 3.13 actually consists of sev-

Fig. 3.14 **Energy sublevels of the M shell.**

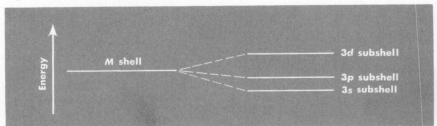

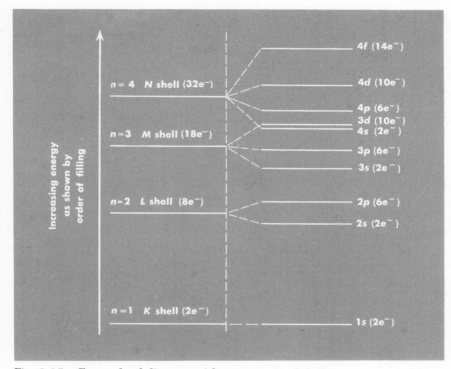

Fig. 3.15   *Energy-level diagram with component subshells.*

eral energy levels closely bunched together. Technically, this is described by saying that each *main shell* consists of one or more *subshells*, or energy sublevels. The number of subshells in any main shell is equal to the principal quantum number *n*. Thus, the *K* shell ($n = 1$) consists of only one energy level. The *L* shell ($n = 2$) consists of two subshells. This means that not all the electrons in the *L* shell are of precisely the same energy. One group of electrons has an energy that is slightly higher than that of the other group. In the *M* shell ($n = 3$) there are three energy levels; in the *N* shell, four energy levels, etc. The subshells are designated by various devices. We shall find it most convenient to designate the lowest subshell of a given shell as an *s* subshell. The next higher subshell is labeled a *p* subshell; the next higher, a *d* subshell; the one above that, an *f* subshell.*

To illustrate subshells, we can look at the *M* shell of electrons, characterized by principal quantum number 3. These electrons fall into three

---

* The letters *s*, *p*, *d*, and *f* were originally chosen on the basis of observations of line spectra of elements such as sodium. Certain lines were observed to belong to a "sharp" series, and these were associated with energy transitions involving the *s* subshell; other spectrum lines were classified as belonging to a "principal," "diffuse," or "fundamental" series; hence the designations *p*, *d*, and *f*.

groups of energy. The 3s subshell is slightly lower in energy than the 3p subshell, which in turn has lower energy than the 3d. Instead of having the third shell represented by a single line on an energy scale, we must use three closely spaced levels, as shown in Fig. 3.14.

The energy-level diagram must now be redrawn. To the left of the dotted line in Fig. 3.15 are shown the main shells. To the right of the dotted line are shown the component subshells. A distinctive feature is the overlapping of the higher energy subshells, an overlapping which gets more complicated as the fifth and sixth main shells are added to the picture.

Just as the number of electrons that can be put in any main shell is limited, the population of a subshell is similarly limited. An s subshell can hold 2 electrons, a p subshell 6, a d subshell 10, and an f subshell 14. In Fig. 3.15, the numbers in parentheses indicate the maximum population of the shells and subshells.

How does the existence of subshells affect the building of atoms from electrons and nuclei? So far as the first 18 elements are concerned, the number of electrons per main shell is as predicted before. As shown in Table 3.5, element 18, argon, has 2 electrons in the 1s subshell, 2 in the 2s, 6 in the 2p, 2 in the 3s, and 6 in the 3p. Because the next subshell is so much higher in energy than the 3p (see Fig. 3.15), argon behaves as an inert atom. There seems to be special stability associated with 8 electrons in any main shell everywhere in the periodic table.

In the next element, potassium, number 19, the nineteenth electron goes into the 4s subshell, since the 4s is lower in energy than the 3d (Fig. 3.15), even though the third shell is not yet completely populated. For calcium, element 20, another electron is added to the 4s energy level. For element 21, scandium, the 21st electron goes into the next available state, the 3d level. With minor irregularities the build-up of the third subshell proceeds in this fashion for the next eight elements. The addition of electrons to the

Table 3.5   Electronic Configurations

Element	Atomic no.	Electron population									
		1s	2s	2p	3s	3p	3d	4s	4p	4d	4f
Argon	18	2	2	6	2	6					
Potassium	19	2	2	6	2	6		1			
Calcium	20	2	2	6	2	6		2			
Scandium	21	2	2	6	2	6	1	2			
Titanium	22	2	2	6	2	6	2	2			

$3d$ subshell, while the $4s$ subshell is occupied, has the interesting effect on the chemistry of the elements from calcium through zinc that the chemical properties of these elements do not change drastically with increasing atomic number. In the sixth period there is an even better example of this. The elements 57 through 71, called the *lanthanides,* or *rare-earth elements,* are built up by the addition of electrons primarily to the third-outermost shell. Such changes deep within the atom do not affect chemical properties very much. All the lanthanides have nearly identical properties.

The electronic configurations of all the elements are shown in Table 3.6. These configurations apply to the atoms in their lowest energy states. The detailed assignment of electrons is based on observations of the spectra and of the magnetic properties (Sec. 3.11) of the individual elements. The question marks denote cases where the assignment is in doubt. Unfortunately, electronic configurations by themselves do not account for all chemical properties of the elements. Predictions made from these configurations alone are sometimes not borne out.

3.10   ELECTRON PROBABILITY DISTRIBUTIONS

The periodic table can be accounted for by assuming that the electrons in atoms have various energy levels. It would be nice to describe these different energy levels as being associated with different kinds of motion of the electrons. Unfortunately, this is not possible. As a consequence of Heisenberg's *uncertainty principle* (1927), it is impossible to know simultaneously the momentum and the position of an electron precisely enough to draw a picture of the path of an electron in a particular energy level. Any experiment, no matter how perfectly designed, to measure the location or the momentum of an electron must, by the measuring process, change either its momentum or location. Since tracks cannot be drawn for electrons, the best we can do is to speak of the probability, or relative chance, of finding an electron at a given location within the atom.

The calculation of the probability of finding an electron at various points in an atom is an extremely involved mathematical problem. It is solved by applying the principles of *wave mechanics,* the description of small particles in terms of waves. What wave mechanics does is to take the mathematical equations which describe the motion of waves and use them to describe the probability of finding small particles such as electrons.

The probability of finding an electron, as calculated from wave mechanics, can be specified by a *probability distribution,* such as that given in Fig. 3.16a. Here the probability of finding a 1s electron at a given location in space is plotted as a function of the distance of that location from

Table 3.6   Electronic Configurations

Z	Element	1	2		3			4				5				6				7
		s	s	p	s	p	d	s	p	d	f	s	p	d	f	s	p	d	f	s
1	H	1																		
2	He	2																		
3	Li	2	1																	
4	Be	2	2																	
5	B	2	2	1																
6	C	2	2	2																
7	N	2	2	3																
8	O	2	2	4																
9	F	2	2	5																
10	Ne	2	2	6																
11	Na	2	2	6	1															
12	Mg	2	2	6	2															
13	Al	2	2	6	2	1														
14	Si	2	2	6	2	2														
15	P	2	2	6	2	3														
16	S	2	2	6	2	4														
17	Cl	2	2	6	2	5														
18	Ar	2	2	6	2	6														
19	K	2	2	6	2	6		1												
20	Ca	2	2	6	2	6		2												
21	Sc	2	2	6	2	6	1	2												
22	Ti	2	2	6	2	6	2	2												
23	V	2	2	6	2	6	3	2												
24	Cr	2	2	6	2	6	5	1												
25	Mn	2	2	6	2	6	5	2												
26	Fe	2	2	6	2	6	6	2												
27	Co	2	2	6	2	6	7	2												
28	Ni	2	2	6	2	6	8	2												
29	Cu	2	2	6	2	6	10	1												
30	Zn	2	2	6	2	6	10	2												
31	Ga	2	2	6	2	6	10	2	1											
32	Ge	2	2	6	2	6	10	2	2											
33	As	2	2	6	2	6	10	2	3											
34	Se	2	2	6	2	6	10	2	4											
35	Br	2	2	6	2	6	10	2	5											
36	Kr	2	2	6	2	6	10	2	6											
37	Rb	2	2	6	2	6	10	2	6			1								
38	Sr	2	2	6	2	6	10	2	6			2								
39	Y	2	2	6	2	6	10	2	6	1		2								
40	Zr	2	2	6	2	6	10	2	6	2		2								
41	Nb	2	2	6	2	6	10	2	6	4		1								
42	Mo	2	2	6	2	6	10	2	6	5		1								
43	Tc	2	2	6	2	6	10	2	6	6		1?								
44	Ru	2	2	6	2	6	10	2	6	7		1								
45	Rh	2	2	6	2	6	10	2	6	8		1								
46	Pd	2	2	6	2	6	10	2	6	10										
47	Ag	2	2	6	2	6	10	2	6	10		1								
48	Cd	2	2	6	2	6	10	2	6	10		2								
49	In	2	2	6	2	6	10	2	6	10		2	1							
50	Sn	2	2	6	2	6	10	2	6	10		2	2							

Table 3.6   Electronic Configurations (Continued)

Z	Element	1	2		3			4				5				6				7
		s	s	p	s	p	d	s	p	d	f	s	p	d	f	s	p	d	f	s
51	Sb	2	2	6	2	6	10	2	6	10		2	3							
52	Te	2	2	6	2	6	10	2	6	10		2	4							
53	I	2	2	6	2	6	10	2	6	10		2	5							
54	Xe	2	2	6	2	6	10	2	6	10		2	6							
55	Cs	2	2	6	2	6	10	2	6	10		2	6			1				
56	Ba	2	2	6	2	6	10	2	6	10		2	6			2				
57	La	2	2	6	2	6	10	2	6	10		2	6	1		2				
58	Ce	2	2	6	2	6	10	2	6	10	2	2	6			2?				
59	Pr	2	2	6	2	6	10	2	6	10	3	2	6			2?				
60	Nd	2	2	6	2	6	10	2	6	10	4	2	6			2				
61	Pm	2	2	6	2	6	10	2	6	10	5	2	6			2?				
62	Sm	2	2	6	2	6	10	2	6	10	6	2	6			2				
63	Eu	2	2	6	2	6	10	2	6	10	7	2	6			2				
64	Gd	2	2	6	2	6	10	2	6	10	7	2	6	1		2				
65	Tb	2	2	6	2	6	10	2	6	10	9	2	6			2?				
66	Dy	2	2	6	2	6	10	2	6	10	10	2	6			2?				
67	Ho	2	2	6	2	6	10	2	6	10	11	2	6			2?				
68	Er	2	2	6	2	6	10	2	6	10	12	2	6			2?				
69	Tm	2	2	6	2	6	10	2	6	10	13	2	6			2				
70	Yb	2	2	6	2	6	10	2	6	10	14	2	6			2				
71	Lu	2	2	6	2	6	10	2	6	10	14	2	6	1		2				
72	Hf	2	2	6	2	6	10	2	6	10	14	2	6	2		2				
73	Ta	2	2	6	2	6	10	2	6	10	14	2	6	3		2				
74	W	2	2	6	2	6	10	2	6	10	14	2	6	4		2				
75	Re	2	2	6	2	6	10	2	6	10	14	2	6	5		2				
76	Os	2	2	6	2	6	10	2	6	10	14	2	6	6		2				
77	Ir	2	2	6	2	6	10	2	6	10	14	2	6	7		2				
78	Pt	2	2	6	2	6	10	2	6	10	14	2	6	9		1				
79	Au	2	2	6	2	6	10	2	6	10	14	2	6	10		1				
80	Hg	2	2	6	2	6	10	2	6	10	14	2	6	10		2				
81	Tl	2	2	6	2	6	10	2	6	10	14	2	6	10		2	1			
82	Pb	2	2	6	2	6	10	2	6	10	14	2	6	10		2	2			
83	Bi	2	2	6	2	6	10	2	6	10	14	2	6	10		2	3			
84	Po	2	2	6	2	6	10	2	6	10	14	2	6	10		2	4?			
85	At	2	2	6	2	6	10	2	6	10	14	2	6	10		2	5?			
86	Rn	2	2	6	2	6	10	2	6	10	14	2	6	10		2	6			
87	Fr	2	2	6	2	6	10	2	6	10	14	2	6	10		2	6			1?
88	Ra	2	2	6	2	6	10	2	6	10	14	2	6	10		2	6			2
89	Ac	2	2	6	2	6	10	2	6	10	14	2	6	10		2	6	1		2?
90	Th	2	2	6	2	6	10	2	6	10	14	2	6	10		2	6	2		2
91	Pa	2	2	6	2	6	10	2	6	10	14	2	6	10	2	2	6	1		2?
92	U	2	2	6	2	6	10	2	6	10	14	2	6	10	3	2	6	1		2
93	Np	2	2	6	2	6	10	2	6	10	14	2	6	10	4	2	6	1		2?
94	Pu	2	2	6	2	6	10	2	6	10	14	2	6	10	5	2	6	1		2?
95	Am	2	2	6	2	6	10	2	6	10	14	2	6	10	7	2	6			2?
96	Cm	2	2	6	2	6	10	2	6	10	14	2	6	10	7	2	6	1		2?
97	Bk	2	2	6	2	6	10	2	6	10	14	2	6	10	8	2	6	1		2?
98	Cf	2	2	6	2	6	10	2	6	10	14	2	6	10	9	2	6	1		2?
99	Es	2	2	6	2	6	10	2	6	10	14	2	6	10	10	2	6	1		2?
100	Fm	2	2	6	2	6	10	2	6	10	14	2	6	10	11	2	6	1		2?
101	Md	2	2	6	2	6	10	2	6	10	14	2	6	10	12	2	6	1		2?
102	(?)	2	2	6	2	6	10	2	6	10	14	2	6	10	14	2	6			2?

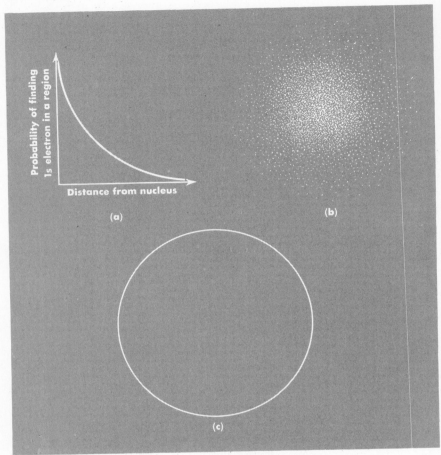

Fig. 3.16   *Representations of spatial distribution of 1s electron.*

the nucleus. The position of greatest probability is at the nucleus. Nowhere
is the probability equal to zero. Even at points at very great distances from
the nucleus there is some chance, although it is small, of finding the electron. Figure 3.16*b* is another way of representing the same electronic distribution. Here the intensity of the shading shows the relative probability
of finding the 1s electron. Consistent with this picture, one can visualize
an electron as forming a rather fuzzy charge cloud about a central nucleus.
Sometimes, it is convenient simply to indicate the shape of the charge
cloud, as is done in Fig. 3.16*c*. Remembering that atoms are three-dimensional, Fig. 3.16*c* should be thought of as a sphere within which the chance
of finding the 1s electron is great. Thus we have in Fig. 3.16 three different ways of representing the spatial distribution of an electron in a 1s
energy level. Since these representations replace the Bohr idea of a simple

orbit, they can properly be said to represent $1s$ orbits. To reduce any possible confusion between the old and new ideas, it has become customary to use the term *orbital* when referring to an energy level associated with a given electronic probability distribution.

There is still another way of describing an electron in a $1s$ orbital, a way that serves to relate the idea of electronic "shells" to probability concepts. First we raise the question: If we imagine starting out from the nucleus and working our way along a straight line from the nucleus to the outside of the atom, how does the chance of finding the $1s$ electron change? Evidently, the chance decreases, consistent with Fig. 3.16a. But now, suppose, as we work our way out of the atom, at each radial distance r from the nucleus, we investigate all the possible locations in three-dimensional space at that distance r from the nucleus and determine the chance of finding the $1s$ electron. Then, we move farther from the nucleus and investigate all the locations at a slightly bigger r. How does the chance of finding the $1s$ electron change? The answer is not immediately obvious since we have to consider both of the following factors. The chance of finding the electron at a given location decreases as we move away from the nucleus; but the number of locations to be investigated increases as we move away from the nucleus. Mathematically, this is equivalent to considering the atom to be divided into concentric layers and multiplying the probability per unit volume in a given layer by the volume of that layer. The result for a $1s$ electron is the probability curve shown in Fig. 3.17. On this plot, the greatest probability of finding the $1s$ electron occurs at the distance a, which can be thought of as corresponding to the radius of an "electron shell."

Electrons that are in different energy levels differ from each other in having different probability distributions. For example, Fig. 3.18 shows the

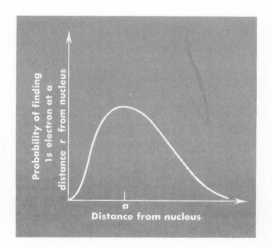

Fig. 3.17   Probability plot for $1s$ electron.

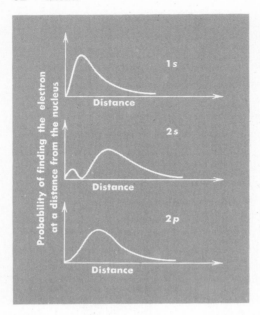

Fig. 3.18   Probability plots for various electrons.

probability that a 1s, a 2s, and a 2p electron are at various distances from a given nucleus. It should be noted that the distances of maximum probability for the 2s and 2p electrons are approximately the same and considerably larger than that for the 1s electron. This is consistent with the fact that the 2s and 2p electrons are of about the same energy and that this energy is considerably greater than that of the 1s electron. The peculiar little bump in the 2s distribution indicates that the 2s electron spends more of its time close to the nucleus than does the 2p electron. This can account for the fact that the 2s electron is bound more tightly to the nucleus (is of lower energy) than the 2p electron. Furthermore, it should be noted that all three of the distributions shown in Fig. 3.18 overlap, implying that outer electrons penetrate the region occupied by inner electrons.

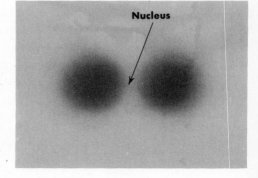

Fig. 3.19   A p-type charge cloud.

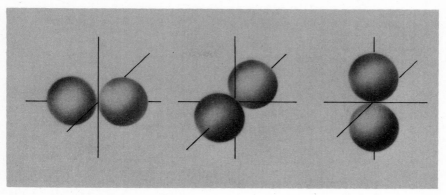

Fig. 3.20   **Shapes of p orbitals.**

Actually, there is an essential difference between s and p electrons which is not evident from Fig. 3.18. The spatial distribution of an s electron is spherically symmetrical; that is, its probability of being found is identical in all directions from the nucleus. On the other hand, p electrons are more probably found in some directions from the nucleus than in others. In fact, the probability distribution of a p electron can be thought of as forming two diffuse spheres, one on each side of the nucleus, as shown in Fig. 3.19. This is called a p orbital, and the electron in a p orbital has equal probability of being found in either half of it. A p subshell is constructed of three such orbitals all perpendicular to each other, as shown in Fig. 3.20.

The d subshells consist of five orbitals, and the f subshells of seven orbitals. Their spatial distribution is considerably more complicated.

3.11   ELECTRON SPIN

In the preceding section it was noted that there is one orbital in an s subshell, three orbitals in a p subshell, five in a d, and seven in an f. Since these subshells can accommodate 2, 6, 10, and 14 electrons, respectively, it follows that any orbital can hold 2 electrons. Actually the 2 electrons in the same orbital differ in one important respect—they have opposite "spin."* The reason for talking about electron spin comes from observations on the magnetic behavior of substances.

---

* The spin is the fourth characteristic needed to describe fully an electron in an atom. The other three are the principal quantum level, the type of subshell, and the particular orbital within the subshell. Customarily, a quantum number is used for each of these four features so that there is a set of four quantum numbers associated with an electron in an atom. In 1925 Wolfgang Pauli pointed out, in what has become known as the Pauli exclusion principle, that no two electrons in the same atom can have the same set of four quantum numbers.

It is a familiar observation that certain solids such as iron are strongly attracted to magnets. Such materials are called *ferromagnetic.* Other substances (not necessarily in the solid state) such as oxygen gas and copper sulfate are weakly attracted to magnets. These are called *paramagnetic.* Still other substances such as sodium chloride are very feebly repelled by magnets and are called *diamagnetic.* Ferromagnetism is exclusively a property of the solid state (as will be discussed in Sec. 21.1), but all three types of magnetic behavior just described are believed to arise from electrons in atoms.

Information about the magnetic behavior of individual atoms can be obtained from an experiment like the one first performed by Stern and Gerlach in 1921. In this experiment, shown in Fig. 3.21, a beam of neutral silver atoms (from the vaporization of silver) was passed between the poles of a specially designed magnet. The beam was found to be split into two separate beams; i.e., half of the atoms were deflected in one direction and the rest in the opposite direction.

In interpreting this experiment, it is assumed that an electron can be thought of as a spinning negative charge, and since any spinning charge is magnetic, an electron behaves like a tiny magnet. Two directions of spin are possible; an electron might spin about its axis in either a clockwise or a counterclockwise manner. These two directions of spin would correspond to two magnets oriented in opposite directions. If we have two electrons of opposite spin, we might expect them to attract each other, as two magnets would; but the electrical repulsion due to like negative charges is very much greater than the magnetic attraction. When electrons are required to be together, as in a completely filled subshell of an atom, each electron will pair up with another electron of opposite spin. The electron pair in an

Fig. 3.21   *Stern-Gerlach experiment showing splitting of beam of silver atoms.*

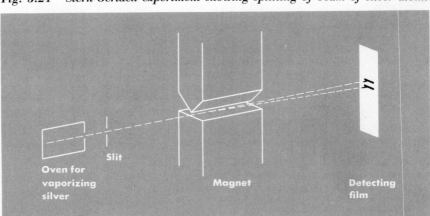

orbital is nonmagnetic, because the magnetism of one spin is canceled by the magnetism of the opposite spin.

In silver atoms, as shown by the electronic configuration given in Table 3.6, all the electrons are found in completed subshells except the one 5s electron. This electron obviously cannot be paired with another. Hence, its uncanceled spin gives magnetism to the silver atom. The two deflections observed in the Stern-Gerlach experiment presumably result from a separation of silver atoms of two types, which differ in the direction of spin of the unpaired electron, one having clockwise spin and the other, counterclockwise.

Any atom which, like the silver atom, contains an odd number of electrons must be paramagnetic. Furthermore, atoms which have an even number of electrons can also be paramagnetic provided that there is an unfilled subshell of electrons. These more complex cases will be considered in Sec. 20.2. When all the electrons in an atom are paired, there is no paramagnetism. There is only diamagnetism, which occurs in all matter, even though in paramagnetic substances it may be obscured. Diamagnetism arises not from the spin of electrons but from their electric charge. A detailed discussion of diamagnetism is beyond the scope of this course.

3.12   ELECTRONIC SYMBOLS

In preceding sections we have described some of the complexities of the electronic structure of atoms. Before proceeding to a discussion of the relationship between properties of atoms and their electronic configurations, it will be convenient to set up a simplified way of expressing electronic configurations. As already pointed out, it is the number of electrons in the outermost shell which usually determines many properties of atoms. The number of outermost electrons in an atom is shown by its electronic symbol. Examples of electronic symbols are:

$$\text{Na}\cdot \qquad \text{Ca:} \qquad :\overset{..}{\text{S}}\cdot \qquad \text{H}\cdot \qquad :\overset{..}{\text{F}}\cdot \qquad \cdot\overset{..}{\text{N}}\cdot$$

As indicated, *electronic symbols* consist of the symbol of the element surrounded by dots. The letters represent the entire *core*, or *kernel*, of the atom. The core includes not only the *nucleus* but also the *electrons in inner shells*. The surrounding dots represent the outermost electrons. These are sometimes called the *valence electrons,* since they are thought to be the electrons that are mainly responsible for the *valence,* or *combining capacity, of atoms.*

The sulfur atom, for example, has a nucleus with a positive charge of 16. It has 2 electrons in the K shell, 8 electrons in the L shell, and 6 electrons in the M shell. In the electronic symbol only the 6 outermost electrons are represented by dots. The rest of the atom (nucleus, K shell, and L shell) makes up the core and is represented by the symbol S. Since the core contains 16 positive charges and 10 negative charges, the net charge on the core is $+6$. This $+6$ charge is balanced in the neutral atom by the 6 negative charges of the outermost electrons. In writing electronic symbols, it does not matter where the dots are placed; *they have no significance so far as the actual positions of the electrons are concerned.* The dots are simply a convenient way of counting up the outermost electrons.

3.13   ATOMIC SIZES

The size of an atom is a difficult property to determine. For one thing, the electronic probability distribution (Sec. 3.10) never becomes exactly zero, even at great distances from the nucleus. Therefore, the distance designated as the boundary of the atom is an arbitrary choice. For another thing, the electronic probability distribution is affected by neighboring atoms; hence the size of the atom may change in going from one condition to another, as, for example, in going from one compound to another. Therefore, in examining any table of atomic radii we must remember that the values listed may be meaningful only in providing a comparison of sizes. Table 3.7 gives such a set of atomic radii deduced from interatomic spacings, the distances between centers of adjacent atoms. These interatomic spacings can be determined from X-ray and spectral studies of bound atoms.

In general, the atomic radii decrease in going from left to right across the periodic table and increase in going from top to bottom. How can we explain these trends?

Table 3.8 shows the change of atomic radius within the second period. It also includes the nuclear charge and the electronic configuration. Within the period, the nuclear charge increases from $+3$ to $+9$. What effect might this have on the K electrons? In each of these elements, there are two K electrons. The two electrons are attracted to the nucleus by a force proportional to the nuclear charge. As the nuclear charge increases, the pull on the electrons is increased, and the maximum in the K probability distribution curve (see Fig. 3.17) gets closer to the nucleus.

What about the L electrons? Here the problem is complicated by the fact that the L electrons are screened from the nucleus by the K electrons, so that the attractive force of the nuclear positive charge is reduced by the intervening negative charges. In lithium, for example, the outermost electron is attracted not by a charge of $+3$ but by a charge of $+3$ screened by two intervening negative electrons. The net attractive charge is closer to a $+1$ charge than to a $+3$ charge. In the beryllium atom, the L electrons

Table 3.7 Atomic Radii of the Elements

(Number above symbol is atomic number; that below is atomic radius in angstrom units, units of 10^{-8} cm.)

1 H 0.37																	2 He —
3 Li 1.23	4 Be 0.89											5 B 0.80	6 C 0.77	7 N 0.74	8 O 0.74	9 F 0.72	10 Ne —
11 Na 1.57	12 Mg 1.36											13 Al 1.25	14 Si 1.17	15 P 1.10	16 S 1.04	17 Cl 0.99	18 Ar —
19 K 2.03	20 Ca 1.74	21 Sc 1.44	22 Ti 1.32	23 V 1.22	24 Cr 1.17	25 Mn 1.17	26 Fe 1.17	27 Co 1.16	28 Ni 1.15	29 Cu 1.17	30 Zn 1.25	31 Ga 1.25	32 Ge 1.22	33 As 1.21	34 Se 1.17	35 Br 1.14	36 Kr —
37 Rb 2.16	38 Sr 1.91	39 Y 1.62	40 Zr 1.45	41 Nb 1.34	42 Mo 1.29	43 Tc —	44 Ru 1.24	45 Rh 1.25	46 Pd 1.28	47 Ag 1.34	48 Cd 1.41	49 In 1.50	50 Sn 1.41	51 Sb 1.41	52 Te 1.37	53 I 1.33	54 Xe —
55 Cs 2.35	56 Ba 1.98	*	72 Hf 1.44	73 Ta 1.34	74 W 1.30	75 Re 1.28	76 Os 1.26	77 Ir 1.26	78 Pt 1.29	79 Au 1.34	80 Hg 1.44	81 Tl 1.55	82 Pb 1.54	83 Bi 1.52	84 Po 1.53	85 At —	86 Rn —
87 Fr —	88 Ra —	†															

*	57 La 1.69	58 Ce 1.65	59 Pr 1.65	60 Nd 1.64	61 Pm —	62 Sm 1.66	63 Eu 1.85	64 Gd 1.61	65 Tb 1.59	66 Dy 1.59	67 Ho 1.58	68 Er 1.57	69 Tm 1.56	70 Yb 1.70	71 Lu 1.56
†	89 Ac —	90 Th 1.65	91 Pa —	92 U 1.42	93 Np —	94 Pu —	95 Am —	96 Cm —	97 Bk —	98 Cf —	99 Es —	100 Fm —	101 Md —	102 (?) —	

Table 3.8   Change of Atomic Radius within a Period

	Li	Be	B	C	N	O	F
Atomic radius, A.	1.23	0.89	0.80	0.77	0.74	0.74	0.72
Nuclear charge	+3	+4	+5	+6	+7	+8	+9
K-level population	$2e^-$	$2e^-$	$2e^-$	$2e^-$	$2e^-$	$2e^-$	$2e^-$
L-level population	$1e^-$	$2e^-$	$3e^-$	$4e^-$	$5e^-$	$6e^-$	$7e^-$

are attracted by a $+4$ nucleus screened by two negative charges, or effectively a $+2$ charge. Despite screening, in going from left to right across the period, the L electrons have a higher and higher positive charge attracting them to the center of the atom. Just as the K shell becomes smaller because of this effect, the L shell gets smaller also.

How does the size of atoms change within a group? Table 3.9 gives the data for the alkali elements. There is an increase of size in going from top to bottom. Going down the sequence, the number of levels populated is increasing stepwise. The more levels used, the bigger the atom. Because the nuclear charge progressively increases down the sequence, the individual shells get smaller, but apparently adding a shell is such a big effect that it dominates. Similar behavior is found for many of the other groups of the periodic table. There are, however, some places in the periodic table where the size does not change much within the same group. This is particularly true when elements number 57 through 71 intervene between the two atoms compared.

There is another method which is occasionally used for estimating the size of atoms. This method makes use of the *gram-atomic volume, the volume occupied in the solid state by one gram-atom of the element at its melting point*. It contains the Avogadro number of atoms and therefore gives some idea of the volume apparently occupied by each atom. This is not a

Table 3.9   Change of Atomic Radius within a Group

Element	Atomic radius, A.	Nuclear charge	Electronic configuration					
Li	1.23	+3	$2e^-$	$1e^-$				
Na	1.57	+11	$2e^-$	$8e^-$	$1e^-$			
K	2.03	+19	$2e^-$	$8e^-$	$8e^-$	$1e^-$		
Rb	2.16	+37	$2e^-$	$8e^-$	$18e^-$	$8e^-$	$1e^-$	
Cs	2.35	+55	$2e^-$	$8e^-$	$18e^-$	$18e^-$	$8e^-$	$1e^-$

Table 3.10   *Gram-atomic Volumes of the Elements*

(Volumes, below symbols, are in cubic centimeters)

1 H 13																	2 He 32
3 Li 13	4 Be 5											5 B 5	6 C 5	7 N 14	8 O 11	9 F 15	10 Ne 17
11 Na 24	12 Mg 14											13 Al 10	14 Si 12	15 P 17	16 S 16	17 Cl 19	18 Ar 24
19 K 46	20 Ca 26	21 Sc 15	22 Ti 11	23 V 8	24 Cr 7	25 Mn 7	26 Fe 7	27 Co 7	28 Ni 6	29 Cu 7	30 Zn 9	31 Ga 12	32 Ge 13	33 As 16	34 Se 16	35 Br 23	36 Kr 33
37 Rb 56	38 Sr 34	39 Y 21	40 Zr 14	41 Nb 11	42 Mo 9	43 Tc —	44 Ru 8	45 Rh 8	46 Pd 9	47 Ag 10	48 Cd 13	49 In 16	50 Sn 16	51 Sb 18	52 Te 21	53 I 26	54 Xe 43
55 Cs 71	56 Ba 38	*	72 Hf 13	73 Ta 11	74 W 10	75 Re 9	76 Os 9	77 Ir 9	78 Pt 9	79 Au 10	80 Hg 14	81 Tl 17	82 Pb 18	83 Bi 21	84 Po —	85 At —	86 Rn 50
87 Fr —	88 Ra 45	†															

*	57 La 22	58 Ce 21	59 Pr 21	60 Nd 21	61 Pm —	62 Sm 20	63 Eu 29	64 Gd 20	65 Tb 19	66 Dy 19	67 Ho 19	68 Er 18	69 Tm 18	70 Yb 25	71 Lu 18
†	89 Ac —	90 Th 20	91 Pa —	92 U 13	93 Np —	94 Pu —	95 Am —	96 Cm —	97 Bk —	98 Cf —	99 Es —	100 Fm —	101 Md —	102 (?) —	

reliable method in all cases because elements may differ in the way their atoms are packed in a solid. Table 3.10 gives values of the gram-atomic volumes for most of the elements. Except for the right-hand part of the table, where packing varies considerably, the general trends in size parallel those mentioned above—that is, size decreases from left to right and increases from top to bottom.

3.14   IONIZATION POTENTIAL

When an electron is pulled off a neutral atom, the particle which remains behind is a positively charged particle, or a *positive ion*. The process, called *ionization*, can be described by writing the following:

$$Na \cdot \rightarrow Na^+ + e^-$$

The electronic symbol on the left indicates the neutral sodium atom. In the process there is formed the positive sodium ion, shown on the right with a superscript $+$ to indicate a $+1$ charge. The electron is shown separately as e^-. The *ionization potential* is the work that is required to separate the negatively charged electron from the positively charged sodium ion that is attracting it. In other words, the ionization potential is the *energy required to pull an electron off an isolated atom*. It can be measured experimentally by placing the atoms of interest in a gas discharge tube and gradually increasing the voltage between the two plates. Practically no electric current flows through the tube until the voltage reaches a value high enough that electrons get ripped off the atoms. From this voltage, the ionization potential can be calculated. Usually, the ionization potential is expressed in units of *electron volts*, one electron volt being a small chunk of energy corresponding to 3.8×10^{-20} cal. One electron volt per atom is equivalent to 23 kcal. per Avogadro number of atoms.

Table 3.11 lists the values of the ionization potential for each atom of the second period. With some exceptions, there is a fairly steady increase from left to right. Why is it harder to pull an electron off neon than off lithium? At least two factors must be considered. First, the nuclear charge increases from left to right across the period. By itself this predicts that the ionization potential increases from lithium to neon. Second, the size of the atoms apparently decreases from left to right. The size effect by itself would also predict that the ionization potential should increase, since the closer an electron is to the nucleus, the harder it is to pull it off.

A shell of eight electrons, the so-called *octet*, is a grouping particularly difficult to break up. It is especially hard to pull an electron off an atom having eight electrons in its outermost shell, and atoms such as neon have very high ionization potentials. Many of the apparent irregularities in the ionization potential (see Table 3.11) can be explained by the fact that completed subshells and half-completed subshells have extra stability. Thus, the ionization potentials of Be (2s subshell completed) and N (2p half completed) are higher than expected. In general, it is sufficient to remember that the elements of high ionization potential are on the right side of the periodic table and those of low ionization potential are on the left.

Table 3.11   Ionization Potentials for Second-period Elements

Element	Li	Be	B	C	N	O	F	Ne
Electron volts	5.4	9.3	8.3	11.3	14.5	13.6	17.4	21.6

Table 3.12   Ionization Potentials for the Alkali Elements

Element	Ionization potential, e.v.	Electronic configuration				
Li	5.4	$2e^-$	$1e^-$			
Na	5.1	$2e^-$	$8e^-$	$1e^-$		
K	4.3	$2e^-$	$8e^-$	$8e^-$	$1e^-$	
Rb	4.2	$2e^-$	$8e^-$	$18e^-$	$8e^-$	$1e^-$
Cs	3.9	$2e^-$	$8e^-$	$18e^-$	$18e^-$	$8e^-$ $1e^-$

How about the trend within a group? Table 3.12 shows the values of the ionization potential for the alkali elements. There is a progressive decrease of the ionization potential in going from top to bottom. This is as predicted by the size change alone. The lithium atom is quite small; the electron which is being pulled off is close to the nucleus. It is more firmly bound than in the case of cesium, where the electron is much farther from the nucleus. The increase in nuclear charge essentially cancels out because of the screening effect of the intervening electrons.

Values of the ionization potentials of the elements are given in Table 3.13. For each element, the value given refers to the first ionization, i.e., the removal of but one electron from the neutral atom.

3.15   ELECTRON AFFINITY

Also important for determining chemical properties is the tendency of an atom to pick up additional electrons. This property can be measured by the *electron affinity*, the *energy released when an electron is added to an isolated neutral atom*. When a neutral atom picks up an electron from some source, it forms a negative ion, as indicated by writing

$$X + e^- \rightarrow X^-$$

The amount of energy released in this process is the electron affinity. Thus, the electron affinity measures the tightness of binding of an additional electron to an atom. The values for the halogen elements are given in Table 3.14.

Group VII elements are expected to have high electron affinity, because addition of one electron leads to formation of a stable octet. The decrease of electron affinity observed from Cl to I is not unexpected, because the size increases in going down the group. In iodine, the electron to be added goes into the fifth shell. Being farther from the nucleus, the added electron is not

Table 3.13 Ionization Potentials of the Elements

(in Electron Volts)

1 H 13.6																	2 He 24.6
3 Li 5.4	4 Be 9.3											5 B 8.3	6 C 11.3	7 N 14.5	8 O 13.6	9 F 17.4	10 Ne 21.6
11 Na 5.1	12 Mg 7.6											13 Al 6.0	14 Si 8.1	15 P 11.0	16 S 10.4	17 Cl 13.0	18 Ar 15.8
19 K 4.3	20 Ca 6.1	21 Sc 6.6	22 Ti 6.8	23 V 6.7	24 Cr 6.8	25 Mn 7.4	26 Fe 7.9	27 Co 7.9	28 Ni 7.6	29 Cu 7.7	30 Zn 9.4	31 Ga 6.0	32 Ge 8.1	33 As 10	34 Se 9.8	35 Br 11.8	36 Kr 14.0
37 Rb 4.2	38 Sr 5.7	39 Y 6.6	40 Zr 7.0	41 Nb 6.8	42 Mo 7.2	43 Tc —	44 Ru 7.5	45 Rh 7.7	46 Pd 8.3	47 Ag 7.6	48 Cd 9.0	49 In 5.8	50 Sn 7.3	51 Sb 8.6	52 Te 9.0	53 I 10.4	54 Xe 12.1
55 Cs 3.9	56 Ba 5.2	*	72 Hf 5.5	73 Ta 6	74 W 8.0	75 Re 7.9	76 Os 8.7	77 Ir 9.2	78 Pt 9.0	79 Au 9.2	80 Hg 10.4	81 Tl 6.1	82 Pb 7.4	83 Bi 8	84 Po —	85 At —	86 Rn 10.7
87 Fr —	88 Ra 5.3	†															

*	57 La 5.6	58 Ce 6.9	59 Pr 5.8	60 Nd 6.3	61 Pm —	62 Sm 5.6	63 Eu 5.7	64 Gd 6.2	65 Tb 6.7	66 Dy 6.8	67 Ho —	68 Er —	69 Tm —	70 Yb 6.2	71 Lu 5.0
†	89 Ac —	90 Th —	91 Pa —	92 U 4	93 Np —	94 Pu —	95 Am —	96 Cm —	97 Bk —	98 Cf —	99 Es —	100 Fm —	101 Md —	102 (?) —	

Table 3.14 Electron Affinities for Group VII

Element	Electron affinity, e.v.	Electronic configuration				
F	3.6	$2e^-$	$7e^-$			
Cl	3.75	$2e^-$	$8e^-$	$7e^-$		
Br	3.53	$2e^-$	$8e^-$	$18e^-$	$7e^-$	
I	3.2	$2e^-$	$8e^-$	$18e^-$	$18e^-$	$7e^-$

so tightly bound as one added to the other elements of the group. The unexpectedly low value for fluorine cannot be explained by any simple theory.

A knowledge of electron affinities can be combined with a knowledge of ionization potentials to predict which atoms can remove electrons from others. Unfortunately, the measurement of electron affinity is difficult and has been carried out for only a few elements. A method for describing the electron-attracting ability of other atoms will be discussed in the next chapter.

QUESTIONS

3.1   *Atomic structure.* Describe briefly the essential differences between the Dalton, Thomson, and present-day models of the atom.

3.2   *Nuclear atom.* Show how Rutherford's experiment caused the rejection of the Thomson model.

3.3   *Energy levels.* In terms of quantum levels describe the build-up of the first 11 atoms. Show also that the periodic law is a natural consequence of this type of build-up.

3.4   *Energy levels.* By suitable reference to an energy-level diagram, account for the fact that the periodic table has two elements in the first period but eight elements in the second period.

3.5   *Ionization potential.* How can you account for the change of ionization potential within a group and within a period?

3.6   *Energy levels.* Account for the fact that the third period has 8 and not 18 elements.

3.7   *Periodic table.* Where in (1) a period and (2) a group will you most probably find atoms having (*a*) the smallest ionization potential, (*b*) the largest ionization potential? Explain.

3.8   *Faraday's laws.* In two different electrolysis experiments it is observed that the same amount of electricity which plates out 3.177 g. of copper from a copper salt solution also plates out 10.788 g. of silver from a solution of a silver salt. Show how these data illustrate one of Faraday's laws.

3.9   *Discharge tubes.* What qualitative information about atoms can be learned from experiments with discharge tubes?

3.10   *Mass of electron.* Show how the experiments of Thomson and of Millikan can be combined to give the mass of the electron.

3.11   *Radioactivity.* How could you show experimentally the difference between alpha, beta, and gamma radiations?

3.12 *Periodic law.* By looking up information in the second half of this book, show that the variation of chemical properties through the second period is similar to that through the third.

3.13 *Electron probability distribution.* Account for the fact that $2s$ electrons are lower in energy than $2p$ electrons in the same atom.

3.14 *Wave mechanics.* Account for the fact that $1s$ electrons are lower in energy than $2s$ electrons in the same atom.

3.15 *Electronic configurations.* Why are Ca ($Z = 20$) and Zn ($Z = 30$) not placed in the same group, even though each has two electrons in the outermost shell?

3.16 *Periodic table.* Without looking at a periodic table, select from each of the following lists those elements which belong to the same group or subgroup: (a) $Z = 11, 37, 3, 27$; (b) $Z = 8, 16, 24, 2$; (c) $Z = 10, 18, 26, 4$; (d) $Z = 24, 42, 29, 47, 55$.

3.17 *Electron structure.* Indicate how the two electrons of highest energy in each of the following atoms differ from each other: Na, B, N, Mg.

3.18 *Atomic structure.* A neutral atom of an element has 2 K electrons, 8 L electrons, and 5 M electrons. Supply as many of the following quantities as possible from the information given above: (a) atomic weight; (b) atomic number; (c) the total number of s electrons; (d) the total number of p electrons; (e) the total number of d electrons; (f) the number of neutrons in the nucleus.

3.19 *Electronic symbols.* Write the electronic symbols for the elements of the second period and for those of the second group of the periodic table.

3.20 *Gram-atomic volume.* The density of solid magnesium is 1.74 g. per cc. Calculate the gram-atomic volume and compare it with Table 3.10.

3.21 *Periodic law.* Using the data in Table 3.13, make a graph showing the variation of ionization potential with atomic number. (Plot ionization potential on the vertical axis and atomic number on the horizontal axis.) (a) Show how this graph illustrates the periodic law. (b) Try to account for the graph in terms of electronic configurations.

3.22 *Periodic law.* Based on location in the periodic table, which of the following hydroxy compounds would you expect to be basic and which acidic: $Sr(OH)_2$, $BrOH$, $SeO_2(OH)_2$, IOH, $FrOH$?

3.23 *Spectra.* What is meant by the term "line spectrum"? What information do line spectra give about electrons in atoms?

3.24 *Magnetism.* Suppose you had a way to measure the magnetic properties of individual atoms. Using Table 3.6, predict which of the following atoms should be paramagnetic: Li ($Z = 3$), Be (4), B (5), F (9), Ne (10), Sc (21), Tm (69), Pt (78).

3.25 *Atomic sizes.* (*a*) In getting information about atomic sizes from gram-atomic volumes, it is assumed that atoms are packed together about the same way for all solid elements. However, the halogens form solids in which the atoms are on the average farther apart than are the atoms of a metal. What effect does this have on deducing directly atomic sizes from gram-atomic volumes? (*b*) Show that your answer is in the right direction to account for the apparent discrepancy between what is indicated for the trend of size within a period by gram-atomic volumes and by atomic radii.

3.26 *Orbitals.* (*a*) Account for the fact that a *p* subshell containing three electrons has one in each orbital rather than two in one orbital and the third in another. Note that each configuration is allowed by the Pauli exclusion principle. (*b*) Draw a sketch showing in perspective the charge density for the three electrons in the *p* subshell.

3.27 *Charge distributions.* Which of the following atoms would you expect to have nonspherical charge distribution: H, He, Li, Be, B? Explain.

3.28 *Pauli exclusion principle.* Show that the Pauli principle accounts for the fact that the fluorine atom has but one unpaired electron.

3.29 *Atomic size.* The atomic volume of magnesium is 14.0 cc. per gram-atom. The arrangement of atoms in solid magnesium corresponds to an arrangement of spheres in which only 74% of the total volume available is actually occupied. (*a*) Calculate the apparent radius of the magnesium atom. (*b*) In magnesium atoms the *K*-shell electrons have the maximum in their probability distribution at 0.042×10^{-8} cm. from the nucleus; the *L*-shell electrons have their maximum probability at 0.27×10^{-8} cm. Draw a diagram showing the relative positions of the nucleus, the *K*-shell maximum, the *L*-shell maximum, and the apparent radius of the atom.

3.30 *Sizes.* Suppose you had a shot glass, of volume 45.0 cc., which is filled with mercury. Mercury has atomic weight 200.61 a.m.u. (*a*) If the density of mercury is 13.5 g. per cc., how many grams are there in the shot glass? How many atoms? (*b*) Calculate the weight of 1 Hg atom. (*c*) If the mass of an electron is 0.00055 a.m.u. and if the Hg atom contains 80 electrons, what is the mass of a single mercury nucleus? (*d*) Of the total mass of mercury in the shot glass, how many grams are contributed by the electrons and how many grams by the nuclei? (*e*) What is the apparent volume occupied by a single mercury atom? (*f*) What is the density of the nuclear region? (Assume the nucleus to be a cube 8×10^{-13} cm. on edge.) (*g*) What is the apparent density of the electronic region of the atom? (*h*) Using your answer to (*g*), calculate the weight of the contents of the shot glass when filled only with electrons. (*i*) Using (*f*), calculate the weight when filled only with nuclei of mercury. How many tons is this?

 Ans. (*a*) 608 g.; 1.82×10^{24} atoms. (*b*) 3.33×10^{-22} g. (*c*) 3.33×10^{-22} g. (*d*) 0.13 g.; 608 g. (*e*) 2.47×10^{-23} cc. (*f*) 7×10^{14} g./cc. (*g*) 3.0×10^{-3} g./cc. (*h*) 0.13 g. (*i*) 3×10^{16} g.; 3×10^{10} tons

3.31 *Isotopes.* The element magnesium has atomic weight 24.32. Show how this atomic weight is consistent with the following distribution of isotopes: 78.6% of $_{12}Mg^{24}$, 10.1% of $_{12}Mg^{25}$, and 11.3% of $_{12}Mg^{26}$. Isotopic masses are 23.99, 24.99, and 25.98, respectively.

3.32 *Probability plot.* (*a*) Assume that the curves given in Fig. 3.18 can be applied to a boron atom. By combining these curves, draw a graph to represent the distance probability of finding any electron in a boron atom. Note that a boron atom contains two 1s electrons, two 2s electrons, and one 2p electron. (*b*) If the nuclear charge could be increased, what effect would this have on the probability distribution?

4 *Chemical Bond*

IN PRECEDING CHAPTERS we have discussed the idea that matter is composed of atoms and have indicated some properties of individual atoms. One property that we did not discuss is the ability of individual atoms to bind to each other. That atoms do bind together is evident from the existence of solids and liquids. Even in some gases, as for example in hydrogen or oxygen, we shall find that individual atoms are bound together as small aggregates. Any electrically neutral aggregate of atoms held together strongly enough to be considered as a unit is called a *molecule*. The attraction between two atoms within a molecule is called a *chemical bond*.

Hydrogen gas is composed of aggregates of two hydrogen atoms. Water vapor is composed of aggregates containing two hydrogen atoms and one oxygen atom. Solid sulfur consists of aggregates of eight sulfur atoms. In each of these cases, the aggregate is called a molecule. On the other hand, in solid sodium chloride there are no simple aggregates consisting of a few atoms. All the sodium atoms and all the chlorine atoms in a given crystal are bound into one giant aggregate. The term molecule is not useful in cases such as solid sodium chloride.

In this chapter we consider the following questions: Why do atoms bind together to form molecules? Why is there a limit to the number of atoms

bound together in a single molecule; why, for example, does a water molecule contain only two hydrogen atoms and but one oxygen atom? Finally,
how can the structure of molecules be described?

4.1   ELECTRONS IN MOLECULES

In an isolated atom each electron is under the influence only of the nucleus
and the other electrons. When two atoms come together, the electrons of
one atom come under the influence of the electrons and nucleus of the other.
The interaction might produce an attraction between the two atoms. If this
is the case, an electronic rearrangement must have occurred to give a more
stable state. In other words, the formation of a chemical bond indicates that
the molecule represents a state of lower energy than the isolated atoms.

A detailed description of electrons in molecules is a difficult problem.
There are two general approaches which can be used. One is to consider
the entire molecule as a unit with all the electrons moving under the influence of all the nuclei and all the other electrons. This approach recognizes
that each electron belongs to the molecule as a whole and may move
throughout the entire molecule. The energy levels that the electrons occupy
in the molecule are called *molecular orbitals* and can be thought of in the
same way as the energy levels of electrons in isolated atoms. The other approach to describing molecules is simpler but less correct. It assumes that
the atoms in a molecule are very much like isolated atoms, except that one
or more electrons from the outer shell of one atom are accommodated in
the outer shell of another atom. This method of describing molecules is
called the *atomic-orbital* method because it utilizes directly the energy levels
of isolated atoms.

In order to point up the difference in the two ways of viewing molecules, let us consider first the case of the hydrogen molecule. As already
indicated, the hydrogen molecule is formed from two hydrogen atoms, each
with one proton and one electron. In the molecular-orbital approach, the
molecule is visualized as consisting of two protons at some distance apart
with two electrons placed in an energy level that is characteristic of the
whole molecule. In the atomic-orbital approach, the molecule is visualized
as consisting of two hydrogen *atoms* close together, with the electron shell
of each atom the same as for an isolated hydrogen atom except that part
of the time it may contain both electrons. No matter which picture is used,
the molecule is held together because the attraction of the two positive protons for the two negative electrons exceeds the repulsion between the two
protons plus the repulsion between the two electrons.

In the more complicated case of hydrogen chloride, the molecule is formed from one hydrogen atom and one chlorine atom. The hydrogen atom contributes a $+1$ nucleus and one electron; the chlorine atom, a $+17$ nucleus and 17 electrons. In the molecular-orbital approach, the molecule is visualized as consisting of the two nuclei at some distance apart, with 18 electrons placed in various energy levels of the molecule as a whole. In the atomic-orbital approach, the molecule is visualized as consisting of one hydrogen *atom* and one chlorine *atom* close together. The hydrogen atom is assumed to be the same as when it is alone, except that part of the time it now may contain, besides its own electron, one of the electrons from the chlorine atom. For the chlorine atom, it is assumed that the two inner shells are unchanged. However, part of the time the outer shell may contain, besides the original seven electrons, one additional electron from the hydrogen atom. The one electron from the hydrogen together with one electron from the chlorine are considered as a pair of electrons which is shared between the atoms. The pair holds the molecule together because it is attracted to both nuclei.

Certainly in a molecule the energy levels of many if not all of the electrons are changed from those of isolated atoms. Therefore, it would be desirable to discuss chemical bonding exclusively in terms of molecular orbitals. However, the atomic-orbital approach is so much simpler that it will be used in the following discussions.

4.2   IONIC BONDS

In discussing chemical bonds, we shall assume first that molecules can be described in terms of individual atoms. Second, we shall assume that bonds can be described as being *ionic bonds*, in which electrons are completely transferred from one atom to another, or as *covalent bonds*, in which electrons are shared between atoms, or as combinations of the two.

The formation of an ionic bond is favored in the reaction of an atom of low ionization potential with an atom of high electron affinity. An example of such a reaction is the one between sodium atoms and chlorine atoms. A sodium

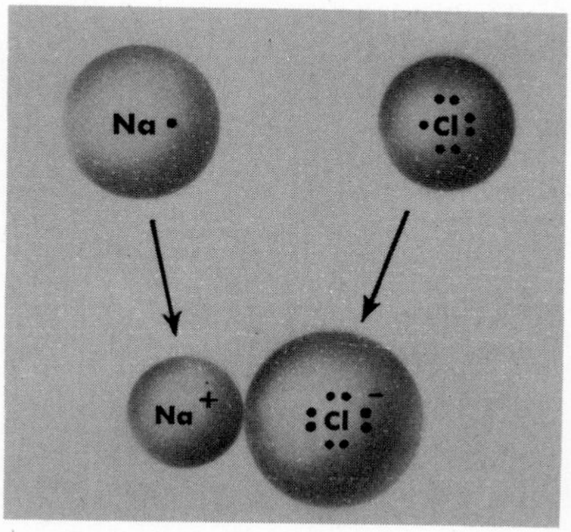

Fig. 4.1   Formation of an ionic bond.

atom has a low ionization potential, i.e., not much energy is required to pull off the outer electron. A chlorine atom has a high electron affinity, i.e., considerable energy is released when an electron is added to its outer shell. Suppose these two atoms collide. As shown in Fig. 4.1, sodium initially has one valence electron, and chlorine, seven. After collision, chlorine has all eight of the valence electrons. The sodium now has a positive charge because of the loss of a negative electron. The chlorine has a negative charge because of the gain of an electron. Thus, a positive ion and a negative ion are formed. Because the ions are of opposite electrical charge, they attract each other to produce an ionic bond. The ionic bond is sometimes called the *electrovalent bond.**

The formation of an ionic bond can be thought of in three steps:

$$\text{Na} \cdot \rightarrow \text{Na}^+ + e^- \tag{1}$$

$$:\overset{..}{\underset{..}{\text{Cl}}}\cdot + e^- \rightarrow [:\overset{..}{\underset{..}{\text{Cl}}}:]^- \tag{2}$$

$$\text{Na}^+ + [:\overset{..}{\underset{..}{\text{Cl}}}:]^- \rightarrow \text{Na}^+[:\overset{..}{\underset{..}{\text{Cl}}}:]^- \tag{3}$$

Step (1) requires energy equal to the ionization potential of sodium. Step (2) releases energy equal to the electron affinity of chlorine. Step (3) releases energy, because of the attraction between positive and negative ions. The ionic bond is formed only because the energy released in steps (2) and (3) is greater than that required in step (1).

In forming compounds by this process of electron transfer, it is necessary that there be a balance of electrons gained and lost. The reaction between sodium and chlorine requires one atom of sodium for every atom of chlorine. It should be noted that after reaction the sodium and chlorine are left with complete octets in their outermost shells. It is a general rule that, when ionic bonds are formed, enough electrons are transferred so that the ions produced have completed octets of electrons, which, as we saw in Chap. 3, tend to be rather stable. As a more complicated example, when calcium reacts with chlorine, each calcium atom loses its two valence electrons to form Ca^{++}. Two chlorine atoms, each picking up one electron, are required to balance this. The compound formed, calcium chloride, contains one doubly positive calcium ion for every two singly negative chloride ions. The formula of the compound is CaCl_2. The subscript 2 for chlorine and the subscript 1 (understood) for calcium indicates that in the compound there are two chlorine atoms for each calcium atom.

Since in general the elements on the left of the periodic table have low

---

* A discrete unit consisting of one sodium ion and one chloride ion can properly be called a molecule. Such discrete units can exist only in gaseous sodium chloride. In the solid, each Na^+ is attracted to more than one Cl^-, and each Cl^- to more than one Na^+. Thus, each crystal of salt is a "giant molecule" containing a huge number of ionically bound Na^+ and Cl^- ions.

ionization potentials and the elements on the right have high electron affinity, ionic bonds are favored in reactions between these elements. Thus, any alkali metal (group I) reacts with any halogen (group VII) to form an ionic compound. Similarly most of the group II elements react with the halogens or with group VI elements to form ionic bonds. In general, these ionic compounds resemble sodium chloride in that they are white, brittle solids at room temperature which dissolve in water to give conducting solutions. They melt at relatively high temperatures.

4.3   COVALENT BONDS

Most bonds cannot be adequately pictured by assuming a complete transfer of electrons from one atom to another. For example, in the hydrogen molecule it seems unreasonable that one hydrogen atom should pull an electron from the other, exactly similar, hydrogen atom. In such cases, it is assumed that electrons are shared between the atoms, and the bond is called covalent. As we have noted already, in the atomic-orbital picture each bond is considered to be a shared pair of electrons. In H_2, Cl_2, and HCl, as discussed below, bonds are described as shared electron pairs.

  The simplest case of a shared-pair bond is found in the case of hydrogen. When two hydrogen atoms collide, as shown in Fig. 4.2, a shared pair of electrons results because each atom can accommodate another electron in its shell. (In Chap. 3, we noted that the K level is not filled until it has a population of two electrons.) Neither atom is able to gain complete possession of both electrons. At the bottom of Fig. 4.2 is shown the conventional way of expressing the formation of a covalent bond using electronic symbols. The formula of hydrogen is written as H_2, to indicate that there are two atoms per molecule; the molecule is *diatomic*. We emphasize again that the pictures with dots and letters are only schematic representations of a complicated situation and tell little about the electronic probability distribution. In the case of hydrogen, for example, the charge distribution is such that the electron pair occupies the whole molecule, spending equal time in the vicinity of each nucleus. The distribution is like that shown

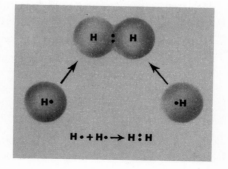

Fig. 4.2   Formation of a covalent bond.

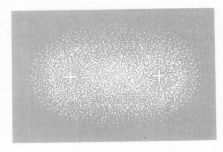

Fig. 4.3   Charge distribution in an H_2 *molecule.*

in Fig. 4.3. The $+$ represents a nucleus. The shading indicates the relative probability of finding the electron pair.

In the case of chlorine, the formation of a covalent bond is pictured as follows: Each chlorine atom has seven valence electrons, one short of a stable octet. When two chlorine atoms collide, each tries to gain another electron. Neither atom is able to pull an electron off the other. The atoms share two electrons, so that at least part of the time each has a filled shell. The formation of the covalent bond in terms of electronic symbols and an electronic formula can be expressed as follows:

$$:\overset{..}{\underset{..}{Cl}}\cdot\ +\ :\overset{..}{\underset{..}{Cl}}\cdot\ \rightarrow\ :\overset{..}{\underset{..}{Cl}}:\overset{..}{\underset{..}{Cl}}:$$

The shared pair of electrons constitutes a *single bond* and is frequently designated by a dash, as, for example, Cl—Cl. In other cases, as in $:\overset{..}{O}::C::\overset{..}{O}:$ and in $:N:::N:$, *double* and *triple bonds* are made possible by sharing two pairs or three pairs of electrons between atoms. Electronic formulas showing shared-pair bonds are an oversimplification. They imply that certain pairs of electrons, those shown between the cores, are the only ones that are shared. What actually goes on is more complicated. All the electrons in the molecule are attracted to both nuclei and do not belong to an individual atom but to the molecule as a whole.

The formation of hydrogen chloride can be expressed as follows:

$$H\cdot\ +\ :\overset{..}{\underset{..}{Cl}}\cdot\ \rightarrow H:\overset{..}{\underset{..}{Cl}}:$$

Although chlorine has a greater attraction for electrons than does hydrogen, the attraction is not great enough to give complete possession of the electron pair to chlorine. Again the electrons are shared, and a single covalent bond results. However, in this case the electron pair is not shared equally by the two atoms but is considered to spend more time under the influence of the chlorine than it spends associated with the hydrogen.

4.4   POLARITY OF BONDS

Because electrons may be shared unequally between atoms, it is necessary to have some way of describing the electric charge distribution in a bond. This is usually done by classifying bonds as *polar* or *nonpolar*. For example, the bonds in H_2 and Cl_2 are called nonpolar; the bond in HCl, polar.

Why are the covalent bonds in H_2 and Cl_2 called nonpolar? In both of these cases, the "center of gravity" of the negative charge distribution is at the center of the molecule, since the electron pair is just as probably found with one nucleus as with the other. The molecule is electrically neutral in two senses of the word. Not only does it contain an equal number of positive and negative charges (protons and electrons), but also the center of the positive charge coincides with the center of the negative charge. The molecule is a *nonpolar molecule;* it contains a *nonpolar bond* because an *electron pair is shared equally* between two atomic kernels.

In the case of HCl, the bond is called polar because the center of positive charge does not coincide with the center of negative charge. The molecule as a whole is electrically neutral, because it contains an equal number of positive and negative particles. However, owing to the unequal sharing of the electron pair, the chlorine end of the molecule appears negative, and the hydrogen end positive. This arises because the shared pair of electrons spends more time on the chlorine atom than on the hydrogen atom. (Polarity does not arise simply from the fact that chlorine has more electrons than hydrogen; the charge of the *unshared* electrons is balanced by the greater positive charge of the chlorine nucleus.)

As another example of a polar covalent bond, we consider the bond between chlorine and bromine in the molecule BrCl. Each of these atoms has seven valence electrons, one less than the inert configuration. By sharing a pair of electrons, each completes its octet. However, the bromine atom is bigger than the chlorine atom, and it has a smaller attraction for electrons. In the covalent bond between Cl and Br, the pair of electrons is not shared equally but (as discussed in Sec. 4.5) spends more of its time with the chlorine. The chlorine end of the molecule therefore appears negative with respect to the bromine end. In Fig. 4.4 this polarity is indicated by a $+$ at the center of distribution of the positive charge and a $-$ at the center of distribution of the negative charge. The molecule as a whole is electrically neutral—there are just as many positive charges as there are negative charges in the whole molecule—but there is a dissymmetry in the electrical distribution. Molecules in which the positive and negative centers of charge do not coincide are called *polar molecules,* and any bond in which the sharing between two kernels is *unequal* is a *polar bond.*

In the molecule BrCl there are two centers of charge. Such a molecule (or such a bond) is called a *dipole.* A dipole consists of a *positive and an*

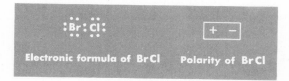

Fig. 4.4   The BrCl mole-cule.

Electronic formula of BrCl   Polarity of BrCl

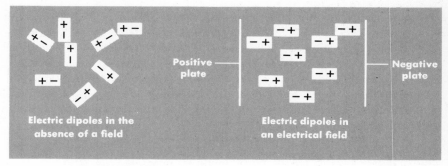

Positive plate

Negative plate

Electric dipoles in the absence of a field

Electric dipoles in an electrical field

Fig. 4.5   Behavior of dipoles.

equal negative charge separated by some distance. Quantitatively, a dipole is described by giving its *dipole moment*, which is equal to the *charge times the distance* between the positive and negative centers. This number measures the tendency of the dipole to turn when placed in an electric field. As shown in Fig. 4.5, each dipole turns because its positive end is attracted to the negative plate and its negative end to the positive plate. Since the positive and negative centers are part of the same molecule, the molecules can only turn; there is no migration toward the plates.

The behavior of dipoles in an electric field gives an experimental method for distinguishing between polar and nonpolar molecules. The experiments involve the determination of a property called the dielectric constant (see Appendix 4.5). This property can be measured as follows: It is observed that an electric condenser (two parallel metallic plates, like those shown in Fig. 4.5) has the ability to store electric charge. The capacity of a condenser, i.e., the amount of charge that can be put on the plates for a given voltage, depends upon the material between the plates. The *dielectric constant* of the substance is defined as the ratio of the condenser's capacity with the substance between the plates to its capacity with a vacuum between them.

In general, a substance which consists of polar molecules has a high dielectric constant, i.e., a condenser can store much more charge when such a substance is between its plates. This high dielectric constant can be thought of as arising in the following way: As shown in Fig. 4.5, dipoles tend to turn in a charged condenser, so that negative ends are near the positive plate and positive ends are near the negative plate. This partially neutralizes the charge on the plates and permits more charge to be added. Thus, measurement of the dielectric constant gives information about the polarity of molecules. The fact that hydrogen gas has essentially no effect on the capacity of a condenser (dielectric constant 1.00026) confirms the idea that H_2 molecules are nonpolar. The quantitative calculation of dipole

*Fig. 4.6   Nonpolar molecule contain-
ing polar bonds.*

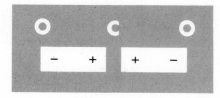

moments of bonds from measured dielectric constants is complicated, because in some cases unshared electrons can contribute to the electrical
dissymmetry of the molecule. Also, the presence of the charged plates can
temporarily distort the charge distribution in molecules.

It is possible to predict whether a diatomic molecule is polar or nonpolar. If the two atoms are alike, the *bond* between them must be nonpolar,
and therefore the *molecule* is nonpolar. If the two atoms are different, the
bond is polar, and the *molecule* is also polar. The degree of polarity of
diatomic molecules increases as the atoms become more unlike in electron-
pulling ability. It is not so easy to predict the polar nature of a molecule
containing more than two atoms. Such a *molecule* can be nonpolar even
though all the *bonds* in the molecule are individually polar. Carbon dioxide,
CO_2, is an example. As shown in Fig. 4.6, the two oxygen atoms are bonded
to the carbon atom. Since oxygen attracts the shared electrons more than
carbon does, each carbon-oxygen bond is polar, with the shared electrons
spending more time near the oxygen than near the carbon. The polarity of
each bond is shown in the figure. Because the molecule is linear, the effect
of one dipole cancels the effect of the other dipole. As a result, when CO_2
molecules are placed in an electric field, they do not line up, because any
turning action of one bond is counteracted by the opposite turning action
of the other bond. Carbon dioxide has a low dielectric constant.

Water, H_2O, is a triatomic molecule in which two hydrogen atoms are
bonded to the same oxygen atom. There are two different possibilities for
its structure. It may have a linear structure with the three atoms arranged
in a straight line, or the atoms may be arranged in the form of a bent chain.
The two possibilities are shown in Fig. 4.7. The fact that water has a very
high dielectric constant supports the structure on the right. The structure
on the left represents a nonpolar molecule in which the two polar bonds
are placed in line, so that there is no net dipole moment; whereas the bent-

*Fig. 4.7   Possible struc-
tures of an H_2O molecule.*

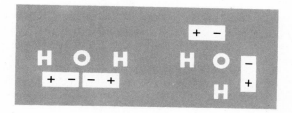

chain structure, on the right, could orient the two positive ends toward a negative plate.

In the light of the foregoing discussion of polar bonds, it is interesting to note that *there is no sharp distinction between ionic and covalent bonds.* In the chemical bond between atoms A and B, all gradations of polarity are possible, depending on the nature of A and B. If A and B have the same ability to attract electrons, the bond is nonpolar. If the electron-pulling ability of B is increased (by taking different elements for B), the shared electrons spend more time on B, and the bond becomes more polar. In the limit, the electron pair is not shared at all but spends all its time on B. The result is a negative ion B^- and a plus ion A^+; the bond is ionic.

4.5 ELECTRONEGATIVITY

In the preceding section we have referred to the electron-pulling ability of atoms in molecules. A quantitative measure of this property could be obtained by considering both the ionization potential and the electron affinity of the individual atoms. That both these quantities must be considered can be seen from the following argument: The bond in BrCl consists of an electron pair shared unequally between Br and Cl. The preference of the electron pair for one atom or the other depends on how much energy is required to pull an electron off one atom (the ionization potential) and how much energy is released when the electron is added to the other atom (the electron affinity). The electron pair will spend more of its time on the Cl, because the energy required to transfer an electron from Br to Cl is less than the net energy required to transfer an electron from Cl to Br. In calculating the energy required for these transfers, it is necessary to know the ionization potential and electron affinity of each atom. Unfortunately, electron affinities have been measured for only a very few elements, so this method of evaluating the electron-pulling ability of atoms in molecules cannot be generally used.

By measuring various properties of molecules, such as dipole moments and energies required to break bonds, it is possible to arrange elements in order of their tendency to attract shared electrons. This listing of the elements is called the scale of *electronegativity*, and one method for its determination is outlined in the next section. Numerical values assigned for the electronegativities of the various elements are shown in Table 4.1. These numbers describe the relative tendency of an atom in forming a bond to go to a negative condition, i.e., to attract a shared electron pair. Fluorine is assigned the highest electronegativity of any element in the periodic table.

The inert elements do not normally form chemical bonds and hence are not assigned values. In general, as we go from left to right across a period (increasing nuclear charge), the electronegativity increases. The elements at the far left of the periodic table have low electronegativity. The elements at the far right, with the exception of group 0, have high electronegativity. On the scale of electronegativity, the group VII elements are assigned the values F, 4.0; Cl, 3.0; Br, 2.8; and I, 2.5. The decreasing order is regular, unlike the order of electron affinities. In general, electronegativity decreases going down a group (size increases).

Of what use are these values of electronegativity? For one thing, they can be used in predicting which bonds are ionic and which covalent. Since the electronegativity indicates the relative attraction for electrons, two elements of very different electronegativity, such as Na (0.9) and Cl (3.0), are expected to form ionic bonds. Thus, electronegativities support the expectation that the alkali elements and the group II elements form essentially ionic bonds with the elements of groups VI and VII. Two elements of about

Table 4.1   Electronegativities of the Elements

1 H 2.1																	2 He —
3 Li 1.0	4 Be 1.5											5 B 2.0	6 C 2.5	7 N 3.0	8 O 3.5	9 F 4.0	10 Ne —
11 Na 0.9	12 Mg 1.2											13 Al 1.5	14 Si 1.8	15 P 2.1	16 S 2.5	17 Cl 3.0	18 Ar —
19 K 0.8	20 Ca 1.0	21 Sc 1.3	22 Ti 1.5	23 V 1.6	24 Cr 1.6	25 Mn 1.5	26 Fe 1.8	27 Co 1.8	28 Ni 1.8	29 Cu 1.9	30 Zn 1.6	31 Ga 1.6	32 Ge 1.8	33 As 2.0	34 Se 2.4	35 Br 2.8	36 Kr —
37 Rb 0.8	38 Sr 1.0	39 Y 1.2	40 Zr 1.4	41 Nb 1.6	42 Mo 1.8	43 Tc 1.9	44 Ru 2.2	45 Rh 2.2	46 Pd 2.2	47 Ag 1.9	48 Cd 1.7	49 In 1.7	50 Sn 1.8	51 Sb 1.9	52 Te 2.1	53 I 2.5	54 Xe —
55 Cs 0.7	56 Ba 0.9	57–71 — 1.1–1.2	72 Hf 1.3	73 Ta 1.5	74 W 1.7	75 Re 1.9	76 Os 2.2	77 Ir 2.2	78 Pt 2.2	79 Au 2.4	80 Hg 1.9	81 Tl 1.8	82 Pb 1.8	83 Bi 1.9	84 Po 2.0	85 At 2.2	86 Rn —
87 Fr 0.7	88 Ra 0.9	89– — 1.1—															

equal electronegativity, such as Cl (3.0) and Br (2.8), are expected to form covalent bonds.

Furthermore, electronegativities can be used to predict polarity of covalent bonds. The farther apart in electronegativity two elements are, the more polar the bond should be. Thus, the bond between H and Cl is more polar than that between Br and Cl. In both cases, the chlorine end should be more negative, since Cl has the higher electronegativity.

4.6   BOND ENERGIES AND THE SCALE OF ELECTRONEGATIVITY

One method for setting up the scale of electronegativities involves the use of bond energies. *Bond energy* is defined as the *energy required to break a bond and form neutral atoms.* It can be determined experimentally by measuring the heat involved in chemical reaction. (The determination of heats of reaction is discussed in Sec. 5.9.) The relation between bond energy and electronegativity can be seen from the following example: It is found that 103 kcal. of heat is required to break the Avogadro number of H_2 molecules into individual atoms. Thus, the bond energy of H_2 is 103 kcal. per Avogadro number of bonds, or 17.1×10^{-23} kcal. per bond. Because the sharing of the electron pair is equal between the two atoms, it would be reasonable to assume that each bonded H atom contributes half of the bond energy, or 8.55×10^{-23} kcal. Furthermore, it would be reasonable to assume that, in any bond where hydrogen shares an electron pair *equally* with another atom, the contribution by H to the bond energy should be 8.55×10^{-23} kcal. Similarly, from the bond energy found for Cl_2, 57.2 kcal. per Avogadro number of bonds, we deduce that a chlorine atom should contribute 4.75×10^{-23} kcal. to any bond in which the sharing of an electron pair is equal.

Suppose we now consider the bond in HCl. We have already indicated that this bond is polar, but for the moment let us imagine that the electron pair is shared equally. This amounts to picturing H in HCl to be the same as in H_2, and Cl, the same as in Cl_2. If H contributes 8.55×10^{-23} kcal. and if Cl contributes 4.75×10^{-23} kcal., the expected bond energy of HCl would be the sum of these contributions, or 13.3×10^{-23} kcal. Actually, the bond energy of HCl found by experiment is 102 kcal. per Avogadro number of bonds, or 16.9×10^{-23} kcal. per bond. The fact that the observed bond energy, 16.9×10^{-23} kcal., is significantly greater than the *calculated* value, 13.3×10^{-23} kcal., indicates that the electrons are *not* equally shared in HCl. The bond in question is actually more stable (re-

Table 4.2   Bond Energies

Bond	Energy, kcal./Avogadro number bonds			
	X = F	X = Cl	X = Br	X = I
H—H	103.2	103.2	103.2	103.2
X—X	38	57.2	45.4	35.5
H—X (calc.)	71	80.2	74.3	69.4
H—X (obs.)	135	102.1	85.9	70.4
Difference	64	21.9	11.6	1.0

quires more energy to break) than would be predicted by equal sharing.

The enhanced stability of HCl can be attributed to unequal sharing of the electron pair. If the electron pair spends more time on the chlorine, that end of the molecule would become negative and the hydrogen end positive. Since the positive and negative ends would attract each other, there would be additional binding energy. The amount of additional binding energy would depend on the relative electron-pulling ability of the bonded atoms, since the greater the charge difference between the ends of the molecule, the greater the additional binding energy. Thus, it should be possible to estimate relative electronegativities from the difference between experimental bond energies and those calculated assuming equal sharing.

In Table 4.2, experimental values of bond energies of the hydrogen halides are compared with values calculated assuming equal sharing of electrons. It is evident that the discrepancy is greatest in HF and least in HI. This implies that the sharing of electrons between H and F is more unequal than the sharing between H and I. Apparently, the electron-pulling ability, or electronegativity, of H and I are nearly the same. Numerical values of electronegativity have been selected by a complex procedure so as to account for the discrepancies listed in Table 4.2. As shown in Table 4.1, the electronegativity value assigned to H is 2.1. The values assigned to F (4.0), Cl (3.0), Br (2.8), and I (2.5) are consistent with the trend toward equal sharing in the sequence HF, HCl, HBr, HI.

Support for the assignment of electronegativity values comes from measurements of dipole moments. For the hydrogen halides, the observed dipole moments are HF, 1.91; HCl, 1.03; HBr, 0.78; and HI, 0.38, expressed in arbitrary units. The decreasing polarity from HF to HI also indicates a trend toward equal sharing of electrons, consistent with decreasing electronegativity from F to I.

4.7   SATURATION OF VALENCE

In the next chapter we shall consider methods for determining formulas of compounds from experimental data. When such methods are applied to most substances, it is found that there is a limit to the combining ability atoms of one element have for atoms of another. For example, when calcium is combined with chlorine, no more than two chlorine atoms per calcium atom are found; when carbon is combined with hydrogen, no more than four hydrogen atoms per carbon are found. If we use the term *valence* to describe the *ability of atoms to bind together*, then we can summarize the above observations by saying that there is a *limit to the valence one atom shows for others*; i.e., there is *saturation of valence*.

Consider the compounds that fluorine forms with sodium, calcium, and aluminum. All three of these compounds are believed to be ionic, because fluorine is so much more electronegative than Na, Ca, or Al. In the combination of fluorine with sodium, there is only one fluorine atom per sodium atom. This can be accounted for by noting that each sodium atom (Na·) has one valence electron (Sec. 3.12) and each fluorine atom ($:\overset{..}{\underset{..}{F}}\cdot$) has seven. If a fluorine atom takes one electron away from a sodium atom, the resulting fluoride ion ($:\overset{..}{\underset{..}{F}}:^-$) has a complete octet of electrons. The sodium ion (Na$^+$) has no more valence electrons to lose to other fluorine atoms. Therefore, in sodium fluoride (NaF), only one fluorine atom is combined per sodium atom.

In the combination of fluorine with calcium, there are only two fluorine atoms per calcium atom. Apparently, the two valence electrons of the calcium atom (Ca:) can be lost to two fluorine atoms. However, no more than two electrons are lost, because the calcium ion (Ca^{++}) has a stable octet of inner electrons. When fluorine is combined with aluminum, no more than three fluorine atoms react per aluminum atom, because the aluminum atom (:Al·) has but three valence electrons.

It should be emphasized that the above discussion tells us nothing about the actual number of atoms in molecules. All three of the fluorides mentioned normally exist as white solids consisting of aggregates of tremendous numbers of positive and negative ions. For such ionic solids, saturation of valence simply indicates the relative numbers of positive and negative ions. For instance, in a sample of aluminum fluoride there are three fluoride ions per aluminum ion, no matter how many aluminum ions are present.

When covalent bonds are formed, not only is the relative number of atoms fixed, but also the actual number of atoms in the molecule may be limited. For example, in the combination of carbon with hydrogen, there are no more than four hydrogen atoms per carbon atom. Furthermore, the compound formed (methane) consists of discrete molecules, each of which has in the case of methane but one carbon atom and four hydrogen atoms. How can we account for this saturation of valence in methane? Each carbon atom ($\cdot \overset{\cdot}{\underset{\cdot}{C}} \cdot$) has four valence electrons; each hydrogen (H$\cdot$) has one.

Since the electronegativities of C and H are similar, covalent rather than ionic bonds are expected. If a carbon atom contributes one electron to each covalent bond formed, four such bonds can be established. We can represent the formation of the compound as follows:

$$4\text{H}\cdot \; + \; \cdot\overset{\cdot}{\underset{\cdot}{\text{C}}}\cdot \rightarrow \text{H}\!:\!\overset{\displaystyle \text{H}}{\underset{\displaystyle \text{H}}{\overset{\cdot\cdot}{\underset{\cdot\cdot}{\text{C}}}}}\!:\!\text{H}$$

By sharing electrons, the carbon atom gets a complete octet of electrons in its outer shell, and each hydrogen atom gets two electrons, all that its valence shell can accommodate. Since the molecule as a whole is electrically neutral and since all valence shells are filled with shared electrons, no other atoms can bind to the molecule. The valence is saturated.

Other examples of valence saturation in covalent bonds are provided by hydrogen compounds of fluorine, oxygen, and nitrogen. The formation of the compounds can be represented as follows:

$$\text{H}\cdot \; + \; :\!\overset{\cdot\cdot}{\underset{\cdot\cdot}{\text{F}}}\!\cdot \rightarrow \text{H}\!:\!\overset{\cdot\cdot}{\underset{\cdot\cdot}{\text{F}}}\!:$$
Hydrogen fluoride

$$2\text{H}\cdot \; + \; \cdot\overset{\cdot\cdot}{\text{O}}\!: \rightarrow \text{H}\!:\!\overset{\displaystyle}{\underset{\displaystyle \text{H}}{\overset{\cdot\cdot}{\text{O}}}}\!:$$
Water

$$3\text{H}\cdot \; + \; \cdot\overset{\cdot\cdot}{\underset{\cdot}{\text{N}}}\cdot \rightarrow \text{H}\!:\!\overset{\displaystyle}{\underset{\displaystyle \text{H}}{\overset{\cdot\cdot}{\text{N}}}}\!:\!\text{H}$$
Ammonia

In each case, the number of hydrogen atoms bonded is equal to the number of electrons required to complete the octet. It should be noted that, in these compounds, but not in methane, there are pairs of valence electrons which do not appear to be shared between atoms. One might imagine that these electron pairs could be used to bind to other atoms, but this can occur only if the additional atom has room for two more electrons in its valence shell. The unshared electron pairs cannot bind additional hydrogen atoms (H$\cdot$), because three electrons cannot be accommodated by a single H atom.

Although hydrogen atoms cannot accommodate an additional pair of electrons, there are other species which can. For example, the hydrogen *ion* (H^+), which has one electron less than a hydrogen atom, has room for a pair of electrons. Therefore, a hydrogen *ion* can bind to a molecule, such as ammonia, in which there is an unshared pair of electrons. Apparently, this is the explanation for the formation of ammonium salts. When ammonia (NH_3) is treated with hydrogen chloride (HCl), the white solid ammonium chloride (NH_4Cl) is formed. The process can be pictured as follows:

$$H : \overset{\displaystyle \cdot\cdot}{\underset{\displaystyle H}{N}} : H \ + \ H : \overset{\displaystyle \cdot\cdot}{\underset{\displaystyle \cdot\cdot}{Cl}} : \ \longrightarrow \ H : \overset{\displaystyle H}{\underset{\displaystyle H}{N}} : H^+ : \overset{\displaystyle \cdot\cdot}{\underset{\displaystyle \cdot\cdot}{Cl}} : {}^-$$

We can imagine that first the HCl splits to give a hydrogen ion, leaving all the electrons on the chlorine, and then the hydrogen ion attaches to the NH_3. The hydrogen ion is bound to the NH_3 by sharing the nitrogen's extra pair of electrons. Since the original NH_3 molecule was electrically neutral and the hydrogen ion had a $+1$ charge, the resulting ammonium ion (NH_4^+) carries a positive charge. Also, since the chlorine ends up with full possession of the hydrogen's electron, the resulting chloride ion bears a negative charge. In ammonium chloride, positive ammonium ions and negative chloride ions attract each other. Once the ammonium ion is formed, all four nitrogen-hydrogen bonds are alike, even though the mode of formation of one of the bonds was different from that of the other three. Covalent bonds which are formed by donation of an electron pair from a single atom are sometimes called *donor-acceptor*, or *coordinate covalent*, bonds.

Saturation of valence is not restricted to bonding between unlike atoms. It also may occur when an atom forms covalent bonds with atoms of its own kind, as in the following examples:

$: \overset{\cdot\cdot}{\underset{\cdot\cdot}{F}} : \overset{\cdot\cdot}{\underset{\cdot\cdot}{F}} :$	$: \overset{\cdot\cdot}{\underset{}{O}} : \overset{\cdot\cdot}{\underset{}{O}} :$	$H : \overset{\cdot\cdot}{\underset{}{N}} : \overset{\cdot\cdot}{\underset{}{N}} : H$	
	H H	H H	
Fluorine	*Hydrogen peroxide*	*Hydrazine*	*Propane*

$$\begin{array}{ccc} & H & H & H \\ H : & C : C : C & : H \\ & H & H & H \end{array}$$

In order to get complete octets, the elements fluorine, oxygen, nitrogen, and carbon must form one, two, three, and four electron-pair bonds, respectively. The number of bonds is the same, whether the atom is bonded only to H or to other atoms of its own kind.

In addition to "saturation of valence," the terms "saturated" and "unsaturated" are also used when describing compounds. In unsaturated compounds of carbon there are double or triple bonds between adjacent carbon atoms. These compounds are called unsaturated because they can undergo chemical reaction in which atoms are added to the molecule. For example,

$$\begin{matrix} H & \cdot & \cdot & H \\ & :C::C: & \\ H & \cdot & \cdot & H \end{matrix} + 2H\cdot \rightarrow \begin{matrix} H & H \\ :\ : & :\ : \\ H:C:C:H \\ :\ : & :\ : \\ H & H \end{matrix}$$

The compound on the left, ethylene, is unsaturated; each carbon atom has a complete octet of electrons made possible by sharing two pairs of electrons with the other carbon atom. The compound on the right, ethane, is saturated; the carbon atoms are joined by sharing but one pair of electrons. If each electron pair is designated by a dash, the above equation is written

$$\begin{matrix} H & & H \\ & \diagdown \ \diagup & \\ & C=C & \\ & \diagup \ \diagdown & \\ H & & H \end{matrix} + 2H \rightarrow \begin{matrix} H & H \\ | & | \\ H-C-C-H \\ | & | \\ H & H \end{matrix}$$

Another unsaturated compound acetylene consists of molecules containing two carbon atoms and two hydrogen atoms. These atoms are arranged in a straight line with the carbons in the center. What is the electronic formula of this molecule? Each carbon atom makes available four valence electrons, and each hydrogen atom one valence electron, giving a total of 10 bonding electrons. Bonds between each hydrogen and its carbon take care of four electrons. There are six electrons left. To satisfy the octet rule, these six occur as three pairs of electrons shared between the two carbon atoms. This is a triple bond.

$$H:C:::C:H \quad \text{or} \quad H-C\equiv C-H$$

In general, for the same pair of bonded atoms, triple bonds are shorter than double bonds, and double bonds are shorter than single bonds. Experiment shows that the carbon-carbon distance (center to center) is 1.20×10^{-8} cm. in acetylene, 1.33×10^{-8} cm. in ethylene, and 1.54×10^{-8} cm. in ethane.

As a fitting conclusion to this section, we should note that the explanation of bonding in terms of octets of electrons is not complete. For a complete explanation we would need to justify the *octet rule*, the supposition that, *when atoms combine, the bonds formed are such that each atom is surrounded by a complete octet of electrons.* Unfortunately, there is no explanation for the outer shell's stopping at eight electrons. In fact, there are some cases where the outer shell does not stop at eight. However, for the majority of compounds the octet rule seems to be a useful generalization.

4.8 RESONANCE

Occasionally, no reasonable electronic picture can be drawn for a molecule which satisfactorily accounts for its observed properties. Such a problem is encountered in the case of sulfur dioxide, SO_2. This molecule has a high dipole moment; hence we conclude that it is nonlinear, with the atoms arranged in a bent chain. Sulfur has six valence electrons, and oxygen also has six. There are thus a total of 18 valence electrons. To agree with the octet rule, these can be disposed in several ways:

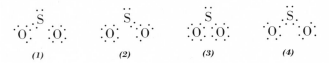

Neither (1) nor (2) is consistent with experimental fact, because each formula indicates that the SO_2 molecule has one double (short) sulfur-oxygen bond and one single (long) sulfur-oxygen bond. Experiments show the two bonds to be exactly the same length. The dilemma might be resolved by assuming that SO_2 is one of the compounds that violates the octet rule. In such case, possible formulas would be (3) and (4). Formula (4) is excluded because it contains unpaired electrons. Molecules containing unpaired electrons are paramagnetic (Sec. 3.11); sulfur dioxide is not. Formula (3) is traditionally excluded because of the convenience of maintaining the sanctity of the octet rule.

A situation in which *no single electronic formula conforms both to observed properties and to the octet rule* is described as *resonance*. In SO_2, the molecule is described by a combination of formulas (1) and (2). The actual electronic distribution in the molecule is said to be a *resonance hybrid* of these contributing formulas. The choice of the word resonance for this situation is unfortunate, because it encourages people to think that the molecule resonates from one structure to the other, or that the extra electron pair jumps back and forth from one bond to the other. *Such is not the case.* The molecule has only one real electron structure. The problem is in describing it. As a homely analogy of resonance, the mule is a hybrid of a jackass and a horse. When we look at a mule, we do not see a jackass at one glance and a horse a bit later. We see a mule. In the same way, the properties of a resonance hybrid do not oscillate from those of one contributing resonance structure to those of the other. The properties are fixed and are those of the actual hybrid structure.

Since resonance represents a problem in describing molecules, the difficulty lies in the description and not in the molecule itself. In the molecular-orbital description of molecules (Sec. 4.1), the problem does not arise. All the electrons belong to the molecule as a whole, and in SO_2 the troublesome electron pair need not be pictured as being in two places at once.

4.9   SHAPES OF MOLECULES

In the preceding sections, the formation of molecules has been represented in schematic fashion by using electronic symbols. It has been emphasized that the dot representation of electrons says nothing about the spatial distribution of the electron clouds. Furthermore, the over-all shape of a molecule is poorly presented in such electron-dot formulas. The theory of molecular shapes is a difficult subject but we might look at some of the simpler aspects of it.

Molecules which contain two atoms are necessarily linear but those containing three or more atoms present complications. For example, why is the water molecule nonlinear? To answer this question we must consider the nature of the orbitals involved in bonding the hydrogen to the oxygen and specifically the spatial distribution of the electronic charge clouds about each of the nuclei. Imagine assembling the molecule H_2O from two H atoms and one O atom. Each H atom has originally a single electron in a $1s$ orbital, which is spherically symmetrical about the nucleus. The oxygen atom has originally in its outer shell two $2s$ electrons (spherically symmetric) and four $2p$ electrons. Recalling the three p-type orbitals shown in Fig. 3.20, we find two of these $2p$ electrons in one of the p orbitals and one electron in each of the other two p orbitals. In the atomic-orbital description of bonds, the O to H bond arises from the sharing of the $1s$ electron of hydrogen with one of the unpaired $2p$ electrons of the oxygen. Such sharing will tend to concentrate the electronic charge along the direction of the $2p$ orbital used. To tie on two H atoms will require use of two $2p$ orbitals, which are at right angles to each other (see Fig. 3.20). Thus, on this simple picture we would expect the two O—H bonds in H_2O to be perpendicular to each other. Actually, they form the somewhat greater angle of $104°31'$. We shall return to this discrepancy later.

Methane, CH_4, has a tetrahedral shape, as shown in Fig. 4.8, with the carbon at the center of a tetrahedron and the four hydrogens at the corners. (A tetrahedron is a pyramid whose four faces are equilateral triangles.) The angles between the C—H bonds are $109°28'$. There are obvious problems with this molecule in that the bond angles are not right angles and furthermore there are four equivalent C—H bonds to be formed and we have but three p orbitals. Evidently we need to use the $2s$ orbital of carbon also. In

Fig. 4.8   Tetrahedral CH₄ *molecule.*

fact, the formation of the CH₄ molecule can be pictured as involving the replacement of the one 2*s* and the three 2*p* orbitals on the carbon by a new set of four equivalent orbitals directed to the corners of a tetrahedron. Electron sharing between these tetrahedral orbitals and the 1*s* orbitals of the hydrogens leads to the observed shape.

The use of tetrahedral orbitals can account for the observed shapes of molecules other than methane even in cases where there are not four attached atoms. For example, the NH₃ molecule can be imagined as having been built from a nitrogen atom with its five valence electrons distributed between four equivalent tetrahedral orbitals such that two of the electrons are paired and occupy one orbital. The other three electrons are shared with the H atoms using the other three tetrahedral orbitals. The result, as shown in Fig. 4.9, is a pyramidal molecule in which the three hydrogens form the base, and the lone pair of electrons the apex. The observed angles between N—H bonds in NH₃ are 108°, which is very nearly that expected for a tetrahedron.

Tetrahedral orbitals can also help explain the observed bond angle in H₂O. Following the reasoning of the preceding paragraph, we expect to find that H₂O is similar to NH₃ except there are two lone pairs of electrons in the case of H₂O. Figure 4.10 attempts to show that the two lone pairs of

Fig. 4.9   Ammonia molecule.

Fig. 4.10 Water molecule.

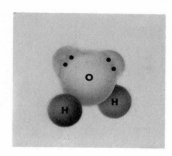

electrons and the two bound hydrogens are directed approximately to the corners of a tetrahedron.

QUESTIONS

4.1 Bond type. (*a*) What is the essential difference between an electrovalent bond and a covalent bond? Give an example of each. (*b*) What is the essential difference between a polar bond and a nonpolar bond? Give an example of each.

4.2 Molecular description. What is the essential difference between the molecular-orbital and the atomic-orbital descriptions of the water molecule?

4.3 Bond type. (*a*) Describe and account for the chemical bond formed when fluorine atoms ($Z = 9$) combine to form a molecule. (*b*) Describe and account for the chemical bond formed when lithium ($Z = 3$) reacts with oxygen ($Z = 8$). Write the formula of the resulting compound.

4.4 Dielectric constant. (*a*) What is meant by the term "dielectric constant"? (*b*) How might a measurement of the dielectric constant help you decide whether a given diatomic molecule is polar or nonpolar? (*c*) How might a measurement of the dielectric constant help you decide whether a given triatomic molecule is linear or bent?

4.5 Atomic-orbital description. Write the electronic formula for the I_2 molecule. What does this formula imply about: (*a*) inner electrons; (*b*) shared electrons; (*c*) unshared valence electrons?

4.6 Electronegativity. (*a*) What is meant by the term "electronegativity"? (*b*) What relation is there between electronegativity and polarity of bonds?

4.7 Electronegativity. Where in (*a*) a period and (*b*) a group would you expect to find atoms having the greatest electronegativity? Explain.

4.8 Saturation of valence. Show how saturation of valence accounts for Cl_2, HCl, CCl_4, and $BaCl_2$.

4.9 Donor-acceptor bonding. When sulfur is added to barium sulfide (BaS), a new compound BaS_2 may be obtained. By writing electronic formulas for sulfide (S^{--}) and disulfide (S_2^{--}) ions, show that donor-acceptor bonding can account for this result.

4.10 Bond type. Atoms X, Y, and Z occur in the same period and have two, six, and seven valence electrons, respectively. (*a*) Write the electronic formula for the compound most probably formed between X and Z. Will the bond between X and Z be predominantly electrovalent or covalent? Explain. (*b*) Write the electronic formula for the compound most probably formed between Y and Z. Give the formula also. Describe the bond between Y and Z.

4.11   General. Given atoms A, B, C, and D in the same period with one, three, five, and seven valence electrons, respectively. (*a*) What will be the formula of the compound between A and D, between B and D, and between C and D? (*b*) Compare the electronegativity of A with that of D. Will the compound between A and D be ionic or covalent? Write the electronic formula of the compound. (*c*) Write the electronic formula of the compound formed between C and D. (*d*) Which of these atoms might form a diatomic molecule? Write the electronic formula. (*e*) Which of these four atoms has the highest and which has the lowest ionization potential?

4.12   Multiple bonds. Assuming that the octet rule applies, show by writing electronic formulas that each of the following contains either double or triple bonds: CO, CO_2, C_3H_6, HCN, N_2.

4.13   Charge distribution. Draw diagrams for the probable charge distribution (similar to Fig. 4.3) in the nonpolar molecule F_2, the ionic molecule NaF, and the polar covalent molecules HF and ClF.

4.14   Bond energies. The bond energies of Cl_2 and Br_2 are 57.2 and 45.4 kcal. per Avogadro number of bonds. (*a*) What bond energy might you expect for $BrCl$, assuming equal sharing of electrons? (*b*) Would the observed bond energy be greater or less than this value? Explain.

4.15   Polarity. (*a*) Assuming that the valence is saturated, write the electronic formulas for the simplest hydrogen compounds of

$$:\overset{..}{\underset{.}{X}}\cdot \qquad\qquad \cdot\overset{..}{\underset{.}{Y}}\cdot \qquad\qquad :\overset{..}{\underset{..}{Z}}\cdot$$

(*b*) What shapes would you predict for these molecules? (*c*) Assuming that the electronegativity of H is different from that of X, Y, and Z, which of these compounds must be polar? Explain.

4.16   Resonance. The ozone molecule, O_3, contains three oxygen atoms arranged in a bent chain. The two bonds in the molecule are found to be equivalent. Show how resonance accounts for this.

4.17   Resonance. The nitrate ion, NO_3^-, contains a central nitrogen atom, to which the oxygen atoms are bound. The three nitrogen-oxygen bonds are found to be equivalent. Draw electronic formulas for the three contributing resonance forms. Note that, since the nitrate ion has a charge of -1, it contains one electron more than the 23 valence electrons contributed by the four neutral atoms.

4.18   Resonance. (*a*) The benzene molecule, C_6H_6, contains six carbon atoms arranged in a hexagon, with one hydrogen bound to each carbon. All six carbon-

carbon bonds are equivalent. Draw electronic formulas for two contributing resonance forms. (*b*) In benzene, the carbon-carbon distance is 1.39×10^{-8} cm. How is this consistent with the resonance picture?

4.19 *Bond energies and electronegativity.* Show how the data in Table 4.2 indicate that chlorine is more electronegative than bromine.

4.20 *Saturation of valence.* In Cl_2O_7 and $NaClO_4$, each chlorine atom is bound covalently to four oxygen atoms. Show how saturation of valence accounts for these compounds.

4.21 *General.* Elements *A*, *B*, and *C* have atomic numbers of z, $z + 1$, and $z + 2$. *B* is an inert element. *A* and *C* form a compound. (*a*) What kind of bonding do you predict in this compound? (*b*) Is the bond between *A* and *C* polar or nonpolar? Explain. (*c*) In what group of the periodic table do you expect to find *A*? *C*? *A* also forms a compound *AX* with the element *X* just above it in the periodic table. (*d*) What kind of bonding do you predict for the compound *AX*? (*e*) Is the bond between *A* and *X* polar or nonpolar? Explain.

4.22 *Molecular shapes.* Predict on the basis of Sec. 4.9 shapes for the following: ethane (C_2H_6), propane (C_3H_8), hydrogen peroxide (H_2O_2), hydrazine (N_2H_4).

5 Stoichiometry

THE WORD STOICHIOMETRY comes from the Greek *stoicheion,* meaning element. Strictly speaking, it refers to the determination of the combining weights of elements. In a broader sense it signifies the weight relations in chemical formulas and chemical equations. We have in preceding chapters used formulas in describing substances. These formulas are shorthand designations giving information about the composition of matter and are the result of experimental measurements.

5.1 SIMPLEST FORMULAS

The simplest formula, also called the empirical formula, gives the bare minimum of information about a compound, since it states only the *relative* number of gram-atoms in the compound. The convention used in writing the simplest formula is to write the symbols of the elements with subscripts to designate the relative numbers of gram-atoms of these elements. The formula $A_x B_y$ represents a compound in which there are x gram-atoms of A for every y gram-atoms of B. Because of the relationship between gram-atoms and atoms, the simplest formula also gives information about the rela-

100

tive number of atoms in the compound. In A_xB_y there are x atoms of element A for every y atoms of type B. Nothing is to be inferred about the nature of this association—in particular, nothing about the size or make-up of the molecular aggregate—except the *relative* number of atoms in it.

The simplest formula is always the direct result of an experiment. This procedure is illustrated in the following examples:

Example 1

When a weighed piece of metal M is heated with excess sulfur, a chemical reaction occurs between the metal and sulfur. The excess sulfur is then driven off, leaving only the compound, consisting of combined metal and sulfur. From the weight of M and weight of compound, the weight of sulfur in the compound can be deduced. Here are some sample figures from an experiment of this type:

Weight of metal	2.435 g.
Weight of compound	3.397 g.
Weight of sulfur	0.962 g.

What is the simplest formula of the compound?

Since the simplest formula gives the relative numbers of gram-atoms in the compound, we must calculate how many gram-atoms of M and of S have combined. If the atomic weight of M is 121.76 and that of S is 32.066, then

$$\text{Number of gram-atoms of } M = \frac{\text{weight of } M}{\text{weight of 1 gram-atom of } M}$$

$$= \frac{2.435 \text{ g.}}{121.76 \text{ g./gram-atom}}$$

$$= 0.0200 \text{ gram-atom of } M$$

$$\text{Number of gram-atoms of S} = \frac{\text{weight of S}}{\text{weight of 1 gram-atom of S}}$$

$$= \frac{0.962 \text{ g.}}{32.066 \text{ g./gram-atom}}$$

$$= 0.0300 \text{ gram-atom of S}$$

In this compound there is 0.0200 gram-atom of M combined with 0.0300 gram-atom of S. Since the relative number of gram-atoms of M to S is 0.0200 to 0.0300, or 2 to 3, the simplest formula is M_2S_3.

Example 2

The analysis of a compound is often given in terms of percentage composition. What is the simplest formula of a compound which on analysis shows 50.05% S and 49.95% O by weight?

For the simplest formula we need the relative numbers of gram-atoms of sulfur and oxygen in the compound. Since only relative numbers are involved, we may consider any amount of compound, 1 g., 32.066 g., or any other weight. We shall work this problem in two ways for illustration.

(*a*) *In 32.066 g. of compound* there are 16.05 g. of sulfur (50.05% of 32.066 g.) and 16.02 g. of oxygen (49.95% of 32.066 g.).

$$\text{Number of gram-atoms of S} = \frac{\text{weight of S}}{\text{weight of 1 gram-atom of S}}$$

$$= \frac{16.05 \text{ g.}}{32.066 \text{ g./gram-atom}}$$

$$= 0.5005 \text{ gram-atom of S}$$

$$\text{Number of gram-atoms of O} = \frac{\text{weight of O}}{\text{weight of 1 gram-atom of O}}$$

$$= \frac{16.02 \text{ g.}}{16.000 \text{ g./gram-atom}}$$

$$= 1.001 \text{ gram-atoms of O}$$

The simplest formula is $S_{0.5005}O_{1.001}$, or SO_2.

(*b*) *In 100.0 g. of compound* there are 50.05 g. of sulfur and 49.95 g. of oxygen.

$$\text{Number of gram-atoms of S} = \frac{\text{weight of S}}{\text{weight of 1 gram-atom of S}}$$

$$= \frac{50.05 \text{ g.}}{32.066 \text{ g./gram-atom}}$$

$$= 1.561 \text{ gram-atoms of S}$$

$$\text{Number of gram-atoms of O} = \frac{\text{weight of O}}{\text{weight of 1 gram-atom of.O}}$$

$$= \frac{49.95 \text{ g.}}{16.000 \text{ g./gram-atom}}$$

$$= 3.122 \text{ gram-atoms of O}$$

The simplest formula is $S_{1.561}O_{3.122}$, or SO_2.

5.2   MOLECULAR FORMULAS

A second type of formula is the molecular formula. The amount of information which the molecular formula gives is greater than that given by the simplest formula. In the molecular formula the subscripts give the *actual* number of atoms of an element in one molecule of the compound. The molecule was defined previously as an aggregate of atoms bonded together tightly enough to be conveniently treated as a recognizable unit. In order to write the molecular formula, it is necessary to know how many atoms constitute the molecule. To find the actual number of atoms in a molecule, various experimental techniques can be used. For instance, X-ray determination of the positions of atoms in solids can give this information. Furthermore, as discussed in Chaps. 6 and 10, some of the properties of gases and solutions depend on the number of atoms in each molecular aggregate. A few molecular formulas thus determined are shown in Table 5.1, where they are compared with the corresponding simplest formulas. In some cases, as for water and sucrose, the molecular and simplest formulas are identical. In other cases, they are not. We cannot tell from a formula whether it is molecular or simplest. However, if the subscripts given have a common divisor, it is a good bet that it is a molecular formula. The molecular formula gives all the information which is in the simplest formula, and more besides.

5.3 FORMULA WEIGHTS AND MOLES

The *formula weight* is the sum of all the atomic weights in the formula under consideration, be it simplest or molecular. For NaCl, the formula weight is the atomic weight of sodium, 22.991 a.m.u., plus the atomic weight of chlorine, 35.457 a.m.u., a total of 58.448 a.m.u. For $C_{12}H_{22}O_{11}$, the formula weight is equal to twelve times the atomic weight of carbon plus twenty-two times the atomic weight of hydrogen plus eleven times the atomic weight of oxygen, or 342.308 a.m.u. In all cases, the formula weight depends on which formula is written. If the molecular formula is used, the formula weight is called the *molecular weight*. For example, 342.308 a.m.u. is the molecular weight of sucrose.

Table 5.1 *Molecular and Simplest Formulas*

Substance	Molecular formula	Simplest formula
Benzene	C_6H_6	CH
Acetylene	C_2H_2	CH
Oxygen	O_2	O
Sulfur	S_8	S
Phosphorus	P_4	P
Water	H_2O	H_2O
Sucrose (a sugar)	$C_{12}H_{22}O_{11}$	$C_{12}H_{22}O_{11}$
Glucose (a sugar)	$C_6H_{12}O_6$	CH_2O

As noted above, the formula weight is given in atomic mass units. An amount of a substance whose weight in grams numerically equals the formula weight is called a *gram-formula*. A gram-formula is usually referred to as a *gram-mole*, or simply a *mole*. In the case of $C_{12}H_{22}O_{11}$, where the formula weight is 342.308 a.m.u., 1 gram-formula or 1 gram-mole weighs 342.308 g. A pile of this sugar weighing 342.308 g. is 1 gram-mole. The formula weight can also be used in terms of tons, ounces, pounds, or other units of weight to give ton-moles, ounce-moles, etc. (see discussion of gram-atoms in Sec. 2.6). In other words, 342.308 tons of sugar is 1 ton-formula, or 1 ton-mole, of sugar. Since we are primarily concerned with gram-moles, it is convenient to omit the prefix "gram-" and to understand that "mole" means gram-mole.

There is an important relationship between number of moles and number of particles. Let us consider sulfur chloride, the molecular formula of which is S_2Cl_2. One mole of S_2Cl_2 weighs 135 g. and contains 64 g. of sulfur and 71 g. of chlorine. In 64 g. of S (atomic weight 32), there are 64/32, or 2, gram-atoms of S; in 71 g. of Cl (atomic weight 35.5), there are 71/35.5, or 2, gram-atoms of Cl. Since 1 gram-atom contains the Avogadro number of atoms, 2 gram-atoms of S contains $2 \times 6.02 \times 10^{23}$ atoms of S, and 2 gram-atoms of Cl contains $2 \times 6.02 \times 10^{23}$ atoms of Cl. The molecular formula, S_2Cl_2, indicates that two atoms of S and two atoms of Cl comprise one molecule of S_2Cl_2. Therefore, $2 \times 6.02 \times 10^{23}$ atoms of S and $2 \times 6.02 \times 10^{23}$ atoms of chlorine comprise 6.02×10^{23} molecules. For any substance whose molecular formula is known, 1 mole contains the Avogadro number of molecules.

Let us consider the relationship between number of moles and number of particles for a compound whose molecular formula is not known. Such a compound is phosphorus dichloride, whose simplest formula is PCl_2. One mole of PCl_2 weighs 102 g. and contains 31 g. of phosphorus and 71 g. of chlorine. In 31 g. of P (atomic weight 31), there is 31/31, or 1, gram-atom of P; in 71 g. of Cl (atomic weight 35.5), there is 71/35.5, or 2, gram-atoms of Cl. One gram-atom of P contains 6.02×10^{23} atoms of P; 2 gram-atoms of Cl contains $2 \times 6.02 \times 10^{23}$ atoms of Cl. Since the molecular formula of PCl_2 is not known, the number of atoms in the molecule is not known. Therefore we can make no statement about the number of molecules in 1 mole of PCl_2. If we define a *formula unit* as consisting of one P atom and two Cl atoms, there are then 6.02×10^{23} such formula units in 1 mole of PCl_2. For any substance, 1 *mole contains the Avogadro number of formula units*. Only if the formula is a molecular formula is the formula unit the same as the molecule.

Even though formulas are based on experimentally determined percentage composition, it is sometimes necessary to calculate percentage composition from a formula.

Example 3

What is the percentage composition of $C_{12}H_{22}O_{11}$? Atomic weights are C, 12.01; H, 1.008; O, 16.00.

One mole $C_{12}H_{22}O_{11}$ contains

12 gram-atoms C, or 12 × 12.01 g. C, or 144.12 g. C

22 gram-atoms H, or 22 × 1.008 g. H, or   22.18 g. H

11 gram-atoms O, or 11 × 16.00 g. O, or 176.00 g. O

342.30 g. total weight

$$\% \text{ carbon} = \frac{\text{wt. of C in 1 mole} \times 100}{\text{total wt. of 1 mole}} = \frac{144.12}{342.30} \times 100 = 42.103\%$$

$$\% \text{ hydrogen} = \frac{\text{wt. of H in 1 mole} \times 100}{\text{total wt. of 1 mole}} = \frac{22.18}{342.30} \times 100 = 6.480\%$$

$$\% \text{ oxygen} = \frac{\text{wt. of O in 1 mole} \times 100}{\text{total wt. of 1 mole}} = \frac{176.00}{342.30} \times 100 = 51.417\%$$

5.4   CHEMICAL REACTIONS

The other principal division of stoichiometry is concerned with weight changes in chemical reactions. Before considering these quantitative aspects, we need to examine ways of describing chemical change. It is possible to group chemical reactions into two broad classes: (*a*) reactions in which there is no electron transfer and (*b*) reactions in which there is electron transfer from one atom to another atom.

Reactions in which there are no electrons transferred usually involve the joining or separating of ions or molecules. An example of a "no-electron-transfer" reaction occurs when a solution of sodium chloride is mixed with a solution of silver nitrate. The solution of sodium chloride contains sodium ions and chloride ions (Sec. 10.4). The solution of silver nitrate contains silver ions and nitrate ions. Figure 5.1 shows one beaker with sodium ions and chloride ions and another with silver ions and nitrate ions. On mixing the two solutions, a chemical reaction occurs, as shown by the formation of a white precipitate. This white solid consists of silver ions and chloride ions clumped together in large aggregates. In the final solution, sodium ions and nitrate ions remain just as they were initially. In the chemical reaction, the only thing that has happened is that the silver ions have combined with chloride ions to form solid silver chloride, which is insoluble in the water. In shorthand form, the reaction is indicated

$$Ag^+(\text{soln.}) + \cancel{NO_3^-(\text{soln.})} + \cancel{Na^+(\text{soln.})} + Cl^-(\text{soln.}) \rightarrow$$

$$AgCl(s) + \cancel{Na^+(\text{soln.})} + \cancel{NO_3^-(\text{soln.})}$$

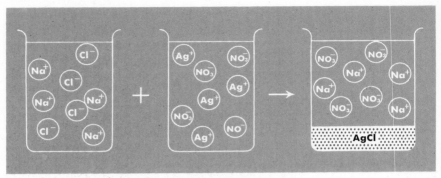

Fig. 5.1 *Chemical reaction without electron transfer.*

where the abbreviation (soln.) indicates that the ion is in solution and the notation (*s*) emphasizes the fact that AgCl is formed as a solid; the strikeovers indicate cancellation of ions which do not change in the course of the reaction. The final net reaction is

$$Ag^+(\text{soln.}) + Cl^-(\text{soln.}) \rightarrow AgCl(s)$$

Reactions in which electrons are transferred from one atom to another are known as *oxidation-reduction reactions*. Many of the most important chemical reactions fall into this class. For example, the combining of the sodium atom with a chlorine atom can be regarded as resulting from the transfer of an electron from the sodium to the chlorine, as shown schematically in Fig. 5.2. A less obvious example of an oxidation-reduction reaction is that in which hydrogen and oxygen form water. In this case there is a change of the sharing of electrons during the course of the reaction:

$$H\!:\!H + \overset{..}{:}\!\overset{..}{O}\!: \rightarrow H\!:\!\overset{..}{\underset{..}{O}}\!:$$
$$H$$

What has happened to the hydrogen in the course of this reaction? In the initial state, two hydrogen nuclei share a pair of electrons. Since the two hydrogen nuclei are identical, they share the pair equally, and each hydrogen atom has a half-time share of an electron pair. In the final state, the hydrogen shares a pair of electrons with oxygen. Since oxygen is the more electronegative, the electron pair is not shared equally but belongs more to the oxygen than to the hydrogen. In the course of the reaction, there is a change in the electron sharing; i.e., a partial transfer of electrons.

Fig. 5.2 *Chemical reaction with electron transfer.*

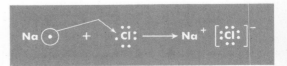

5.5   OXIDATION NUMBERS

In order to keep track of electron shifts in oxidation-reduction reactions, it is convenient to use the *oxidation number*, sometimes called the *oxidation state*. The oxidation number is defined as the charge which an atom appears to have (with emphasis on the word *appears*) when electrons are counted according to some rather arbitrary rules. The first of these rules is that electrons shared between two unlike atoms are counted with the more electronegative atom. The second rule is that electrons shared between two like atoms are divided equally between the sharing atoms.

What is the oxidation number of hydrogen in the H_2 molecule? The electron pair is shared by two identical atoms, and so, according to the second rule, half of the electrons are counted with each atom, as shown by the dotted line in Fig. 5.3. Since the hydrogen kernel has a $+1$ charge and since one negative charge is counted with the kernel, the apparent charge of each hydrogen atom is zero. The oxidation number of hydrogen in H_2 is 0.

What are the oxidation numbers of hydrogen and oxygen in H_2O? Oxygen is the more electronegative, and so, according to the first rule, the shared electrons are counted with the oxygen, as shown by the dotted line in Fig. 5.4. The hydrogen appears to have a charge of $+1$ and is assigned an oxidation number of $+1$. Since eight electrons are counted with the $+6$ oxygen kernel, the apparent charge of oxygen is -2. Oxygen has an oxidation number of -2 in H_2O.

In principle, electronic pictures can be drawn for all molecules and electrons counted in this way to deduce the oxidation numbers of the various atoms. This is laborious. It is more convenient to use the following operational rules which are derived from the above:

1   In the free elements, each atom has an oxidation number of 0, no matter how complicated the molecule is. Hydrogen in H_2, sodium in Na, sulfur in S_8, and phosphorus in P_4 all have oxidation numbers of 0.

2   In simple ions (ions which contain one atom) the oxidation number is equal to the charge on the ion. In these cases, the apparent charge of the atom is the real charge of the ion. In the tripositive aluminum ion, the oxidation number of the aluminum atom is $+3$. Iron, which can form a dipositive or a tripositive ion, sometimes has an oxidation number of $+2$ and sometimes $+3$. In the dinegative oxide ion, the oxidation number of oxygen is -2. It is useful to remember that elements of group I of the periodic table, lithium, sodium, potassium, rubidium, cesium, and francium,

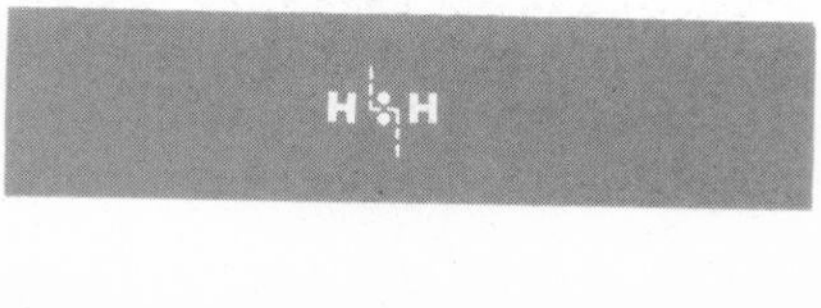

Fig. 5.3   Assignment of oxidation number in H_2.

Fig. 5.4 Assignment of oxidation numbers in H_2O.

form only $+1$ ions. Their oxidation number is $+1$ in all compounds. The group II elements, beryllium, magnesium, calcium, strontium, barium, and radium, form only $+2$ ions and hence always have oxidation numbers of $+2$ in all compounds.

3   *In most compounds containing oxygen, the oxidation number of each oxygen atom is* -2. This covers the vast majority of oxygen compounds. There are two kinds of exceptions. One arises in the case of the peroxides, compounds of oxygen in which there is an oxygen-oxygen bond. In peroxides, e.g., hydrogen peroxide (H_2O_2), only seven electrons are counted with the $+6$ kernel of oxygen. Figure 5.5 shows how the electrons are assigned. In the hydrogen-oxygen bond, the electrons are counted with oxygen, the more electronegative atom. In the oxygen-oxygen bond, the electron pair is shared between two like atoms and is split equally between the sharing partners. The apparent charge of the oxygen is thus -1. Oxygen has an oxidation number of -1 in all peroxides. The second exception is even less common. It occurs when oxygen is bonded to fluorine, the only atom which is more electronegative than oxygen. When oxygen is bonded to fluorine, shared electrons are counted with the fluorine. The assignment of oxidation numbers in the compound oxygen fluoride is shown in Fig. 5.6. The oxidation number of fluorine is -1 and the oxidation number of oxygen is $+2$.

4   *In most compounds containing hydrogen, the oxidation number of hydrogen is* $+1$. This rule covers practically all the hydrogen compounds. It fails in the case of the hydrides, in which hydrogen is bonded to an atom less electronegative than hydrogen. For example, when hydrogen is bonded to sodium in the compound sodium hydride, NaH, the hydrogen is the more electronegative atom, and two electrons are counted with it. In hydrides, the oxidation number of hydrogen is -1.

5   *All oxidation numbers must be consistent with the conservation of charge.* Charge must be conserved in the sense that the sum of all the apparent charges in a particle must equal the net charge of that particle. This leads to the following conditions: (*a*) *for neutral molecules, the oxidation numbers of all the atoms must add up to zero;* (*b*) *for complex ions (charged particles*

Fig. 5.5 Assignment of oxidation numbers in H_2O_2.

Fig. 5.6   Assignment of oxidation numbers in OF_2.

O kernel $+6$

F kernel $+7$

which contain more than one atom), the oxidation numbers of all the atoms must add up to the charge on the ion. As an example of a neutral molecule, we consider the case of H_2O. The oxidation number of hydrogen is $+1$. There are two hydrogen atoms. The total apparent charge contribution by hydrogen is $+2$. The oxidation number of oxygen is -2. The whole molecule looks to be neutral. The neutrality rule enables us to assign oxidation numbers to any atom. For example, what is the oxidation number of sulfur in H_2SO_4? The oxidation number of hydrogen is $+1$; the oxidation number of oxygen is -2. The two hydrogens give an apparent charge of $+2$; the four oxygens give an apparent charge of -8. For neutrality the sulfur must contribute $+6$. Since there is but one sulfur atom, the oxidation number of sulfur is $+6$. In $H_2S_2O_3$ hydrogen contributes an apparent charge of $+2$; oxygen contributes a total apparent charge of -6. For neutrality the sulfur contribution must be $+4$. Since there are two sulfur atoms, the oxidation number of each is $+2$.

Since oxidation numbers are quite arbitrary, they may have values which at first sight appear strange. For example, in cane sugar, $C_{12}H_{22}O_{11}$, the oxidation number of carbon is 0. The total apparent charge of 22 hydrogen atoms is canceled by that of 11 oxygen atoms. According to the oxidation number, each carbon atom appears to contribute no charge to the molecule. Fractional oxidation numbers are also possible, as in $Na_2S_4O_6$, where the oxidation number of sulfur is $+1\frac{1}{4}$.

In complex ions the apparent charges of all the atoms must add up to equal the charge on the ion. This is true in hydroxide ion, OH^-, for example, where the dash indicates that the ion has a net charge of -1. Since oxygen has an oxidation number of -2 and since hydrogen has an oxidation number of $+1$, the total apparent charge is $-2 + 1 = -1$, which is the same as the actual charge of the ion. In $Cr_2O_7^{--}$, a dinegative ion, the seven oxygen atoms contribute -14. Chromium must contribute $+12$ in order to make the ion have a net charge of -2. Since there are two chromium atoms in the complex, each chromium has an oxidation number of $+6$.

In order to avoid confusion with the actual charge on an ion, which is written as a superscript, the oxidation number of an atom, when needed, is written beneath the atom to which it applies. For example, in

$$P_2O_7^{-4}$$
$$\underset{+5\ \ -2}{}$$

the charge on the ion is -4; the oxidation numbers are $+5$ and -2. It should be emphasized strongly that oxidation numbers are not actual charges of atoms. In the specific case of $P_2O_7^{-4}$ it can be shown experimentally that the aggregate carries a -4 charge; however, it cannot be shown experimentally that the charge of P is $+5$ and that of the O is -2. The $+5$ and -2 are arbitrarily assigned numbers, and we must not conclude that $P_2O_7^{-4}$ contains P^{+5} ions and O^{-2} ions.

Oxidation number is not the same thing as valence. Valence, or combining capacity, can be interpreted in several ways. For example, it represents the number of hydrogen atoms which can be combined with a given atom. It also represents the number of single bonds which an atom can form. In any case valence is a pure number and has no plus or minus associated with it. On the other hand, oxidation number is positive or negative. For example, in water the valence of oxygen is two, but its oxidation number is *minus* two. Furthermore, there may actually be a difference in the magnitude of the valence and the oxidation number. In hydrogen peroxide (Fig. 5.5) each oxygen atom has two single bonds, one that goes to oxygen and one to hydrogen. The valence of oxygen is therefore two. As indicated before, the oxidation number of oxygen in H_2O_2 is -1.

5.6   OXIDATION-REDUCTION

The term *oxidation* refers to any chemical change in which there is an *increase in oxidation number*. For example, when hydrogen, H_2, reacts to form water, H_2O, the hydrogen atoms change oxidation number from 0 to $+1$. The H_2 is said to undergo oxidation. When sugar, $C_{12}H_{22}O_{11}$, is burned to give carbon dioxide, CO_2, carbon atoms increase in oxidation number from 0 to $+4$. The sugar is oxidized. The term *reduction* applies to any *decrease in oxidation number*. For example, when oxygen, O_2, reacts to form H_2O, oxygen atoms change oxidation number from 0 to -2. This is a decrease in oxidation number; hence O_2 is said to undergo reduction. In oxidation and reduction the increase and decrease of oxidation numbers result from a shift of electrons. The only way by which electrons can be shifted away from an atom is for them to be pulled toward another atom. In this process the oxidation number of the first atom increases, and the oxidation number of the second atom decreases. Oxidation and reduction must always occur together and must just compensate each other.

The *oxidizing agent* is, by definition, the *substance that does the oxidizing*. It is that substance containing the atom which shows a decrease in oxidation number. For example, if in a reaction $KClO_3$ is converted to KCl, each chlorine atom decreases in oxidation number from $+5$ to -1. This amounts to getting six electrons (six negative charges) from other atoms. Thus, $KClO_3$ must cause oxidation and is acting as an oxidizing agent.

Table 5.2 **Oxidation-reduction Terms**

Term	Oxidation-number change	Electron change
Oxidation	Increase	Loss of electrons
Reduction	Decrease	Gain of electrons
Oxidizing agent	Decrease	Picks up electrons
Reducing agent	Increase	Supplies electrons
Substance oxidized	Increase	Loses electrons
Substance reduced	Decrease	Gains electrons

Similarly a *reducing agent* is the *substance that does the reducing*. It is the substance containing the atom which shows an increase in oxidation number. In the reaction of $C_{12}H_{22}O_{11}$ to give CO_2, $C_{12}H_{22}O_{11}$ is a reducing agent, because it contains carbon atoms which increase in oxidation number. It should be evident that when a substance acts as a reducing agent, it itself must be oxidized in the process. Table 5.2 summarizes the terms used to describe oxidation-reduction.

Listed in Table 5.3 are some examples of oxidation-reduction processes. The numbers below the formulas indicate the oxidation numbers of interest. It must be emphasized that the term oxidizing agent or reducing agent refers to the entire substance and not to just one atom. For example, in the next to last reaction of the table, the oxidizing agent is $KClO_3$ and not $+5$ Cl. It can be shown that $KClO_3$ picks up electrons and therefore is an oxidizing agent, but it *cannot* be shown that it is the chlorine atom in $KClO_3$ that picks up electrons, because of the arbitrary rules for assigning oxidation numbers.

Table 5.3 **Oxidation-reduction Reactions**

Oxidizing agents	+	Reducing agents	→	Products
O_2 0		H_2 0		H_2O $+1-2$
Cl_2 0		Na 0		NaCl $+1-1$
H^+ $+1$		Mg 0		$Mg^{++} + H_2$ $+2 \quad\quad 0$
$KClO_3$ $+5$		$C_{12}H_{22}O_{11}$ 0		$KCl + CO_2 + H_2O$ $-1 \quad +4$
H_2O_2 -1		H_2O_2 -1		$H_2O + O_2$ $-2 \quad\; 0$

In the last reaction listed in Table 5.3, H_2O_2 acts both as a reducing agent and an oxidizing agent. In oxidizing and reducing itself, it is said to undergo *auto-oxidation,* or *disproportionation.*

5.7 CHEMICAL EQUATIONS

Chemical equations are shorthand designations which give information about a chemical reaction. We shall generally use *net equations,* which *specify only the substances used up and the substances formed* in the chemical reaction. Net equations omit anything which remains unchanged. The convention used in writing equations is to place what disappears (the *reactants*) on the left-hand side and what appears (*the products*) on the right-hand side. The reactants and products are separated by a single arrow $\rightarrow$, an equal sign $=$, or a double arrow $\rightleftharpoons$, depending on what aspect of the chemical reaction is being emphasized. An example of a net equation is

$$Cl_2(g) + H_2O + Ag^+ \rightarrow AgCl(s) + HOCl + H^+$$

The reactants and products are designated by symbols or formulas. The symbol can be thought of as representing either 1 atom or 1 gram-atom. The formula represents either 1 formula unit or 1 mole. The notation (g) indicates the gas phase, and (s) the solid phase. When no such phase notation appears, the liquid phase is understood.

To be valid, a chemical equation must satisfy three conditions. First, it must be consistent with the experimental facts—that is, it must state what chemical species disappear and appear. Second, it must be consistent with the conservation of mass. (Since we cannot destroy mass, we must account for it. If an atom disappears from one substance, it must appear in another.) Third, the chemical equation must be consistent with the conservation of electrical charge. (Since we cannot destroy electrical charge, we must account for it.) Conditions two and three are expressed by saying that the equation must be *balanced.* A balanced equation contains the same numbers of atoms of the different kinds on the left- and right-hand sides; furthermore, the net charge is the same on both sides.

How do we go about writing balanced equations? One method, usually reserved for simple reactions, is to balance the equation by inspection. For example, in the reaction between a solution of silver nitrate and a solution of sodium chloride, silver ions and chloride ions disappear, and solid silver chloride appears. The equation for the reaction is

$$Ag^+ + Cl^- \rightarrow AgCl(s)$$

Since there is one silver atom on the left and one on the right and since there is one chlorine atom on the left and one on the right, mass balance is satisfied. The net electrical charge on the left is zero ($+1$ for the silver ion plus -1 for the chloride ion totals zero), and the net charge on the right is zero. Therefore the equation is also electrically balanced.

In the reaction between solid sodium and gaseous diatomic chlorine, solid sodium chloride is formed, so we write first

$$Na(s) + Cl_2(g) \rightarrow NaCl(s)$$

To balance this equation, we note that we have two chlorine atoms on the left, so we ought to have two chlorine atoms on the right. We cannot change the subscript of Cl in the formula NaCl, because that would give the formula of a different compound. We can change only the coefficients; hence we put 2 in front of the NaCl. With two sodium atoms on the right we now need two sodium atoms on the left; therefore we also place a 2 in front of the Na.

The equation now reads

$$2Na(s) + Cl_2(g) \rightarrow 2NaCl(s)$$

and has been balanced by inspection.

There are more complicated reactions involving electron transfer where balancing by inspection gets to be quite a chore. For example, suppose that in the reaction which occurs between potassium dichromate, sulfur, and water, the products are sulfur dioxide, potassium hydroxide, and chromic oxide.

$$K_2Cr_2O_7(s) + H_2O + S(s) \rightarrow SO_2(g) + KOH(s) + Cr_2O_3(s)$$

Although the equation may be balanced by inspection, it is easier to balance it by matching up the electron transfer, i.e., the oxidation and the reduction. So far as electron transfer is concerned, we have to worry only about those atoms which change oxidation number. Applying the rules for assigning oxidation numbers, we see that sulfur changes oxidation number from 0 to $+4$, and chromium from $+6$ to $+3$. As indicated below, each sulfur atom appears to lose four electrons and each chromium atom appears to gain three electrons.

$$K_2Cr_2O_7(s) + H_2O + S(s) \rightarrow SO_2(g) + KOH(s) + Cr_2O_3(s)$$

$+6$ $\qquad\qquad\qquad$ 0 $\qquad$ $+4$ $\qquad\qquad\qquad$ $+3$

$\uparrow$ 3e^- per atom
6e^- per formula
$\quad$ unit

$\downarrow$ 4e^-

Since each formula unit of $K_2Cr_2O_7$ contains two chromium atoms, a formula unit will pick up 6 electrons. These electrons must be furnished by the S. In order that the electron loss and the electron gain be equal, for every two $K_2Cr_2O_7$ formula units that disappear (12 electrons picked up) three S atoms must be used up (12 electrons furnished). This is indicated by writing 2 in front of the $K_2Cr_2O_7$ and the Cr_2O_3 and 3 in front of the S and the SO_2 to give

$$2K_2Cr_2O_7(s) + H_2O + 3S(s) \rightarrow 3SO_2(g) + KOH(s) + 2Cr_2O_3(s)$$

Although the tough part is over, the equation is not balanced. To complete the job, the other coefficients must be made consistent with this. We can do this by inspection. From the above equation we can see that we get four potassium atoms on the right, so we place a 4 in front of the KOH. The result

$$2K_2Cr_2O_7(s) + H_2O + 3S(s) \rightarrow 3SO_2(g) + 4KOH(s) + 2Cr_2O_3(s)$$

is still not balanced. Balance may be achieved by counting up either the H atoms or the O atoms on the right. This shows that two molecules of H_2O are required. The balanced equation is

$$2K_2Cr_2O_7(s) + 2H_2O + 3S(s) \rightarrow 3SO_2(g) + 4KOH(s) + 2Cr_2O_3(s)$$

Here in summary for future reference are the steps followed:

1. Assign oxidation numbers for those atoms which change.
2. Decide on number of electrons to be shifted per atom.
3. Decide on number of electrons to be shifted per formula unit.
4. Compensate electron gain and loss by writing appropriate coefficients for the oxidizing agent and the reducing agent.
5. Insert other coefficients consistent with the conservation of matter.

A chemical equation is valuable from two standpoints. It gives information on an atomic scale and also on a laboratory scale. For example,

$$8KClO_3(s) + C_{12}H_{22}O_{11}(s) \rightarrow 8KCl(s) + 12CO_2(g) + 11H_2O(g)$$

Atomic scale:

8 formula units + 1 formula unit $\rightarrow$
(molecule)

8 formula units + 12 formula units + 11 formula units
(molecule)   (molecule)

Lab scale:

8 moles + 1 mole $\rightarrow$ 8 moles + 12 moles + 11 moles

980.456 g. + 342.308 g. $\rightarrow$ 596.456 g. + 528.132 g. + 198.176 g.

On an atomic scale, the equation states that 8 formula units of $KClO_3$ (each formula unit containing a potassium atom, a chlorine atom, and three oxygen atoms) react with 1 formula unit of $C_{12}H_{22}O_{11}$ to produce 8 formula units of KCl, 12 formula units of CO_2, and 11 formula units of H_2O. Since the numbers are important only in a *relative* sense, the equation also indicates, for example, that eight *dozen* formula units of $KClO_3$ react with one *dozen* formula units of $C_{12}H_{22}O_{11}$ to produce eight *dozen* formula units of KCl, 12 *dozen* formula units of CO_2, and 11 *dozen* formula units of H_2O. Multiplying the equation through by the same number does not change its significance. Multiplying the equation through by Avogadro's number converts it from the atomic scale to something which is useful in the laboratory. The Avogadro number of formula units is 1 mole, so that the equation signifies that 8 moles of $KClO_3$ reacts with 1 mole of $C_{12}H_{22}O_{11}$ to give 8 moles of KCl plus 12 moles of CO_2 plus 11 moles of H_2O. From the formula weights of the various compounds we can get further quantitative information from the equation. Eight moles of $KClO_3$ weighs eight times the formula weight, or 8×122.557 g., or 980.456 g.; 1 mole of sucrose weighs 342.308 g.; 8 moles of KCl weighs 8×78.557, or 596.456, g.; 12 moles of CO_2 weighs 12×44.011, or 528.132, g.; and 11 moles of H_2O weighs 11×18.016, or 198.176, g. The total mass on the left-hand side of the equation is 1,322.764 g., and that on the right-hand side, 1,322.764 g. Mass is conserved as it must be.

Once a balanced chemical equation is obtained, it can be used for solution of problems involving weight relationships in chemical reactions. This is illustrated by the following examples:

Example 4

How many grams of $KClO_3$ *must be decomposed to give 0.96 g. of oxygen?*

It is known that, on heating, the white solid $KClO_3$ decomposes to form the white solid KCl and the gas oxygen, O_2. To answer the question, we need the equation for the decomposition. In this equation $KClO_3$ is placed on the left, and KCl and O_2 on the right.

$$KClO_3(s) \rightarrow KCl(s) + O_2(g)$$

The chlorine atom changes oxidation number from $+5$ to -1. It appears to gain six electrons. Oxygen changes oxidation number from -2 to 0; each atom appears to lose two electrons. The formula unit is such that there are three oxygen atoms for every chlorine atom, so that the compound itself has taken care of the electron gain and the electron loss. One K and one Cl on the left require one K and one Cl on the right. Three oxygen atoms on the left require three oxygen atoms on the right. We can get these three oxygen atoms on the right by placing the coefficient ½ before the formula O_2, giving

$$KClO_3(s) \longrightarrow KCl(s) + \tfrac{3}{2}O_2(g)$$

Multiplying through by 2 to get rid of the fraction gives

$$2KClO_3(s) \longrightarrow 2KCl(s) + 3O_2(g)$$

We now have the balanced equation and can proceed to solve the problem. Since a chemical equation may always be read directly in terms of moles, it is convenient to solve problems in terms of moles.

One mole of O_2 weighs 32 g.

0.96 g. of O_2 is equal to 0.96/32, or 0.030, mole

The equation states that 2 moles of $KClO_3$ yields 3 moles of O_2.

For 1 mole of O_2, need ⅔ mole of $KClO_3$

For 0.030 mole of O_2, need (⅔)(0.030), or 0.020, mole of $KClO_3$

One mole of $KClO_3$ weighs 122.56 g., as found by adding atomic weights

0.020 mole of $KClO_3$ weighs (0.020)(122.56), or 2.5, g.

Example 5

On heating, 4.90 g. of $KClO_3$ shows a weight loss of 0.384 g. What percentage of the original $KClO_3$ has decomposed?

The weight loss is due to the fact that a gas is driven off. The only gas formed in this reaction is oxygen, as seen from the equation obtained in Example 4.

$$2KClO_3(s) \longrightarrow 2KCl(s) + 3O_2(g)$$

0.384 g. of O_2 formed is 0.384/32.0, or 0.0120, mole

To get 3 moles of O_2, decompose 2 moles of $KClO_3$

To get 1 mole of O_2, decompose ⅔ mole of $KClO_3$

To get 0.0120 mole of O_2, decompose (⅔)(0.0120), or 0.00800, mole of $KClO_3$. Originally we had 4.90 g. of $KClO_3$ (formula weight 122.5), or 4.90/122.5, or 0.0400, mole.

$$\% \text{ decomposed} = \frac{\text{moles decomposed}}{\text{moles available}} \times 100 = \frac{0.00800}{0.0400} \times 100, \text{ or } 20\%$$

Example 6

In the reaction of vanadium oxide, VO, with iron oxide, Fe_2O_3, the products are V_2O_5 and FeO. How many grams of V_2O_5 can be formed from 2.00 g. of VO and 5.75 g. of Fe_2O_3?

In solving this problem, we first write the balanced equation

$$2VO(s) + 3Fe_2O_3(s) \longrightarrow 6FeO(s) + V_2O_5(s)$$

Next we decide which reactant limits the amount of products and which reactant is present in excess. To do this, we convert the data into moles. The formula weight of VO is 66.95; the formula weight of Fe_2O_3 is 159.70.

In 2.00 g. of VO there is 2.00/66.95, or 0.0299, mole of VO

In 5.75 g. of Fe_2O_3 there is 5.75/159.70, or 0.0360, mole of Fe_2O_3

According to the equation, 2 moles of VO requires 3 moles of Fe_2O_3

One mole of VO requires 3/2 moles of Fe_2O_3

Therefore, 0.0299 mole of VO requires (3/2)(0.0299), or 0.0449, mole of Fe_2O_3

Since the 0.0360 mole of Fe_2O_3 is less than the 0.0449 mole required, there is not enough Fe_2O_3 to react with all the VO. The VO is present in excess, and the reaction is limited by the amount of Fe_2O_3.

Three moles of Fe_2O_3 produces 1 mole of V_2O_5

One mole of Fe_2O_3 produces 1/3 mole of V_2O_5

0.0360 mole of Fe_2O_3 produces (1/3)(0.0360), or 0.0120, mole of V_2O_5

One mole of V_2O_5 is 181.9 g.

0.0120 mole of V_2O_5 is (0.0120)(181.9), or 2.18, g.

5.8   GRAM-EQUIVALENTS

In solving the above problems, it was necessary to use a balanced chemical equation. In many cases balancing the equation can be bypassed by introducing a new quantity, the *gram-equivalent*. One *gram-equivalent of an oxidizing agent* is defined as that *weight of the substance that picks up the Avogadro number of electrons* in a particular reaction. One *gram-equivalent of a reducing agent* is defined as that *weight of the substance that releases the Avogadro number of electrons* in a particular reaction. The gram-equivalents are defined in this way so that 1 gram-equivalent of any oxidizing agent reacts exactly with 1 gram-equivalent of any reducing agent.

In the reaction of aluminum, Al, and oxygen, O_2, to produce Al_2O_3, aluminum changes oxidation number from 0 to $+3$, and oxygen changes oxidation number from 0 to -2. Each atom of Al releases three electrons, so 1 gram-atom of Al (which is the Avogadro number of Al atoms) releases three times the Avogadro number of electrons. That weight of Al which releases the Avogadro number of electrons is one-third a gram-atom. So, for Al, 1 gram-equivalent is one-third a gram-atom, or (1/3)(26.98), or 8.993, g. Each atom of O picks up two electrons. Each O_2 molecule picks up four electrons. One mole of O_2 picks up four times the Avogadro number of electrons. That weight of O_2 which picks up the Avogadro number of electrons is one-fourth a mole. So, for O_2, 1 gram-equivalent is one-fourth a mole, or (1/4)(32.00), or 8.000, g. In the reaction of Al with O_2, 8.993 g. of aluminum reacts exactly with 8.000 g. of oxygen.

Example 7

When magnesium burns in oxygen, it forms magnesium oxide. In a given experiment 1.2096 g. of oxide is formed from 0.7296 g. of magnesium. What is the weight of 1 gram-equivalent of magnesium in this reaction?

Weight of oxygen combined = 1.2096 − 0.7296 = 0.4800 g.

Since oxygen changes from oxidation number 0 to −2 (see rule 3, Sec. 5.5), each oxygen atom appears to gain two electrons. For oxygen to gain the Avogadro number of electrons, ½ gram-atom, or 8 g., of oxygen is required. So, for this reaction, 1 gram-equivalent of oxygen is 8 g.

In 0.4800 g. of O, there is 0.4800/8, or 0.06000, gram-equivalent

One gram-equivalent of O requires 1 gram-equivalent of Mg

0.06000 gram-equivalent of O requires 0.06000 gram-equivalent of Mg

The weight of Mg used is 0.7296 g.

Therefore, 0.06000 gram-equivalent of Mg weighs 0.7296 g.

One gram-equivalent of Mg weighs 0.7296/0.06000, or 12.16, g.

Example 8

When zinc reacts with acid, hydrogen gas is liberated. From 13.076 g. of zinc, 0.4032 g. of hydrogen is obtained. Calculate the number of gram-equivalents in 1 gram-atom of zinc for this reaction.

Hydrogen changes oxidation number from +1 to 0

Each H atom appears to gain one electron

Therefore, 1 gram-atom, or 1.008 g., of H, is 1 gram-equivalent

In 0.4032 g. of H, there is 0.4032/1.008, or 0.4000, gram-equivalent

0.4000 gram-equivalent of H requires 0.4000 gram-equivalent of Zn

Since 13.076 g. is 0.4000 gram-equivalent, 1 gram-equivalent of Zn weighs 13.076/0.4000, or 32.69, g.

From the atomic weight table, 1 gram-atom of Zn weighs 65.38 g.

In 65.38 g. of Zn there is 65.38/32.69, or 2, gram-equivalents.

In the above examples, the discussion was limited to individual elements. For compounds, the weight of 1 gram-equivalent can be calculated by dividing the weight of 1 gram-formula (or mole) by the electron gain or loss per formula unit. This calculation requires knowledge of products. As an illustration, when HNO_3 (formula weight 63.016) is reduced to NO, the change in oxidation number of nitrogen is from +5 to +2; therefore the weight of 1 gram-equivalent of HNO_3 is 63.016/3, or 21.005, g. However, when HNO_3 is reduced to NH_3, the nitrogen changes oxidation number from +5 to −3, and the weight of 1 gram-equivalent of HNO_3 is 63.016/8, or 7.8770, g. Thus, the weight of 1 gram-equivalent depends on what product is formed.

Example 9

How many grams of hydrogen sulfide, H_2S, react with 6.32 g. of potassium permanganate, $KMnO_4$, to produce K_2SO_4 and MnO_2?

Mn changes oxidation number from +7 to +4 in this reaction

One gram-equivalent of $KMnO_4$ weighs 158.04/3, or 52.680, g.

6.32 g. of $KMnO_4$ is 6.32/52.680, or 0.120, gram-equivalent

One gram-equivalent of $KMnO_4$ requires 1 gram-equivalent of H_2S

0.120 gram-equivalent of $KMnO_4$ requires 0.120 gram-equivalent of H_2S

S changes oxidation number from -2 to $+6$ in this reaction

One gram-equivalent of H_2S weighs 34.082/8, or 4.26, g.

0.120 gram-equivalent of H_2S is (0.120)(4.26), or 0.511, g.

It might be noted that the examples of this section illustrate that problems in stoichiometry involving oxidation-reduction reactions can be solved without use of balanced equations.

5.9   HEATS OF REACTION

In addition to weight relations, another quantitative aspect of chemical reactions is the heat change that accompanies reaction. Experimentally, the heat liberated or absorbed when a known amount of material reacts is determined by using a calorimeter, like that shown in Fig. 5.7. This type of calorimeter consists of an insulated box filled with water in which the reaction vessel is placed, along with a thermometer and a stirrer. The principle on which the calorimeter is based is that the temperature change of a given weight of water depends on the amount of heat added or subtracted. Suppose that the reaction of A with B is exothermic, so that when A and B are mixed, heat is liberated to the water. (A and B can be mixed by simply inverting the reaction tube.) Measurement of the water temperature before and after reaction gives the temperature rise of a known weight of water. Since 1 cal. of heat raises the temperature of 1 g. of water by $1°C.$, the total number of calories liberated can be calculated. The stirrer ensures that the water temperature is uniform.

Example 10

When solutions of barium chloride ($BaCl_2$) and sodium sulfate (Na_2SO_4) are mixed, a white solid, barium sulfate ($BaSO_4$), precipitates. The net reaction is $Ba^{++} + SO_4^{--} \longrightarrow BaSO_4(s)$. Suppose that, in Fig. 5.7, A is a solution of $BaCl_2$ and B is a solution of Na_2SO_4. In a given experiment it is observed that, when 0.100 mole of $BaSO_4$ is formed, the temperature changes from $20.123°C.$ to $20.316°C.$ If there is a total of 3.000 kg. of water in the calorimeter, calculate the amount of heat liberated when 1 mole of $BaSO_4$ is formed from Ba^{++} and SO_4^{--}.

The temperature rise is $20.316 - 20.123$, or $0.193°C.$

This rise requires 0.193 cal. for each gram of water, or $0.193 \times 3,000 = 579$ cal. for 3,000 g. of water

If 579 calories are liberated when 0.100 mole of $BaSO_4$ is formed, then 579/0.100, or 5,790, cal. is liberated when 1 mole of $BaSO_4$ is formed. (This answer can be converted to kilocalories by dividing 5,790 by 1,000 to give 5.79 kcal.)

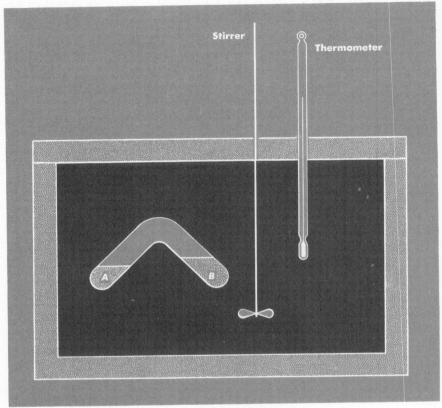

Fig. 5.7 Calorimeter for measuring heat of reaction.

The heat change accompanying chemical reaction can be indicated by including heat in the chemical equation. Common practice is to specify the amount of heat corresponding to the equation read in moles. For example, the equation

$$2H_2(g) + O_2(g) \rightarrow 2H_2O(g) + 116 \text{ kcal.}$$

indicates that, when 2 moles of hydrogen gas react with 1 mole of oxygen gas to form 2 moles of water vapor, 116 kcal. of heat is liberated. This means that 58 kcal. is liberated per mole of $H_2O(g)$ formed.

It is quite important in equations that include heat to specify the state of each reactant and product. This must be done because the heat of a reaction depends upon the state of the chemicals involved. For instance, the equation

$$2H_2(g) + O_2(g) \rightarrow 2H_2O(l) + 135 \text{ kcal.}$$

which differs from the preceding one in that the water formed is liquid instead of gaseous, indicates that per mole of *liquid* water, 67.5 kcal. is liberated.

The above reactions show heat as one of the products; i.e., the reactions are exothermic. In endothermic reactions, heat is absorbed from the surroundings. This can be shown by including heat on the left of the equation as a reactant or by writing heat with a minus sign on the right of the equation. For example, the conversion of sodium bicarbonate, $NaHCO_3$, to sodium carbonate, Na_2CO_3, is endothermic. The equation may be written in either of the following ways:

$$2NaHCO_3(s) + 31 \text{ kcal.} \rightarrow Na_2CO_3(s) + CO_2(g) + H_2O(g)$$

$$2NaHCO_3(s) \rightarrow Na_2CO_3(s) + CO_2(g) + H_2O(g) - 31 \text{ kcal.}$$

QUESTIONS
3, 4, 5.

5.1 *Chemical equations.* Given the balanced equation

$$2NO(g) + O_2(g) \rightarrow 2NO_2(g)$$

(*a*) What information do you get from each of the three formulas? (*b*) What information do you get from the coefficients in the equation? (*c*) What information can you get by combining the equation with the atomic weights of N and O?

5.2 *Moles.* How many moles in each of the following: (*a*) 1.40 g. of N_2; (*b*) 92.0 g. of NO_2; (*c*) 1.5×10^{21} molecules of N_2O; (*d*) the amount of NH_3 that contains 0.69 gram-atom of H? *Ans.* 0.0500; 2.00; 2.5×10^{-3}; 0.23

5.3 *Moles.* A given bottle contains some colored compound. Analysis of the contents shows the presence of 0.100 gram-atom of vanadium and 0.250 gram-atom of oxygen. (*a*) How many grams of compound are there in the bottle? (*b*) Calculate the percentage of the compound weight contributed by each element. (*c*) What is the simplest formula of the compound? (*d*) How many moles of the compound are there in the bottle?

5.4 *Weight relations.* How many grams of oxygen can be made by decomposing: (*a*) 2.0 moles; (*b*) 0.64 mole; (*c*) 1.1 g. of $KClO_3$ by the reaction

$$2KClO_3(s) \rightarrow 2KCl(s) + 3O_2(g)$$

5.5 *Weight relations.* How many grams of oxygen are required to react completely with 7.004 g. of nitrogen by the reaction

$$N_2(g) + 2O_2(g) \rightarrow 2NO_2(g)$$

5.6 *Weight relations.* When water is decomposed by electrolysis, how many grams of oxygen are formed in an experiment which produces 5.04 g. of hydrogen? *Ans.* 40.0 g.

5.7 *Chemical equations.* Write a balanced equation for each of the following changes: (*a*) solid $CaCO_3$ is decomposed to give solid CaO and gaseous CO_2; (*b*) H_2 gas and Cl_2 gas combine to form HCl gas; (*c*) CO gas reacts with solid Fe_2O_3 to produce CO_2 gas and solid Fe_3O_4; (*d*) H^+ in solution combines with CO_3^{--} in solution to produce liquid water and CO_2 gas.

5.8   *Moles.* A bottle contains 31.6 g. of a colored compound which by weight consists of 24.7% potassium, 34.8% manganese, and 40.5% oxygen. (*a*) Calculate the number of gram-atoms of each of these elements present. (*b*) Calculate the number of atoms in the bottle. (*c*) What is the simplest formula of the compound? (*d*) How many moles of the compound are there in the bottle?

   Ans. (*a*) 0.200 gram-atom of K, 0.200 gram-atom of Mn, 0.800 gram-atom of O; (*b*) 7.22×10^{23} atoms; (*c*) $KMnO_4$; (*d*) 0.200 mole

5.9   *Weight relations.* Bismuth has atomic weight 209.00. (*a*) What is the weight of one bismuth atom? (*b*) How many atoms in 6.27 g. of Bi? (*c*) How many gram-atoms of Bi in 6.27 g. of Bi? (*d*) How many grams of oxygen are required to react with 6.27 g. of Bi to form Bi_2O_3? (*e*) How many grams of Bi_2S_3 can be produced from 6.27 g. of Bi and 1.28 g. of S?

5.10   *Simplest formulas.* What are the simplest formulas of the following compounds? (*a*) contains 2 gram-atoms of N with 3 gram-atoms of O; (*b*) contains 0.125 gram-atom of N with 0.250 gram-atom of O; (*c*) contains 7.0 g. of N with 20.0 g. of O; (*d*) contains 4.2 g. of N with 0.15 gram-atom of O; (*e*) contains by weight 46.7% N and 53.3% O.   *Ans.* N_2O_3; NO_2; N_2O_5; N_2O; NO

5.11   *Percentage composition.* In 0.370 g. of *X* there are 3.01×10^{21} atoms of *X*. This weight of *X* just combines with 9.03×10^{21} atoms of *Y* to form a compound. Atom *Y* has an atomic weight of 87.0 a.m.u. (*a*) What is the atomic weight of *X?* (*b*) What is the simplest formula of the compound formed? (*c*) What is the percentage composition by weight of the compound?

5.12   *Formula weights.* A molecule of a given compound contains six atoms of *A* and ten atoms of *B*. The weight of 0.25 gram-atom of *A* is 23 g. One atom of *B* weighs 1.6×10^{-22} g. (*a*) What is the atomic weight of *A?* (*b*) What is the atomic weight of *B?* (*c*) What is the percentage composition by weight of the compound? (*d*) What is the simplest formula of the compound? (*e*) What is the molecular formula of the compound? (*f*) What is the molecular weight of the compound? (*g*) What is the weight of 3.0×10^{19} molecules of the compound?

   Ans. 92 a.m.u.; 96 a.m.u., 37% *A* and 63% *B*; A_3B_5; A_6B_{10}; *1,510* a.m.u.; 0.076 g.

5.13   *Oxidation numbers.* Consider the process

$$2H_2 + O_2 \rightarrow 2H_2O$$

Show clearly how the term "oxidation number" is applied to each atom in this reaction, and indicate what assumptions are made in assigning these oxidation numbers.

5.14   *Oxidation numbers.* (*a*) What is the oxidation number of chlorine in the following compounds: NaCl, NaClO, $NaClO_2$, $NaClO_3$, $NaClO_4$? (b) What is the oxidation number of manganese in the following compounds: Na_2MnO_4, MnO_2, $NaMnO_4$, Mn_3O_4, Mn_2O_7? (c) What is the oxidation number of chromium in the following ions: CrO_2^-, $Cr_2O_7^{--}$, CrO_4^{--}, $HCrO_4^-$, $CrOH^{++}$?

5.15 *Oxidation-reduction.* Diagnose the following reactions as oxidation-reduction reactions, indicating the substance oxidized, the substance reduced, the reducing agent, and the oxidizing agent: (a) $2Ca + O_2 \rightarrow 2CaO$; (b) $H_2 + 3Fe_2O_3 \rightarrow H_2O + 2Fe_3O_4$; (c) $2F_2 + O_2 \rightarrow 2OF_2$.

5.16 *Chemical equations.* Balance the following:

    (a) $H_2(g) + V_2O_3(s) \rightarrow VO(s) + H_2O(g)$

    (b) $NH_3(g) + O_2(g) \rightarrow NO(g) + H_2O(g)$

    (c) $NH_3(g) + O_2(g) \rightarrow NO_2(g) + H_2O(g)$

    (d) $NH_3(g) + O_3(g) \rightarrow N_2O_5(s) + H_2O(g)$

    (e) $KClO_3(s) + C_2H_4O \rightarrow CO_2(g) + KCl(s) + H_2O(g)$

    (f) $Ag(s) + NO_3^- + H^+ \rightarrow Ag^+ + NO(g) + H_2O$

    (g) $\underset{\text{peroxide}}{H_2O_2} + MnO_4^- + H^+ \rightarrow O_2(g) + Mn^{++} + H_2O$

    (h) $ClO^- \rightarrow ClO_3^- + Cl^-$

5.17 *Gram-equivalents.* Balance the following:

$$HNO_3 + SO_2(g) + H_2O \rightarrow H_2SO_4 + NO(g)$$

(a) Indicate for this reaction the oxidizing agent, the reducing agent, the substance oxidized, and the substance reduced. (b) Calculate the weight of 1.00 gram-equivalent of the oxidizing agent and of the reducing agent. (c) How many gram-equivalents are there in 0.017 mole of oxidizing agent in this reaction?

5.18 *Percentage composition.* The following minerals are among the world's major sources of the element silver: AgCl, Ag_3AsS_3, Ag_2S, Ag_5SbS_4. Arrange these minerals in order of increasing tonnage which must be processed to get a given weight of silver. (Assume all the silver can be extracted.)

Ans. Ag_2S, AgCl, Ag_5SbS_4, Ag_3AsS_3

5.19 *Simplest formula.* In the synthesis of a compound there are used up 1.26 g. of carbon, 0.240 gram-atom of hydrogen, and 9.01×10^{21} atoms of oxygen. What is the simplest formula of the compound?

5.20 *Gram-equivalents.* (a) Balance the following:

$$H_2C_2O_4(s) + KMnO_4(s) \rightarrow H_2O(g) + CO_2(g) + MnO(s) + KOH(s)$$

(b) Show for this reaction that 9.00 g. of $H_2C_2O_4$ is required to react with 6.32 g. of $KMnO_4$ and that 8.80 g. of CO_2 is formed in the process. (c) Show for this reaction that 9.00 g. of $H_2C_2O_4$ represents 0.200 gram-equivalent of reducing agent and 6.32 g. of $KMnO_4$ represents 0.200 gram-equivalent of oxidizing agent.

5.21 *Calorimetry.* In a bomb-type calorimeter, chemical reaction can be initiated by an electrical spark. In a given experiment, palmitic acid ($C_{16}H_{32}O_2$) is burned in excess oxygen. From the following data, calculate the heat of combustion of 1.00 mole of palmitic acid:

Weight burned	1.00 g.
Initial temperature of water	21.05°C.
Final temperature of water	22.92°C.
Weight of water in calorimeter	5.00 kg.

5.22 *Pound-moles.* (a) How many pound-moles of $Ca(OH)_2$ are there in 3.7 lb. of $Ca(OH)_2$? (b) How many pound-moles of $Ca(NO_3)_2$ can be made from 3.7 lb. of $Ca(OH)_2$ by the reaction

$$Ca(OH)_2(s) + 2HNO_3 \rightarrow Ca(NO_3)_2(s) + 2H_2O(g)$$

(c) How many pounds of $Ca(NO_3)_2$ can be made from 3.7 lb. of $Ca(OH)_2$?

5.23 *Oxidation numbers.* Assign oxidation numbers to each atom in the following compounds: K_2Se, Na_3PO_3, H_3PO_4, NH_3, N_2H_4, $Ca(HSO_4)_2$, Cr_8O_{21} (not a peroxide).

5.24 *Weight relations.* By using oxidation numbers, balance the equation for the change

$$KMnO_4(s) + FeO(s) \rightarrow K_2O(s) + MnO(s) + Fe_2O_3(s)$$

How many moles of MnO can be prepared from 32.6 g. of $KMnO_4$ and 64.7 g. of FeO?

5.25 *Calorimetry.* Using the equations in Sec. 5.9, calculate the amount of heat required to decompose 1.0 g. of each of the following: (a) $H_2O(g)$; (b) $H_2O(l)$; (c) $NaHCO_3(s)$. *Ans.* 3.2 kcal.; 3.7 kcal.; 0.18 kcal.

5.26 *General.* (a) Balance the following and label the substances oxidized and reduced:

$$KClO_4(s) + C_6H_{10}O_5(s) \rightarrow KCl(s) + CO(g) + H_2O(g)$$

(b) In 8.10 g. of $C_6H_{10}O_5$, there are how many moles of $C_6H_{10}O_5$, molecules of $C_6H_{10}O_5$, gram-atoms of carbon, grams of hydrogen, gram-equivalents of $C_6H_{10}O_5$ for this reaction?
Ans. 0.0500 mole; 3.00×10^{22} molecules; 0.300 gram-atom; 0.505 g.; 0.600 gram-equivalent

5.27 *General.* (a) Balance the following and label the substance oxidized and the substance reduced:

$$K_2Cr_2O_7(s) + S_8(s) \rightarrow SO_2(g) + Cr_2O_3(s) + K_2O(s)$$

(b) In 1.6 g. of sulfur, there are how many gram-atoms of sulfur, atoms of sulfur, moles of S_8, molecules of S_8, gram-equivalents of sulfur for this reaction?

5.28 *Chemical equations.* (a) Write a balanced equation for the reaction in which HBr is oxidized by OF_2 to form Br_2, HF, and H_2O. (b) Compute (1) the number of moles, (2) the number of grams, and (3) the number of molecules of Br_2 that can be formed when 9.71 g. of HBr is oxidized in the above reaction by an excess amount of OF_2.

Ans. (b) 0.0600 mole; 9.59 g.; 3.61×10^{22} molecules

5.29 *Gram-equivalents.* I_2 can be oxidized by NO_3^- to form IO_3^- and NO_2. (a) Calculate the weight of 1 gram-equivalent of I_2 for this reaction. (b) How many moles of NO_3^- will react with 1 gram-equivalent of I_2? (c) How many grams of I_2 will react with 1 mole of NO_3^-?

5.30 *Weight relations.* If 18.0 g. of an element X exactly reacts with 5.76 g. of oxygen to form a compound whose molecular formula is shown from other experiments to be X_4O_6, what is the atomic weight of X?

5.31 *Weight relations.* When solid PbO_2 is heated, it forms solid PbO and O_2 gas. Heating solid BaO_2 yields solid BaO and O_2 gas. A mixture of PbO_2 and BaO_2 is heated until both decompositions are complete. If the initial weight of the mixture was 10.564 g. and the final weight was 9.764 g., what weight of PbO_2 was present in the original mixture?

5.32 *Weight relations.* A test tube containing $KClO_3$ is heated until all the $KClO_3$ decomposes according to the reaction

$$KClO_3(s) \rightarrow KCl(s) + O_2(g)$$

If the original tube plus contents weighs 21.68 g. and the loss in weight is 0.960 g., what is the weight of the test tube? *Ans.* 19.23 g.

5.33 *Calorimetry.* Using the equations in Sec. 5.9, calculate the heat liberated by the formation of 5.0 g. of *liquid* H_2O from the decomposition of $NaHCO_3(s)$.

Ans. −6.0 kcal.

5.34 *Balancing equations.* Balance the following:

(a) $Na_2S(s) + Na_2SO_4(s) + SiO_2(s) \rightarrow Na_2SiO_3(s) + SO_2(g)$
(b) $HNO_2 \rightarrow H^+ + NO_3^- + NO(g) + H_2O$
(c) $NO_2(g) + H_2(g) \rightarrow NH_3(g) + H_2O(g)$
(d) $C_2H_6O + Cr_2O_7^{--} + H^+ \rightarrow C_2H_4O(g) + Cr^{+3} + H_2O$
(e) $HO_2^- + CrO_2^- \rightarrow CrO_4^{--} + OH^- + H_2O$
     Peroxide

(f) $MnO_4^- + H_2C_2O_4 + H^+ \rightarrow Mn^{++} + CO_2(g) + H_2O$
(g) $ICl + H_2O \rightarrow Cl^- + IO_3^- + I_2 + H^+$
(h) $HBrO_3 + SO_2 + H_2O \rightarrow Br_2 + H_2SO_4$
(i) $P_4(s) + OH^- + H_2O \rightarrow H_2PO_2^- + P_2H_4(g)$

5.35 *Weight relations.* A given sample weighing 1.00 kg. contains $CaCO_3$, $NaHCO_3$, and inert material. When heated sufficiently, reaction occurs as follows:

$$CaCO_3(s) \rightarrow CaO(s) + CO_2(g) - 43 \text{ kcal.}$$

$$2\, NaHCO_3(s) \rightarrow Na_2CO_3(s) + CO_2(g) + H_2O(g) - 31 \text{ kcal.}$$

What is the weight of inert material in the sample if the weight loss observed on heating is 0.36 kg. and the amount of heat absorbed is 295 kcal.?

Ans. 0.13 kg.

6   *Gases*

HAVING DISCUSSED ATOMS and the forces which hold them together in molecules, we can now look at large collections of atoms, as in a sample of solid,
liquid, or gas. Since in many respects the gaseous state is the simplest, it
will be considered first. The general approach will be to define the terms
used to describe gases, then to discuss the laws which summarize observed
behavior, and finally to consider the theories which have been proposed to
account for the observations.

6.1   VOLUME

The volume of any substance is the space occupied by that substance. For
gases, the volume of a sample is the same as the volume of the container
in which it is held. Ordinarily, this volume is specified in units of liters
(l.), milliliters (ml.), or cubic centimeters (cc.). As the name implies, 1 cc.
is the volume of a cube 1 cm. on an edge. A liter, on the other hand, is
not derived from units of length but is defined as the volume occupied by
1 kg. of water at the temperature of its maximum density, which is near
$4°C$. There are almost exactly 1,000 cc. in 1 liter. For most purposes 1

ml., exactly a thousandth of a liter, can be considered the same as 1 cc. Actually, 1 ml. is equal to 1.000027 cc.

For liquids and solids, volume does not change much with a change of pressure or temperature. Consequently, to describe the amount of a solid or liquid being handled, e.g., the number of moles, it is usually sufficient to specify only the volume of the sample. For gases, this cannot be done. As an example, 1 ml. of hydrogen at a certain pressure and temperature will contain a different number of moles and have a different weight from 1 ml. at some other pressure and temperature. In order to determine the number of moles in a given volume of gas, it is necessary to know its pressure and temperature.

When solids or liquids are mixed together, the total volume is roughly equal to the sum of the original volumes. However, this is not necessarily true for gases. For example, if gaseous bromine is added to a bottle full of air, the brown bromine gas spreads through the whole bottle, so that both the air and the bromine now occupy the same volume which originally contained only air. Since all gases can *mix in any proportion,* they are said to be *miscible.*

6.2   TEMPERATURE

We have already referred (Sec. 1.6) to temperature as a measure of the degree of hotness of a substance. It is a familiar observation that a hot and a cold substance placed in contact with each other change so that the hot substance gets colder and the cold substance hotter. This is interpreted as resulting from a flow of heat energy from the hot body to the cold body. The hot body is said to have a higher temperature; the cold body, a lower temperature. Therefore, temperature determines the direction of heat flow, in the sense that heat always flows from a region of higher temperature to one of lower temperature.

Quantitative scales for measuring temperature are based on properties, such as expansion, which depend on changes of temperature. For the centigrade scale, two arbitrary points are selected, zero for the normal freezing point of water and one hundred for the normal boiling point of water.* Because of the arbitrary selection of the zero point, negative temperatures are possible on the centigrade scale, corresponding to temperatures below that of freezing water. It is not immediately obvious that the centigrade scale cannot be extended indefinitely to infinitely negative temperatures.

---

* As we shall see later, both the freezing point and the boiling point of pure water depend on what pressure is exerted on the sample. The significance of the term "normal boiling point" is discussed in Sec. 7.3.

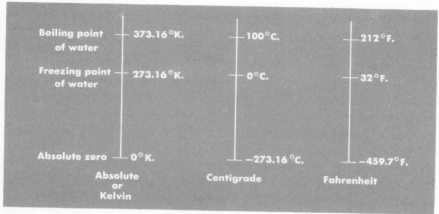

Fig. 6.1   Temperature scales.

However, as we shall see later, the experimental behavior of gases leads us to believe that temperatures below −273.16°C. are impossible to attain. This lowest limit of temperature gives us a zero for an absolute temperature scale.

On the absolute scale of temperature, negative temperatures are impossible, since the scale starts from absolute zero. On this scale, the size of the degree is chosen to be the same as on the centigrade scale. The absolute scale is frequently referred to as the Kelvin scale after Lord Kelvin, who first proposed it in 1848. A comparison of the Kelvin scale with the centigrade and Fahrenheit scales is shown in Fig. 6.1. It should be noted that the size of one degree is the same on the centigrade and Kelvin scales, but that the Fahrenheit degree is only five-ninths as large. Temperature on the centigrade scale is converted to temperature on the Kelvin scale by adding 273.16°.

$$°C. + 273.16 = °K.$$

To convert Fahrenheit temperature to absolute temperature, it is also necessary to correct for the difference in the size of the degree.

$$(°F. - 32) \times \tfrac{5}{9} + 273.16 = °K.$$

6.3   PRESSURE

Just as temperature determines the direction of heat flow, pressure is a property which determines the direction of mass flow. Unless otherwise constrained, matter tends to move from a place where it is at higher pressure to a place of lower pressure. For example, when air escapes from an automobile tire, it moves from a region of higher pressure to one of lower pressure. Quantitatively, *pressure* is defined as *force per unit area.* Though the concept of force as a push is a familiar one, force is more rigorously defined as that which tends to change the state of rest or motion of an object. As discussed in Appendix 4.2, the fundamental unit of force is the dyne, which is the force required to change the speed of 1 g. of matter by 1 cm. per sec. in 1 sec. Force can also be expressed in terms of pounds weight. The units for expressing pressure can thus be dynes per square centimeter or pounds per square inch.

In *fluids,* a general term which includes *liquids and gases,* the pressure at a given point is the same in all directions. This can be visualized by considering a swimmer under water. At a given depth, no matter how he turns, the pressure exerted on him by the water is always the same. However, as he increases his depth, the pressure increases. This comes about because of the pull of gravity on the water above him. We can picture his body as supporting the weight of the column of water directly above him. In general, for all fluids, the greater the depth of immersion, the greater the pressure.

The earth is surrounded by a blanket of air approximately 500 miles thick. So, in effect, we live at the bottom of a fluid, the atmosphere, which exerts a pressure. The existence of this pressure can be shown by evacuating a tin can. As the air is pumped out, atmospheric pressure crushes the can. A more subtle indication of atmospheric pressure can be obtained by filling a long test tube with mercury and inverting it in a dish of mercury. (Any other liquid would do, but mercury has the advantage of not requiring too long a test tube.) Some of the mercury runs out of the tube, but the important thing we observe is that not all of it runs out. The experiment is represented in Fig. 6.2. No matter how large the diameter of the tube and no matter how long the tube, the difference in height between the mercury level inside and outside the tube is the same. The fact that all the mercury

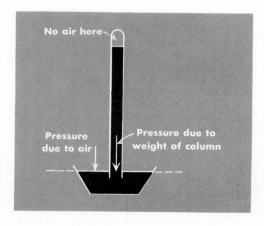

Fig. 6.2   Barometer.

does not run out shows that there must be a pressure exerted on the surface of the mercury in the dish sufficient to support the column of mercury. There is essentially nothing in the space above the mercury level in the tube, because at room temperature mercury does not evaporate much. To a good approximation, the space is a vacuum and exerts no pressure on the upper mercury level. The pressure at the bottom of the mercury column is therefore due only to the weight of the mercury column. As noted, it is a general property of liquids that at any given level in the liquid the pressure is constant. In Fig. 6.2 the dotted line represents the level which is of interest. At this level, outside the tube, the force per unit area is due to the atmosphere and can be labeled as P_{atm}. The pressure inside the tube is due to the pressure of the column of mercury and can be labeled P_{Hg}. The equality $P_{atm} = P_{Hg}$ provides us with a method for measuring the pressure exerted by the atmosphere. The device shown in Fig. 6.2 is called a barometer.

The atmospheric pressure changes from day to day and from one altitude to another. A *standard atmosphere* is defined as the pressure which supports a column of mercury that is 76.0 cm. high at 0°C. at sea level.* A standard atmosphere is referred to as 1 atm. Pressure can be expressed either in terms of number of atmospheres or number of centimeters of mercury (cm. Hg). We can also express pressure by the height of a water column. Since water has a density of 1 g. per ml., whereas mercury has a density of 13.6 g. per ml., a given pressure supports a column of water that is 13.6 times as high as one of mercury. One atmosphere pressure supports 76 cm. of mercury, or (76) (13.6) cm. of water, the latter being roughly 34 ft. In terms of pounds per square inch, a standard atmosphere is 14.7 p.s.i.

The device shown in Fig. 6.3 is a *manometer,* used to measure the pressure of a sample of gas. This manometer is constructed by placing a liquid in the bottom of a U tube with the gas sample in one arm of the U. If the right-hand tube is open to the atmosphere, the pressure which is exerted on the right-hand surface is atmospheric pressure P_{atm}. At the same level in both arms of the tube, the pressure must be equal; otherwise, there would be a flow of liquid from one arm to the other. At the level indicated by the dotted line in Fig. 6.3, the pressure in the left arm is equal to the pressure of the trapped gas P_{gas} plus the pressure of the column of liquid above the dotted line P_{liq}. We can therefore write

$$P_{atm} = P_{gas} + P_{liq}$$

or

$$P_{gas} = P_{atm} - P_{liq}$$

* If we think of pressure as weight per unit area, then we can see why it is necessary that both 0°C. and sea level be specified in defining the standard atmosphere. The density of liquid mercury changes with temperature, and therefore the weight of a 76-cm.-high Hg column of fixed cross section changes with temperature. Hence the temperature must be specified. Similarly, the force of gravity changes slightly with altitude, and hence the weight of the Hg column changes when moved away from sea level.

The atmospheric pressure can be measured by a barometer, and P_{liq} can be obtained from the difference in height between the liquid level in the right and left arms and the known density of the liquid. P_{atm} and P_{liq} must be expressed in the same units. For example, if P_{atm} is in millimeters of mercury and the manometer liquid is not mercury, the difference in height must be converted to its mercury equivalent. If the bottom of the U tube consists of flexible rubber tubing, the right arm can be raised with respect to the left arm until the two liquid levels are at the same height, in which case $P_{liq} = 0$, so $P_{gas} = P_{atm}$.

6.4 BOYLE'S LAW

A characteristic property of gases is their great compressibility. This behavior is summarized quantitatively in Boyle's law (1662). *Boyle's law states that at constant temperature a fixed weight of gas occupies a volume inversely proportional to the pressure exerted on it.* If the pressure is doubled, the volume becomes one-half as large. Figure 6.4 shows a sample of gas trapped in a cylinder with a movable piston. When the weight on the piston is doubled, the pressure exerted on the gas is doubled, and the gas volume shrinks to half its original volume. Boyle's law can be summarized by a pressure-volume, or *P-V*, plot like that shown in Fig. 6.5. In this graph the horizontal axis represents the pressure of a given sample of gas, and the vertical axis, the volume occupied. The curve is a hyperbola, the equation for which is $PV = $ constant, or $V = $ constant$/P$. (The size of the constant is fixed once the weight of the sample and its temperature are specified.) If at 4 atm. the volume is 1 liter, then at 1 atm. the volume is 4 liters. This can be seen from either the graph or the equation.

The behavior specified by Boyle's law is not always observed. For any gas, the law is most nearly followed at lower pressures and at higher temperatures, but as the pressure is increased or as the temperature is lowered, deviations may occur. This can be seen by considering the experimental data listed in Table 6.1. In each of these

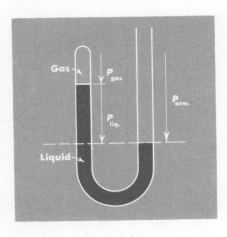

Fig. 6.3   Manometer.

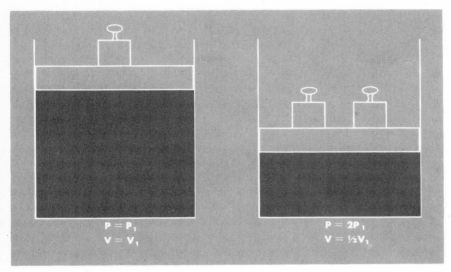

Fig. 6.4   Boyle's law experiment.

experiments, the quantity of gas is fixed at 39.94 g., and the temperature is
fixed either at 100°C. or at −50°C. The pressure is measured when the
given weight of gas is contained in different volumes. The *PV* products in
the last column, obtained by multiplying the values in the second and third
columns, should be, according to Boyle's law, constant at a constant temperature. The data shown indicate that, at the high temperature, Boyle's law
is closely obeyed. However, at the low temperature, the *PV* product is not
constant but drops off significantly as the pressure increases; Boyle's law is
not obeyed. In other words, as the temperature of argon is decreased, its
behavior deviates from that specified in Boyle's law.

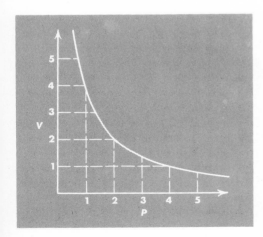

Fig. 6.5   P-V plot for a gas.

Table 6.1   Pressure-volume Data for 39.94 g. of Argon Gas

Temperature, °C	V, liters	P, atm.	P × V
100	2.000	15.28	30.560
	1.000	30.52	30.520
	0.500	60.99	30.500
	0.333	91.59	30.530
−50	2.000	8.99	17.980
	1.000	17.65	17.650
	0.500	34.10	17.050
	0.333	49.50	16.500

The fact that deviations from the law increase at higher pressures can be seen from the experimental data for acetylene given in Table 6.2. When the pressure is doubled from 0.5 to 1.0 atm., the *PV* product is essentially unchanged, so that in this pressure range acetylene follows Boyle's law reasonably well. However, when the pressure is doubled from 4.0 to 8.0 atm., the *PV* product decreases by more than 3 per cent; in this pressure range, Boyle's law is not followed so well. For any gas, the lower the pressure, the closer the approach to Boyle's law behavior. When the law is obeyed, the gas is said to show *ideal* behavior.

The following examples show how Boyle's law is used. In both cases, it is assumed that the temperature remains constant and that the behavior is ideal.

Example 1

Eight grams of a gas occupies 12.3 liters at a pressure of 40.0 cm. Hg. What is the volume when the pressure is increased to 60.0 cm. Hg?

Pressure changes to 60.0/40.0 of the original pressure
Volume changes inversely
Volume changes to 40.0/60.0 of the original volume
Final volume = (40.0/60.0)(initial volume)
= (40.0/60.0)(12.3) = 8.20 liters

Table 6.2   PV Products for a Sample of Acetylene at 0° C.

P, atm.	0.5	1.0	2.0	4.0	8.0
PV	1.0057	1.0000	0.9891	0.9708	0.9360

Example 2

To what pressure must a gas be compressed in order to get into a 3.00-cu.-ft. tank the entire weight of gas that occupies 400 cu. ft. at atmospheric pressure?

Volume changes to 3.00/400 of the original volume

Pressure changes inversely

Pressure changes to 400/3.00 of original, or 133 atm.

6.5   CHARLES' LAW

Another characteristic property of gases is their thermal expansion. Like most other substances, all gases increase in volume when their temperature is raised. Experimentally, the increase of volume with increasing temperature can be measured by confining a fixed weight of gas in a cylinder fitted with a sliding piston, as shown in Fig. 6.6. The weight on top of the piston is constant, so that the gas sample remains at constant pressure. It is observed that, as the gas is heated, the piston moves out and the volume increases. Typical numerical data are plotted in Fig. 6.7. The points fall on a straight line, indicating that the volume varies linearly with temperature. If the temperature is lowered sufficiently, the gas liquefies, and no more experimental points can be obtained. However, if the straight line is extended, or extrapolated, to lower temperatures, as shown by the dotted line, it reaches a point of zero volume. The temperature at which the dotted line reaches zero volume is $-273.16°$C. It is significant that the value, $-273.16°$C., does not depend on the kind of gas used or on the pressure at which the experiment is performed. Designating $-273.16°$C. as absolute zero is reasonable, since temperatures below this would correspond to negative volume.

If volume-temperature data like those plotted in Fig. 6.7 are given in terms of absolute temperature, then it is found that, *at constant pressure, the volume occupied by a fixed weight of gas is directly pro-*

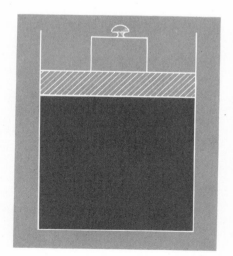

Fig. 6.6   Gas cylinder with movable piston.

136 *Gases*

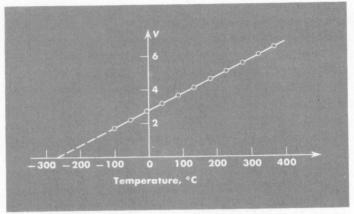

Fig. 6.7   Volume of a gas as a function of centigrade temperature.

portional to the absolute temperature. This summarization of gas behavior is called *Charles' law* (1787) and can be expressed mathematically as $V =$ (constant) $\times T$, where T is in degrees Kelvin. The value of the constant depends on pressure and on the weight of gas.

Actually, Charles' law like Boyle's law represents the behavior of an *ideal*, or *perfect*, gas. For any *real* gas at high pressures and at temperatures near the liquefaction point, deviations from Charles' law are observed. Near the liquefaction point the observed volume is less than that predicted by Charles' law. For simplicity, in solving gas problems, we shall assume ideal behavior, which is usually a good approximation.

Example 3

A sample of nitrogen gas weighing 9.3 g. at a pressure of 75.0 cm. Hg occupies a volume of 12.3 liters when its temperature is 450° K. What is its volume when its temperature is 300° K.?

Absolute temperature changes to 300/450 of its original value

Volume changes proportionally

Volume changes to 300/450 of its original value

Final volume is (300/450)(12.3), or 8.20 liters

Because of the Charles' law relation of volume to absolute temperature, calculations involving gases usually require conversion of temperatures to the Kelvin scale (Sec. 6.2). It is also convenient in working with gases to have a reference point. The customary reference point for gases is at 273° K. (0° C.) and 1 standard atmosphere (760 mm. Hg) pressure. These conditions are called *standard temperature and pressure* (STP).

6.6   DALTON'S LAW OF PARTIAL PRESSURES

The behavior observed when two or more gases are placed in the same container is summarized in Dalton's law of partial pressures (1801). *Dalton's law* states that the *total pressure exerted by a mixture of gases is equal to the sum of the partial pressures* of the various gases. The *partial pressure* of a gas in a mixture is defined as the *pressure the gas would exert if it were alone in the container.* Dalton's law can be illustrated with the aid of Fig. 6.8. Each of the boxes is of the same volume, and each has a manometer for measuring pressure. Suppose a sample of hydrogen is pumped into the first box, and its pressure found to be 6 cm. Hg; a sample of oxygen is pumped into the second box, and its pressure found to be 10 cm. Hg. If now both samples are transferred to the third box, the pressure is observed to be 16 cm. For the general case, Dalton's law can be written

$$P_{\text{total}} = P_1 + P_2 + P_3 + \cdots$$

where the subscripts denote the various gases occupying the same volume. Actually, Dalton's law is an idealization but is closely obeyed by most mixtures of gases.

In many laboratory experiments dealing with gases, the gases are collected above water, and water vapor contributes to the total pressure measured. Figure 6.9 illustrates an experiment in which oxygen gas is collected by water displacement. If the water level is the same inside and outside the bottle, then we may write

$$P_{\text{atm}} = P_{\text{oxygen}} + P_{\text{water vapor}}$$

or

$$P_{\text{oxygen}} = P_{\text{atm}} - P_{\text{water vapor}}$$

Fig. 6.8   Dalton's law of partial pressures.

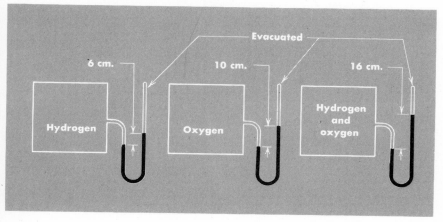

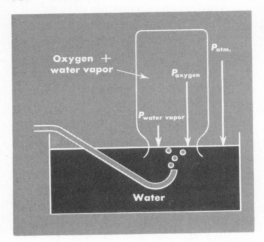

Fig. 6.9   Oxygen collected over water.

P_{atm} is obtained from a barometer. As we shall see later (Sec. 7.2), $P_{water\ vapor}$ depends only on the temperature of the water. This so-called vapor pressure of water has been measured at various water temperatures and is recorded in tables such as the one given in Appendix 6. Thus, the partial pressure of oxygen can be determined from an observed pressure and temperature and reference to a table of vapor-pressure data.

The following example shows how Dalton's law of partial pressures enters into calculations involving gases.

Example 4

If 40.0 liters of nitrogen is collected over water at 22° C. when the atmospheric pressure is 727 mm. Hg, what is the volume of the dry nitrogen at standard temperature and pressure, assuming ideal behavior?

	Initial	**Final**
Volume, liters	40.0	?
Pressure, mm. Hg	$727 - 20 = 707$	760
Temperature, °K.	295	273

The initial volume of the nitrogen is 40.0 liters. The final volume is unknown. The initial pressure of the nitrogen gas is the atmospheric pressure, 727 mm. Hg, minus the vapor pressure of water. From Appendix 6, it is noted that, at 22°C., water has a vapor pressure of 20 mm. Hg. The initial temperature of the nitrogen is 22°C., or $273 + 22 = 295$°K. Final conditions are standard; i.e., the final pressure is 760 mm. Hg, and the final temperature is 273°K. The problem is solved by considering separately how the volume is affected by a change in pressure and a change in temperature.

Pressure changes to 760/707 of its original value

Volume changes inversely

Volume changes to 707/760 of its original value

Temperature changes to 273/295 of its original value

Volume changes proportionally

Volume changes to 273/295 of its original value

$$V_{final} = V_{initial} \times \text{correction for} \quad \times \text{correction for}$$
$$\qquad\qquad\qquad\qquad \text{pressure change} \quad \text{temperature change}$$
$$= 40.0 \text{ liters} \times (707/760) \times (273/295)$$
$$= 34.4 \text{ liters}$$

6.7   GAY-LUSSAC'S LAW OF COMBINING VOLUMES

In the previous section we assumed that, when gases are mixed, they do not react with each other. However, sometimes they do react. For example, when a spark is passed through a mixture of hydrogen and oxygen gas, reaction occurs to form gaseous water. Similarly, when a mixture of hydrogen and chlorine gas is exposed to ultraviolet light, reaction occurs to form the gas hydrogen chloride. In any such reaction involving gases, it is observed that at constant temperature and pressure the volumes of the individual gases which actually react are simple multiples of each other. As a specific example, in the reaction of hydrogen with oxygen to form water, 2 liters of hydrogen is required for every liter of oxygen. In the reaction of hydrogen with chlorine, each liter of hydrogen requires 1 liter of chlorine, and 2 liters of hydrogen chloride gas is formed. These observations are summarized in *Gay-Lussac's law of combining volumes* (1809), which states that, *at a given pressure and temperature, gases combine in simple proportions by volume, and the volume of any gaseous product bears a whole-number ratio to that of any gaseous reactant.*

6.8   AVOGADRO'S PRINCIPLE

In the law of multiple proportions (Sec. 2.3), the observation of simple ratios between combining weights of elements implies that matter is atomic. Similarly, the occurrence of simple ratios between combining volumes of gases suggests that there is a simple relation between gas volume and number of molecules. Avogadro, in 1811, was the first to propose that equal volumes of gases at the same temperature and pressure contain equal numbers of molecules. That this principle accounts for Gay-Lussac's law can be seen from the following example:

When hydrogen combines with chlorine, the product, hydrogen chloride, can be shown by chemical analysis to contain equal numbers of hydrogen and chlorine atoms. These equal numbers of H and Cl atoms come from the original molecules of hydrogen gas and chlorine gas. If we assume that hydrogen and chlorine molecules are both diatomic, then equal numbers of hydrogen and chlorine molecules are required for reaction. According to the Avogadro principle, these occupy equal volumes, consistent with the observation that the combining volumes of hydrogen and chlorine gas are equal.

The assumption that hydrogen and chlorine molecules are diatomic rather than monatomic can be justified as follows: If hydrogen were monatomic, i.e., consisted of individual H atoms, and if chlorine were also monatomic, then 1 liter of hydrogen (n atoms) would combine with 1 liter of chlorine (n atoms) to give 1 liter of HCl gas (n molecules). This is contrary to the observation that the volume of HCl formed is *twice* as great as the volume of hydrogen or of chlorine reacted. It must be that the hydrogen and chlorine molecules are more complex than monatomic. If hydrogen and chlorine are diatomic, then 1 liter of hydrogen (n molecules, or $2n$ atoms) will combine with 1 liter of chlorine (n molecules, or $2n$ atoms) to form 2 liters of hydrogen chloride ($2n$ molecules). This agrees with experiment.*

As first shown by Cannizzaro (1858), the Avogadro principle can be used as a basis for the determination of molecular weights. If two gases at the same temperature and pressure contain the same number of molecules in equal volumes, the weights of equal volumes give directly the relative weights of the two kinds of molecules. For example, at STP 1 liter of hydrogen is observed to weigh 0.0900 g., and 1 liter of oxygen, 1.43 g. Since the number of molecules is the same in both samples, according to the Avogadro principle, each hydrogen molecule must be 0.0900/1.43, or 0.0630, times as heavy as each oxygen molecule. By international convention the diatomic oxygen molecule is assigned a molecular weight of 32.0000 a.m.u.; so, on this scale, the molecular weight of hydrogen is 2.016 a.m.u.

The volume occupied at STP by 32.00 g. of oxygen (1 mole) has been determined by experiment to be 22.4 liters. This is called the *molar volume*

---

* The footnote to Sec. 2.5 indicated that Dalton believed water to contain one H for each O. This error could have been corrected by accepting the following reasoning: two volumes of hydrogen react with one volume of oxygen to form two volumes of gaseous water. Since one volume of oxygen gives two volumes of water, the oxygen molecule must contain an even number of oxygen atoms. If oxygen, like hydrogen, is diatomic, the fact that two volumes of hydrogen are needed per volume of oxygen implies that the water molecule contains twice as many H atoms as O atoms.

of oxygen at STP, and, within the limits of ideal behavior, it should be the volume occupied by 1 mole of any gas at STP. Table 6.3 shows the observed molar volumes of some gases. The value for the ideal gas is obtained from measurements made on gases at high temperatures and low pressures (where gas behavior is more nearly ideal) and extrapolated to STP by using Boyle's and Charles' laws. For the first three gases, agreement with ideality is quite satisfactory. Even for the fourth, carbon dioxide, the agreement is better than 1 per cent. Consequently, in the future, we shall assume that at STP the molar volume of any gas is 22.4 liters. The following example shows how the molar volume can be used to determine molecular weight and molecular formula:

Example 5

Chemical analysis shows that ethylene has a simplest formula corresponding to one atom of carbon for two atoms of hydrogen. It has a density of 1.25 g. per liter at standard temperature and pressure. What is the molecular weight and the molecular formula of ethylene?

At STP 1 mole of any gas (if ideal) has a volume of 22.4 liters. Each liter of ethylene weighs 1.25 g., so 1 mole of ethylene weighs 22.4 times 1.25 g., or 28.0 g. One mole is equal to the gram-formula weight. Since the simplest formula is CH_2, the molecular formula must be some multiple of that, or $(CH_2)_x$. The formula weight of CH_2 is the atomic weight of carbon plus twice the atomic weight of hydrogen, or 14.0. For $(CH_2)_x$, the formula weight is equal to x times 14.0. By experiment this is equal to 28.0, so x must be equal to 2. The molecular formula of ethylene is $(CH_2)_2$, or C_2H_4.

6.9   EQUATION OF STATE

Boyle's law, Charles' law, and Avogadro's principle can be combined to give a general relation between the volume, pressure, temperature, and number of moles of a gas sample. Such a general relation is called an *equa-*

Table 6.3   *Molar Volumes at STP*

Gas	Molar volume, liters
Hydrogen	22.432
Nitrogen	22.403
Oxygen	22.392
Carbon dioxide	22.263
Ideal gas	22.414

tion of state, because it tells how, in going from one gaseous state to another, the four variables *V, P, T,* and *n* (the number of moles) change. For an ideal gas, the equation of state can be deduced as follows: According to Boyle's law, *V* is inversely proportional to *P;* according to Charles' law, *V* is directly proportional to *T;* according to Avogadro's principle, *V* is directly proportional to *n.* More exactly, using the symbol $\propto$ for "is proportional to," this can be written

$$V \propto \frac{1}{P} \text{ at constant } T \text{ and } n$$

$$V \propto T \text{ at constant } P \text{ and } n$$

$$V \propto n \text{ at constant } T \text{ and } P$$

or, in general,

$$V \propto \left(\frac{1}{P}\right)(T)(n)$$

(That this last relation embodies each of the other three can be seen by imagining any two of the variables, such as *T* and *n,* to be constant and noting the relation of the other two.) Written as a mathematical equation, the general relation becomes

$$V = R\left(\frac{1}{P}\right)(T)(n) \qquad \text{or} \qquad PV = nRT$$

where *R* is inserted as the constant of proportionality and is called the universal gas constant (see Appendix 3.1 for discussion of proportionality constants). The equation $PV = nRT$ is called the *equation of state for an ideal gas,* or the *perfect-gas law.*

The numerical value of *R* can be found by substituting experimental quantities in the equation. At STP, $T = 273.16°$K., $P = 1$ atm., and, for 1 mole of gas ($n = 1$), $V = 22.414$ liters. Consequently

$$R = \frac{PV}{nT} = \frac{(1)(22.414)}{(1)(273.16)} = 0.082054$$

The units of *R* in this case are liter-atmospheres per degree per mole. In order to use this value of *R* in the equation of state, *P* must be expressed in atmospheres, *V* in liters, *n* in number of moles, and *T* in degrees Kelvin.

Example 6

The density of an unknown gas at 98° C. and 740 mm Hg pressure is 2.50 g. per liter. What is the molecular weight of this gas, assuming ideal behavior?

Temperature is $98 + 273 = 371°K$.

Pressure is $740/760 = 0.974$ atm.

From the equation of state, $PV = nRT$, we can calculate the number of moles in 1 liter.

$$\frac{n}{V} = \frac{P}{RT} = \frac{(0.974)}{(0.0821)(371)} = 0.0320$$

Since 0.0320 mole weighs 2.50 g., 1 mole weighs 2.50/0.0320, or 78.1 g.

6.10   GRAHAM'S LAW OF DIFFUSION

As already noted, a gas spreads to occupy any volume accessible to it. This spontaneous spreading of a substance throughout a phase is called *diffusion*. Diffusion can readily be observed by liberating some ammonia gas in a room. Its odor soon fills the room, indicating that the ammonia has become distributed throughout the entire volume of the room. Furthermore, it is found for a series of gases that the lighest gas (i.e., the one of lowest molecular weight) diffuses most rapidly. Quantitatively, under the same conditions the *rate of diffusion of a gas is inversely proportional to the square root of its molecular weight*. This is *Graham's law of diffusion* (1829) and in mathematical form is written

$$R = \frac{\text{constant}}{\sqrt{m}} \quad \text{or} \quad \frac{R_1}{R_2} = \frac{\sqrt{m_2}}{\sqrt{m_1}}$$

R_1 and R_2 are the rates of diffusion of gases one and two, and m_1 and m_2 are their respective molecular weights. In the case of oxygen gas and hydrogen gas

$$\frac{R_{H_2}}{R_{O_2}} = \frac{\sqrt{m_{O_2}}}{\sqrt{m_{H_2}}} = \sqrt{\frac{32}{2}} = \sqrt{16} = 4$$

The fact that heavier gases diffuse more slowly than light gases has been applied on a mammoth scale to effect the separation of uranium isotope U^{235} from U^{238}. Natural uranium consisting of 99.3 per cent U^{238} and 0.7 per cent U^{235} is converted to the gas UF_6, and the mixture of the gases is passed at low pressure through a porous solid. The heavier $U^{238}F_6$ diffuses less rapidly than $U^{235}F_6$; hence the gas mixture which first emerges from the solid is richer in the light isotope than is the starting mixture. Since the square root of the ratio of molecular masses is only 1.0043, the step must be repeated thousands of times, but eventually substantial enrichment of the desired 235 isotope is obtained.

6.11   BROWNIAN MOTION

One aspect of observed gas behavior which gives the strongest clue to the nature of gases is the phenomenon known as *Brownian motion*. This motion, first observed by the Scotch botanist Robert Brown, in 1827, is the *irregular zigzag movement of extremely minute particles when suspended in a liquid or a gas*. Brownian motion can be observed by focusing a microscope on a particle of cigarette smoke illuminated from the side. The particle does not settle to the bottom of its container but moves continually to and fro and shows no sign of coming to rest. The smaller the suspended particle observed, the more violent is this permanent condition of irregular motion. The higher the temperature of the fluid, the more vigorous is the movement of the suspended particle.

6.12   KINETIC THEORY

The existence of Brownian motion contradicts the idea of matter as a quiescent state and suggests rather that the molecules of matter are constantly moving. A particle of cigarette smoke appears to be jostled by its neighboring molecules, and thus indirectly the motion of the smoke particle reflects the motion of the submicroscopic, invisible molecules of matter. Here then is powerful support for the suggestion that matter consists of extremely small particles which are ever in motion. This "moving-molecule" theory is known as the kinetic theory of matter. Its two basic postulates are that molecules of matter are in motion and that heat is a manifestation of this motion.

Like any theory, the kinetic theory represents a model which is proposed to account for an observed set of facts. In order that the model be practical, certain simplifying assumptions must be made about its properties. The validity of each assumption and the reliability of the whole model can be checked by how well the facts are explained. For a perfect gas, the following assumptions are made:

1. Gases consist of tiny molecules, which are so small and so far apart on the average that the actual volume of the molecules is negligible compared to the empty space between them.

2. In the perfect gas, there are no attractive forces between molecules. The molecules are completely independent of each other.

3. The molecules of a gas are in rapid, random, straight-line motion, colliding with each other and with the walls of their container. In each collision, it is assumed that there is no net loss of kinetic energy, although there may be a transfer of energy between the partners in the collision.

4. At a particular instant in any collection of gas molecules, different molecules have different speeds and, therefore, different kinetic energies. However, the average kinetic energy of all the molecules is assumed to be directly proportional to the absolute temperature.

Before discussing each of these assumptions, we might ask how the model is related to the observable quantities V, P, and T. The accepted model of a gas is that it consists mostly of empty space in which billions of tiny points representing molecules move in violent motion, colliding with each other and with the walls of the container. Figure 6.10 shows an exaggerated version of this model. The *volume* of a gas is mostly empty space but is *occupied*, in the sense that moving particles occupy the entire region in which they move. *Pressure*, defined as force per unit area, is exerted by gases because molecules collide with the walls of the container. Each collision produces a tiny push, and the sum of all the pushes on 1 sq. cm. of wall in 1 sec. is the pressure. *Temperature* gives a quantitative measure of the average motion of the molecules.

That the first of the four assumptions listed is reasonable can be seen from the fact that the compressibility of gases is so great. Calculations show that, in oxygen gas, for example, at STP, 99.96 per cent of the total volume is empty space at any instant. Since there are 2.7×10^{19} molecules per cubic centimeter of oxygen gas at STP, the average spacing between molecules is about 37×10^{-8} cm., which is about thirteen times the molecular diameter. When oxygen or any other gas is compressed, the average spacing between molecules is reduced, i.e., the fraction of free space is diminished.

The validity of the second assumption is supported by the observation that gases spontaneously expand to occupy all the volume accessible to them. This behavior occurs even for a highly compressed gas, where the molecules are fairly close together and any intermolecular forces should be greatest. It must be that there is no appreciable binding of one molecule of a gas to its neighbors.

As already indicated, the observation of Brownian motion implies that molecules of a gas move, in agreement with assumption 3. Like any moving body, molecules have an amount of kinetic energy equal to $\frac{1}{2}ms^2$, where m is the mass of the molecule and s is its speed. That molecules move in

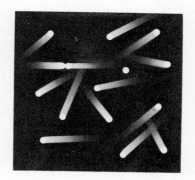

Fig. 6.10   Kinetic model of a gas.

straight lines follows from the assumption of no attractive forces. Only if there were attractions between them could molecules be swerved from straight-line paths. Because there are so many molecules in a gas sample and because they are moving so rapidly (at 0°C. the average speed of oxygen molecules is about 1,000 miles per hour), there are frequent collisions between molecules. It is necessary to assume that the collisions are elastic (like those between billiard balls). Otherwise, kinetic energy would be lost by conversion to potential energy (as by distorting molecules); motion of the molecules would eventually stop, and the molecules would settle to the bottom of the container. It might be noted that the distance a gas molecule has to travel before colliding elastically with another gas molecule is much greater than the average spacing between molecules, because the molecules have many near misses. In oxygen at STP the average distance between successive collisions, called the *mean free path*, is approximately 1,000 times the molecular diameter.

The fourth assumption has two parts: (1) that there is a distribution of kinetic energies and (2) that the average kinetic energy is proportional to the absolute temperature. The distribution, or range, of energies comes about as the result of molecular collisions, which continually change the speed of a particular molecule. A given molecule may move along with a certain speed until it hits another, to which it loses some of its kinetic energy, perhaps, later, it gets hit by a third and gains kinetic energy. This exchange of kinetic energy between neighbors is constantly going on, so that it is only the total kinetic energy of a gas sample that stays the same—provided, of course, that no energy is added to the gas sample from the outside, as by heating. The total kinetic energy of a gas is made up of the contributions of all the molecules, each of which may be moving at a different speed. At a particular instant, a few molecules may be standing still with no kinetic energy; a few may have high kinetic energy; most will have kinetic energies near the average. The situation is summarized in Fig. 6.11, which indicates the usual distribution of kinetic energies in a gas sample. Each point on the curve tells what fraction of the molecules have the specified value of the kinetic energy.

The temperature of a gas may be raised by the addition of heat. What happens to the molecules as the temperature is raised? The heat which is

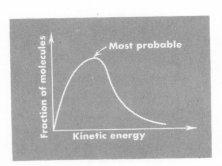

Fig. 6.11   Energy distribution in a gas.

Fig. 6.12   Energy distribution in a gas at two temperatures.

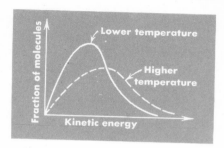

added is a form of energy and so can be used to increase the speed of the molecules and, therefore, the average kinetic energy. This is shown in Fig. 6.12, where the dotted curve describes the situation at higher temperature. At the higher temperature the molecules have a higher average kinetic energy than at the lower temperature. Thus, temperature serves to measure the average kinetic energy. The assumption that average kinetic energy is directly proportional to the absolute temperature is supported by the fact that predictions based on this assumption agree with experiment.

The kinetic theory, presented above, accounts for the observed behavior of gases as follows:

1   Boyle's law. The pressure exerted by a gas depends only on the number of molecular impacts per unit wall area per second, if the temperature is kept constant so that the molecules move with the same average speed. As shown in Fig. 6.13, when the volume is reduced, the molecules do not have so much volume in which to move. They must collide with the walls more frequently; hence the walls receive more pushes per second, and the observed pressure is greater in the smaller volume.

2   Charles' law. The effect of raising the temperature of a gas is to raise the average kinetic energy of the molecules. As the molecules

Fig. 6.13   Kinetic theory explanation of Boyle's law.

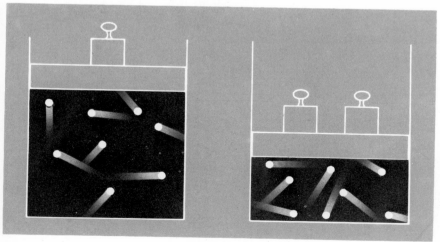

move more energetically, they collide with the walls of the container more frequently and more vigorously, thus producing a greater pressure. As shown in Fig. 6.14, if the external pressure on a balloon is constant but the temperature is raised, the gas expands the balloon to a larger volume in which the more vigorous molecular motion is compensated for.

3 Dalton's law. According to the kinetic theory, there are no attractive forces between the molecules of an ideal gas. In a mixture of gas molecules, each molecule strikes the walls the same number of times per second and with the same force as if no other molecules were present. Therefore, the partial pressure of a gas is not changed by the presence of other gases in the container.

4 Brownian motion. When a particle is suspended in a gas, gas molecules collide with it. If the particle is very large, the number of bombarding molecules on one side is about equal to the number of bombarding molecules on the other side. However, if the particle is small, so that the number of bombarding molecules at any instant is small, collisions on one side of the particle may predominate, so that the particle experiences a net force which causes it to move. This is illustrated in Fig. 6.15. An analogue of Brownian motion is observed when a small chunk of bread is thrown on the surface of a pool in which there are many small fish. The bread darts to and fro as if propelled by some unseen force, the invisible force being due to the bumping of the nibbling fish. The larger the piece of bread, the less its erratic motion.

5 Graham's law. This law follows directly from the fourth postulate of the kinetic theory, that the average kinetic energy of molecules is fixed for a given temperature. When gas 1 and gas 2 are compared at the same temperature,

Average kinetic energy of gas 1 molecules
$$= \text{average kinetic energy of gas 2 molecules}$$

$$\tfrac{1}{2}m_1 s_1{}^2 = \tfrac{1}{2}m_2 s_2{}^2$$

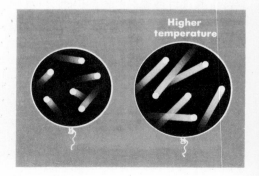

Fig. 6.14 Kinetic theory explanation of Charles' law.

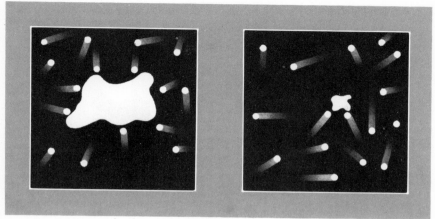

Fig. 6.15   *Kinetic theory explanation of Brownian motion.*

where m_1 and m_2 are the masses of the different molecules and s_1 and s_2 are their average speeds.

$$\frac{s_1{}^2}{s_2{}^2} = \frac{\frac{1}{2}m_2}{\frac{1}{2}m_1} = \frac{m_2}{m_1}$$

$$\frac{s_1}{s_2} = \sqrt{\frac{m_2}{m_1}}$$

Qualitatively, this last equation indicates that heavier molecules move more slowly than light ones. It is reasonable to assume that the relative rates of diffusion of molecules are measured by their relative average velocities, so that

$$\frac{\text{Rate of diffusion of gas 1}}{\text{Rate of diffusion of gas 2}} = \frac{R_1}{R_2} = \sqrt{\frac{m_2}{m_1}}$$

This is Graham's law.

6   *Equation of state.* The equation of state of an ideal gas, $pV = nRT$, can be derived from kinetic theory by considering in detail how the pressure of a gas arises from molecular impacts. Suppose we imagine a gas confined in a box, as in Fig. 6.10. The pressure of the gas is proportional to the *number of molecular impacts* on a square centimeter of wall area per second and is also proportional to the *impulse*, or change of momentum (Appendix 4), *of each impact*. The number of impacts multiplied by the impulse of each is the total pressure.

The *number of impacts* per square centimeter per second depends on three factors. First, it is directly proportional to N, the number of molecules in the box. If there are twice as many molecules in the box, there are twice as many collisions per unit wall area per second. Second, it is inversely proportional to V, the volume of the box. If there are N molecules in a box and if then the size of the box is doubled, the number of collisions per second per unit wall area becomes half as great. Finally, the number of impacts is directly proportional to s, the average speed of the molecules. If the molecules are moving slowly, they collide with the walls less frequently than if they are moving rapidly. In summary, the number of impacts is proportional to N, $1/V$, and s, which can be written

$$\text{Number of impacts per cm.}^2 \text{ per sec. } \propto N \frac{1}{V} s$$

The *impulse* of each impact depends on two factors. First, it is directly proportional to m, the mass of the molecule. If a light molecule strikes a wall, it does not push the wall very hard. A heavy molecule moving at the same speed exerts a larger force. The impulse is also directly proportional to the average speed of the molecules. If a molecule is moving slowly when it collides with the wall, the force exerted is not so great as if it were moving fast. Therefore we may write

$$\text{Impulse of each impact} \propto ms$$

Since the pressure is proportional to the product of the number of impacts and the impulse of each impact, we can write

$$P \propto N \frac{1}{V} sms$$

or, by rearranging,

$$P \propto \frac{N}{V} ms^2$$

Since the average kinetic energy $\frac{1}{2}ms^2$ is assumed to be proportional to the absolute temperature, the factor ms^2 is proportional to T. We can therefore write

$$P \propto \frac{N}{V} T$$

The number of molecules N is, of course, proportional to the number of moles n.

$$P \propto \frac{n}{V} T$$

The constants of proportionality in the various steps combine to give R, the universal gas constant; hence

$$P = R \frac{n}{V} T$$

or

$$PV = nRT$$

This derivation is given mainly to show how the observed behavior of gases is related to molecular properties. A more rigorous derivation which considers in detail the collision process and the various proportionality constants can be found in most elementary physics texts.

6.13   DEVIATIONS FROM IDEAL BEHAVIOR

We have seen that, at high pressures and at low temperatures, gases deviate from ideal behavior. For example, although a gas compressed at constant temperature from 1 to 2 atm. changes its volume to one-half the original, the same gas compressed from 1,000 to 2,000 atm. may change its volume to something other than one-half the original. Similarly, at constant low pressure a gas cooled from 300 to 200°K. changes its volume to two-thirds the original volume, but the same gas cooled from 30 to 20°K. may change its volume to something other than two-thirds the original. At sufficiently high pressures and sufficiently low temperatures, the volume of the gas phase disappears. The gas liquefies, a phenomenon which is the extreme case of nonideal behavior.

What are the sources of deviations from ideal behavior? In the kinetic theory of gases, two assumptions might be questioned: (1) that the actual volume of the molecules is negligible compared to the empty space between them; (2) that there are no attractive forces between the molecules. Under what conditions would these assumptions break down? The volume of the molecules is not negligible when the molecules are close together, as they are at high pressure. Further compression is resisted by the impenetrability of molecules. Eventually the volume cannot be reduced any more, because all the free space is gone. Considering this molecular-volume effect alone, volumes observed at high pressure would be greater than predicted by the ideal-gas law. Assumption two is not strictly true, since it is known that there *are* attractive forces between molecules. However, at high temperatures, molecules are in violent motion, so that these attractions are not important. At low temperature, the attractions are important, and they tend to make the observed volume less than that predicted by the ideal-gas law.

6.14   ATTRACTIVE FORCES

In some cases it is easy to see the reason for attractive forces between molecules. For example, in polar molecules, the positive end of one molecule may attract the negative end of another molecule. It is not surprising, therefore, that polar substances deviate markedly from ideal behavior. Water vapor, as an illustration, is so nonideal that, even at room temperature, it liquefies under slight pressure. It is not so easy to see the reason for attractive forces between nonpolar molecules. That these forces do exist was suggested by the Dutch physicist van der Waals, for whom they are named. The *van der Waals forces* arise from the motion of electrons in atoms and molecules. They are present in all matter.

The van der Waals forces can be described in the following way: Suppose we consider two neon atoms extremely close together, as shown in Fig. 6.16. We can imagine that *instantaneously* the electron distribution in atom I is unsymmetrical, with a slight preponderance on one side. For a fraction of a microsecond, the atom is in a state in which one end appears slightly negative with respect to the other end; i.e., the atom is momentarily a dipole. The neighboring atom as a result is distorted, because the positive end of atom I displaces the electrons in atom II. As shown in the figure, there is an instantaneous dipole in each of the neighboring atoms, with a consequent attraction. This picture persists only for an extremely short time, because the electrons are in motion. As electrons in atom I move to the other side, electrons in atom II follow. In fact, we can think of van der Waals forces as arising because electrons in adjacent molecules are beating in time, so as to produce fluctuating dipoles which give rise to an instantaneous attraction. The attraction is strong when particles are close together but rapidly weakens as they move apart. The more electrons there are in a molecule and the less tightly bound these electrons are, the greater are the van der Waals forces.

Under what conditions do the forces of attraction produce the biggest effect? The closer the molecules are together, the greater the attraction. This means that the attractive forces become more important as the pressure increases and the molecules are crowded together. The attractive forces become less important as the temperature increases, because a rise in temperature produces an effect that opposes the attractive forces. This effect is a disordering one due to the molecular motion, which increases in speed as the temperature rises. Disordering arises because the molecules of a gas move in random fashion. The attractive forces try to draw the molecules together, but the latter, because of their motion, stay apart. As the temperature is lowered, the molecules become sluggish. They have less ability to overcome the attractive forces. The attractive forces are unchanged, but the motion of the molecules decreases; hence the attraction becomes relatively

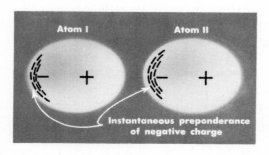

Instantaneous preponderance of negative charge

Fig. 6.16   Model of van der Waals attraction.

Table 6.4   Critical Constants

Substance	Critical temperature, °K.	Critical pressure, atm.
Water, H_2O	647	217.7
Sulfur dioxide, SO_2	430	77.7
Hydrogen chloride, HCl	324	81.6
Carbon dioxide, CO_2	304	73.0
Oxygen, O_2	154	49.7
Nitrogen, N_2	126	33.5
Hydrogen, H_2	33	12.8
Helium, He	5.2	2.3

more important. At sufficiently low temperature the attractive forces, no matter how weak they are, take over and draw the molecules together to form a liquid. The *temperature at which gas molecules coalesce to form a liquid* is called the *liquefaction temperature*. Liquefaction is easier at high pressures, where distances between molecules are smaller and hence intermolecular forces are greater. The higher the pressure of a gas, the easier it is to liquefy it and the less it needs to be cooled to accomplish liquefaction. Thus, the liquefaction temperature increases with increasing pressure.

6.15   CRITICAL TEMPERATURE

There is for each gas a temperature above which the attractive forces are not strong enough to produce liquefaction, no matter how high the pressure. This temperature is called the *critical temperature* of the substance and is designated by T_c. It is defined as the *temperature above which the substance can exist only as a gas*. Above the critical temperature the motion of the molecules is so violent that, no matter how high the pressure, the molecules occupy the entire available volume as a gas. The critical temperature depends on the magnitude of the attractive forces between the molecules of a substance. Table 6.4 contains values of the critical temperature for some common substances. Listed also is the *critical pressure, the pressure which must be exerted to produce liquefaction at the critical-temperature.* Above the critical temperature, no amount of pressure, not even billions of atmospheres, can produce liquefaction. For example, above 647°K. (374°C.), H_2O exists only in the gaseous state. The high critical temperature indicates that the attractive forces between the polar water molecules are so great that, even at 647°K., they can produce coalescence. The attractive forces between SO_2

molecules are less than those between water molecules; hence the critical temperature of SO_2 is lower than that of water, and liquefaction cannot be achieved above 430°K. (157°C.). In the extreme case of helium the attractive forces are so weak that liquid helium can exist only below 5.3°K. (−267.9°C.). At this very low temperature the molecular motion is so slow that the weak van der Waals forces can hold the atoms together in a liquid. In Table 6.4, the order of decreasing critical temperature is also the order of decreasing attractive forces, and we can think of the critical temperature as giving a measure of the attractive forces between molecules.

6.16   COOLING BY EXPANSION

Substances with high critical temperatures are easy to liquefy. Substances with low critical temperatures must be cooled before they can be liquefied. For example, oxygen cannot be liquefied at room temperature (298°K. or so). It must be cooled below 154°K. (−119°C.) before liquefaction can occur. This cooling would be quite difficult except that gases sometimes cool themselves on expansion.* For example, if a gas expands against a piston, then the gas does work in pushing the piston out. The energy for this work can come from the kinetic energy of the gas molecules. A decrease in the kinetic energy of the molecules is observed as a lowering of the temperature. However, a temperature drop is sometimes observed for an expanding gas which does no external work.

The cause of cooling by unrestrained expansion can be seen by considering the experiment shown in Fig. 6.17. The box shown is perfectly insulated from its surroundings, so that no heat can get in from the outside. It is divided into two compartments by a diaphragm. The left-hand compartment contains compressed gas. The right-hand compartment is originally empty. If a hole is now punched in the diaphragm, the gas streams into the vacuum. A thermometer in the path of the streaming gas would show a drop in temperature. At the original temperature, the molecules have a definite average kinetic energy. As the gas streams into the empty space, molecules work against the attractive forces of their neighbors. This requires energy, and since no outside energy is available, the molecules must use up some of their kinetic energy. The average kinetic energy, as measured by

---

* The word "sometimes" takes into consideration the fact that cooling does not occur at *any* temperature but only below the *inversion temperature*, which for most gases is roughly six times the critical temperature. Above the inversion temperature, a gas warms when suddenly expanded; below the inversion temperature, it cools. Since most inversion temperatures are above room temperature, most gases near room temperature cool on expanding and heat on compression. However, for hydrogen and helium the inversion temperatures are below room temperature (195°K. and 45°K., respectively) and consequently these gases at room temperature heat up when allowed to expand into a vacuum.

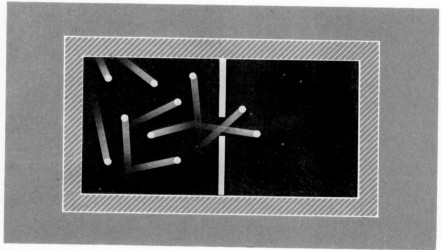

Fig. 6.17   Sudden expansion of a gas.

the temperature, drops. If there were no attractive forces between molecules, there would be no cooling effect. Indeed, the fact that cooling is observed indicates that there *are* attractive forces between gas molecules.*

The commercial liquefaction of gases makes use of cooling by expansion. In order to liquefy air, for example, it is first compressed to high pressure, cooled with a refrigerant to remove the heat that accompanies compression, and then allowed to expand. Some of the air liquefies as a result of cooling on expansion; the rest is passed over the incoming pipes containing the compressed air to cool it further.

QUESTIONS

6.1   *Manometer.* What happens to the right-hand level of the manometer shown in Fig. 6.3 when: (*a*) the gas sample is heated; (*b*) more gas is added; (*c*) atmospheric pressure increases; (*d*) a small amount of manometer liquid is removed?

6.2   *Pressure.* What happens to the pressure exerted by the gas in each case in Question 6.1?

6.3   *Boyle's law.* Given that 2.0 g. of an ideal gas occupies 8.4 liters at STP. What is its volume at 0°C. and a pressure of 84 cm. Hg?

---

* The opposite effect, warming on unrestrained expansion above the inversion temperature, indicates that there are also repulsive forces between gas molecules. Below the inversion temperature, these repulsions are masked by the larger attractions; however, as the temperature is raised above the inversion temperature, the attractive forces become less important and the repulsive forces, small as they are, dominate. The repulsions can be viewed as arising from the noninterpenetrability of molecules.

6.4   *Barometer.* If atmospheric pressure on a given day is 29 in. Hg, how high a column of water can be supported? (Neglect the water vapor pressure.)

Ans. 33 ft.

6.5   *Kinetic theory.* Show how the kinetic theory accounts for these observations: (*a*) gases are easily compressible; (*b*) gases are miscible; (*c*) gases exert pressure; (*d*) the pressure exerted by a gas increases as its temperature is increased; (*e*) when observed with a microscope, smoke particles show Brownian motion; (*f*) 2 g. of hydrogen gas in a given box at a given temperature exerts twice the pressure of 1 g. of hydrogen gas in the same box at the same temperature.

6.6   *Charles' law.* Given that 2.0 g. of an ideal gas occupies 8.4 liters at STP. What is its volume at 91°C. and a pressure of 76 cm. Hg?   *Ans.* 11 liters

6.7   *Gas laws.* Given that 2.0 g. of an ideal gas occupies 8.4 liters at STP. What is its volume at 91°C. and a pressure of 84 cm. Hg?

6.8   *Gas laws.* Design an apparatus suitable for an experiment to illustrate each of the following: (*a*) Charles' law; (*b*) Boyle's law.

6.9   *Comparison of gases.* Given 4.80 g. of O_2 gas and 2.80 g. of N_2 gas. Calculate for each of these samples: (*a*) the number of moles; (*b*) the number of molecules; (*c*) the number of atoms; (*d*) the volume as an ideal gas at STP; (*e*) the volume as an ideal gas at 38.0 cm. Hg pressure and 273°C.

Ans. 0.150 and 0.100 mole; 9.03×10^{22} and 6.02×10^{22} molecules; 1.81×10^{23} and 1.20×10^{23} atoms; 3.36 and 2.24 liters; 13.4 and 8.96 liters

6.10   *Molar volume.* Show from the ideal equation of state that the molar volume of an ideal gas at 25.00°C. and 1.000 atmosphere pressure is 24.465 liters.

6.11   *Molar volume.* What is the molar volume of an ideal gas at 91°C. and 84.0 cm. Hg pressure?

6.12   *Temperature.* Convert the critical temperature of hydrogen into degrees centigrade and degrees Fahrenheit. See Table 6.4.

6.13   *Temperature.* What is room temperature (68°F.) in degrees centigrade and degrees Kelvin?

6.14   *Nonideality.* Discuss briefly two causes of nonideality in gases. Under what conditions of pressure and/or temperature would you expect the nonideality to be pronounced? Why?

6.15   *Kinetic theory.* If the average speed of O_2 molecules is 1.0×10^3 miles per hour at STP, what is the average speed of SO_2 molecules at the same conditions?   *Ans.* 7.1×10^2 miles/hour

6.16   *General.* Given a sample of 1.76 g. of C_3H_8. How many of each of the following does it contain: (*a*) moles of C_3H_8; (*b*) molecules of C_3H_8; (*c*) atoms of carbon; (*d*) gram-atoms of hydrogen; (*e*) liters as an ideal gas at STP; (*f*) liters as an ideal gas at 60.0 cm. Hg pressure and 77°C.?

6.17 *Comparison of gases.* Two flasks of the same size are maintained at the same temperature. H_2 gas is put into one. An equal weight of O_2 gas is put into the other. (*a*) Which flask contains the greater number of molecules? How many times as many? (*b*) In which flask is the pressure greater? How many times as great? (*c*) In which flask are the molecules moving faster? How many times as fast?

6.18 *Avogadro number.* When radium undergoes radioactive disintegration, alpha particles (helium nuclei) are formed. These alpha particles pick up electrons and form neutral helium atoms. The number of alpha particles can be counted with a Geiger counter. In an actual experiment 1.82×10^{17} alpha particles were counted, and the resultant helium gas occupied a volume of 0.00734 ml. at 19°C. and a pressure of 745 mm. Hg. Using 22.414 liters for the molar volume of an ideal gas at STP and assuming the helium gas to behave in ideal fashion, calculate the Avogadro number. *Ans.* 6.07×10^{23}

6.19 *Pressure.* A mercury barometer like that diagramed in Fig. 6.2 is entirely submerged under water. What happens to the difference in mercury-level heights? Explain.

6.20 *Combining volumes.* Show that, when two gases react chemically, the volumes that react (measured at the same temperature and pressure) are in a ratio expressible by small whole numbers.

6.21 *Gas laws.* In a particular experiment 0.0273 mole of O_2 gas is to be collected over water at 17°C. and a barometer reading of 715 mm. Hg. What volume will be occupied by this oxygen assuming it is saturated with respect to water vapor?

6.22 *Kinetic theory.* Consider two samples of ideal gas in two different 1-liter containers. The pressure of the two samples is equal, but the temperature (in °K.) of sample 1 is half that of sample 2. Compare the two quantitatively with respect to each of the following: (*a*) number of molecules; (*b*) molecular speed; (*c*) number of collisions per second with the walls; (*d*) average kinetic energy per molecule; (*e*) effect of an average collision with the wall in producing the pressure found in the two containers.

6.23 *Pressure.* (*a*) What is the difference between pressure and force? (*b*) Show that the diameter of the tube used to make a barometer does not affect the height of the mercury column.

6.24 *Temperature.* Sample A consists of 1 g. of hydrogen; sample B consists of 10 g. of hydrogen. Both are at the same temperature. One hundred calories of heat are added to each of these samples at constant pressure. Which sample has the higher final temperature? Explain.

6.25 *Combining volumes.* By using Gay-Lussac's law and the Avogadro principle, show that oxygen gas cannot be monatomic.

6.26 *Gas laws.* (*a*) Simultaneously, 0.202 g. of H_2 gas and 0.80 g. of O_2 gas are injected into an empty box which has a volume of 2.24 liters and is kept at

273°C. What is the final pressure in the box? (*b*) Suppose a spark is passed through the box so that the hydrogen and oxygen can react to form water by the reaction

$$2H_2(g) + O_2(g) \rightarrow 2H_2O(g)$$

What will be the final pressure in the box if the volume and temperature are kept the same?   *Ans.* 2.50 atm.; 2.00 atm.

6.27   *Molecular weight.* The molecular weight of a volatile liquid can be measured by adding an excess of the liquid to a weighed bulb, heating the assembly to volatilize all the liquid and to expel through a nozzle the excess vapor, cooling, and then weighing the bulb with the condensed liquid. From the following data, calculate the molecular weight of an unknown liquid. Assume the vapor is ideal.

Weight of dry bulb	83.192 g.
Weight of bulb + condensed liquid	83.913 g.
Temperature of the heating	98.6°C.
Volume of the bulb	226 ml.
Pressure	746 mm. Hg

6.28   *Molecular formula.* If the compound in Question 6.27 analyzes to 24.3% carbon, 71.6% chlorine, and 4.1% hydrogen, what is its molecular formula?

Ans. $C_2H_4Cl_2$

6.29   *Kinetic theory.* Given a 1-liter sample of H_2 at STP, and a 1-liter sample of O_2 at 0°C. and 2.00 standard atm. pressure. Compare quantitatively the two samples with respect to each of the following: (*a*) number of molecules; (*b*) average kinetic energy of the molecules; (*c*) speed of the molecules; (*d*) total number of collisions per second with the walls; (*e*) effect of an average collision with the wall on giving the observed pressure.

6.30   *Vapor pressure.* Suppose that 4.20 g. of N_2 gas and 3.20 g. of O_2 gas are mixed and placed in a container that holds some unknown liquid at 0°C. If the volume of the gas phase is 7.60 liters and the pressure of the gas phase is 581 mm. Hg, what is the vapor pressure of the unknown liquid at 0°C.?

6.31   *Gas laws.* An unknown mixture of scandium and zinc powders can be analyzed by reacting a weighed amount of unknown with excess acid and collecting the liberated hydrogen by water displacement. From the following data, calculate the percentage composition of the unknown mixture:

Weight of unknown	2.4478 g.
Volume of H_2 collected	1.248 liters
Temperature of water	21°C.
Barometric pressure	753.6 mm. Hg

Equations:

$$Sc(s) + 3H^+ \rightarrow Sc^{+3} + \tfrac{3}{2}H_2(g)$$
$$Zn(s) + 2H^+ \rightarrow Zn^{++} + H_2(g)$$

Ans. 71.6% Zn and 28.4% Sc by weight

6.32 *Air density*. A typical sample of air shows the following analysis as per cent by weight:

Nitrogen, N_2	74.7%
Oxygen, O_2	22.9%
Argon, Ar	1.3%
Water vapor, H_2O	1.0%
Carbon dioxide, CO_2	0.1%

Calculate the density of air at 20°C. and 740 mm. Hg pressure.

Ans. 1.16 g./liter

6.33 *Model of a gas.* (*a*) Calculate approximately the average distance between the centers of argon atoms in the gas at STP, by finding the edge length of a cube containing one molecule. (*b*) If the argon atom has a radius of 1.54 A.(1.54 × 10⁻⁸cm.), what fraction of an argon gas sample at STP is actually empty space? (*c*) If an argon atom at 0°C. has an average velocity of 381 cm. per sec., what is its average velocity at 20°C.?

Ans. 3.34 × 10⁻⁷ cm.; 99.960%; 395 cm./sec.

7   *Liquids*

IN THIS CHAPTER WE CONSIDER THE LIQUID STATE and compare it with the gaseous state. When a sample of gas is cooled or compressed, or both, it liquefies. In the process the molecules of the gas, originally far apart on the average, are slowed down and brought close enough together that attractive forces become appreciable. The individual molecules coalesce into a cluster which settles to the bottom of the container as liquid. What are the properties of liquids? How can they be accounted for by the kinetic theory?

7.1   PROPERTIES OF LIQUIDS

Liquids are practically incompressible. Unlike gases, there is not much change in the volume of a liquid when the pressure on it is changed, even when pressures of thousands of atmospheres are involved. The kinetic theory accounts for this by saying that the amount of free space between the molecules of a liquid has been reduced almost to a minimum. Any attempt to compress the liquid meets with resistance as the electron cloud of one molecule repels the electron cloud of an adjacent molecule.

160

Liquids maintain their volume, no matter what the shape or size of the container. A 10-ml, sample of liquid occupies a 10-ml. volume, whether it is placed in a small beaker or in a large flask, whereas a gas spreads out to fill the whole volume accessible to it. Gases do not maintain their volume, because the molecules are essentially independent of each other and can move into any space available. In liquids, the molecules are close together, so that mutual attractions (Sec. 6.14) are strong. Consequently, the molecules are clustered together.

Liquids have no characteristic shape. A liquid sample assumes the shape of the bottom of its container. The kinetic theory explains this property by saying that there are no fixed positions for the molecules. The molecules are free to slide over each other in order to occupy positions of the lowest possible potential energy with respect to the earth.

Liquids diffuse, but they do so slowly. When a drop of ink is carefully released in water, there is a rather sharp boundary between the ink cloud and the water. Eventually the black color diffuses throughout the rest of the liquid. In gases, diffusion is much more rapid. Diffusion occurs because molecules have kinetic energy and move from one place to another. In a liquid, molecules do not move very far before they collide with neighboring molecules. The mean free path, which is the average distance between collisions, is short. Eventually each molecule of a liquid does migrate from one side of its container to the other, but it has to suffer many billions of collisions in doing so. In gases, there is less obstruction to the migrating molecule. Because a gas is mostly empty space, the mean free path is much longer. Hence the molecules of one gas can rather quickly mix with those of another.

Liquids evaporate from open containers. Although there are attractive forces which hold the molecules together in a clump, apparently it is possible for molecules to escape. The molecules with kinetic energy great enough to overcome the attractive forces can escape into the gas phase. In any collection of molecules, any given molecule does not have the same energy all the time. There is perpetually an exchange of energy between colliding molecules. The collection might start out with all molecules of the same energy, but this situation would not persist long. Two or more molecules may simultane-

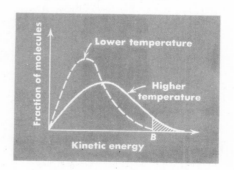

Fig. 7.1   Energy distribution in a liquid.

ously collide with a third molecule. Molecule 3 now has not only its initial energy but possibly some extra energy received from its neighbors. Molecule 3 is now a molecule which is higher than average in kinetic energy. If it happens to be near the surface of the liquid, it may be able to overcome the attractive forces of neighbors and go off into the gas phase. Figure 7.1 shows a typical energy distribution for the molecules of a sample of liquid at a given temperature. The curve is quite similar to the one given previously for a gas. The value marked B corresponds to the minimum kinetic energy required by a molecule to overcome attractive forces and escape from this liquid. All the molecules in the shaded area of the curve have enough energy to overcome attractive forces. These are the molecules that have the possibility of escaping, provided that they are close enough to the surface. If these highly energetic molecules leave the liquid, the average kinetic energy of those left behind is lower. This is because each molecule that escapes carries along with it more than an average amount of energy, part of which it uses in working against the attractive forces. Since the average kinetic energy of the remaining molecules is lower, their temperature drops. Evaporation is therefore accompanied by cooling.

When a liquid evaporates from a noninsulated container such as a beaker, the temperature of the liquid cannot fall very far before there is an appreciable heat flow from the surroundings into the liquid. If the rate of evaporation is not too great, this flow of heat is sufficient to supply the energy required for evaporation. As a consequence, the temperature of a liquid remains at room temperature, even though the liquid is evaporating. Eventually, the liquid disappears. When evaporation proceeds from a container insulated to reduce heat flow, the heat flow from the surroundings is slower, and the temperature of the liquid drops. An example of such an insulated container is the Dewar flask shown in Fig. 7.2. A Thermos bottle is a Dewar flask. The essential feature of the Dewar flask is double-walled construction of glass with vacuum between the walls. The vacuum jacket acts as an insulator to retard heat flow into or out of the container. When a liquid evaporates from such a container, the flow of

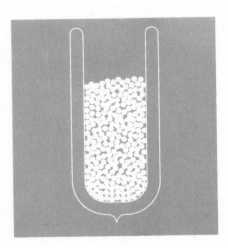

Fig. 7.2 Schematic representation of liquid in a Dewar flask.

heat from outside may not be fast enough to compensate for the evaporation. The temperature of the liquid drops; the average kinetic energy of the molecules decreases; and the rate of evaporation diminishes until the heat flow inward just equals the heat required for evaporation. At the lower temperature the distribution of the kinetic energies is shifted to the left, as shown by the dotted line in Fig. 7.1. As the temperature decreases, the fraction of energetic molecules decreases, and the rate of evaporation decreases. The liquid level stays nearly constant. The temperature now stays constant but at a value which may be considerably lower than the original temperature. Liquid air, an extremely volatile liquid, remains in an open Dewar flask at approximately $-190°$C. for many hours.

7.2   EQUILIBRIUM VAPOR PRESSURE

When a bell jar is placed over a beaker of evaporating liquid, as shown in Fig. 7.3, the liquid level drops for a while and then becomes constant. This can be explained as follows: Molecules escape from the liquid into the gas, or vapor, phase. After escaping, they are confined to a limited space. As the molecules accumulate in the space above the liquid, there is an increasing chance that in their random motion some of them will go back to the liquid. The longer the experiment proceeds, the better the chance that the molecules return. Eventually, a situation is established in which molecules are returning to the liquid just as fast as other molecules are leaving it. At this point the liquid level no longer drops, because the number of molecules evaporating per second is equal to the number of molecules condensing per second. A condition in which two changes exactly oppose each other is referred to as *dynamic equilibrium*. Although the system is not at a state of rest, there is no net change in the system. The amount of liquid in the beaker stays constant; the concentration of molecules in the vapor above the liquid is constant. A particular molecule spends part of its time in the liquid and part in the vapor phase. As molecules pass from liquid to gas, other molecules move from gas to liquid, keeping the number of molecules in each phase constant.

Fig. 7.3   Evaporation in a confined space.

The molecules which are in the vapor exert a pressure. At equilibrium, this pressure is characteristic of the liquid and is known as the *equilibrium vapor pressure.* As the term implies, it is the *pressure exerted by a vapor when in equilibrium with its liquid.* The magnitude of the equilibrium vapor pressure depends (1) on the nature of the liquid and (2) on its temperature.

1. The nature of the liquid is involved, since each liquid has characteristic attractive forces between its molecules. Molecules which have large mutual attraction have a small tendency to escape into the vapor phase. Such a liquid has a low equilibrium vapor pressure. Liquids composed of molecules with small mutual attraction have a high escaping tendency and therefore a high equilibrium vapor pressure.

2. As the temperature of a liquid is raised, the average kinetic energy of its molecules increases. The number of high-energy molecules capable of escaping also becomes larger, so that the equilibrium vapor pressure increases.

There are various devices for measuring equilibrium vapor pressure, one of which is shown in Fig. 7.4. It consists of a barometer set up in the usual manner. The difference between the upper mercury level and the lower mercury level represents the atmospheric pressure. Above the mercury there is a vacuum. By squeezing on the rubber bulb, a drop of liquid can be ejected into the mercury. Since practically all liquids are less dense than mercury, they float to the top of the mercury, where enough liquid evaporates to establish its equilibrium vapor pressure. This vapor pressure pushes down the mercury column. (The excess liquid also helps to push down the mercury column, but this is a negligible effect, especially when there is little excess.) The extent to which the mercury level is depressed gives a quantitative measure of the vapor pressure of the liquid. At 20°C., water, H_2O, has an equilibrium vapor pressure of 17.5 mm. Hg; carbon tetrachloride,

Fig. 7.4   Measurement of vapor pressure.

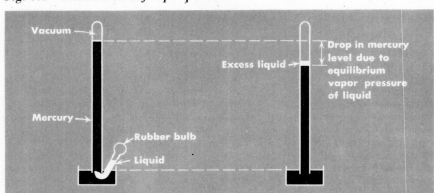

Fig. 7.5   Change of vapor pressure with temperature.

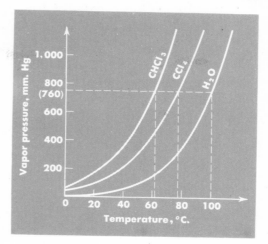

CCl_4, 91.0 mm. Hg; and chloroform, $CHCl_3$, 160 mm. Hg. These values of the vapor pressure give an idea of the escaping tendencies of molecules from the various liquids. In water, the attractive forces between molecules are apparently quite large; hence relatively few water molecules escape. In chloroform, the attractive forces between molecules are small, and it evaporates readily to give a high vapor pressure.

By repeating the above experiment at different temperatures, it is possible to determine vapor pressure of liquids as a function of temperature. Appendix 6 is a table showing the results for water in great detail. The general behavior of water, carbon tetrachloride, and chloroform is shown by the graph in Fig. 7.5. The vertical scale represents the vapor pressure and the horizontal scale the temperature. As the temperature increases, the vapor pressure rises, first slowly and then more steeply, until at high temperatures it is rising almost vertically. The curve continues to the critical temperature. It does not go beyond the critical temperature, because above the critical temperature the liquid cannot exist.

7.3   BOILING POINTS

Boiling is a special case of vaporization and is the passage of a liquid from an open vessel into the vapor state through the formation of bubbles.* A liquid is said to boil at its *boiling point* (abbreviated b.p.), which is the

---

* When water is heated in an open container, it is usually observed that, as the liquid is warmed, tiny bubbles gradually form at first, and then, at a higher temperature, violent bubbling commences. The first bubbling should not be confused with boiling. The tiny bubbles are due to the expulsion of the air usually dissolved in water.

temperature at which the vapor pressure of the liquid is equal to the prevailing atmospheric pressure. At the boiling point, the vapor pressure of the liquid is high enough that the atmosphere can be pushed aside. Therefore, bubbles of vapor can form in the interior of the liquid, allowing vaporization to occur at any point in the liquid. In general, a molecule can evaporate only if two requirements are met: it must have enough kinetic energy, and it must be close enough to a liquid-vapor boundary. At the boiling point, bubbling infinitely increases the liquid-vapor boundary, and therefore it is necessary only that molecules have enough kinetic energy to escape from the liquid. Any heat added to a liquid at its boiling point is used to give more molecules sufficient energy to escape; hence the average kinetic energy of molecules remaining in the liquid cannot increase. The temperature of a pure boiling liquid is therefore constant.

The boiling point of a liquid depends on pressure. For instance, when the atmospheric pressure is 700 mm. Hg, water boils at 97.7°C.; at 760 mm. Hg, it boils at 100°C. To avoid ambiguity, it is necessary to define a *standard*, or *normal, boiling point*. The normal boiling point is the temperature at which the vapor pressure of a liquid is equal to one standard atmosphere, or 760 mm. Hg. The normal boiling point is the one usually listed in handbooks and textbooks. It can be determined from the vapor-pressure curve by finding the temperature which corresponds to 1 atm. pressure. Figure 7.5 shows that the normal boiling point of water is 100°C.; that of carbon tetrachloride is 76.8°C.; and that of chloroform is 61°C. In general, the higher the normal boiling point, the greater must be the attractive forces between the molecules of a liquid.*

QUESTIONS

7.1   *Liquid-gas comparison.* Given a substance in the liquid and gaseous states in equilibrium at some temperature, compare the following properties for the liquid and gas phases: (*a*) compressibility; (*b*) rate of diffusion; (*c*) average kinetic energy of molecules; (*d*) potential energy of molecules. Explain briefly in terms of kinetic theory.

7.2   *Liquid-gas comparison.* In experiments with liquids, amounts of chemicals are usually specified by giving the volumes. With gases, volume, pressure, and temperatures must be specified. Justify such procedure.

---

* It is usually observed that, in a series of similar compounds such as CH_4, C_2H_6, and C_3H_8, the normal boiling point is highest for the compound of greatest molecular weight. Although it is tempting to explain a high boiling point in terms of large gravitational attraction between heavy molecules, gravitational attraction in reality is small. A more reasonable explanation is that heavy molecules usually contain more electrons than light molecules and hence have greater van der Waals attractions.

7.3 *Evaporation.* Separate portions of chloroform and water at the same temperature are poured on each of your hands. The chloroform feels colder. Account for this in terms of attractive forces.

7.4 *Liquid properties.* In terms of kinetic theory, account for the fact that the volume of most liquids increases with a rise of temperature.

7.5 *Boiling.* When a stream of air is bubbled through water, the water evaporates faster. Show how this is related to boiling.

7.6 *Molecular forces.* The normal boiling point of liquid HCl is $-84°C$. At this temperature the vapor pressure of SO_2 is less than 10 mm. Hg. (*a*) Are the intermolecular attractions greater in liquid SO_2 or liquid HCl? (*b*) Which should have the higher critical temperature? (Check your answer with Table 6.4.)

7.7 *Vapor pressure.* (*a*) If 0.80 g. of oxygen and 0.202 g. of hydrogen are placed in an evacuated container of volume 2.24 liters at $0°C.$, what is the total pressure? (*b*) If now a spark is passed through the gas so as to give the reaction

$$2H_2(g) + O_2(g) \rightarrow 2H_2O(l)$$

what will be the final pressure of the gas phase at $27°C.$?

Ans. 1.25 atm.; 0.585 atm.

7.8 *Vapor pressure.* (*a*) Given a sealed evacuated container into which liquid water is injected. How does the pressure in the vapor phase depend on the temperature and on the amount of liquid water in the container? Explain. (*b*) Suppose the sealed container was originally filled with air. What would happen to the total pressure of the vapor phase as more liquid water is injected? What happens to the vapor pressure of the water? Explain.

7.9 *Model of a liquid.* The density of liquid argon is 1.40 g. per ml. at $-186°C.$ If the argon atom is assumed to be a sphere of radius 1.54×10^{-8} cm., what percentage of liquid argon is apparently empty space? *Ans.* 67.7%

7.10 *Molecular forces.* Carbon tetrachloride, CCl_4, is a symmetrical, nonpolar molecule; chloroform, $CHCl_3$, is unsymmetrical and polar. Still, the normal boiling point of CCl_4 is higher. Explain.

7.11 *Liquid-gas comparison.* Given a room that is $4.0 \times 4.0 \times 3.0$ meters in volume. How many liters of liquid water are used up in producing the equilibrium vapor pressure of H_2O throughout this room at $25°C.$ (in other words, to produce 100% relative humidity)?

8　*Solids*

WHEN A GAS IS COOLED, the molecules coalesce into the random arrangement characteristic of liquids. On further cooling, the liquid freezes to a solid. What are the properties characteristic of the solid state and how does the kinetic theory account for them?

8.1　PROPERTIES OF SOLIDS

Solids are practically incompressible. This is not surprising, since the molecules are in contact with each other, even in the liquid. Like liquids, solids are quite difficult to compress, because here too the molecules are in contact.

　Solids maintain their volume, which is independent of the size or shape of their container. In a solid there are strong attractive forces which keep the molecules together, just as in a liquid.

　Solids have definite shape. Solids are rigid and do not flow under ordinary circumstances. In this respect, solids are unlike liquids and gases, which are fluid. The shape of a liquid sample can change because the

168

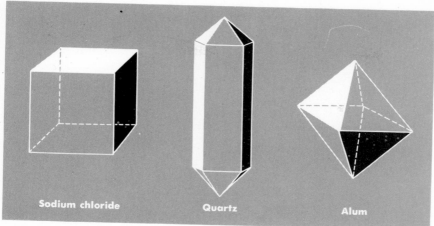

Sodium chloride   **Quartz**   **Alum**

Fig. 8.1   Crystals.

molecules are free to slide over each other to take up different positions. The fact that a solid is rigid suggests that the molecules have fixed positions, from which they cannot move appreciably.

Solids diffuse extremely slowly compared to liquids or gases. Direct evidence for this comes from the fact that rock layers have been in contact with each other for millions of years and still retain sharp boundaries. Such lack of diffusion can be accounted for by saying that in the solid state the molecules have permanent positions, from which they do not move far.

Solids form crystals, definite geometric forms which are distinctive for the substance in question. The crystals of a given substance are bounded by plane surfaces, which are called *faces.* The faces always intersect at an angle characteristic of the substance. For example, sodium chloride crystallizes in the form of cubes with faces which intersect at an angle of 90°. When a crystal is broken, it splits, or shows *cleavage,* along certain preferred directions, so that the characteristic faces and angles result even when the material is ground to a fine powder. In Fig. 8.1 are shown the usual crystal shapes of some common chemicals. It should be pointed out that the same chemical substance can under different conditions form different kinds of crystals. For instance, although NaCl almost always crystallizes as cubes, it can also be made to crystallize as octahedral crystals like that shown for alum. The occurrence of different crystal forms of the same chemical is called *polymorphism.* The existence of crystals can be accounted for by assuming that the molecules or atoms which make up a crystal are arranged in orderly patterns characteristic of the substance. Unlike the liquid, where the constituent molecules or atoms are arranged at random with respect to each

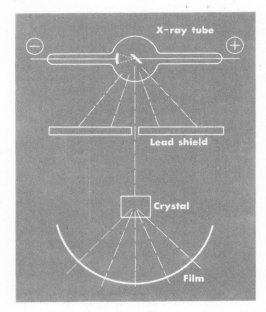

Fig. 8.2 X-ray determination of structure.

other, in the crystal there is an orderly arrangement of the fundamental particles which repeats itself throughout the whole structure.*

8.2   DETERMINATION OF STRUCTURE

Information about the arrangement of fundamental particles in solids can be gained from the external symmetry of crystals. However, much more information is obtained from X-ray diffraction. X rays are a form of radiant energy much like light, but more energetic and of greater penetrating power. They can be produced by bombarding a metal with energetic electrons. The energy of the electrons is transferred to the atoms of the metal and excites electrons of the atoms of the metal to a higher energy level (Sec. 3.8). When the electrons fall from a high energy level to a low energy level, they emit energy in the form of X rays. The target metal is usually copper or molybdenum. Figure 8.2 shows a simple X-ray tube. It is essentially a gas discharge tube, with the cathode connected to the negative side of a high voltage and the anode to the positive side. The cathode is concave, so that the electrons which come from it are focused to a point on the metal target. The resultant X rays radiate from the target in all directions, and precautions are required to shield living tissue from overexposure.

*Not all solids are crystalline in form. There are some substances, such as glass, which have the solid-state properties of extremely slow diffusion and virtually complete maintenance of shape and volume but do not have the ordered crystalline state. These substances are sometimes called amorphous solids.

For the study of crystalline materials, X rays are collimated into a beam by a lead shield with a hole in it. If sufficiently thick, the shield stops all X rays except the beam which comes through the hole. A well-formed crystal is mounted in the path of the X-ray beam, as shown in Fig. 8.2. As the X rays penetrate the crystal, the atoms which make up the crystal scatter or deflect some of the X rays from their original path. The X rays are detected by a piece of photographic film at some distance from the crystal. The X-ray beam exposes the film, and when the film is developed, a spot appears at points where the beam struck it. The developed film shows not just one spot, but a pattern, which is uniquely characteristic of the crystal investigated.

In Fig. 8.3 is shown the pattern for a crystal of sodium chloride. The big spot in the center corresponds to the main unscattered beam. The other spots represent a scattering of part of the original beam through various characteristic angles. The creation of many beams from one is like the effect observed when a light beam falls on a diffraction grating—a piece of glass on which are scratched thousands of parallel lines that are opaque and leave, in effect, many narrow slits of unscratched surface for light to pass through. The spreading of the light wave from each slit results in interference between waves from different slits, giving rise to alternate regions of light and dark. The diffraction of X rays by crystals is similar to diffraction by a grating and suggests that crystalline materials consist of regular arrangements of atoms in space in which the lines of atoms form tiny slits for the X rays.

The diffraction of X rays by a crystal is a complex phenomenon involving the interaction between incoming X rays and the electrons that make up atoms. We can consider the X rays to consist of electrical pulsations and their interactions with atoms as producing a corresponding pulsation of the

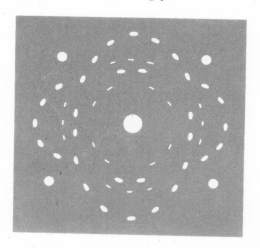

Fig. 8.3   *X-ray pattern of* NaCl.

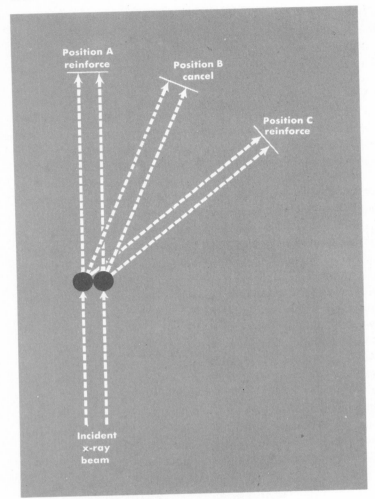

Fig. 8.4   Two-atom model for X-ray scattering.

electrons in each atom. Thus, each atom in the path of an X-ray beam receives pulsations and regenerates them in all directions. Consider (as shown in Fig. 8.4) two atoms, side by side in an X-ray beam, set into electrical pulsation at the same frequency. Viewed from head on (position *A*), the signals from the two are received "in step" so that the signal from one reinforces that from the other. This need not be true when viewed at some angle to the incident beam. In general, the signals will be out of step with each other (position *B*), because one signal has to travel farther than the other. If, however, the path difference is just exactly equivalent to a whole pulsation (position *C*), there will again be reinforcement of the signals. For a real crystal consisting of many atoms regularly arranged, there will be certain angles (relative to the incident X-ray beam) at which there will be reinforcement in the emergent beam so as to produce spots on a photographic film.

8.3   SPACE LATTICE

A careful mathematical analysis of a spot pattern resulting from X-ray diffraction enables X-ray crystallographers to calculate the positions particles might occupy in order to produce such a pattern. The process of calculation is an indirect one which involves guessing probable structures, calculating the X-ray patterns they would produce, and comparing these with experiment. The pattern of points which describes the arrangement of molecules or atoms in a crystal is known as a *space lattice*. In Fig. 8.5 is shown the space lattice of sodium chloride, NaCl.* Each of the points corresponds to the position of the center of an ion. X's locate positive sodium ions, and circles, negative chloride ions. The points do not represent sodium ions and chloride ions but only the positions occupied by the centers. In fact, in sodium chloride the ions are of different size and are practically touching each other, as shown in Fig. 8.6.

The space lattice has to be thought of as extending in all directions throughout the entire crystal. In discussing the space lattice, it is sufficient to consider only enough of it to represent the order of arrangement. This small fraction of a space lattice, which sets the pattern for the whole lattice, is called the *unit cell*. It is defined as the smallest portion of the space lattice which, moved a distance equal to its own dimensions in various directions, generates the whole space lattice. A unit cell of sodium chloride is the cube shown in Fig. 8.7. If this cube is moved through its edge length in the x direction, the y direction, and the z direction, many times, eventually the whole space lattice is reproduced.

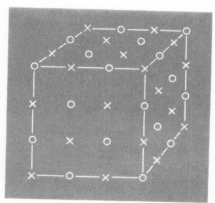

* In the strictest sense, a space lattice is concerned only with points and, hence, all points in a space lattice must be identical. In this sense, NaCl can be represented by two identical interpenetrating space lattices, one for the positions of the sodium ions and one for those of the chloride ions.

Fig. 8.5   Space lattice of NaCl. (Circles represent centers of chloride ions; X's, the centers of sodium ions.)

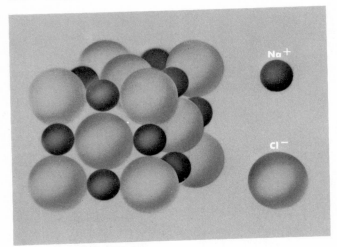

Fig. 8.6   Model of NaCl.

There are several different kinds of symmetry which occur in crystal-line substances. The simplest is known as *simple cubic*. The unit cell is shown in Fig. 8.8a. Each point at the corner of the cube represents a position occupied by an atom or a molecule. The dotted lines represent the three characteristic directions of space, or *axes*, along which the structure must be extended to reproduce the entire space lattice. Closely related to the simple-cubic symmetry is *body-centered cubic*, the unit cell for which is shown in Fig. 8.8b. It is made up of points at the corners of a cube, with an additional point in the center. In *face-centered-cubic* symmetry there are points at the corners of the cube with additional points in the middle of each face, as shown in Fig. 8.8c.

Other kinds of symmetry are considerably more complicated. To produce *tetragonal* symmetry, the cube is elongated in one direction. The lines of atoms still form right angles with each other, but the distance between points along one axis differs from that along the other two. Figure 8.9a shows

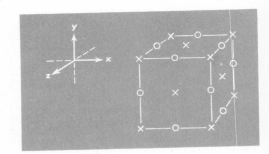

Fig. 8.7   Unit cell of NaCl.

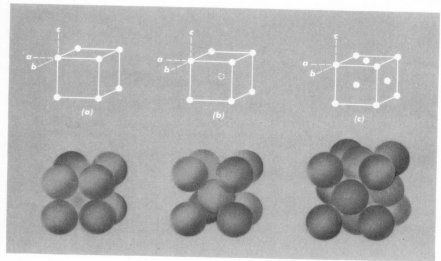

Fig. 8.8   Unit cells: (a) simple cubic; (b) body-centered cubic; (c) face-centered cubic.

a tetragonal unit cell. The separation of points along the a axis is the same as that along the b axis, but that along the c axis is different. In *rhombic*, or *orthorhombic*, symmetry, the unit cell retains mutually perpendicular edges, but the point separation is unequal in the a, b, and c directions. In *monoclinic* crystals the three axes a, b, and c are no longer perpendicular to each other. Monoclinic symmetry differs from rhombic symmetry in that the c axis does not make a right angle with the ab plane. An example is shown in Fig. 8.9b. In *triclinic* symmetry none of the three axes a, b, and c is perpendicular to any of the others. In the *hexagonal* type of symmetry, as shown in Fig. 8.9c, the atoms or molecules are arranged in the form of hexagons, with the hexagons stacked on top of each other.

Fig. 8.9   Unit cells: (a) tetragonal; (b) monoclinic; (c) hexagonal.

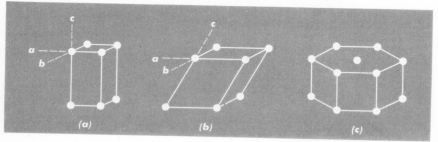

8.4 TYPES OF SOLIDS

Often, instead of classifying by the symmetry of their arrangements, it is more useful to classify solids by the units that occupy the lattice points. There are four types of crystals: *molecular, ionic, covalent,* and *metallic.* Table 8.1 lists for each type the units that occupy lattice points, the forces that bind these units together, characteristic properties, and some typical examples.

Molecular solids are those in which the lattice points are occupied by molecules. In a molecular solid the bonding within the molecule is covalent and, in general, is much stronger than the bonding between the molecules. The bonding between molecules can be of two types, dipole-dipole interaction or van der Waals attraction. Dipole-dipole attraction is encountered in solids consisting of polar molecules. As in the case of water, the negative end of one molecule attracts the positive end of a neighboring molecule. Van der Waals attractions (Sec. 6.14) are present in all molecular solids. Because the total intermolecular attraction is small, molecular crystals usually have low melting temperatures. Furthermore, molecular substances are usually quite soft, because the molecules can be easily pushed around from one place to

Table 8.1 Types of Solids

	Molecular	Ionic	Covalent	Metallic
Units that occupy lattice points	Molecules	Positive ions Negative ions	Atoms	Positive ions in electron gas
Binding force	Van der Waals Dipole-dipole	Electrostatic attraction	Shared electrons	Electrical attraction between $+$ ions and $-$ electrons
Properties	Very soft Low melting point Volatile Good insulators	Quite hard and brittle Fairly high melting point Good insulators	Very hard Very high melting point Nonconductors	Hard or soft Moderate to very high melting point Good conductors
Examples	H_2 H_2O CO_2	NaCl KNO_3 Na_2SO_4	Diamond, C Carborundum, SiC Quartz, SiO_2	Na Cu Fe

Fig. 8.10   Diamond structure.

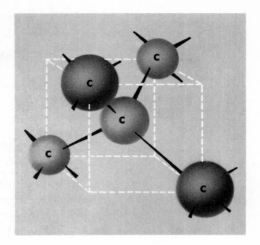

another. Finally, they are non-conductors of electricity, because there is no easy way for an electron associated with one molecule to jump over to another molecule. Most substances which exist as gases at room temperature form molecular solids at low temperature.

In an *ionic solid*, the units that occupy the lattice points are positive and negative ions. For example, in Na_2SO_4 some of the lattice points are occupied by sodium ions, Na^+, and the others by sulfate ions, SO_4^{--}. The forces of attraction are those between a positive and a negative charge and are high. Hence ionic solids usually have fairly high melting points, well above room temperature. Sodium sulfate, for example, melts at $884°C$. Also, ionic solids tend to be brittle and fairly hard, with great tendency to fracture by cleavage. In the solid state, the ions are not free to move; therefore these ionic substances are poor conductors of electricity. However, when melted, they become good conductors.

In a *covalent solid*, the positions are occupied by atoms, which share electrons with their neighbors. The covalent bonds extend in fixed directions, so that the result is a giant interlocking structure. The classic example of a covalent solid is diamond, in which each carbon atom is joined by pairs of shared electrons to four other carbon atoms, as shown in Fig. 8.10. Each of these carbon atoms in turn is bound to four carbon atoms, etc., giving a giant three-dimensional molecule. In any solid of this type the bonds between the individual atoms are covalent and, usually, are quite strong. Substances with covalent structures have high melting points, are quite hard, and, in general, are poor conductors of electricity.

In a *metallic solid*, the points of the space lattice are occupied by positive ions. This array of positive ions is immersed in a cloud of valence electrons. In solid sodium, sodium ions are arranged in a body-centered cubic pattern. The cloud of electrons, or *electron gas*, as it is often called, arises from the contribution by each neutral sodium atom of its lone outermost electron. The electron cloud belongs to the whole crystal. A metal like sodium is held together by the attraction between the positive ions and the cloud of negative electrons. Because electrons can wander at will throughout the metal, a metallic solid is characterized by high electrical conductivity. It is difficult to specify the other properties of metallic solids, because they vary widely. Sodium, for example, has a low melting point; tungsten has a very high melting point. Sodium is soft and can be cut with a knife; tungsten is very hard.

What does the term "molecule" mean in these various solids? In a molecular crystal, e.g., solid CO_2, it is possible to distinguish discrete molecules. Each C atom has two relatively close O atoms as neighbors, and all other atoms are at considerably greater distances. In an ionic substance like sodium chloride this is not true. Each sodium ion is equally bound to its neighboring six chloride ions, as shown in Fig. 8.6. These six chloride ions must be considered as belonging to the same aggregate as the original sodium ion. But each chloride ion in turn is bonded to six sodium ions, which must also be counted as part of the aggregate. Actually, all the ions in the whole crystal belong to the same aggregate, or giant molecule. A similar situation occurs in metallic and covalent crystals, in which all the ions or atoms are bound together as one giant aggregate. The term "molecule" is not useful for ionic, metallic, or covalent solids.

8.5   LATTICE DEFECTS

The preceding discussion concerned only ideal crystals. An ideal crystal is one which can be completely described by the unit cell; i.e., it contains no *lattice defects*. There are several important kinds of lattice defects. One arises if some of the lattice points are unoccupied. Another arises if atoms occupy positions between lattice points. Most crystals are imperfect to a slight extent and contain lattice defects. For example, in NaCl some of the sodium ions and chloride ions are missing from the regular pattern (Fig. 8.11*a*). In silver bromide, AgBr, some of the silver ions are missing from their regular positions and are found squeezed in between other ions (Fig. 8.11*b*).

A more complex kind of lattice defect occurs when there are impurities present in the crystal. A specific instance of this is found in the rather rare, colored crystals of NaCl, which on careful analysis show a very slight excess of Na over Cl. These colored crystals can be considered to contain Na as an impurity in NaCl. It is believed that the Na forms Na^+ ions, which

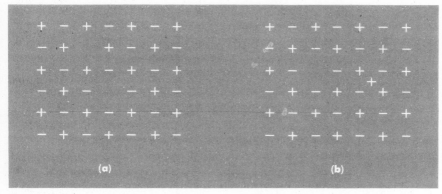

Fig. 8.11 *Lattice defects: (a) vacancies in* **NaCl;** *(b) misplaced* **Ag⁺** *in* **AgBr.**

occupy usual Na$^+$ lattice points, and electrons, which occupy lattice vacancies due to missing Cl$^-$ ions. Another example of impurity defects is observed for germanium crystals which contain traces of other elements. As described in Sec. 24.6, these crystals have special electric properties.

In general, the presence of lattice defects has an important effect on some properties of solids. For example, the strength and hardness of metals depend markedly on defects in their crystal structure. The study of lattice defects is a field of intensive research.

QUESTIONS

8.1 *Model of solid.* In terms of kinetic theory, account for the following facts: (*a*) solids are essentially incompressible, whereas gases can easily be compressed; (*b*) solids maintain their shape, but liquids flow; (*c*) diffusion in solids is many times slower than in liquids or gases; (*d*) solids cleave at characteristic angles.

8.2 *X-ray pattern.* Explain in terms of kinetic theory why crystals give a spot X-ray pattern but liquids do not.

8.3 *Metallic conduction.* Account for the fact that metallic solids conduct but ionic solids do not.

8.4 *Types of solids.* Given an alkali element, *A*, and a halogen, *B*. Compare solid *A*, solid *B*, and solid *AB* with respect to type of solid formed. Predict as many properties as you can for each solid.

8.5 *Model of solid.* Why does the purist prefer not to speak of the molecular weight of solid sodium chloride but uses the term formula weight instead?

8.6 *Unit cell.* Draw a face-centered-cubic unit cell. Show that connecting adjacent face-centered positions gives an octahedron. This relation between a cube and an octahedron accounts for the fact that many substances having face-centered-cubic symmetry crystallize as octahedrally shaped crystals.

8.7 *Gram-atomic volume.* Account for the fact that two elements may have identical gram-atomic volumes but different atomic radii.

8.8 *Unit cell.* Explain why Fig. 8.8*a* is not a unit cell for NaCl but Fig. 8.7 is.

8.9 *Unit cell.* What is the simplest formula of a solid containing A atoms and B atoms in a face-centered-cubic arrangement in which the A atoms occupy the corners of the unit cell and the B atoms occupy the faces? *Hint:* Each A atom belongs partly to eight unit cells at the same time. *Ans.* AB_3

8.10 *Unit cell.* Assuming equal rigid spheres in contact with each other, what fraction of the volume of a solid is empty space if the spheres are arranged with the following symmetry: (*a*) simple cubic; (*b*) body-centered cubic; (*c*) face-centered cubic? *Hint:* Calculate cube edge in terms of the radius of the spheres.
Ans. 48%; 32%; 26%

8.11 *Avogadro number.* Given:

Density of solid NaCl	2.165 g./cc.
Distance between centers of adjacent Na^+ and Cl^- ions (from X-ray studies)	2.819×10^{-8} cm.
Weight of 1 mole of NaCl	58.448 g.

Using only these data, calculate the Avogadro number. *Hint:* First calculate the volume of a cube that contains 1 mole. Calculate the edge length of this cube. Then from the spacing of ions, calculate the number of ions along one edge of the cube. *Ans.* 6.026×10^{23}

8.12 *Lattice defects.* Titanium monoxide, TiO, has the NaCl structure. However, some of the Ti^{++} sites and an equal number of O^{--} sites are vacant. From the observed density, 4.93 g. per cc., and the X-ray-determined unit-cell-edge length, 4.235 A., calculate the fraction of vacant sites. *Ans.* 11.8%

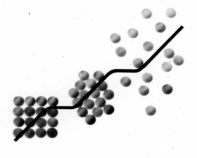

9   *Changes of State*

WHEN A SOLID IS HEATED, it melts to form a liquid, and on further heating, the liquid evaporates to form a gas. In the solid state, the particles are ordered; in the liquid, they are less ordered; in a gas, they are completely disordered. The changes of state, melting and evaporation, are therefore disordering processes. A picture of these changes of state is given in Fig. 9.1.

9.1   HEATING CURVES

The temperature variations which accompany changes of states are represented in Fig. 9.2. The curve shown is a *heating curve* corresponding to the uniform addition of heat to an initially solid substance. Since heat is added at a constant rate, distance on the time axis is also a measure of the amount of added heat.

At time t_0 the temperature is absolute zero. As heat is added, each particle vibrates back and forth about a lattice point, which thus represents the center of this motion. As more heat is added, the vibration becomes greater. Though no change is visible, because the amplitude of the vibration is so small, the crystal progressively becomes slightly less ordered. The heat added increases the kinetic motion of the particles. Since temperature measures average kinetic energy, temperature rises along portion 1 of Fig. 9.2. This continues until the melting point of the substance is reached.

At the melting point (abbreviated m.p.) the vibration of particles is so

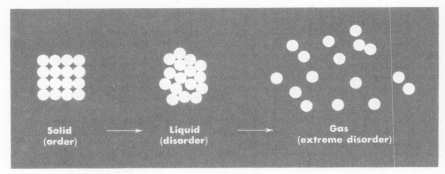

Fig. 9.1   Changes of state.

vigorous that any added heat serves to loosen binding forces between neighboring particles. Consequently, from time t_1 to t_2, added heat goes not to increase the average kinetic energy but to increase the potential energy of the particles. Potential energy is increased because work is done against attractive forces. During this period, there is no change in average kinetic energy, and so the substance stays at the same temperature. From t_1 to t_2 the amount of solid gradually decreases, and the amount of liquid increases. The *temperature at which the solid and liquid coexist* is defined as the *melting point* of the substance.

The amount of heat necessary to melt 1 mole of solid is called the *molar heat of fusion*. It gives a measure of the attractive forces which must be overcome in the melting process. The heat of fusion of NaCl is 7.25 kcal. per mole, and that of H_2O is 1.44 kcal. per mole, values that reflect the greater attractive forces in NaCl.

Eventually (at time t_2), sufficient heat is added to tear all the particles from the crystal structure. Along portion 3 of the curve, added heat increases the average kinetic energy of the particles, and the temperature of the liquid rises. This continues until the boiling point (b.p.) is reached. At the boiling

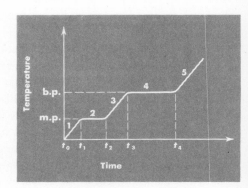

Fig. 9.2   Heating curve.

point, added heat is used to overcome the attraction of one particle for its neighbors in the liquid. Along portion 4 of the curve, there is an increase in the potential energy of the particles but no change in their average kinetic energy. From time t_3 to t_4, liquid converts to gas. Finally, after all the liquid has been converted to gas, added heat raises the kinetic energy of the particles, as shown by the rising temperature along portion 5.

The amount of heat necessary to vaporize 1 mole of liquid is called the *molar heat of vaporization*. This quantity gives a measure of the attractive forces characteristic of the liquid. The heat of vaporization of water is 9.72 kcal. per mole, and that of chloroform is 7.04 kcal. per mole. These values support the notion that attractive forces between water molecules are greater than those between chloroform molecules.

9.2   COOLING CURVES

The *cooling curve* results when heat is removed at a uniform rate from a substance. For a pure substance that is initially a gas, the temperature as a function of time is shown in Fig. 9.3. As heat is removed from the gas, its temperature drops along the line marked g. During this time, the average kinetic energy of the gas particles must decrease in order to compensate for the removal of energy to the outside. This slowing down proceeds until the particles are so sluggish that the attractive forces become dominant.

At t_1 the particles start to coalesce to form a liquid. In the liquefaction process, particles leave the gas and enter the liquid state. Since it requires energy to take a particle from the liquid to the gas state, the reverse process, in which a particle is taken from the gas to the liquid, releases energy. This decrease of potential energy on condensation supplies heat, which compensates for that being removed from the system. Thus, as liquefaction

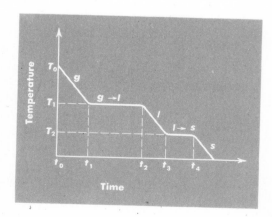

Fig. 9.3   *Cooling curve.*

proceeds, the temperature does not fall, and the particles do not slow down in their motion. As a result, the gas and the liquid are both at the same temperature, and the average kinetic energy of the particles in both phases is the same. From time t_1 to t_2 the temperature remains constant at T_1, the *condensation, or liquefaction, temperature.*

At time t_2 all the gas particles have condensed into the liquid state. Further removal of energy from the system causes the particles to slow down. As the average kinetic energy decreases, the temperature drops, as shown, along the line marked l. This drop continues until t_3, when the liquid begins to convert to solid.

In crystallization, the particles line up in a definite symmetry pattern, and as they go from the liquid state to the solid state, their freedom of motion is diminished. As each particle moves into position to form the crystal structure, the potential energy of the particle drops. The removal of heat energy to the outside is compensated for by the energy available from this decrease in potential energy. The average kinetic energy of the particle stays constant during the crystallization process. At the crystallization temperature, the motion of the particles is not slower when they are in the solid than it is when they are in the liquid, but it is a more restricted motion. From time t_3 to t_4 the temperature remains constant as the liquid converts to solid. When all the particles have crystallized, further removal of heat drops the temperature, as shown, along the final part s of the curve.

The cooling curve is just the reverse of the warming curve. The temperature at which gas converts to liquid (liquefaction point) is the same as the temperature at which liquid converts to gas (boiling point). Similarly, the temperature at which liquid converts to solid (freezing point) is the same as the temperature at which solid converts to liquid (melting point).

9.3 SUPERCOOLING

Most cooling curves are not quite so simple as the one in Fig. 9.3. The complication usually occurs on the portion of the cooling curve corresponding to the transition from liquid to solid. Instead of following three fairly straight segments, as shown by the heavy lines in Fig. 9.4, the temperature follows the dotted line.

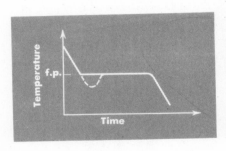

Fig. 9.4 Supercooling.

The liquid does not crystallize at the freezing point but *supercools* along the dotted line. Supercooling arises in the following way: The particles of a liquid have little recognizable pattern and move around in a disordered manner. At the freezing point, they should line up in characteristic crystalline arrangement, but only by chance do the particles start crystallizing correctly. Often they do not snap into the correct pattern immediately, and when heat continues to be removed from the system without crystallization's occurring, the temperature falls below the freezing point. Particles continue moving through various patterns until by accident they hit on the right one. Once this pattern has been built up to sufficient size, other particles rapidly crystallize on it. When a multitude of particles crystallize simultaneously, enough potential energy is converted to kinetic energy to heat up the whole system. The temperature actually increases until it coincides with the freezing-point temperature. From there on, the behavior is normal.

Supercooling may be reduced by two methods. The most frequent is to stir the liquid being cooled as vigorously as possible. This apparently increases the chance of forming the right crystal pattern. A second method involves the introduction of a seed crystal, on which further crystallization can occur, thereby perpetuating the proper structure.

Some substances never crystallize in cooling experiments, but remain permanently in the *undercooled,* or *supercooled,* state. Such substances are called *glasses,* after their most famous example. Glasses owe their existence to the fact that supercooled particles may be trapped in a disordered arrangement typical of liquids because the particles have relatively so little kinetic energy that they are not able to move into an ordered array. Supercooled liquids are quite common. They include, besides glass, many plastics, such as Lucite, bakelite, and celluloid. They have many of the properties of solids. For example, they are usually quite rigid and brittle. They certainly are not what we call fluid.* However, the X-ray pictures of glasses are quite different from the X-ray pictures of solids. As discussed previously, an X-ray picture of a solid gives an orderly pattern of spots corresponding to diffraction from different planes of atoms. In the supercooled liquid there are no planes of atoms from which to get diffraction. Instead of a spot pattern, the X-ray pictures of a supercooled liquid show concentric rings, like those for liquids. The existence of these rings indicates that there is a certain amount of order, but it is far from perfect. Another indication that glasses are not true solids is their behavior on being broken. Instead of showing cleavage with formation of flat faces and characteristic angles between faces,

---

* Strictly speaking, even glasses are somewhat fluid. This is supported by the observation that glass tubing that stands in a corner for many years gradually bends out of shape. However, such flow, which also occurs with crystalline solids, is extremely slow compared to that of usual liquids.

glasses break to give shell-like depressions such as are observed on the chips of a broken bottle.

9.4   VAPOR PRESSURE OF SOLIDS

As in a liquid, particles of a solid can escape into the vapor phase to establish vapor pressure. In a solid, all the particles do not have the same energy. There is a distribution of energy in which most of the particles have average energy, some have less energy than average, while others have more. Those particles which at any one time are of higher than average energy and are near the surface can overcome the attractive forces of their neighbors and escape into the vapor phase. If the solid is confined in a closed container, eventually there will be enough particles in the vapor phase that the rate of escape is equal to the rate of return. A dynamic equilibrium is set up, in which there is an equilibrium vapor pressure characteristic of the solid. Since the escaping tendency of particles depends on the magnitude of the intermolecular forces, the equilibrium vapor pressure differs from one substance to another. If the attractive forces in the solid are small, as in the case of a molecular crystal, the escaping tendency is great, and vapor pressure is high. In the ionic crystal, the binding forces are usually large, and the vapor pressure is low.

The vapor pressure of solids also depends on temperature. The higher the temperature, the more energetic the particles, and the more easily they can escape. The more that escape, the higher the vapor pressure. Quantitative measurements of the vapor pressure of solids can be made in the same way as for liquids. Figure 9.5 shows how the vapor pressure of a given substance changes with temperature. At absolute zero, the particles of a solid have no escaping tendency, so the vapor pressure is zero. As the temperature is raised, the vapor pressure rises. It rarely gets to be very high before the solid melts. Above the melting point the vapor pressure is equal to that of the liquid.

At any point along the portion of the curve marked "Solid," there is equilibrium between vapor and solid. The number of particles leav-

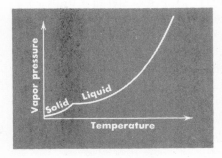

Fig. 9.5   Temperature variation of vapor pressure.

ing the solid is equal to the number returning. When the temperature is raised, there are more particles shaken loose from the crystal than returning. This causes a net increase in the concentration of particles in the vapor phase. There is also a resultant increased rate of condensation to the solid, which eventually becomes equal to the increased rate of evaporation. Equilibrium is reestablished at the new temperature.

The behavior of an equilibrium system when it is upset by the action of an external force is the subject of the famous *principle of Le Chatelier,* first published in 1884. Le Chatelier stated that, *if a stress is applied to a system at equilibrium, then the system readjusts, if possible, to reduce the stress.* Raising the temperature of a solid-vapor equilibrium system amounts to applying to the system a stress in the form of added heat. Since the conversion from solid to gas is endothermic (uses up heat)

$$\text{solid} + \text{heat} \rightleftharpoons \text{gas}$$

the stress of added heat can be absorbed by converting some of the solid to gas. On being cooled, the system adjusts itself to lower temperature by producing heat from the conversion of gas to solid.

At the point where the vapor-pressure curve of a liquid intersects that for the solid (i.e., where vapor pressure of solid equals vapor pressure of liquid), there is simultaneously an equilibrium between solid and gas, between liquid and gas, and between solid and liquid. This point of intersection at which *solid, liquid, and gas coexist in equilibrium* is called the *triple point.* Every substance has a characteristic triple point fixed by the nature of the attractive forces between its particles. For water, the triple-point temperature is 0.0098°C., and the triple-point pressure is 4.58 mm. Hg. It should be noted that the triple-point temperature of water is not quite the same as the normal melting point, which is exactly 0°C. This difference comes about because the normal melting point is defined as the melting point at 1 atm. pressure and because the melting point changes as pressure is changed. At the triple point, the only pressure exerted is the vapor pressure of the substance.

9.5   PHASE DIAGRAMS

The relation between the solid, liquid, and gaseous states of a given substance as a function of the temperature and pressure can be summarized on a single graph known as a *phase diagram.* Each substance has its own particular phase diagram, which has been worked out from experimental observation. Figure 9.6 gives the phase diagram of H_2O. On this diagram, vari-

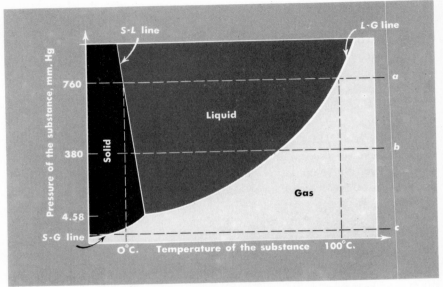

Fig. 9.6   *Phase diagram of* H_2O. *(Scale of axes somewhat distorted.)*

ous points represent the substance H_2O in the solid, liquid, or gaseous states, depending on its temperature and pressure. Each of the three regions corresponds to a one-phase system. For all values of pressure and temperature falling inside such a single-phase region, the substance is in the state specified. For example, at 380 mm. Hg pressure, H_2O at $-10°C$. is in the solid state, at $+10°C$. in the liquid state, and at $+100°C$. in the gas state. The lines which separate one region from another are equilibrium lines, representing an equilibrium between two phases. In the diagram the *S-L* line represents equilibrium between the solid and liquid; the *L-G* line, equilibrium between liquid and gas; and the *S-G* line, equilibrium between solid and gas. The intersection of the three lines corresponds to the triple point, where all three phases are in equilibrium with each other.

The usefulness of a phase diagram can be illustrated by considering the behavior of H_2O when heat is added at a constant pressure. This corresponds to moving across the phase diagram from left to right. We distinguish three typical cases:

1   Pressure of the H_2O *is kept at 760 mm.* Hg. The experiment is this: A chunk of ice is placed in a cylinder so as to fill the cylinder completely, with no empty space. A piston resting on the ice carries a weight which corresponds to 1 atm. of pressure. The H_2O starts as a solid. As heat is added, its temperature is raised. This corresponds to moving along the dashed line *a* in Fig. 9.6. When the *S-L* line is reached, the added heat melts the ice. Solid-liquid equilibrium persists at the normal melting point of 0°C. until all the solid is converted to liquid. There is no gaseous H_2O thus far, because the vapor pressure of solid ice is much lower than the pressure required to push the piston out to make room for the vapor. As heating continues, liquid H_2O warms up from 0°C. until the *L-G* line is reached, at a temperature which corresponds to 100°C. At this temperature, liquid-gas equilibrium is established. The system stays at 100°C. as the liquid converts to gas. At 100°C. the vapor pressure is great enough to move the piston and make room for the voluminous vapor phase. Since the external pressure is fixed at 1 atm., liquid converts completely to gas at the normal boiling temperature. From then on, the gas simply warms up.

2   Pressure of the H_2O *is kept at 380 mm.* Hg. Again the H_2O starts as the solid. The temperature is raised, moving to the right along dashed line *b*. The H_2O stays as a solid until it reaches the temperature that corresponds to melting. Because of the tilt of the *S-L* line toward the left (the tilt has been somewhat exaggerated in Fig. 9.6), the temperature at which melting occurs is slightly higher at 380 mm. than at 760 mm. Hg pressure. At 380 mm. Hg pressure, ice melts not at 0°C. but slightly above zero. The difference in melting-point temperature is only about 0.005°. After all the ice has been converted to liquid at $+0.005°C.$, further addition of heat warms the liquid up until boiling occurs at the *L-G* line. Boiling occurs when the vapor pressure of the water reaches 380 mm. Hg. The temperature at which this happens is 82°C., considerably lower than the normal boiling point of 100°C. Above 82°C. only gaseous water exists at 380 mm. pressure.

3   Pressure of the H_2O *is kept at 1 mm.* Hg. If the pressure exerted by the H_2O is kept at 1 mm. Hg, by a suitable device, the H_2O can exist only along the dashed line marked *c*. As the temperature is raised, solid H_2O warms up until it reaches the *S-G* line. Solid-gas equilibrium is established; solid converts to gas. When all solid has been converted, the temperature of the gas rises. There is no melting in this experiment, and no passage through the liquid state.

An interesting aspect of the H_2O phase diagram is that the *S-L* line, representing equilibrium between solid and liquid, tilts to the left with increasing pressure. This is unusual; for most substances the *S-L* line tilts to the right. The direction of the tilt is important, since it tells whether the melting point rises or falls with increased pressure. In the case of H_2O, as pressure is increased (*up* on the phase diagram), the temperature at which solid and liquid coexist decreases (*left* on the phase diagram). The melting-point decrease is approximately 0.01°C. per atm.

The lowering of the ice melting point by increased pressure is predicted by Le Chatelier's principle. The density of ice is 0.9 g. per cc.; the density of water is 1.0 g. per cc. One gram of H_2O in the solid state occupies a volume of 1.1 cc.; in the liquid state, 1 g. of H_2O occupies 1.0 cc. Thus, a given weight of H_2O occupies a larger volume as solid than as liquid. An equilibrium system consisting of water and ice at 1 atm. is at the normal melting point of $0°C$. If the pressure on the H_2O is increased, a stress exists which the system can relieve by shrinking in volume. It can shrink in volume by converting from ice to water; hence melting is favored. But melting is an endothermic process and requires heat. If the system is insulated, the only source of heat is the kinetic energy of the molecules. The molecules slow down, and the temperature drops. The result is that solid ice and liquid water under increased pressure coexist at a lower temperature.

Another phase diagram of interest is that of carbon dioxide, CO_2. In general appearance, as shown in Fig. 9.7, it is similar to that of H_2O. However, the solid-liquid equilibrium line tilts to the right instead of to the left, since the melting point of CO_2 rises with increased pressure. The triple-point pressure of CO_2 is 5.2 atm.; the triple-point temperature is $-57°C$. Since the triple-point pressure is considerably above normal atmospheric pressure, liquid carbon dioxide is not observed under usual conditions. In order to get liquid carbon dioxide, the pressure must be higher than 5.2 atm. At 1 atm., only solid and gas can exist. When solid carbon dioxide in the form of dry ice is used as a refrigerant at 1 atm. pressure, the conversion of solid to gas occurs at $-78°C$. There is no increase in temperature of the carbon dioxide until all the solid disappears.

Fig. 9.7   Phase diagram of CO_2.

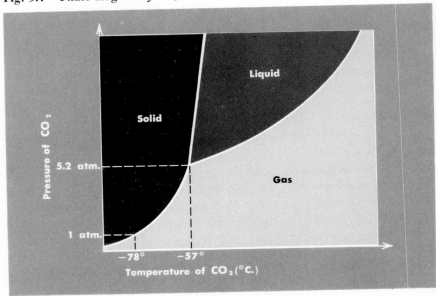

9.6   ENTROPY AND SPONTANEOUS CHANGE

It would seem to be obvious that processes occur spontaneously to produce a state of lower energy. However, we see that a chunk of ice at room temperature spontaneously melts, forming a state of higher energy. Apparently, more than energy is involved in determining the direction of spontaneous changes.

The additional factor which must be considered is the tendency of a system to assume the most random molecular arrangement possible. In other words, systems are likely to become disordered. The reason for this tendency is that random molecular motion more probably produces a disordered than an ordered state. The disorder is described quantitatively in terms of a property called the *entropy* and we say that a more disordered state has a higher entropy than an ordered state. As a specific example, H_2O in the form of liquid water has a higher entropy than does H_2O in the form of solid ice.

In the same sense that natural processes are favored which result in a decrease of energy, those are also favored which result in an increase of entropy. In certain cases, as in melting ice, the two factors may oppose each other so that there is a question of which one wins out. Above the melting point the entropy increase is dominant, so spontaneous melting occurs; below the melting point the energy decrease is dominant, so spontaneous freezing occurs. It turns out that the temperature itself is the critical factor and governs how important the entropy increase is relative to the energy change. At the absolute zero of temperature, the entropy term contributes nothing in determining the direction of spontaneous change, so that the most stable state is that of lowest energy. As the temperature rises, molecular motion increases and the tendency to disorder becomes more important in determining the direction of change. At sufficiently high temperatures, the entropy factor becomes large enough to overcome even an unfavorable energy change.

QUESTIONS

9.1   *Heating curve.* (*a*) Draw a graph showing what happens to the temperature of a pure molecular substance as heat is added at a constant rate. Start with the solid and include the liquid and gas. Label each portion of the curve to show what phases are present. (*b*) Indicate briefly what happens to the average kinetic energy and potential energy along each branch of the curve. (*c*) How does the molecular picture change during the experiment?

9.2   *Heating curve.* Draw the uniform warming curve for H_2O at 1.00 atm., indicate temperatures of the breaks, and account for the general shape in terms of kinetic theory.

9.3   *States of matter.* A given closed container holds ice, water, and water vapor at the triple point. Compare qualitatively these three phases with respect to: (*a*) density of the phase; (*b*) average kinetic energy of the molecules; (*c*) average potential energy of the molecules; (*d*) compressibility of the phase; (*e*) ordering of the molecules; (*f*) pressure of the H_2O.

9.4   *Graphical representations.* Show on suitably labeled graphs each of the following: (*a*) the energy distribution of molecules in a liquid; (*b*) the equilibrium vapor pressure of a liquid as a function of temperature; (*c*) the cooling of a gas through the liquid and solid transitions by uniform removal of heat; (*d*) the supercooling of a liquid followed by a "seeding" operation.

9.5   *Phase diagram.* (*a*) Draw the phase diagram for the substance H_2O. Label the various features of the diagram. (*b*) Indicate by a dotted line what happens when H_2O is heated from -30 to $+150°C$. at 1.00 atm. pressure. Describe in words what will be observed, and compare qualitatively with what happens at 1.01 atm. and 0.99 atm.

9.6   *Le Chatelier principle.* Ice is added to warm water in a well-insulated container at atmospheric pressure. The amount of ice in the mixture decreases for a time and then remains constant. (*a*) What is the temperature of the final mixture? (*b*) If the pressure on the ice-water mixture is greatly increased, what will happen to the temperature? (*c*) What will happen to the amount of ice? (*d*) Explain your answers to (*b*) and (*c*) in terms of the principle of Le Chatelier.

9.7   *Heat of fusion.* (*a*) How much heat is required to melt an ice cube weighing 15.0 g.? (*b*) What will be the final temperature produced by the addition of three such ice cubes to 300 ml. of 20°C. water in an insulated container?

9.8   *Heat of fusion.* In comparing attractive forces in solids, why is the molar heat of fusion used instead of the heat of fusion per gram?

9.9   *Equilibrium.* Given a well-stirred mixture of ice and water. If a small amount of either warm water or dry ice is added, the temperature does not change. Explain.

9.10   *Water.* A barrel of water placed in a cellar keeps fruit from freezing in the winter and from spoiling in the summer. Explain.

9.11   *Melting point.* Ice is placed in a sealed container from which all the air has been evacuated. What is the melting point of the ice? Compare this with what would be observed if the container were open to the air.

9.12   *Ice.* A 50-g. ice cube is enclosed in a fine-mesh wire cage and placed at the bottom of a well-insulated container of water at 0°C. After some time has passed, the wire cage contains only liquid water, and 50 g. of ice is floating on the surface. Explain.

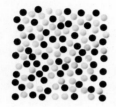

10 Solutions

THE PRECEDING DISCUSSION of the solid, liquid, and gaseous states was limited to pure substances. In practice, we continually deal with mixtures; hence the question arises as to the effect of mixing in a second component. As mentioned previously, a mixture is classified as heterogeneous or homogeneous. By its nature, a heterogeneous mixture consists of distinct phases and the observed properties are just the sum of those of the individual phases. However, a homogeneous mixture consists of a single phase which has properties that may differ drastically from those of the individual components. These homogeneous mixtures, or solutions, are of widespread importance in chemistry and deserve intensive study.

10.1 TYPES OF SOLUTIONS

Solutions, defined as *homogeneous mixtures of two or more components*, can be gaseous, liquid, or solid. Gaseous solutions are made by dis-

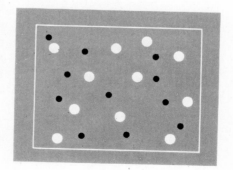

Fig. 10.1   Model of a gaseous solution.

solving one gas in another. Since all gases mix in all proportions, any mixture of gases is homogeneous and is a solution. The kinetic picture of a gaseous solution is like that of a pure gas, except that the molecules are of different kinds. Figure 10.1 represents a gaseous solution of hydrogen and oxygen, where the dark circles represent hydrogen molecules and the white circles represent oxygen molecules. Ideally, the molecules move independently of each other.

Liquid solutions are made by dissolving a gas, liquid, or solid in a liquid. If the liquid is water, the solution is called an *aqueous* solution. The kinetic picture of a sugar-water solution is represented in Fig. 10.2. The white circles represent water molecules, and the dark circles sugar molecules. The sugar molecules are distributed at random throughout the bulk of the solution. It is evident that on this molecular scale the term homogeneous has little significance. However, experiments cannot be performed with less than billions of molecules, so that for practical purposes the solution is homogeneous.

Solid solutions are solids in which one component is randomly dispersed on an atomic or molecular scale throughout another component. An example of a solid solution is shown in Fig. 10.3, where the dark circles represent atoms of one component, and the white circles atoms of the other. As in any crystal, the packing of atoms is orderly, even though there is no particular order as to which lattice points are occupied by which kind of atom. Solid solutions are of great practical importance, since they make up a large fraction of the class of substances known as alloys.

An *alloy* may be defined as a combination of two or more elements which has metallic properties. Sterling silver, for example, is an alloy consisting of a solid solution of copper in silver. In brass, an alloy of copper and zinc, it is possible to have a solid solution in which some copper atoms of the face-centered-cubic structure of pure copper have been replaced by zinc atoms. Some kinds of steel are alloys of iron and carbon and can be considered as solid solutions in which carbon atoms are located in some of the spaces between iron atoms. The iron atoms are arranged in the regular structure of pure iron. It should be pointed out, however, that not all alloys are solid solutions. Some alloys, such as bismuth-cadmium, are heter-

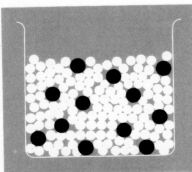

Fig. 10.2   Model of a liquid solution.

ogeneous mixtures containing tiny crystals of the constituent elements. Others, such as $MgCu_2$, are intermetallic compounds which contain atoms of different metals combined in definite proportions.

Two words that are convenient in the discussion of solutions are the terms *solute* and *solvent*. Accepted procedure is to refer to the substance present in larger amount as the solvent and to the substance present in smaller amount as the solute. However, the terms can be interchanged whenever it is convenient. For example, in solutions of sulfuric acid and water, sulfuric acid is sometimes referred to as the solute and water referred to as the solvent, even when the water molecules are in the minority.

10.2   CONCENTRATION

The properties of solutions, e.g., the color of a dye solution or the sweetness of a sugar solution, depend on their concentration. There are several common methods for describing concentration.

The *mole fraction* is the ratio of the number of moles of one component to the total number of moles in the solution. For example, in a solution containing 1 mole of alcohol and 3 moles of water, the mole fraction of alcohol is ¼ and that of water ¾.

The *molarity* of a solute is the number of moles of solute per liter of solution and is usually designated by a capital *M*. A 6.0-molar solution of HCl is labeled 6.0 *M*. The label means that the solution has been made up in a ratio that corresponds to adding 6.0 moles of HCl to enough water to make a liter of solution.

The *molality* of a solute is the number of moles of solute per 1,000 g. of solvent. It is usually designated by a small *m*. The label 6.0 *m* HCl is read "6.0 molal" and represents a solution made by adding to every 6.0 moles of HCl, 1,000 g. of water.

The *normality* of a solute is the number of gram-equivalents (Secs. 5.8 and 10.11) of solute per liter of solution. It is usually designated by a capital *N*. The label 0.25 *N* $KMnO_4$ is read "0.25 normal" and represents a solution which contains 0.25 gram-equivalent of potas-

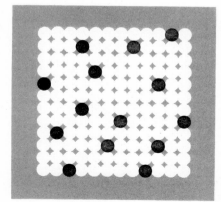

Fig. 10.3   Model of a solid solution.

sium permanganate per liter of solution. (As indicated previously, the size of a gram-equivalent may vary from one reaction to another.)

The *per cent of solute* is an ambiguous designation which may refer to per cent by weight or per cent by volume. If the former is meant, and this is usually the case, it is the per cent of the total solution weight contributed by the solute. Thus, 3 per cent H_2O_2 by weight would be 3 g. of H_2O_2 per 100 g. of solution. Per cent by volume is the per cent of the final solution volume represented by the volume of solute taken to make the solution. For example, 12 per cent alcohol by volume would represent a solution made from 12 ml. of alcohol and enough solvent to bring up the total volume to 100 ml.

Occasionally one finds use of still another concentration designation, the *formality*. This designation (abbreviated F) refers to the number of gram-formulas of solute per liter of solution and is used especially when one wishes to make a distinction between what is formally placed in a solution and what actually is there.

10.3 PROPERTIES OF SOLUTIONS

How are the properties of a solvent affected by the addition of a solute? Specifically, how are the properties of water affected by the addition of sugar? Suppose we consider the following experiment: Two beakers, one containing pure water (beaker I) and the other containing a sugar-water solution (beaker II), are set under a bell jar, as shown in Fig. 10.4. As time goes on, we observe that the level of pure water in beaker I drops, while the level of the solution in beaker II rises. There is transfer of water from pure solvent to solution, presumably through the vapor phase. This transfer occurs because the escaping tendency, or vapor pressure, of pure water is higher than the escaping tendency of H_2O from the sugar-water solution.

Another experimental observation which supports the idea that addition of a solute lowers the escaping tendency of solvent molecules is

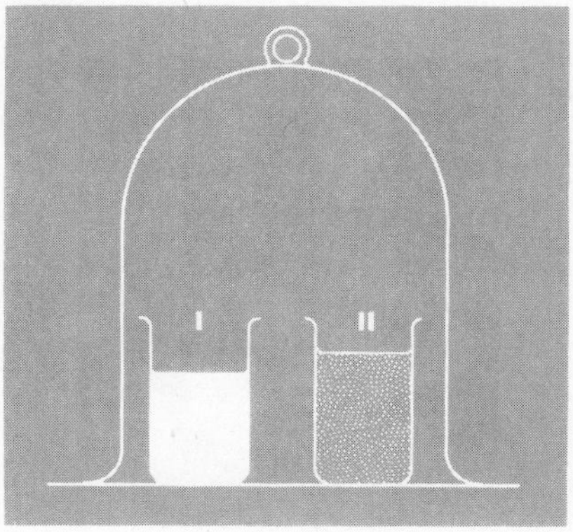

Fig. 10.4 Experimental comparison of the escaping tendency of water from pure water (I) and an aqueous solution (II).

the lowering of the freezing point. For example, when sugar is added to water, it is found necessary to cool below 0°C. in order to freeze out ice. The implication is that the tendency of H_2O to escape from the liquid phase is decreased by the presence of solute.

The lowering of the freezing point and the reduction of the vapor pressure are found, at least in dilute solutions, to be directly proportional to the concentration of added solute particles. Apparently, the most important effect of the solute is to reduce the concentration of H_2O molecules.* In the solution, only a certain fraction of the molecules are H_2O molecules, and therefore the escape of H_2O molecules from the solution is less probable than their escape from pure water.

Figure 10.5 shows on a phase diagram the effect on the solvent, water, of one particular concentration of solute. The solid lines represent the phase diagram of pure H_2O; the dashed lines, that of the solution. The dashed line on the left corresponds to equilibrium between solid H_2O and the liquid solution. It represents the temperatures at which pure solid H_2O freezes out when the particular solution is cooled at different pressures. The dashed line on the right corresponds to equilibrium between gaseous H_2O and the liquid solution. It represents the temperatures at which pure gaseous H_2O boils off when the solution is heated at various pressures.

The most striking feature shown on the phase diagram is the extension, at all pressures, of the liquid range, both to higher temperatures and to lower temperatures. The liquid phase of water has been made more probable by the addition of solute. Associated with this is the fact that the vapor pressure of the water has been reduced. For example, as seen from Fig. 10.5 at 100°C. the vapor pressure of the water is not 1 atm., but less than that. Because the vapor pressure of water is lowered, the solution does not boil at 100°C., but at some other temperature at which vapor pressure becomes equal to 1 atm. If the solute contributes nothing to the vapor pressure (is nonvolatile, as, for example, sugar is), then the normal boiling point of the solution can be read directly from the phase diagram. Similarly, there is a depression of the normal freezing point.

Both the boiling-point elevation and the freezing-point depression de-

---

* On the basis of his observations, the French scientist Francois-Marie Raoult in 1887 stated that the fractional vapor-pressure lowering of a solvent is equal to the mole fraction of solute present. Since the mole fraction of solute is equal to 1 minus the mole fraction of solvent, it follows that the vapor pressure of the solvent is directly proportional to the mole fraction of solvent. Mathematically, Raoult's law can be stated as follows:

$$\frac{p_0 - p}{p_0} = x_2 = 1 - x_1$$

or $\qquad p = p_0 x_1$

where p_0 is the vapor pressure of the pure solvent, and p is the partial pressure of the solvent above a solution in which the mole fraction of solute is x_2 and the mole fraction of solvent is x_1.

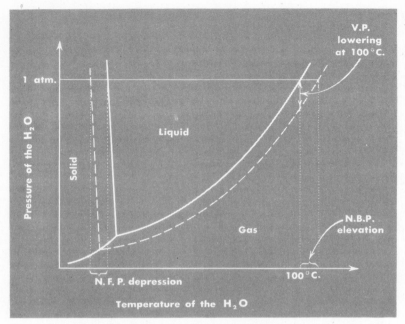

Fig. 10.5 *Comparison of phase diagrams of water and an aqueous solution. (Dashed lines refer to solution.)*

pend on the nature of the solvent and on the concentration of solute particles. In water, the characteristic values for the freezing-point depression and the boiling-point elevation are 1.86°C. and 0.52°C., respectively, per Avogadro number of solute particles per 1,000 g. of water. These constants are referred to as the *molal freezing-point lowering* and the *molal boiling-point elevation* for water. They are called *molal* constants because the concentration of solute is expressed in molal units (Sec. 10.2). One thousand grams of H_2O in which there are dissolved the Avogadro number of particles of solute has a boiling point 0.52°C. higher than that of pure water. Its freezing point is 1.86°C. lower than that of pure water. In the same amount of water, twice the Avogadro number of particles causes twice the boiling-point elevation and twice the freezing-point depression. It does not matter much what the particles are. They may be neutral molecules or electrically charged ions. Since the main role of the solute particles is to cut down the concentration of water molecules, it is the concentration of the solute, not its nature, that determines these particular solution properties.

Freezing-point depression and boiling-point elevation can be used as a means of measuring the concentration of solute particles in a solution.* In

---

* Once the freezing point of a compound is known, measurement of freezing point can be used to determine the purity of samples of that compound. For example, benzene has a freezing point of 5.5°C., and any sample of benzene showing a lower freezing point contains dissolved impurity.

principle, either property can be used. However, the freezing point is more easily measured accurately, and it is the preferred method of counting particles in solution. From the number of particles in solution and the weight of solute, the molecular weight of each particle can be calculated. This can be done easily when the solute molecules remain intact in the solution.

Example 1

When 45 g. of glucose is dissolved in 500 g. of water the solution has a freezing point of $-0.93°C$. *(a) What is the molecular weight of glucose? (b) If the simplest formula is* CH_2O, *what is the molecular formula of glucose?*

(a) The freezing point of H_2O is reduced $1.86°C$. by 1 mole of particles per 1,000 g. of H_2O. If the freezing point of H_2O is reduced $0.93°C$., the solution must have

$0.93/1.86$ mole of particles per 1,000 g. of H_2O, or

0.50 mole of particles per 1,000 g. of H_2O, or

0.25 mole of particles per 500 g. of H_2O

Since there are 45 g. of glucose per 500 g. of H_2O,

45 g. $= 0.25$ mole

1 mole $= 180$ g.

Therefore, molecular weight of glucose is 180 a.m.u.

(b) Molecular formula must be some multiple x of CH_2O, or $(CH_2O)_x$.

The simplest formula weight is $12 + 2 + 16 = 30$ a.m.u.

The molecular weight is 180 a.m.u., or x times 30, so $x = 6$

The molecular formula is $(CH_2O)_6$, or $C_6H_{12}O_6$.

The above calculation assumes that the number of particles in the solution is the same as the number of molecules placed in solution. However, as discussed in the next section, the solution process itself may tear molecules apart.

10.4   ELECTROLYTES

There are many cases in which the solution process is accompanied by dissociation, or breaking apart, of molecules. The dissociated fragments are usually electrically charged, so that electrical measurements can show whether dissociation has occurred. Charged particles, or ions, moving in solution, constitute an electric current, so that a measurement of electrical conductivity of the solution is all that is required. Figure 10.6 is a schematic diagram of an apparatus for determining whether a solute is dissociated into ions. The pair of electrodes is connected, in series with a light bulb, to a source of electricity. So long as the two electrodes are kept separated, no electric current can flow through the circuit, and the lamp stays dark. When the two electrodes are joined by an electrical conductor, the circuit is com-

Table 10.1   Classification of Solutes

Electrolytes		Nonelectrolytes	
HCl	Hydrochloric acid	$C_{12}H_{22}O_{11}$	Sucrose
H_2SO_4	Sulfuric acid	C_2H_5OH	Ethyl alcohol
$HC_2H_3O_2$	Acetic acid	N_2	Nitrogen
NaOH	Sodium hydroxide	O_2	Oxygen
$Ca(OH)_2$	Calcium hydroxide	CH_4	Methane
NaCl	Sodium chloride	CO	Carbon monoxide
Na_2SO_4	Sodium sulfate	CH_3COCH_3	Acetone

plete and the lamp lights. When the electrodes are dipped into a beaker of water, the bulb does not light, indicating that water does not conduct electricity appreciably. When sugar is dissolved in the water, the solution does not conduct, but when NaCl is dissolved in the water, the solution does conduct. By such experiments it is possible to classify substances as those which produce conducting solutions and those which produce essentially nonconducting solutions. Solutes of the first class are called *electrolytes*, and those of the second *nonelectrolytes*. Table 10.1 gives the names and formulas of several examples.

Electrical conductivity requires the existence of charged particles. The greater the number of charges available for carrying electricity, the greater the conductivity observed. By replacing the light bulb in Fig. 10.6 with an

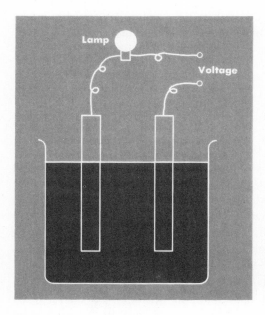

Fig. 10.6   Experiment to determine conductivity of a solution.

Table 10.2   *Classification of Electrolytes*

Strong electrolytes	Weak electrolytes
HCl	$HC_2H_3O_2$
NaOH	NH_4OH
NaCl	$HgCl_2$

ammeter for quantitatively measuring the conductivity, it is possible to get information about the concentration of charges in the solution. When the conductivity of a solution labeled 1 *m* HCl is compared to the conductivity of 1 *m* $HC_2H_3O_2$, it is found that the former conducts to a greater extent than the latter. Both solutions are made up by dissolving 1 mole of solute in 1,000 g. of water. The inference is that HCl yields a higher concentration of charges than $HC_2H_3O_2$. From experimental observations of this kind, electrolytes may be subdivided into two more or less distinct groups: *strong* electrolytes, which give solutions that are good conductors of electricity, and *weak* electrolytes, which give slightly conducting solutions. Table 10.2 lists representative compounds. Weak electrolytes differ from strong electrolytes in that weak electrolytes are only slightly dissociated into ions in solution. Strong electrolytes are essentially 100 per cent dissociated into ions, whereas weak electrolytes may be dissociated only a few per cent.

In a solution of a nonelectrolyte, molecules of solute retain their identity. For example, when sugar dissolves in water, as shown in Fig. 10.7, the sugar molecules exist in the solution as solvated, or hydrated, molecules. The hydrated sugar molecule (consisting of a sugar molecule surrounded by a cluster of water molecules) is an uncharged, or neutral, species. When positive and negative electrodes are inserted in a solution containing hydrated sugar molecules, there is no reason for the particles to move one way or the other, since they are neutral. Hence there is no electrical conductivity.

Fig. 10.7   *Schematic representation of sugar dissolving.*

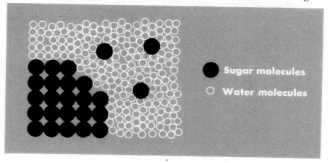

Electrolytes (before being dissolved) may be ionic or molecular substances. For *ionic substances,* it is not surprising that there are charged particles in solution, because the undissolved solid is already made up of charged particles. The solvent rips the lattice apart into its constituent pieces. Figure 10.8 shows what is thought to happen when the ionic solid NaCl dissolves in water. Since the chloride ion is negative, the positive ends of water molecules cluster about the chloride ion, with the hydrogen atoms facing the chloride ion. The chloride ion surrounded by its cluster of water molecules moves off into the solution. It is now a hydrated chloride ion. The species is negatively charged because the chloride ion itself is negatively charged. At the same time the sodium ion undergoes similar hydration, with the difference that the negative or oxygen end of the water molecule faces the positive ion. Since the solution as a whole must be electrically neutral, an equal number of hydrated sodium ions and hydrated chloride ions is formed. When positive and negative electrodes are inserted into this solution, the positively charged hydrated sodium ions are attracted to the negative electrode, and the negatively charged hydrated chloride ions are attracted to the positive electrode. There is a net transport of electrical charge as the positive charge moves in one direction and the negative charge moves in the opposite direction. (Electric conductivity is discussed in greater detail in Sec. 14.1.)

Ions may also be formed when certain *molecular substances* are dissolved in the proper solvent. For example, molecules of HCl are neutral, distinct species, which in the pure solid, liquid, or gaseous state do not conduct electricity because no ions are present. However, when HCl is placed in water, the resulting solution conducts electricity, indicating the formation of charged particles. Electrically neutral HCl molecules have interacted with the solvent to form ions. As shown in the equation,

$$H\!:\!\overset{..}{\underset{H}{O}}\!: \; + \; H\!:\!\overset{..}{\underset{..}{Cl}}\!: \; \rightarrow \; H\!:\!\overset{..}{\underset{H}{O}}\!:\!H^+ \; + \; :\!\overset{..}{\underset{..}{Cl}}\!:^-$$

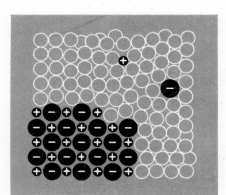

HCl molecules collide with water molecules to form H_3O^+ and Cl^-. Positive and negative ions are formed, even though none is present in pure HCl. The positively charged H_3O^+ is referred to as a

Fig. 10.8   Schematic representation of NaCl dissolving.

hydronium ion. The negative ion is the chloride ion. Both of these ions are hydrated, since there are water molecules stuck on them just as on an ionic solute. The ionization of a solute by water can be considered a chemical reaction and can be described by a chemical equation, such as

$$HCl + H_2O \rightarrow H_3O^+ + Cl^-$$

Since the hydronium ion, H_3O^+, can be considered as a hydrated proton, and since water of hydration is often omitted from chemical equations, the above equation can be written more simply as

$$HCl \rightarrow H^+ + Cl^-$$

with the tacit understanding that all species are hydrated.*

10.5   PER CENT DISSOCIATION

The extent of dissociation of solutes varies widely. Some substances, such as HCl, are essentially completely dissociated into ions in aqueous solution. Other substances, such as $HC_2H_3O_2$, are only slightly dissociated. The per cent dissociation can be determined by measuring any property that depends on the concentration of ions. Conductivity measurements can be used, as well as freezing-point lowering. The latter is somewhat easier in most cases and can be used because the freezing-point depression of a solvent is proportional to the molal concentration of particles dissolved in the solvent. As an example, consider the solution of an electrolyte *AB* in water. If some of the *AB* molecules are dissociated into A^+ and B^- ions, then the solution contains three kinds of particles: undissociated *AB* molecules, A^+ ions, and B^- ions. Each particle contributes to the freezing-point depression. By determining the freezing-point lowering of a specific solution of *AB*, the total concentration of particles and thus the per cent dissociation of *AB* can be calculated.

Example 2

The freezing point of 0.0100 m AB solution is $-0.0193°C$. What per cent of the AB molecules have been dissociated by the water?

The freezing point of water is reduced
1.86°C. for each 1 mole of particles per 1,000 g. H_2O
1.00°C. for each (1/1.86) mole of particles per 1,000 g. H_2O

---

* The practice of omitting water of hydration from chemical equations is dangerous unless we constantly bear in mind that, in aqueous solution, water is always associated with any dissolved species and may affect its properties. The danger is greatest in the case of the hydrogen ion, because a bare hydrogen ion is nothing but a proton (nucleus of H atom). Whereas H^+ is essentially of zero size, H_3O^+ has a volume which is about 10^{15} times as great and is comparable in size to other ions.

$0.0193°C.$ for each (0.0193) $(1/1.86)$ mole of particles per $1,000$ g. H_2O, or for 0.0104 mole of particles per $1,000$ g. H_2O

Let x = moles of AB dissociated per $1,000$ g. H_2O. This forms x moles of A^+ ions per $1,000$ g. H_2O and x moles of B^- per $1,000$ g. H_2O and leaves $(0.0100 - x)$ moles of AB undissociated per $1,000$ g. H_2O.

Total moles of particles per $1,000$ g. $H_2O = x + x + (0.0100 - x) = 0.0100 + x$

The freezing point indicates 0.0104 mole of particles present per $1,000$ g. H_2O, so $0.0100 + x = 0.0104$ and $x = 0.0004$.

Therefore, according to the observed freezing point, a solution of 0.0100 m AB contains 0.0004 mole of A^+, 0.0004 mole of B^-, and 0.0096 mole of AB. Hence the number of moles of AB that have dissociated is 0.0004.

The fraction of AB molecules dissociated is equal to the number of AB molecules dissociated divided by the number of AB molecules initially available.

$$\text{Fraction of } AB \text{ dissociated} = \frac{0.0004}{0.0100} = 0.04, \text{ or } 4\%$$

Measurements on various electrolytes under different conditions indicate that the per cent dissociation of an electrolyte depends on the nature of the solute, the nature of the solvent, the concentration of the solute, and the temperature.

1   Nature of the solute. When a molecule AB is dissociated into ions A^+ and B^-, the bond AB must be broken. The extent to which this operation can be performed depends on the nature of A and B. For example, under comparable conditions, HCl in water is 100 per cent dissociated, whereas HF in water is only 1 per cent dissociated.

2   Nature of the solvent. This point is easily overlooked, because we usually think only of water as the solvent. In solvents other than water the behavior of solutes may be different. As an example, under comparable conditions, in water HCl is 100 per cent dissociated, but in benzene it is less than 1 per cent dissociated. Also, it is possible for an electrolyte which in water is less dissociated than HCl, to be more dissociated than HCl in another solvent.

3   Temperature. There is no simple rule for the effect of temperature on per cent dissociation. For some substances, per cent dissociation increases as the temperature is raised; for other substances, the per cent dissociation decreases or is unchanged. Some substances show a combination of all effects. For example, acetic acid is 1 per cent dissociated in a given solution at room temperature; at higher temperatures and at lower temperatures it is less than 1 per cent dissociated.

4   Concentration. The per cent dissociation of an electrolyte increases as the concentration of the electrolyte decreases. The more dilute a solution, the higher the per cent dissociation. Table 10.3 gives numerical values

Table 10.3   *Concentration Dependence of Per Cent Dissociation*

Concentration	% dissociation
1 M $HC_2H_3O_2$	0.4
0.1 M $HC_2H_3O_2$	1.3
0.01 M $HC_2H_3O_2$	4.3
0.001 M $HC_2H_3O_2$	15
0.00001 M $HC_2H_3O_2$	75

of the per cent dissociation of $HC_2H_3O_2$ into hydrogen ion and acetate ion, $C_2H_3O_2{}^-$, in solutions of various concentrations. In the more dilute solutions, a higher percentage of the electrolyte is dissociated into positive and negative ions. An extreme case of an almost infinitely dilute solution can be imagined as one made by putting one molecule of *AB* in a barrel of solvent. When the molecule breaks up to form ions, the chance that the ions will come together is vanishingly small. Since the one molecule is dissociated, the per cent dissociation must be 100 per cent. At infinite dilution, all electrolytes approach 100 per cent dissociation.

The definition that a strong electrolyte is one that is highly dissociated and a weak electrolyte is one that is slightly dissociated is ambiguous, since in very dilute solutions all electrolytes are almost completely dissociated. The ambiguity is reduced by adopting the convention that a 1 M solution be the criterion. If the substance in 1 M solution is highly dissociated, it is called a strong electrolyte; if in 1 M solution it is slightly dissociated, it is called a weak electrolyte.

10.6   INTERIONIC ATTRACTIONS

In a solution of NaCl in water, the hydrated Na^+ and Cl^- ions are separated, on the average, by many H_2O molecules. It is in this sense that NaCl is 100 per cent dissociated and is expected to depress the freezing point of water by twice the normal amount. However, the solute particles carry electrical charges; hence there are attractions between the separated ions of opposite charge. Owing to these attractions, the positive and negative ions in a water solution of NaCl do not act completely independently of each other. Therefore 1 mole of NaCl is not quite so effective in lowering the freezing point of water as are 2 moles of nonelectrolyte.

The attraction between ions decreases rapidly with increasing distance. In a dilute solution of NaCl, the ions are rather widely separated, and the interionic attractions are small. However, as the concentration is increased, the ions are closer together, the interionic attractions are bigger, and the ions act less independently of each other. The freezing-point lowering *per mole* of NaCl is smaller in concentrated solutions than in dilute solutions, as shown in Table 10.4. Taken at face value, the numbers seem to indicate that, in 0.1 *m* solution, 1

Table 10.4   **Concentration Dependence of Freezing-point Lowering**

Concentration	Observed freezing point, °C.	Freezing-point lowering, °C. (per mole NaCl)
0.1 *m* NaCl	−0.347	3.47
0.01 *m* NaCl	−0.0361	3.61
0.001 *m* NaCl	−0.00366	3.66
0.0001 *m* NaCl	−0.000372	3.72

mole of NaCl produces fewer particles than it does in more dilute solution. The trend is the same as that observed for a weak electrolyte such as $HC_2H_3O_2$. It is not surprising that for many years chemists were unable to decide whether or not NaCl is completely dissociated in water.

The Debye-Hückel interionic-attraction theory of electrolytes, proposed in 1923, accounts quantitatively for the attraction between completely dissociated ions and justifies the view that NaCl and other ionic solids are completely dissociated in water solution. Further, this theory can be applied to calculate the interionic attractions in a solution of a weak electrolyte. This must be done for accurate determination of per cent dissociation from freezing-point data. In concentrated solutions, even the Debye-Hückel theory does not account for the observed freezing-point lowering by electrolytes. One important effect is that there are insufficient water molecules to hydrate all the ions. These concentrated solutions are not well understood at present.

10.7   SOLUBILITY

The term solubility is used in several senses. It describes the qualitative idea of the solution process. It also is used quantitatively to describe the composition of solutions. The solutions considered up to now represent *unsaturated solutions,* to which solute can be added a bit at a time to produce a whole series of solutions differing in concentration. For any solute and solvent, a large number of unsaturated solutions are possible. However, in most cases, the process of adding solute cannot go on indefinitely. Eventually, a stage is reached beyond which the addition of solute to a specified amount of solvent does not produce another solution of higher concentration. Instead, solute remains undissolved. In these cases there is a limit to the amount of solute which can be dissolved in a given amount of solvent. The solution which represents this limit is called a *saturated solution,* and the concentration of the saturated solution is called the *solubility* of the given solute in the particular solvent used.

The best way to ensure having a saturated solution is to have an excess of solute in contact with the solution. If the solution is unsaturated, solute disappears until saturation is established. If the solution is saturated, the amount of excess solute remains unchanged, as does the concentration of the solution. The system is in a state of equilibrium. Apparently, it is a state of dynamic equilibrium, since, for example, an irregularly shaped crystal of solute dropped into the solution changes its shape although remaining constant in weight. In the equilibrium state, dissolving of solute is still occurring but is compensated for by precipitation of solute out of solution. The number of solute particles going into solution per unit time is equal to the number of solute particles leaving the solution per unit time. The concentration of solute in the solution remains constant; the amount of solute in excess remains constant. The amount of excess solute present in contact with the saturated solution does not affect the concentration of the saturated solution. In fact, it is possible to filter or separate the excess solute completely and still have a saturated solution. For convenience, a *saturated solution is defined as one which is or would be in equilibrium with excess solute.*

The concentration of the saturated solution, i.e., the solubility, depends on the nature of the solvent, the nature of the solute, the temperature, and the pressure. In considering these, we should keep in mind that three important interactions operate in the dissolving process: Solute particles are separated one from the other (this takes energy); solvent particles are pushed apart to make a hole to accommodate the solute (this also takes energy); solvent particles attract the solute particles (this provides energy). This set of interactions—solute-solute, solvent-solvent, and solute-solvent— is useful in discussing the magnitude of the solubility.*

1   Nature of the solvent. A useful generalization much quoted in chemistry is that "like dissolves like." More specifically, high solubility occurs when the molecules of the solute are similar in structure and electrical properties to the molecules of the solvent. When there is a similarity of electrical properties, e.g., high dipole moment, between solute and solvent, then solute-solvent attractions are particularly strong. When there is dissimilarity, solute-solvent attractions are weak. For this reason a polar substance such as H_2O usually is a good solvent for a polar substance such as alcohol, but a poor solvent for a nonpolar substance such as gasoline.

---

* As mentioned in Sec. 9.6, the tendency for spontaneous change is decided not only by energy balance but also by entropy changes. In the case of the solution process this means that due consideration must be given to the fact that the solution represents a more disordered and hence more probable state than that of the unmixed components. Thus, dissolving will frequently occur—because of this entropy increase—even in cases where the solute-solvent interactions are not sufficiently energetic to compensate for the sum of the solute-solute and solvent-solvent interactions.

In general, an ionic solid has a higher solubility in a polar solvent than in a nonpolar solvent. For example, at room temperature the solubility of NaCl in H_2O is 311 g. per liter of solution, whereas the solubility of NaCl in gasoline is essentially zero. Also, the more polar the solvent, the greater the solubility of ionic solids. For example, at room temperature, the solubility of NaCl in ethyl alcohol is 0.51 g. per liter of solution, compared to 311 g. per liter of solution in water. The difference is ascribed to the lower polarity (lower dipole moment) of the ethyl alcohol molecule, with resulting lower attractions for the ions.

2   *Nature of the solute.* Changing the solute means changing the solute-solute and solute-solvent interaction. At room temperature the amount of sucrose that can be dissolved in water is 1,311 g. per liter of solution. This is more than four times as great as the solubility of NaCl. However, these numbers are rather misleading. The number of particles involved can better be seen by comparing the molar solubility. For NaCl, the saturated solution is 5.3 *M*, whereas for sugar the saturated solution is 3.8 *M*. On a molar basis NaCl has a higher solubility in H_2O than does sugar. Since the attractions in solid NaCl are greater than those in sugar, the reason for the higher solubility of NaCl apparently lies in the fact that the interactions between Na^+ and Cl^- and water molecules are greater than the interactions between the sugar molecules and water molecules.

What effect does the presence of one solute in a solution have on the solubility of another solute in that same solution? As a crude approximation, unless the concentration of a substance is high, it has little effect on the solubility of other substances in that solution. For example, approximately the same concentration of NaCl can be dissolved in a 0.1 *M* sugar solution as in pure water. However, the solubility of NaCl is drastically affected by a solute having an ion in common, such as KCl or $NaNO_3$.

Table 10.5   *Change of Solubility with Temperature*

(Solubility in grams of solute per 100 g. of H_2O)

Substance	0°	10°	20°	30°	40°	50°
$AgC_2H_3O_2$	0.72	0.88	1.04	1.21	1.41	1.64
$AgNO_3$	122	170	222	300	376	455
KCl	27.6	31.0	34.0	37.0	40.0	42.6
NaCl	35.7	35.8	36.0	36.3	36.6	37.0
Li_2CO_3	1.54	1.43	1.33	1.25	1.17	1.08
CO_2(gas) at 1 atm.	0.33	0.23	0.17	0.13	0.097	0.076
SO_2(gas) at 1 atm.	22.8	16.2	11.3	7.8	5.4	4.5
O_2(gas) at 1 atm.	0.0070	0.0054	0.0044	0.0037	0.0033	0.0030

3   *Temperature.* The solubility of *gases in water* usually decreases as the temperature of the solution increases. The tiny bubbles which form when water is heated are due to the fact that dissolved air becomes less soluble at higher temperatures. The flat taste characteristic of boiled water is largely due to the fact that dissolved air has been expelled. However, for *gases in other liquid solvents* (and, in fact, even for water at higher temperatures) solubility of gases need not decrease with increasing temperature. Similarly, there is no general rule for the temperature change of solubility of *liquids* and *solids.* For example, with increasing temperature, lithium carbonate decreases in solubility in water, silver nitrate increases, and sodium chloride shows practically no change. Specific data are given in Table 10.5 for the solubility of various substances in water.

The change of solubility with temperature is closely related to the heat of solution of the substance. The *heat of solution* is the heat evolved when a solute dissolves to give the saturated solution and can be written as the heat that accompanies the following process:

Solute + solvent → saturated solution + heat of solution

The heat of solution as experimentally determined can be a positive quantity, in which case heat is evolved to the surroundings, or it can be a negative quantity, in which case heat is absorbed from the surroundings. For lithium carbonate, for example, the heat of solution is positive. Heat is evolved and usually appears as a rise in temperature of the solution. For silver nitrate, the heat of solution is negative. We can write for the process

$$AgNO_3(s) + H_2O \rightarrow \text{solution} - \text{heat}$$

or   Heat + $AgNO_3(s)$ + $H_2O \rightarrow$ solution

Heat must be supplied, since the process is endothermic. When a substance with negative heat of solution is dissolved, there is usually a drop in the temperature of the solution.

Whether the heat of solution is positive or negative depends on the nature of the solute and the solvent. Specifically, when solids are dissolved in water, the heat of solution depends on the relative magnitude of two energies, the energy required to break up the solid lattice and the energy liberated when the particles are hydrated. In the case of silver nitrate, the overall process can be imagined to occur in two consecutive steps:

$$AgNO_3(s) \rightarrow Ag^+(g) + NO_3^-(g) \tag{1}$$

$$Ag^+(g) + NO_3^-(g) + H_2O \rightarrow Ag^+(\text{hydrated}) + NO_3^-(\text{hydrated}) \tag{2}$$

The first step, vaporizing the solid, requires energy. Work must be done to separate the positive and negative ions from each other. The amount of energy required per mole is called the *lattice energy*. The second step liberates energy. As the water molecules are separated from each other and attracted to the ions, energy is liberated to the surroundings. This energy is called the *hydration energy*.* When the hydration energy is greater than the lattice energy, the over-all solution process liberates energy to the surroundings and is exothermic. When less energy is furnished by step (2) than is required by step (1), the over-all solution process is endothermic. In a few cases, the lattice energy is approximately equal to the hydration energy. For example, the lattice energy of NaCl is 184.0 kcal. per mole; the hydration energy is 182.8 kcal. per mole. The heat of solution of NaCl is the difference between these two values and is nearly zero.

How is the heat of solution related to the change of solubility with temperature? In a saturated solution in equilibrium with excess solute, the two processes, dissolving and precipitation, occur simultaneously. If the dissolving process is endothermic, as with $AgNO_3$, the precipitation process is exothermic.

$$\text{Heat} + AgNO_3(s) + H_2O \rightleftharpoons \text{solution}$$

The upper arrow indicates the forward process of dissolving read from left to right, and the bottom arrow indicates the reverse process of precipitation read from right to left. In a beaker containing solid $AgNO_3$ in equilibrium with the saturated solution, the two processes occur equally. If heat is now added to the equilibrium system, Le Chatelier's principle predicts that the system will adjust to reduce the stress of added heat. The stress can be reduced in this case by favoring the dissolving process over the precipitation process. Until the stress is relieved, silver nitrate goes into solution faster than it comes out. The amount of solid in solution increases. The solubility of silver nitrate in water is therefore greater at the higher temperature. This behavior is typical of most solids. When placed in water, they dissolve by an endothermic process; hence raising the temperature increases solubility.

4 *Pressure.* The solubility of all *gases* is increased as the partial pressure of the gas above the solution is increased. Probably the most familiar example of this phenomenon is found in carbonated beverages. These are solutions of the gas CO_2 in a liquid solvent. Because of the way in which the beverages are bottled, the pressure of the carbon dioxide gas in the sealed bottle is rather high. The concentration of CO_2 dissolved in

---

* Note that the hydration energy actually takes into account both the solvent-solvent interaction (the energy required to make a hole in the water) and the solvent-solute interaction. These are lumped together because experimentally they are hard to separate. In other words, we cannot hydrate an ion without first making room for it anymore than we can make a hole in the water without putting something in it.

the solution is dependent directly on the partial pressure of CO_2 in the gas phase. When the bottle is opened, the pressure of carbon dioxide drops, its solubility is diminished, and bubbles of carbon dioxide form and escape from the beverage. As far as liquids and solids are concerned, there is essentially no change of solubility with pressure. If there is a change, it can be predicted by Le Chatelier's principle, since it depends on the relative volume of the solution and the component substances. In general, the volume change on solution is so small that the pressure must be made very high, thousands of atmospheres, in order to change the solubility appreciably.

In closing this section on solubility we need to note that it is sometimes possible to prepare solutions which have a higher concentration of solute than that of the saturated solution. Such solutions are *supersaturated* and are unstable with respect to the separation of excess solute. A supersaturated solution of sodium acetate, $NaC_2H_3O_2$, for example, can be made as follows: A saturated solution of $NaC_2H_3O_2$ and H_2O in contact with excess solute is heated until the increase of solubility with temperature is sufficient to dissolve all the excess solute. At sufficiently high temperatures an unsaturated solution results. This unsaturated solution is then cooled very carefully. The system ought to return to its original equilibrium state with the excess solute crystallized out. This, in fact, does happen with most solids. However, for some, such as sodium acetate, cooling can be accomplished without crystallization. The resulting solution has a concentration of solute higher than would correspond to the saturated solution at the lower temperature. It is supersaturated. The situation is reminiscent of that observed for supercooling of a liquid below its freezing point. Supersaturation can usually be destroyed in the same manner, i.e., by seeding. When a tiny seed crystal of sodium acetate is placed in a supersaturated solution of sodium acetate, excess solute crystallizes on it until the remaining solution is just saturated. Occasionally, a mechanical disturbance such as a sudden shock may suffice to break the supersaturation. Dust particles or even scratches on the inner surface of the container may act as centers on which crystallization can start.

10.8   ACIDS AND BASES

In the preceding discussions, it has been assumed that water is a nonconductor of electricity in conductivity determinations. It is found, however, by precise measurement that even very highly purified water does conduct electrical current to a slight extent. It must be that water itself is dissociated into positive and negative ions and should be classified as a weak electrolyte. The electrolytic dissociation of water can be represented by Eq. (1), which shows the splitting of the water molecule to form a positive *hydrogen* ion and a negative *hydroxide* ion.

$$H_2O \rightarrow H^+ + OH^- \tag{1}$$

Each of these ions is hydrated. Perhaps a better way of describing the electrolytic dissociation of water is shown in Eq. (2):

$$H\!:\!\overset{..}{\underset{..}{O}}\!: + H\!:\!\overset{..}{\underset{..}{O}}\!: \rightarrow H\!:\!\overset{..}{\underset{..}{O}}\!:H^+ + :\overset{..}{\underset{..}{O}}\!:H^- \tag{2}$$

$$\qquad H \qquad\quad H \qquad\quad H$$

$$H_2O + H_2O \rightarrow H_3O^+ + OH^-$$

where it is assumed that, on collision of two water molecules, a proton shifts from one oxygen atom to the other oxygen atom, so that a hydronium ion is formed. The residue is a hydroxide ion. Both the hydronium ion and the hydroxide ion are hydrated. For simplicity, the dissociation is usually written as Eq. (1).

The degree of dissociation of water is very small. In pure water the concentration of hydrogen ion is 1.0×10^{-7} *M*. The concentration of hydroxide ion is, of course, the same, since each time a water molecule is split, one hydrogen ion and one hydroxide ion are formed. In a liter of water at room temperature there are approximately 1,000 g., or 55 moles, of H_2O. Thus, the fraction of water dissociated is $1.0 \times 10^{-7}/55$, or 0.0000002 per cent. On the average, only 1 out of 500 million molecules of H_2O is dissociated. Although very small and seemingly trivial, this small per cent of dissociation is probably one of the most important properties of water. For example, many of the metabolic reactions in the body depend very critically on the dissociation of water or, more specifically, on the hydrogen-ion and the hydroxide-ion concentrations in the system.

Substances can be added to water which upset the hydrogen ion–hydroxide ion balance. Those substances which *increase the hydrogen-ion concentration* are called *acids;* those substances which *increase the hydroxide-ion concentration* are called *bases.* For example, HCl and $HC_2H_3O_2$ are acids. HCl is a *strong acid,* one which is *highly dissociated* into hydrogen ions and negative ions; $HC_2H_3O_2$ is a *weak acid,* one which is *slightly dissociated* into hydrogen ions and negative ions. As a class, acids have a set of characteristic properties which are referred to as *acid properties.* Acids have a noticeable sour taste. They affect dye materials in a specific way. For example, the purple dye litmus is turned pink in acid solution, and it serves as an *indicator* for the presence of acids. Litmus paper consists of absorbent paper impregnated with this indicator. Similarly, bases have characteristic *basic properties*. For example, the typical strong base NaOH, sodium hydroxide, has a bitter taste, a slippery feel, and turns litmus blue.

It is not obvious from a formula whether a chemical compound is an acid or a base; it is not safe to generalize that any molecule containing the OH group is a base. For example, the substance $SO_2(OH)_2$ contains two OH groups. When placed in water, the compound shows typical acid properties, indicating dissociation to form a hydrogen ion (proton) and a negative $SO_2(OH)O^-$ ion. The negative ion is usually written HSO_4^-. To emphasize that the compound is an acid and dissociates in water to furnish protons, it is customary to write the formula as H_2SO_4 instead of $SO_2(OH)_2$. In general, the formulas of acids are written so that the available protons appear first in the formula. Thus, the usual formula of hypochlorous acid is HOCl instead of ClOH. On the other hand, it is not safe to assume that all formulas ending with OH denote bases. For example, C_2H_5OH is not a base, but NaOH is. Only a knowledge of the experimental behavior can give an unequivocal decision as to whether a given compound is an acid, a base, or neither.

It might be useful to consider the full implications of the definition of acids and bases, as given in this section, that acids are substances which increase the hydrogen-ion concentration in water and bases are substances which increase the hydroxide-ion concentration in water. One obvious implication is that the definition is limited to aqueous systems. Another implication is that a hydrogen-ion increase can be brought about by substances which themselves do not contain hydrogen. For example, CO_2 is an acid because its addition to water increases the hydrogen-ion concentration so that the resulting solution has acid properties. This can best be represented by the net equation

$$CO_2 + H_2O \rightarrow H^+ + HCO_3^-$$

where HCO_3^- represents the bicarbonate ion. Similarly, NH_3 is a base because its addition to water increases the hydroxide-ion concentration. This can be represented as

$$NH_3 + H_2O \rightarrow NH_4^+ + OH^-$$

There are other less evident reactions (often called hydrolysis reactions— Sec. 17.11) which change the H^+ and OH^- concentrations in water. For example, when certain aluminum compounds are added to water, the solution becomes acidic; when certain sulfides are added to water, the solution becomes basic. Thus, for aluminum chloride $(AlCl_3)$ dissolved in water the increase of hydrogen-ion concentration can be attributed to the net reaction

$$Al^{+3} + H_2O \rightarrow H^+ + AlOH^{++}$$

and for sodium sulfide (Na_2S) dissolved in water the increase of hydroxide-ion concentration can be attributed to the net reaction

$$S^{--} + H_2O \rightarrow OH^- + SH^-$$

In summary, the definition of acid here given would include CO_2 and $AlCl_3$ as well as HCl and $HC_2H_3O_2$, and the definition of base would include NH_3 and Na_2S as well as $NaOH$, $Ca(OH)_2$, etc.

Although the definitions given above are quite general for aqueous solutions and include all the commonly recognized acids and bases, there are other definitions which apply equally well to solutions in water and to systems from which water is completely absent. The Brønsted-Lowry definition, for example, refers to any proton donor as an acid and any proton acceptor as a base, even in nonaqueous solution. Thus, when ammonium chloride (NH_4Cl) and potassium amide (KNH_2) are mixed in liquid ammonia, the reaction that occurs,

$$NH_4^+ + NH_2^- \rightarrow 2NH_3$$

shows NH_4^+ as a proton donor (Brønsted-Lowry acid) and NH_2^- as a proton acceptor (Brønsted-Lowry base). In aqueous solutions, the Brønsted-Lowry definition focuses attention on the acid-base nature of the solvent itself. For example, the equation for the slight dissociation of water,

$$H_2O + H_2O \rightarrow H_3O^+ + OH^-$$

shows H_2O acting as a proton donor (in forming OH^-) and a proton acceptor (in forming H_3O^+). Incidentally, H_3O^+ itself can be a proton donor and is called the *conjugate acid* of H_2O; OH^- can be a proton acceptor and is the *conjugate base* of H_2O. In other words, when a Brønsted-Lowry acid gives up a proton it is converted to the conjugate base. Similarly, when a Brønsted-Lowry base accepts a proton it is converted to the conjugate acid. As another example, in the reaction

$$HCl + H_2O \rightarrow H_3O^+ + Cl^-$$

HCl is a Brønsted acid, H_2O is a Brønsted base, H_3O^+ is the conjugate acid of H_2O, and Cl^- is the conjugate base of HCl.

There is yet another commonly used definition of acid and base, called the Lewis definition. It applies the term acid to any species that acts as an electron-pair acceptor in chemical reaction and the term base to an electron-pair donor. For instance, in the reaction

$$H^+ + \overset{\displaystyle H}{\underset{\displaystyle H}{:\!\overset{..}{N}\!:\!H}} \rightarrow \left[\overset{\displaystyle H}{\underset{\displaystyle H}{H\!:\!\overset{..}{N}\!:\!H}} \right]^+$$

the Lewis acid H^+ accepts a pair of electrons from the Lewis base NH_3.

The choice of definition of acids and bases can be defended equally in the three systems. For our purposes, where major emphasis will be placed on aqueous solutions, the first definition (acids increase H^+, bases increase OH^-) will be sufficient.

10.9 NEUTRALIZATION

The fact that water is only slightly dissociated into H^+ and OH^- indicates that the two ions have great affinity for each other in aqueous solution. Therefore, it is not surprising that, when H^+ and OH^- from separate sources are brought together, they readily combine to form water molecules. In this reaction, which is known as *neutralization*, the H^+ destroys the OH^- by forming H_2O. The process of neutralization is typical of acids and bases and is frequently made part of their definitions.

In the neutralization process there is produced a third class of substances known as *salts*. They consist of the positive ion of a base and the negative ion of an acid and can be defined as the neutralization products of an acid-base reaction. As a specific example, when a solution of H^+ and Cl^- is mixed with a solution of Na^+ and OH^-, the H^+ pairs with the OH^- to form H_2O, and Na^+ and Cl^- are left in the solution. When the solvent water is boiled off, the Na^+ ions and the Cl^- ions conglomerate to form the salt sodium chloride. The net equation for the neutralization reaction is

$$H^+ + OH^- \rightarrow H_2O$$

The net equation for the subsequent formation of the salt on evaporation of the solvent is

$$Na^+ + Cl^- \rightarrow NaCl(s)$$

The equation

$$H^+ + OH^- \rightarrow H_2O$$

describes the neutralization of any strong acid by any strong base. In the reaction, H^+ and OH^- are used up, and H_2O molecules appear. Neither Cl^- nor Na^+ takes part in the neutralization reaction, and therefore neither appears in the net equation. The neutralization of HCl with NaOH is sometimes written as

$$HCl + NaOH \rightarrow H_2O + NaCl$$

but since HCl, NaOH, and NaCl are all strong electrolytes, the species present in solution are ions. The equation is better written as

$$H^+ + Cl^- + Na^+ + OH^- \rightarrow H_2O + Na^+ + Cl^-$$

The Na^+ and Cl^- are canceled because they appear on both sides of the equation. The net equation

$$H^+ + OH^- \rightarrow H_2O$$

is preferred. It does not concern itself with any species not pertinent to the reaction but tells only what disappears and what appears.

For the neutralization of a weak acid by a strong base the net equation can be represented in general terms,

$$HA + OH^- \rightarrow H_2O + A^-$$

where HA stands for any weak acid such as acetic acid, $HC_2H_3O_2$. Since weak acids are only slightly dissociated in aqueous solution into H^+ and A^- ions, the original solution of the weak acid contains predominantly HA molecules. In the neutralization, it is the HA molecules that ultimately disappear, and this must be shown in the net equation. It may well be that the actual mechanism of the neutralization involves, first, dissociation of HA into $H^+ + A^-$, with subsequent union of $H^+ + OH^-$ to give H_2O. The net equation represents only the over-all reaction.

For the neutralization of strong acid by a weak base, the net reaction can be written

$$H^+ + MOH \rightarrow M^+ + H_2O$$

where MOH represents any weak base. For the neutralization of a weak acid by a weak base, the net reaction is represented by

$$HA + MOH \rightarrow M^+ + A^- + H_2O$$

10.10   POLYPROTIC ACIDS

The term *polyprotic acid* (sometimes called polybasic acid) is used to describe those acids which furnish more than one proton per molecule. Two examples of polyprotic acids are H_2SO_4, sulfuric acid, and H_3PO_4, phosphoric acid. In dissociation, polyprotic acids usually dissociate only one proton at a time. For example, when placed in water, H_2SO_4 dissociates to give H^+ and HSO_4^-. This dissociation

$$H_2SO_4 \rightarrow H^+ + HSO_4^-$$

is complete, and in this sense H_2SO_4 is called a strong electrolyte. When a solution containing 1 mole of sodium hydroxide is mixed with a solution containing 1 mole of sulfuric acid, 1 mole of H^+ neutralizes 1 mole of OH^-.

Evaporation of the resulting solution gives 1 mole of the salt $NaHSO_4$, sodium hydrogen sulfate. (This salt is also called sodium bisulfate and used to be called primary sodium sulfate.) The ion HSO_4^- is an acid in its own right. Although fairly weak, it can dissociate to give H^+ and SO_4^{--}. This dissociation

$$HSO_4^- \rightarrow H^+ + SO_4^{--}$$

can be considered as the second step in the dissociation of the diprotic acid H_2SO_4 and occurs only when there is a large demand for protons. For example, when 1 mole of H_2SO_4 is mixed in solution with 2 moles of sodium hydroxide, the 2 moles of OH^- neutralize 2 moles of H^+. Evaporation of the solution produces the salt Na_2SO_4, sodium sulfate (or secondary sodium sulfate).

The triprotic acid H_3PO_4 undergoes dissociation in three steps:

$$H_3PO_4 \ \rightarrow H^+ + H_2PO_4^-$$

$$H_2PO_4^- \rightarrow H^+ + HPO_4^{--}$$

$$HPO_4^{--} \rightarrow H^+ + PO_4^{-3}$$

The extent of dissociation is again governed by the demand for protons. It is possible to get three salts from this acid. The following are the net equations for reaction between 1 mole of H_3PO_4 and 1, 2, and 3 moles of NaOH in solution:

$$H_3PO_4 + OH^- \ \rightarrow \ H_2O + H_2PO_4^-$$

$$H_3PO_4 + 2OH^- \rightarrow 2H_2O + HPO_4^{--}$$

$$H_3PO_4 + 3OH^- \rightarrow 3H_2O + PO_4^{-3}$$

Evaporation of the solutions gives the salts NaH_2PO_4, monosodium dihydrogen phosphate; Na_2HPO_4, disodium monohydrogen phosphate; and Na_3PO_4, trisodium phosphate. These are sometimes referred to as the primary, secondary, and tertiary sodium phosphates, respectively.

10.11   GRAM-EQUIVALENTS OF ACIDS AND BASES

In acid-base neutralization, it is necessary that there be an equal number of H^+ ions and OH^- ions available for the reaction. This can be expressed by writing a non-net equation. For example, in the complete neutralization of $Ca(OH)_2$, calcium hydroxide, by H_3PO_4 the non-net equation is

$$3Ca(OH)_2 + 2H_3PO_4 \rightarrow Ca_3(PO_4)_2 + 6H_2O$$

Since each mole of $Ca(OH)_2$ furnishes 2 moles of OH^- and each mole of H_3PO_4 furnishes 3 moles of H^+, complete neutralization occurs if 3 moles of $Ca(OH)_2$ per 2 moles of H_3PO_4 are used. From such an equation, the usual stoichiometric calculations can be made.

It is more convenient, however, to consider neutralization reactions by fixing attention only on the hydrogen ion and hydroxide ion. For this purpose, gram-equivalents are convenient. One *gram-equivalent of an acid* is the *weight of acid required to furnish* 1 *mole of* H^+; one *gram-equivalent of a base* is the *weight of base required to furnish* 1 *mole of* OH^- *or accept* 1 *mole of* H^+. One gram-equivalent of any acid just reacts with one gram-equivalent of any base.

One of the simplest acids is HCl, hydrochloric acid, 1 mole of which weighs 36.5 g. Since 1 mole of HCl can furnish 1 mole of H^+, 36.5 g. of HCl is 1 gram-equivalent. For HCl, and for all other monoprotic acids, 1 mole is the same as 1 gram-equivalent. This means that the molarity of such solutions numerically equals the normality (Sec. 10.2). For example, a solution labeled 0.59 M HCl requires 0.59 mole of HCl per liter of solution, or 0.59 gram-equivalent of HCl per liter, and so can also be labeled 0.59 N HCl.

For a diprotic acid such as H_2SO_4, 1 mole of acid can furnish on demand 2 moles of H^+. By definition, 2 moles of H^+ is the amount furnished by 2 gram-equivalents of acid. Therefore, for complete neutralization 1 mole of H_2SO_4 is identical with 2 gram-equivalents. Since 1 mole = 98 g. = 2 gram-equivalents, 1 gram-equivalent of H_2SO_4 weighs 49 g. A solution labeled 1 M H_2SO_4, indicating 1 mole of H_2SO_4 per liter of solution, can also be labeled as 2 N H_2SO_4. For complete neutralization of a triprotic acid such as H_3PO_4, 1 mole is equal to 3 gram-equivalents, so the normality of any solution is three times the molarity.

The situation is similar for bases. For NaOH, 1 mole gives 1 mole of OH^-. Therefore, 1 mole of NaOH is 1 gram-equivalent. For all solutions of NaOH the normality is equal to the molarity. For $Ca(OH)_2$, the normality of any solution is twice the molarity.

10.12 STOICHIOMETRY OF SOLUTIONS

Labels on reagent bottles specify what the solution was made from, but not necessarily what the solution contains. For example, the label 0.5 M HCl appears on a solution made from 0.5 mole of HCl and sufficient water to give 1 liter of solution. Despite the label, there are no HCl molecules in the solution. HCl is a strong electrolyte and is 100 per cent dissociated into H^+ and Cl^-. For most quantitative considerations, however, it is not necessary to know what species are actually in the solution. It is necessary to know only what is ultimately available. The label 0.5 M $HC_2H_3O_2$ also tells what the solution was made from, but in this case the solution actually contains $HC_2H_3O_2$ molecules, since it is a weak electrolyte and is very slightly dissociated. There is only a trace of H^+ and $C_2H_3O_2^-$ in the solution. However, if this solution is used for a neutralization reaction, not only the trace of H^+ but also the $HC_2H_3O_2$ is neutralized.

The use of solutions for chemical reactions requires a clear distinction between the *number of moles* of solute in a solution and its *concentration*. To illustrate, let us suppose 15.8 g. of $KMnO_4$, potassium permanganate, is dissolved to make a 0.100 M $KMnO_4$ solution. The formula weight of $KMnO_4$ is 158; hence 15.8 g. is equal to 0.100 mole. To make up the solution, the solute is placed in a graduated container and water is added to it. Not necessarily 1 liter of water is added but only enough to bring the volume to a liter of solution. (Usually, the volume of solute plus the volume of the solvent is not exactly equal to the volume of the solution.) The solution can now be labeled 0.100 M $KMnO_4$, since it contains 0.100 mole of $KMnO_4$ in 1 liter of solution. The concentration does not depend on how much of this solution is taken. Whether one drop or 200 ml. is considered, the solution is still 0.100 M $KMnO_4$. However, the number of moles of $KMnO_4$ taken does depend on the volume of solution. If the volume and the concentration of a sample are known, the number of moles of solute in the sample is the number of moles per liter multiplied by the volume of the sample in liters. In 200 ml. of 0.100 M $KMnO_4$, there is $(200/1,000)(0.100)$, or 0.0200, mole of $KMnO_4$.

Solutions are extremely convenient because they permit measuring amounts of solute not by weighing the solute but by measuring a volume of solution. For example, suppose a given chemical reaction requires 0.0100 mole of $KMnO_4$. This amount of $KMnO_4$ can be provided by 1.58 g. of $KMnO_4$ or by 100 ml. of 0.100 M $KMnO_4$ solution.

To summarize:

Liters of solution $\times$ molarity of solution = moles of solute in sample

Liters of solution $\times$ normality of solution = gram-equivalents of solute
  in sample

Example 3

To what volume must 50.0 ml. of 3.50 M H_2SO_4 be diluted in order to make 2.00 M H_2SO_4?

  50.0 ml. of 3.50 M H_2SO_4 contains $(50.0/1,000)(3.50)$, or 0.175, mole of H_2SO_4

  We wish the final solution to be 2.00 M, i.e., 2.00 moles per liter

  We have only 0.175 mole, which is the fraction $0.175/2.00$ of the number of moles
    in 1 liter of the desired solution

Therefore, we can have only the fraction 0.175/2.00 of 1 liter of the desired solution

0.175/2.00 of 1,000 ml. is 87.5 ml.

Therefore, it is necessary to dilute to 87.5 ml. of final solution.

Example 4

To 50.0 ml. of 0.50 M H_2SO_4, 75.0 ml. of 0.25 M H_2SO_4 is added. What is the concentration of the final solution if its volume is 125 ml.?

In 50.0 ml. of 0.50 M H_2SO_4, there are (50.0/1,000)(0.50) moles H_2SO_4

In 75.0 ml. of 0.25 M H_2SO_4, there are (75.0/1,000)(0.25) moles H_2SO_4

Total moles = (50.0/1,000)(0.50) + (75.0/1,000)(0.25) = 0.044

Final solution contains 0.044 mole in 125 ml.

Final concentration is (0.044/125)(1,000), or 0.35 M H_2SO_4

Example 5

How many milliliters of 0.025 M H_3PO_4 are required to neutralize 25 ml. of 0.030 M $Ca(OH)_2$?

Method 1   Moles. In 25 ml. of 0.030 M $Ca(OH)_2$, there is (25.0/1,000)(0.030), or 0.00075, mole. From the non-net equation

$$3Ca(OH)_2 + 2H_3PO_4 \longrightarrow Ca_3(PO_4)_2 + 6H_2O$$

3 moles of $Ca(OH)_2$ requires 2 moles of H_3PO_4, or

0.00075 mole of $Ca(OH)_2$ requires 0.00050 mole of H_3PO_4

0.025 M H_3PO_4 means 0.025 mole H_3PO_4 per 1,000 ml. of solution. To get 0.00050 mole of H_3PO_4 as required, we take

(0.00050/0.025)(1,000), or 20, ml. of 0.025 M H_3PO_4

Method 2   Gram-equivalents. 0.030 M $Ca(OH)_2$ is 0.060 N $Ca(OH)_2$, and 0.025 M H_3PO_4 is 0.075 N H_3PO_4.

In 25 ml. of 0.030 M $Ca(OH)_2$ there is (25.0/1,000)(0.060), or 0.0015, gram-equivalent of base

Need 0.0015 gram-equivalent of acid for neutralization

Acidic solution has 0.075 gram-equivalent per 1,000 ml., or

0.0015 gram-equivalent in (0.0015/0.075)(1,000), or 20, ml. of solution.

10.13   OXIDATION-REDUCTION IN SOLUTION

In the quantitative consideration of oxidation-reduction reactions in aqueous solution, no new principles need to be introduced. In fact, electrolytic dissociation simplifies consideration of oxidation-reduction. Only the net reaction need be considered; other ions present in the solution can be ignored. As a specific case, we consider the reaction of an acidified solution of $KMnO_4$ with a solution of ferrous sulfate, $FeSO_4$. Before reaction occurs, the mixture contains K^+, MnO_4^-, H^+, HSO_4^-, Fe^{++}, and SO_4^{--}. After the reaction is complete, the mixture contains K^+, HSO_4^-, Mn^{++}, Fe^{+3}, and SO_4^{--}. The K^+, HSO_4^-, and SO_4^{--} are present both in the initial mixture and the final mixture and can be ignored. The net reaction shows the disappearance of MnO_4^-, Fe^{++}, and H^+ and the appearance of Mn^{++}, Fe^{+3}, and H_2O. It can be written

$$Fe^{++} + MnO_4^- + H^+ \rightarrow Fe^{+3} + Mn^{++} + H_2O$$

This equation can be balanced using the procedure outlined previously (Sec. 5.7). The first step is to balance the oxidation-reduction from the electron transfer. Since the manganese atom changes oxidation state from $+7$ to $+2$, it appears to pick up five electrons. Since the iron atom changes oxidation state from $+2$ to $+3$, it appears to release one electron. The electron gain and electron loss must compensate; hence for every MnO_4^-, five Fe^{++} are used. The balancing of electron transfer is shown as follows:

$$5Fe^{++} + 1MnO_4^- + H^+ \rightarrow H_2O + Mn^{++} + Fe^{+3}$$
$$\begin{array}{ccc} {\scriptstyle +2} & {\scriptstyle +7} & \qquad {\scriptstyle +2} \quad {\scriptstyle +3} \\ {\scriptstyle 5 \times \downarrow 1e^-} & {\scriptstyle = \; 1 \times \uparrow 5e^-} & \end{array}$$

Since five atoms of iron disappear on the left, five atoms of iron as Fe^{+3} must appear on the right. Since one manganese atom disappears on the left, one Mn^{++} must appear on the right. Finally, to conserve mass, the four atoms of oxygen from the MnO_4^- must appear on the right as four H_2O molecules. Since there are now eight hydrogen atoms on the right, there must be a corresponding eight H^+ on the left. The final *net ionic equation* reads

$$5Fe^{++} + MnO_4^- + 8H^+ \rightarrow 5Fe^{+3} + Mn^{++} + 4H_2O$$

It can be checked by comparing the net charge on the left, $+17$, with the net charge on the right, $+17$.

Actually, the balanced net ionic equation can be written if the only information given is that MnO_4^- is reduced in the reaction by Fe^{++} to form Mn^{++} and Fe^{+3} in acidic solution. The steps are as follows: (*a*) balance electron transfer; (*b*) balance the net charge by placing H^+ where required in order to maintain net charge balance; and (*c*) place H_2O where it is required to balance the oxygen. The steps are illustrated below in their proper sequence:

Given: In acidic solution, $MnO_4^- + Fe^{++} \rightarrow Fe^{+3} + Mn^{++}$

(*a*) $1MnO_4^- + 5Fe^{++} \rightarrow 5Fe^{+3} + 1Mn^{++}$
$$\begin{array}{cccc} {\scriptstyle +7} & {\scriptstyle +2} & {\scriptstyle +3} & {\scriptstyle +2} \\ {\scriptstyle 1 \times \uparrow 5e^-} & {\scriptstyle = \; 5 \times \downarrow 1e^-} & & \end{array}$$

(*b*) $MnO_4^- + 5Fe^{++} \qquad \rightarrow \qquad 5Fe^{+3} + Mn^{++}$

Net charge: Net charge:

$(-1) + (5)(+2) = +9$ $(5)(+3) + (+2) = +17$

To maintain net charge, need eight more plus charges on left, so insert $8H^+$ on left.

(c) $MnO_4^- + 5Fe^{++} + 8H^+ \rightarrow 5Fe^{+3} + Mn^{++}$

Insert $4H_2O$ on right to balance four oxygen atoms on left.

$MnO_4^- + 5Fe^{++} + 8H^+ \rightarrow 5Fe^{+3} + Mn^{++} + 4H_2O$

Check by counting the number of hydrogen atoms on left and right.

The great advantage of approaching the oxidation-reduction reactions in this way is that it is necessary to remember only the oxidizing and reducing agents and their products. The rest can be figured out. In the reaction between potassium dichromate, $K_2Cr_2O_7$, and sulfur dioxide, SO_2, in acidic solution, the oxidizing agent $Cr_2O_7^{--}$ and the reducing agent SO_2 disappear to form Cr^{+3} and HSO_4^-. The steps used to arrive at the balanced net equation are as follows:

Given: In acidic solution, $Cr_2O_7^{--} + SO_2 \rightarrow Cr^{+3} + HSO_4^-$

(a) $1Cr_2O_7^{--} + 3SO_2 \rightarrow 2Cr^{+3} + 3HSO_4^-$

      $+6$ $+4$ $+3$ $+6$

      $1 \times \uparrow 3e^- \times 2 \quad = 3 \times \downarrow 2e^-$

Note that, since $Cr_2O_7^{--}$ contains two chromium atoms, the gain of $3e^-$ per atom must first be doubled to give the electron gain per dichromate ion, which is then compared with the electron loss of the sulfur.

(b) $Cr_2O_7^{--} + 3SO_2 \quad\rightarrow\quad 2Cr^{+3} + 3HSO_4^-$

Net charge: Net charge:

$(-2) + (3)(0) = -2 \qquad (2)(+3) + (3)(-1) = +3$

To maintain net charge, add $5H^+$ to left.

(c) $Cr_2O_7^{--} + 3SO_2 + 5H^+ \rightarrow 2Cr^{+3} + 3HSO_4^-$

To balance oxygen atoms, add $1H_2O$ to right.

$Cr_2O_7^{--} + 3SO_2 + 5H^+ \rightarrow 2Cr^{+3} + 3HSO_4^- + H_2O$

This method of balancing equations works for basic solutions as well, except that, in basic solution, hydrogen ions do not exist in any appreciable concentration. The balancing of the net charge is done by placing hydroxide ions where needed. As an example, consider the preceding oxidation-reduction as carried out in basic solution. In basic solution, the oxidizing agent exists in the form of CrO_4^{--} and the reducing agent in the form of SO_3^{--}. The products are CrO_2^- and SO_4^{--}. The sequence of steps follows:

Given: In basic solution, $CrO_4^{--} + SO_3^{--} \rightarrow CrO_2^- + SO_4^{--}$

(a) $2CrO_4^{--} + 3SO_3^{--} \rightarrow 2CrO_2^- + 3SO_4^{--}$

$$\underset{2 \times \uparrow 3e^-}{\overset{+6}{}} \quad = \quad \underset{3 \times \downarrow 2e^-}{\overset{+4}{}} \qquad \overset{+3}{} \qquad \overset{+6}{}$$

(b) $2CrO_4^{--} + 3SO_3^{--} \qquad \rightarrow \qquad 2CrO_2^- + 3SO_4^{--}$

Net charge: Net charge:

$(2)(-2) + (3)(-2) = -10 \qquad (2)(-1) + (3)(-2) = -8$

To maintain net charge, we need two plus charges on left, or two minus charges on right. To place $2H^+$ on left is forbidden, since the original solution is basic and does not contain any appreciable concentration of hydrogen ions. The alternative is to place two hydroxide ions on the right.

(c) $2CrO_4^{--} + 3SO_3^{--} \rightarrow 2CrO_2^- + 3SO_4^{--} + 2OH^-$

Place $1H_2O$ on left to balance oxygen atoms.

$$2CrO_4^{--} + 3SO_3^{--} + H_2O \rightarrow 2CrO_2^- + 3SO_4^{--} + 2OH^-$$

Net equations show both the species involved in the reactions and the stoichiometry. The number of moles of reactants can be calculated from the equation. The volumes of solutions necessary for complete reaction are thus specified. In general, principal interest is focused on the oxidizing agent and the reducing agent, since the acidic or basic nature of the solution is usually provided by an excess of an acid or base.

Example 6

How many milliliters of 0.20 M $KMnO_4$ are required to oxidize 25.0 ml. of 0.40 M $FeSO_4$ in acidic solution? The reaction which occurs is the oxidation of Fe^{++} by MnO_4^- to give Fe^{+3} and Mn^{++}.

Method 1   Moles. The balanced net equation obtained above is

$$5Fe^{++} + MnO_4^- + 8H^+ \rightarrow 5Fe^{+3} + Mn^{++} + 4H_2O$$

25.0 ml. of 0.40 M $FeSO_4$ supplies $(25.0/1,000)(0.40)$, or 0.010, mole Fe^{++}
From the equation, 5 moles Fe^{++} require 1 mole of MnO_4^-
Hence 0.010 mole Fe^{++} requires 0.0020 mole MnO_4^-
0.20 M $KMnO_4$ supplies 0.20 mole MnO_4^- per 1,000 ml., or 0.0020 mole MnO_4^-
    per 10 ml.

The problem can also be solved by using gram-equivalents as defined in Sec. 5.8. In this reaction, the reducing agent Fe^{++} changes to Fe^{+3}. Each Fe^{++} loses one electron to the oxidizing agent. The Avogadro number of Fe^{++} ions, or 1 mole of Fe^{++}, can furnish the Avogadro number of electrons. For this reaction, 1 mole of $FeSO_4$ is equal to 1 gram-equivalent of $FeSO_4$, and 0.40 M $FeSO_4$ is 0.40 N. The oxidizing agent, MnO_4^-, changes to Mn^{++} in the course of the reaction. As the manganese changes oxidation state from $+7$ to $+2$, each MnO_4^- appears to gain five electrons. One mole of MnO_4^- requires five times the Avogadro number of electrons and so is equal to 5 gram-equivalents. Therefore, 0.20 M $KMnO_4$ is 1.0 N. In general, the normality of a solution of an oxidizing or reducing agent is equal to the molarity times the electron change per formula unit.

Example 6 can be rephrased using normality instead of molarity: How many milliliters of 1.0 N $KMnO_4$ are required to oxidize 25.0 ml. of 0.40 N $FeSO_4$ in acidic solution?

Method 2   Gram-equivalents

25.0 ml. of 0.40 N $FeSO_4$ supplies $(25.0/1,000)(0.40)$, or 0.010 gram-equivalent of reducing agent

1 gram-equivalent of any reducing agent requires 1 gram-equivalent of any oxidizing agent

0.010 gram-equivalent of reducing agent requires 0.010 gram-equivalent of oxidizing agent

1.0 N $KMnO_4$ supplies 1.0 gram-equivalent of oxidizing agent per 1,000 ml., or 0.010 gram-equivalent of oxidizing agent per 10 ml.

In some cases, a given oxidizing agent can be reduced to different products depending on conditions. For example, MnO_4^- can be reduced to Mn^{++}, MnO_2, or MnO_4^{--}, if the medium is acid, neutral, or basic, respectively. In these reactions, the number of electrons transferred is five, three, and one. A solution that is 1 M $KMnO_4$ is 5 N $KMnO_4$, 3 N $KMnO_4$, or 1 N $KMnO_4$, depending on which product is formed. Thus, the normality given for a particular solution may be ambiguous unless the reaction for which the solution is to be used is specified.

QUESTIONS

10.1 *Saturation.* Given in separate beakers some solid sodium acetate, some water, and a clear solution of sodium acetate in water. Explain what you would do to determine whether the solution is saturated, unsaturated, or supersaturated.

10.2 *Solution process.* Describe what is thought to happen on an atomic scale when a crystal of NaCl is dissolved in water. Discuss the origin of the forces involved.

10.3 *Concentration.* Which of the following solutions is most concentrated? (a) 4.00×10^{-4} mole of sugar $(C_{12}H_{22}O_{11})$ and 5.00×10^{-2} mole of H_2O; (b) 0.25 m sugar solution; (c) 1.00 g. of sugar per 10.00 g. of water.

10.4 *Molarity.* The density of water at room temperature is 0.997 g. per ml. Calculate the molarity of water in pure water.   *Ans.* 55.3 M

10.5   *Acids.* How many moles of HNO_3 are: (*a*) in 2.10 g.; (*b*) in 500 ml. of 0.300 *M* HNO_3; (*c*) neutralized by 0.500 mole NaOH dissolved in 250 ml. of water; (*d*) neutralized by 250 ml. of 0.280 *N* NaOH?

Ans. 0.0333; 0.150; 0.500; 0.0700

10.6   *Definitions.* What experiments would you do to show the difference between each of the following: (*a*) electrolyte and nonelectrolyte; (*b*) strong electrolyte and weak electrolyte; (*c*) acid and base?

10.7   *Acids.* How many moles of H_2SO_4 are: (*a*) in 1.96 g.; (*b*) in 0.196 gram-equivalent; (*c*) in 0.300 liter of 0.50 *M* H_2SO_4; (*d*) in 0.300 liter of 0.50 *N* H_2SO_4; (*e*) neutralized by 0.196 mole of NaOH dissolved in 196 ml. of water; (*f*) neutralized by 25.0 ml. of 2.40×10^{-3} *N* $Ba(OH)_2$?

10.8   *Freezing point.* How can you account for the fact that the freezing-point depression per mole of NaCl is greater in 0.001 *m* NaCl solution than in 0.01 *m* NaCl solution?

10.9   *Equations.* Write balanced equations for reactions in which the following changes are observed to occur:

(*a*) $Cu(s) + NO_3^- \rightarrow Cu^{++} + NO(g)$ (acidic)

(*b*) $Zn(s) + NO_3^- \rightarrow Zn^{++} + NH_4^+$ (acidic)

(*c*) $MnO_4^- + NO_2^- \rightarrow MnO_4^{--} + NO_3^-$ (basic)

(*d*) $Ag_2S(s) + NO_3^- \rightarrow Ag^+ + S(s) + NO(g)$ (acidic)

(*e*) $Al(s) + NO_3^- \rightarrow AlO_2^- + NH_3(g)$ (basic)

(*f*) $H_2O_2 + Cr_2O_7^{--} \rightarrow Cr^{+3} + O_2(g)$ (acidic)
   Peroxide

(*g*) $HO_2^- + CrO_2^- \rightarrow CrO_4^{--}$ (basic)
   Peroxide

10.10   *Solubility.* The dissolving of potassium chlorate, $KClO_3$, is endothermic. (*a*) Which is greater, the hydration energy or the lattice energy? Explain. (*b*) Using Le Chatelier's principle, account for the fact that the solubility of $KClO_3$ increases with temperature.

10.11   *Concentrations.* Calculate the molarity and the normality of the solute in each of the following aqueous solutions: (*a*) 1.20 g. of NaOH in 25.0 ml. of solution; (*b*) 3.43 g. of $Ba(OH)_2$ in 2.50 liters of solution; (*c*) 1.47 g. of H_3PO_4 in 40.0 ml. of solution.

Ans. 1.20 *M* and 1.20 *N*; 0.00800 *M* and 0.0160 *N*; 0.375 *M* and 1.13 *N*

10.12   *Concentrations.* A given aqueous solution contains 4.41 g. of H_2SO_4 in 0.200 liter of solution. What is (*a*) its molarity and (*b*) its normality? When diluted with enough water to make 0.500 liter of solution, what will be (*c*) its molarity and (*d*) its normality? The final solution will neutralize (*e*) how many moles of NaOH; (*f*) how many grams of NaOH; (*g*) how many liters of 0.010 *M* NaOH; (*h*) how many liters of 0.050 *N* NaOH?

10.13 *Vapor pressure.* (*a*) What happens to the equilibrium vapor pressure of a solvent when solute is added? (*b*) Describe how the apparatus shown in Fig. 7.4 can be used to measure this effect. (*c*) Draw a graph showing how the vapor pressure of water changes with temperature. On the same graph, show the effect of added solute. (*d*) Indicate how the change in normal boiling point can be deduced from your graph.

10.14 *Concentrations.* A given solution contains only 2.76 moles of *A* and 1.24 moles of *B*. The volume of the sample is 0.125 liter. The molecular weights of *A* and *B* are 80.0 and 50.0, respectively. Calculate for this solution: (*a*) the mole fraction of *A* and *B*; (*b*) the molarity of *A* and *B*; (*c*) the molality of *A* and *B*.

10.15 *Brønsted-Lowry.* Show specifically how the terms Brønsted-Lowry acid, base, conjugate acid, and conjugate base apply to the following reactions in pure liquid H_2SO_4 as solvent:

$$HF + H_2SO_4 \rightarrow H_2F^+ + HSO_4^-$$

$$HClO_4 + H_2SO_4 \rightarrow H_3SO_4^+ + ClO_4^-$$

10.16 *Lewis acids and bases.* From the following list select the Lewis acids and the Lewis bases: S^{--}, H^+, H_2O, NH_3, BF_3, Al^{+3}, O^{--}.

10.17 *Freezing-point depression.* In a 0.100 *m* aqueous solution, the weak acid H*X* is 5.0% dissociated. Calculate the expected freezing point of this solution.

Ans. $-0.195°C.$

10.18 *Concentration of electrolytes.* (*a*) Assuming complete dissociation, calculate the number of moles of positive ion and of negative ion in each of the following solutions: (1) 20.0 ml. of 0.10 *M* NaCl; (2) 30.0 ml. of 0.30 *M* $CaCl_2$; (3) 50.0 ml. of 0.20 *M* $Ca(NO_3)_2$. (*b*) When the three above samples are mixed, the final volume is 100.0 ml. Calculate the concentration of Na^+, Ca^{++}, Cl^-, and NO_3^- in the final solution.

Ans. (*b*) 0.020 *M* Na^+; 0.20 *M* Cl^-; 0.19 *M* Ca^{++}; 0.20 *M* NO_3^-

10.19 *Oxidation-reduction.* (*a*) To make up 35.0 ml. of 1.0×10^{-3} *M* $KMnO_4$ requires how many grams of $KMnO_4$? (*b*) This sample of solution requires how many milliliters of 0.040 *M* $FeSO_4$ solution for complete reaction in acidified solution, where the reaction is $Fe^{++} + MnO_4^- \rightarrow Fe^{+3} + Mn^{++}$? (*c*) To make up the solution needed in (*b*) requires how many grams of $FeSO_4$?

10.20 *Oxidation-reduction.* (*a*) Complete and balance the equation for the following change in acidic solution:

$$Cr_2O_7^{--} + Sn^{++} \rightarrow Cr^{+3} + Sn^{+4}$$

(*b*) Calculate (1) the number of moles, (2) the number of gram-equivalents, (3) the volume of 0.10 *M* solution, (4) the volume of 0.10 *N* solution of $K_2Cr_2O_7$ required just to oxidize 75 ml. of 0.30 *M* $SnCl_2$ by the above reaction.

10.21 *Solution properties.* (*a*) Show by labeled dotted lines what happens to the liquid range on the H_2O phase diagram when 1 mole of a strong electrolyte and 1 mole of a nonelectrolyte are added separately to equal quantities of water. (*b*) How will the normal boiling point and the normal melting point be affected in these two cases?

10.22 *Molecular-weight determination.* (*a*) Outline the principle involved in the determination of the molecular weight of sugar by freezing-point depression. List the experimental data required for such a determination. (*b*) If the dissolved sugar molecules were dissociated, would the determined molecular weight be higher than, lower than, or the same as the true value? Explain.

10.23 *Molarity.* Given a bottle of 18 *M* H_2SO_4. You wish to make up 0.60 liter of 3.0 *M* H_2SO_4. How many milliliters of concentrated H_2SO_4 and how many milliliters of water must you mix? Assume volumes are additive.

Ans. 100 ml. of acid and 500 ml. of water

10.24 *Molarity.* Given a bottle of 0.75 *M* H_2SO_4 and a bottle of 3.00 *M* H_2SO_4. Using only these two solutions (no additional water), how much of each would you use to make 0.120 liter of 1.5 *M* H_2SO_4?

Ans. 0.080 liter of 0.75 *M* and 0.040 liter of 3.00 *M*

10.25 *Neutralization.* What is the normality of a solution of an unknown base, 22.50 ml. of which just neutralize 28.00 ml. of 0.100 *M* H_2SO_4?

Ans. 0.249 *N*

10.26 *Neutralization.* How many milliliters of 0.100 *N* H_2SO_4 would be required just to neutralize a solution made by mixing 20.0 ml. of 0.0100 *M* $Ca(OH)_2$ and 30.0 ml. of 0.0300 *M* NaOH?

10.27 *Gram-equivalents.* The neutralization of 0.900 g. of an unknown solid acid requires 30.00 ml. of 0.150 *N* NaOH. What is the weight of 1 gram-equivalent of the acid?

10.28 *Oxidation-reduction.* What is the normality of an unknown reducing agent, 22.50 ml. of which just reduce 28.00 ml. of 0.100 *M* $KMnO_4$ to Mn^{++} in acid solution?

Ans. 0.622 *N*

10.29 *Cooling curve.* Draw a cooling curve to show what happens when H_2O vapor at 1 atm. pressure is cooled by uniform removal of heat to give finally a solid. Show by dotted lines what modification you would have to make in your cooling curve if the steam starts out in contact with a small amount of water-soluble solid.

10.30 *Freezing-point depression.* An automobile radiator is filled with 2.0 gal. of antifreeze and 8.0 qt. of water. How cold can it get before this radiator "freezes"? (Assume the antifreeze to be the nonelectrolyte ethylene glycol, $C_2H_6O_2$, having a density of 1.12 g. per ml. Assume water to have a density of 1.0 g. per ml. The molal freezing-point depression constant of water is 3.35°F. per mole per 1,000 g. of water.)

Ans. −29°F.

10.31 *Neutralization.* The heat evolved when 1 mole of a strong acid is neutralized by 1 mole of a strong base is 13.7 kcal., no matter what strong acid or strong base is used. However, for neutralizations involving weak acids or weak bases, less than 13.7 kcal. of heat may be evolved per mole of water formed. Explain.

10.32 *General.* (a) Complete and balance the following in acidic solution: $NO + ClO_3^- \rightarrow NO_3^- + Cl^-$. (b) How many milliliters of 0.10 M $HClO_3$ solution would be required to react completely with 1.5 g. of NO according to this reaction? (c) What would be the concentration of Cl^- in the final solution if the final total volume of solution were 0.400 liter? (d) What would be the normality label you would put on a bottle of 0.10 M $HClO_3$ as used for this reaction? (e) How many gram-equivalents of $Ba(OH)_2$ would you need to neutralize completely 50.0 ml. of the solution in (d)?

10.33 *Normality.* Given a bottle of solution labeled 0.020 M $K_2Cr_2O_7$. How would you relabel this solution in terms of normality for use in each of the following reactions?

(a) $Cr_2O_7^{--} + Fe^{++} \rightarrow Cr^{+3} + Fe^{+3}$ (acidic)

(b) $Cr_2O_7^{--} + Zn(s) \rightarrow Zn^{++} + Cr^{++}$ (acidic)

What is the weight of a gram-equivalent of $K_2Cr_2O_7$ for each of these reactions?

10.34 *Per cent dissociation.* Suppose you dissolve 1.200×10^{-3} mole of HX in 25.0 ml. of water. If the freezing point is determined to be $-0.100°C.$, what is the per cent dissociation of the weak acid HX?   *Ans.* 12%

10.35 *General.* (a) Write a complete balanced equation for the following change in basic solution:

$$Cl_2(g) + S_2O_3^{--} \rightarrow SO_4^{--} + Cl^-$$

(b) Given 0.15 mole of Cl_2 gas. (1) How many grams does the sample weigh? (2) How many atoms does the sample contain? (3) How many gram-atoms does the sample contain? (4) How many molecules does the sample contain? (5) How many liters does the sample occupy at STP? (6) How many liters does the sample occupy at 1.5 atm. pressure and 27°C.?

(c) Given 50.0 ml. of 0.20 M $Na_2S_2O_3$ solution. (1) How many moles of $S_2O_3^{--}$ are in this sample? (2) How many gram-equivalents of reducing agent are in this sample for the above reaction? (3) What is the normality of this solution?

(d) Given 150.0 ml. of 2.0 M NaOH solution. (1) What is the normality of this solution? (2) How many gram-equivalents of base does the sample contain? (3) How many grams of NaOH were used to prepare the sample? (4) How many molecules of undissociated NaOH in the sample? (5) How many gram-equivalents of H_3PO_4 are required just to neutralize the sample? (6) How many milliliters of 0.50 M H_3PO_4 are required just to neutralize the sample?

(e) The samples given in (b), (c), and (d) are mixed, so that reaction occurs according to the equation in (a). Calculate the molarity of OH^-, Cl^-, and SO_4^{--} in the final solution assuming the final volume of solution is 200 ml.

Ans. (e) 1.0 M OH^-; 0.40 M Cl^-; 0.10 M SO_4^{--}

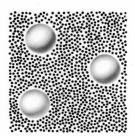

11   *Colloids*

IN INTRODUCING THE TOPIC OF SOLUTIONS, it was more or less implied that it is easily possible to distinguish between a homogeneous mixture and a heterogeneous mixture. However, this distinction is not a sharp one. There are systems which are neither obviously homogeneous nor obviously heterogeneous. They are classed as intermediate and are known as *colloids*.

11.1   PARTICLE SIZE

In order to get an idea of what a colloid is, we imagine a process in which a sample of solid is placed in a liquid and subdivided. So long as distinct particles of solid are visible to the naked eye, there is no question that the system is heterogeneous. On standing, these visible particles separate out. Depending on the relative density of the solid and the liquid, the solid particles float to the top or settle to the bottom. They can be separated easily by filtration.

As the solid is progressively subdivided, eventually a state is reached in which the dispersed particles have been broken down to individual molecules or atoms. In this limit, a solution is produced in which two phases can no longer be distinguished. No matter how powerful a microscope is used, a solution appears uniform throughout, and individual molecules cannot be seen. On standing, the dispersed particles do not separate out, nor can they be separated by filtration.

Between coarse suspensions and true solutions, there is a region of change from heterogeneity to homogeneity. In this region, dispersed particles are so small that they do not form an obviously separate phase, but they are not so small that they can be said to be in true solution. This state of subdivision is called the *colloidal state.* On standing, the particles of a colloid do not separate out at any appreciable rate; they cannot be seen under a microscope; nor can they be separated by filtration. The dividing lines between colloids and solutions and between colloids and discrete phases are not rigorously fixed, since a continuous gradation of particle size is possible. Usually, however, colloids are defined as a separate class on the basis of size. When the particle size lies between about 10^{-7} cm. and 10^{-4} cm., the dispersion is called a *colloid,* a *colloidal suspension,* or a *colloidal solution.*

The size of a dispersed particle does not tell anything about the constitution of the particle. The particle may consist of atoms, of small molecules, or of one giant molecule. For example, colloidal gold consists of various-sized particles each containing a million or more gold atoms. Colloidal sulfur can be made with particles containing a thousand or so S_8 molecules. An example of a huge molecule is hemoglobin, the protein responsible for the red color of blood. The molecular weight of this molecule is 66,800. It has a diameter of approximately 3×10^{-7} cm.

11.2   TYPES OF COLLOIDS

Colloids are frequently classified on the basis of the states of aggregation of the component phases, even though the separate phases are not visibly distinguishable once the colloid is formed. The more important classifications are *sols, emulsions, gels,* and *aerosols.*

In *sols,* a solid is dispersed through a liquid, so that the liquid forms the continuous phase and bits of solid form the discontinuous phase. Milk of magnesia is a sol consisting of solid particles of magnesium hydroxide dispersed through water. Sols can be made by breaking down large particles or building up small particles to colloidal dimensions. Colloidal gold can be made by striking an electric arc between two gold electrodes under water. It can also be made by the chemical reduction of chlorauric acid, $HAuCl_4$, by a slow reducing agent such as hydrazine, N_2H_4. A gold sol made in 1857 by Michael Faraday is still in the London museum without any detectable settling. Investigation of gold sol by X rays has shown that the particles of gold which are dispersed throughout the water are crystalline in nature.

Emulsions are colloids in which a liquid is dispersed through a liquid. A common example is ordinary milk, which consists of butterfat globules dispersed through an aqueous solution. In the creaming process the larger globules separate out. In the process of homogenization, milk is forced under pressure through small openings in a metal plate to break up the globules and thereby reduce creaming.

A *gel* is an unusual type of colloid in which a liquid contains a solid arranged in a fine network extending throughout the system. Both the solid and the liquid phases are continuous. Examples of gels are jellies, gelatin, agar, and slimy precipitates such as aluminum hydroxide. The so-called "canned heat," or "solid alcohol," is a gel made by mixing aqueous calcium acetate with alcohol.

An *aerosol* is a colloid made by dispersing either a solid or a liquid in a gas. The former is called a smoke and the latter a fog. Cigarette smoke is an aerosol of solid ash dispersed in air. The fog spray produced from DDT bombs is an aerosol of the DDT solution dispersed in air.

11.3 TYNDALL EFFECT

One of the most characteristic features that distinguish colloids, especially sols, from true solutions is the *Tyndall effect*. When a beam of light is passed through a solution or a pure liquid, the path of the beam is not visible from the side. The dissolved particles are too small to scatter light, and therefore the light goes on through. In a colloid, the particles are big enough to scatter the light. Therefore, when a beam of light is turned on a colloid, an observer to one side can see the path of the beam. The situation is shown in Fig. 11.1. The Tyndall effect can be produced readily by turning a flashlight on an aqueous solution of sodium thiosulfate, $Na_2S_2O_3$, and adding a

Fig. 11.1 *Tyndall effect.*

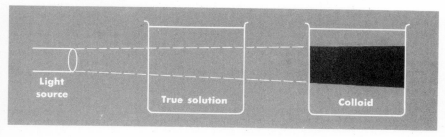

few drops of dilute acid. A chemical reaction occurs which produces elemental sulfur. The light beam is invisible until the sulfur particles aggregate to colloidal dimensions.

By taking into consideration the wave nature of light, information can be obtained from the Tyndall effect about the size and shape of the scattering particles. In an ordinary solution, the particles of solute are much smaller than the wavelength of the light. Visible light has a wavelength ranging from 4,000 to 7,200 A., or from 4.0×10^{-5} to 7.2×10^{-5} cm. Solute particles that are 5 A. or so in diameter are too small to affect a wave of such length. However, when solute particles are of the order of several thousand angstrom units in diameter, the light beam is scattered or diffracted and becomes visible from the side. Careful studies of this scattering have been used to determine the size of particles in colloids such as suspensions of rubber.

11.4 BROWNIAN MOTION

The particles of a colloid are too small to be visible under a microscope. However, they are big enough to reflect light. When a microscope is focused on a Tyndall beam, light is reflected up into the microscope. The details of the shape of the particle are not apparent, but the position of the particle may be fixed by noting the position at which the light appears. When observed in this way, colloidal particles are seen to undergo Brownian motion, the rapid, random, zigzag motion previously mentioned in discussing gases (Sec. 6.11). The smaller the particle size, the more violent the Brownian motion.

Under ordinary circumstances, it is observed that a colloid in an uninsulated container does not settle out. However, when the colloid is kept in a well-insulated container, settling is observed, and after a time there will be a gradation in the concentration of colloidal particles from the top to the bottom of the sample. This gradation in concentration develops because there are two opposing effects: (1) the attraction due to gravity, which tends to pull heavier particles down, and (2) the dispersing effect due to Brownian motion. The more massive the particles, the more important is effect (1) and the more pronounced is the concentration gradation.* Why then is there no appreciable concentration gradient observed for colloids in uninsulated containers? Apparently, the main reason is that in an uninsulated container

---

* Two extreme cases can be imagined. For rocks in water, the settling is so pronounced that all the rocks are at the bottom. For a true solution such as sugar in water, the gradation in concentration is so slight that only the most careful experiments involving very tall columns and precise temperature control could show any difference in concentration between the top and bottom of the sample.

there are convection currents due to nonuniform temperature. These currents keep the colloidal suspension constantly stirred up.

11.5   ADSORPTION OF CHARGES

In some colloids, the colloidal particles adsorb electrical charges. For example, ferric oxide sol consists of positively charged aggregates of ferric oxide units. The positive charge enhances the stability of the colloid. Normally, when one particle in its Brownian motion hits another, they coagulate to form a larger particle. From collisions between large particles, a particle results which is so large that Brownian motion cannot keep it in suspension. However, ferric oxide has great adsorption power for H^+. By the proper method of preparation, it is possible to get ferric oxide particles formed with H^+ adsorbed on the surface, as shown on the left in Fig. 11.2. Presumably the H^+ ions are stuck on oxygen atoms which protrude from the particles. A particle which has H^+ adsorbed on it has a net positive charge and thereby repels any similarly charged particle. The charged ferric oxide particles try to stay as far apart from each other on the average as possible. There is little chance that they will come together to form a large mass which settles out.

Arsenious sulfide, As_2S_3, forms a negative sol by adsorbing SH^- or OH^- ions, as shown in Fig. 11.2. It is not surprising that mixing a positively charged ferric oxide sol with a negatively charged arsenious sulfide sol coagulates them both.

That some colloidal particles are electrically charged can be shown by studying *electrophoresis, the migration of colloidal particles in an electric field*. Figure 11.3 shows the experimental setup. A U tube is partly filled with the colloidal solution. Very carefully, so as not to disturb the colloid, the remainder of the U tube is filled with a solution of an electrolyte. The electrolytic solution needs to be of lower density (so that it will stay on top), different in appearance from the colloid (so that the boundary can be clearly

Fig. 11.2   Adsorption of charges on colloidal aggregates.

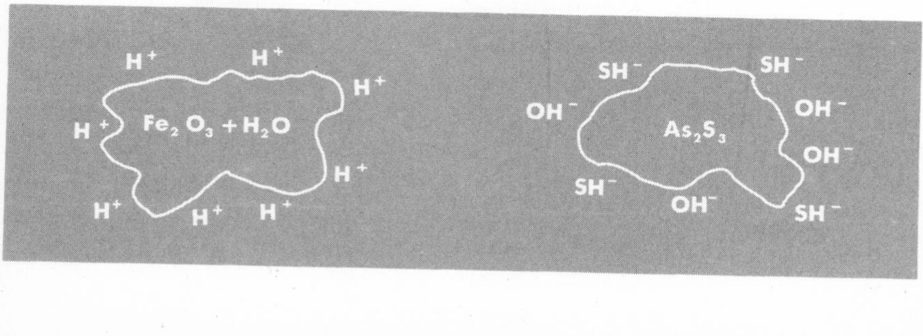

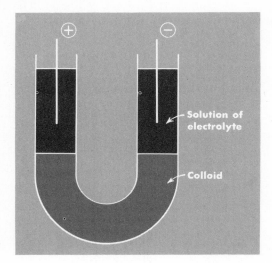

Fig. 11.3   Electrophoresis.

seen), and appreciably electrically conducting. The choice of electrolyte is limited by the fact that many electrolytes coagulate colloids, but usually a salt, such as sodium bromide, can be found which does not affect the colloid. Electrodes are inserted into the solution, with one electrode positively charged and the other negatively charged. After a time that may range from 30 min. to 48 hr., the boundaries between the colloid and the electrolyte solution have shifted because of migration of the colloid through the solvent. From the direction of migration of the colloid, the sign of the charge of the colloidal particles can be determined. For example, when the electrophoresis of ferric oxide sol is observed in this cell, the boundary moves toward the negative electrode and away from the positive electrode, suggesting that the colloid is positively charged. By observing the rate at which migration occurs, it is also possible to get information about the size and the shape of the colloidal particles. Recently, the study of electrophoresis has been applied with great success to protein molecules. In acidic solution, protein molecules pick up hydrogen ions to become positively charged. From their migration in an electric field, it has been possible to draw inferences about their size and shape. Some, like gamma globulin, seem to be spherical in shape. Others, such as fibrinogen, the blood-clotting agent, are shaped like cigars. Knowledge of the size and shape of protein molecules should help in understanding their behavior.

Some colloidal particles adsorb films of molecules, which shield them from other particles. An example of this adsorption is found in gelatin. Gelatin is a high-molecular-weight protein which has the property of tying to itself a sheath of water. This film of very tightly bound water protects the gelatin particle from coagulating with another gelatin particle. If two gelatin particles collide, they do not coagulate, because the gelatin parts have not been able to get in contact with each other. This property of gelatin is used in stabilizing colloids of silver bromide in preparing photographic film. When finely divided silver bromide is stirred up with water, it settles out. However, if the silver bromide is mixed with gelatin, the gelatin forms a film on the outside of the silver bromide. The gelatin in turn adsorbs a layer of water, so that essentially two protective films have formed on silver bromide to keep it in suspension.

11.6 SURFACE ADSORPTION

One of the most characteristic properties of matter in a finely divided condition is the extremely large surface area. Subdivision of a solid, for example, may increase its surface area by many factors of 10. One cubic centimeter of sulfur in the form of a cube 1 cm. on edge has a surface area of 6 sq. cm., or about 1 sq. in. However, 1 cc. of sulfur ground up into cubes which are 10^{-5} cm. on the edge has its surface area increased to 6×10^5 sq. cm., or about 700 sq. ft. In the former case, most of the sulfur atoms are not surface atoms. In the latter case, the fraction of atoms that are surface atoms is appreciable compared to the number of atoms that are in the interior. This would make no difference except that surface atoms have special properties. For example, the valence of surface atoms is usually not satisfied, since the atom is designed to bond in three dimensions, which it cannot do at the surface.

Charcoal is a substance in which the surface atoms are an appreciable fraction of the total number. It consists of solid carbon with a fine network of tunnels extending through the specimen. The surface area is enormous and has been determined to be of the order of 1,000 sq. ft. per. g. On all of this large surface area are carbon atoms which have unsaturated valence. They can attract molecules, especially polar molecules, thus accounting for the high adsorption that is characteristic of charcoal. When a mixture of hydrogen sulfide, H_2S, and oxygen is passed over a charcoal surface, the H_2S is selectively adsorbed. Because H_2S is a polar molecule with the sulfur end more negative than the hydrogen end, it is more strongly adsorbed than the oxygen molecule, which is symmetrical and nonpolar. The charcoal gas mask makes use of this principle of selective adsorption. The charcoal selectively adsorbs poisonous gases, which are usually complicated polar molecules, and lets the oxygen through for respiration.

At higher temperatures, molecular motion makes adsorption more difficult. Thus, charcoal with its surface completely covered may be reactivated by heating it up to drive off adsorbed gases. At low temperatures, where molecular motion is slight, adsorption increases. In fact, at very low temperatures, selectivity is less pronounced, and even nonpolar molecules may be adsorbed, presumably because of van der Waals attraction. At liquid-nitrogen temperatures ($-196°$C.) even oxygen gas is strongly adsorbed on charcoal.

QUESTIONS

11.1   *Sol.* How can you show experimentally that a given liquid is a sol?

11.2   *Surface area.* Suppose 1.0 cc. of gold is subdivided into spherical particles of radius 25 A. Calculate: (*a*) the total number of particles formed; (*b*) their total surface area; (*c*) the molecular weight, assuming the density is 19.3 g. per cc.   *Ans.* 1.5×10^{19}; 1.2×10^7 sq. cm.; 7.7×10^5 a.m.u.

11.3   *Adsorption.* If an H_2S molecule takes up an area of 12 sq. A. when adsorbed, what volume at STP of H_2S can be adsorbed on 1.0 g. of charcoal? (See Sec. 11.6 for surface area of charcoal.)

11.4   *Coagulation.* How might you coagulate a sol which has been stabilized by adsorption of H^+?

11.5   *Tyndall effect.* (*a*) What is the difference in experimental equipment needed to observe Brownian motion and the Tyndall effect? (*b*) What is observed in each case?

11.6   *Tyndall effect.* (*a*) What is the relation between Tyndall effect and the decreased effectiveness of automobile headlights in a fog? (*b*) Yellow light is of longer average wavelength than white light. Why are fog lights usually yellow?

11.7   *Adsorption.* Which of the following would be most strongly adsorbed on charcoal: O_2, CO_2, H_2O? Explain.

11.8   *Colloidal charges.* How could you show experimentally that a given colloidal suspension contains charged particles?

11.9   *Freezing-point lowering.* Suppose you have 1.0 g. of sulfur dispersed in 100.0 g. of water. If the particle diameter is 20.0 A. and its density is 2.0 g. per cc., what would be the freezing point of the sol?   *Ans.* $-0.0037°$C.

11.10   *Protein size.* Given that the insulin molecule under certain conditions has a molecular weight of 12,000 a.m.u. If the density is 1.4 g. per cc., what is the apparent radius of the insulin molecule?

11.11   *Particle-size determination.* Suppose you have a sample of ferric oxide sol that is being examined with a microscope. You find on the average 2.7 particles in a field of view that is 0.0040 cm. in diameter and 0.0010 cm. in depth. The sol contains 0.00028 g. per liter of ferric oxide (density 5.2 g. per cc). Assuming the particles are spherical, calculate their probable average radius.
Ans. 3.9×10^{-6} cm.

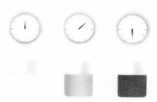

12   *Chemical Kinetics*

CHEMICAL KINETICS is the branch of chemistry concerned with the velocity of chemical reactions and the mechanism by which chemical reactions occur. The term *reaction velocity* is used to describe the rate at which chemical change occurs. The term *reaction mechanism* is used to describe the sequence of stepwise reactions by which the over-all change occurs. For most reactions, it is only the disappearance of starting materials and the appearance of final products that can be detected; i.e., only the net reaction is observable. In general, however, the net reaction is not the whole story but simply represents a summation of all the changes that occur. The net change may actually consist of several consecutive reactions, each of which constitutes a step in the formation of final products. In discussing chemical reactions, it is important to keep clear the distinction between a net reaction and one step in that reaction.

When a reaction occurs in steps, there are probably intermediate species formed which may not be detectable because they may be promptly used up in a subsequent step. However, by investigating the influence that various factors have on the rate at which the net change occurs, it is sometimes possible to elucidate what the intermediates are and how they are involved in the mechanism of the reaction.

What are the factors which influence the rate of chemical reaction? Experiments show that four important factors are (1) nature of reactants, (2) concentration of reactants, (3) temperature, and (4) catalysis.

12.1   NATURE OF REACTANTS

In a chemical reaction, bonds are formed, and bonds are broken. The rate should therefore depend on the specific bonds involved. Experimentally, the reaction velocity depends on the specific substances brought together in reaction. For example, the reduction of permanganate ion in acidic solution by ferrous ion is practically instantaneous. MnO_4^- disappears as fast as ferrous sulfate solution is added; the limiting factor is the rate of mixing the solutions. On the other hand, the reduction of permanganate ion in acidic solution by oxalic acid, $H_2C_2O_4$, is not instantaneous. The violet color characteristic of MnO_4^- persists long after mixing the solutions. In these two reactions everything is identical except the nature of the reducing agent, but still the rate is quite different.

The rates observed for different reactants vary widely. There are reactions, such as occur in acid-base neutralization, which may be over in a microsecond, so that the rate is difficult to measure. There are also very slow reactions, such as those occurring in geological processes, which may not reach completion in a million years. The changes in a lifetime may be too small to be detected. Most information has been accumulated about the reactions that occur at rates intermediate between these extremes.

12.2   CONCENTRATION OF REACTANTS

It is found by experiment that the rate of a homogeneous chemical reaction depends on the concentration of the reactants. A homogeneous reaction is one which occurs in only one phase. Heterogeneous reactions involve more than one phase. It is found for *heterogeneous* reactions that the rate of reaction is proportional to the area of contact between the phases. An example is the rusting of iron, a heterogeneous reaction involving a solid phase, iron, and a gas phase, oxygen. Rusting is slow when the surface of contact is small, as is the case with a bar of iron. If the bar is ground into powder, rusting is more rapid because of greater area of contact.

For *homogeneous* reactions, the rate depends on the concentration (amount per unit volume) of the reactants in solution. The solution may be liquid or gaseous. In a liquid solution, the concentration of a reactant can be changed either by its addition or removal or by changing the volume of the system, as by addition or removal of solvent. The specific effect has to be determined by experiment. Thus, in the reaction of substance *A* with substance *B*, the addition of *A* may cause an increase, a decrease, or no change in rate depending on the particular reaction. Quantitatively, the rate may double, triple, become half as great, etc. A priori, it is not possible to look at the net equation for a chemical reaction and tell how the rate is affected by a change of concentration of reactants. The quantitative influence of concentration on the rate can be found only by experiment.

The determination of how the rate of reaction changes with concentration of reactants is an experimental problem beset by many difficulties. The usual procedure is to keep everything constant except the concentration of one reactant. As the concentration of the one reactant is systematically changed, the reaction rate is measured. This may be done by noting the rate of disappearance of a reactant or the rate of formation of a product. Experimental difficulties usually come in determining the instantaneous concentration of a component as it changes.

The reaction between hydrogen and nitric oxide

$$2H_2(g) + 2NO(g) \rightarrow 2H_2O(g) + N_2(g)$$

is a homogeneous reaction which can be investigated kinetically by following the change in pressure of the gaseous mixture as the reaction proceeds. The pressure drops because 4 moles of gas are converted to 3 moles of gas. Typical data for several experiments at 800°C. are given in Table 12.1.

Table 12.1   Rate of Reaction of NO and H_2

Experiment	Initial molar concentration × 10^3 *		Initial rate, mm. Hg/min.
	NO	H_2	
I	6.00	1.00	20
II	6.00	2.00	40
III	6.00	3.00	60
IV	1.00	6.00	3
V	2.00	6.00	12
VI	3.00	6.00	27

* "Initial molar concentration × 10^3" means that the values of molar concentration have been multiplied by 10^3 before being entered in the table. Hence in experiment I, the concentration of NO is 6.00×10^{-3} *M* and that of H_2 is 1.00×10^{-3} *M*.

Since reactants are being used up during the course of the reaction, their concentrations and their rate of reaction are constantly changing. The concentrations and rates listed are those at the very beginning of the reaction when little change has occurred. The first three experiments have the same initial concentration of NO but different initial concentrations of H_2. The last three experiments have the same initial concentration of H_2 but different initial concentrations of NO.

The data for experiments I and II show that, when the initial concentration of NO is constant, doubling the concentration of H_2 doubles the rate; I and III show that tripling the concentration of H_2 triples the rate. The rate of reaction is therefore found to be directly proportional to the concentration of H_2. The data for experiments IV and V show that, when the initial concentration of H_2 is constant, doubling the concentration of NO quadruples the rate; IV and VI show that tripling the concentration of NO triply triples the rate. The rate of reaction is therefore found to be proportional to the square of the concentration of NO. Quantitatively, the data can be summarized by stating that the reaction rate is proportional to (concentration of H_2) × (concentration of NO)^2. This can be written mathematically as

$$\text{Rate} = k[H_2][NO]^2$$

The equation is known as the *rate law* for the reaction and states that the rate is equal to a proportionality constant times the concentration of H_2 to the first power times the concentration of NO to the second power. Square brackets represent concentration of a substance in moles per liter. The proportionality constant k is called the *specific rate constant* and is characteristic of a given reaction but varies with temperature.

The general form of any rate law is

$$\text{Rate} = k[A]^n[B]^m \cdots$$

where n is the appropriate power to which the concentration of A must be raised, and m is the appropriate power to which the concentration of B must be raised, in order to summarize the data. The three dots represent other reactants which may be involved in the rate law. The exponents n and m may be fractions and, in fact, may be negative. Negative exponents express inverse proportionality. The important thing to note is that the rate law is determined by experiment. A common error is to assume that the coefficients in the balanced net equation are the exponents in the rate law. This, in general, is not true. For example, in the reaction between H_2 and NO the exponents in the rate law are 1 and 2, whereas the coefficients in the balanced equation are 2 and 2. The only way to determine unambiguously the exponents in the rate law is to do the experiment.

1 2 . 3   TEMPERATURE

How does the temperature of a reaction affect its rate? Observations on rate experiments like that described in the previous section indicate that a rise in temperature increases the rate of any reaction. Furthermore, a decrease in temperature decreases the rate, no matter whether the reaction is exothermic or endothermic. The change of rate with temperature is expressed by a change in the specific rate constant k. For every reaction, k increases with increasing temperature. As to the magnitude of the effect, no generalization can be made. The magnitude varies from one reaction to another and also from one temperature range to another. A rule, which must be used with caution, is that a 10°C. rise in temperature approximately doubles or triples the reaction rate. For each specific reaction it is necessary to determine from experiment the quantitative effect of a rise in temperature.

1 2 . 4   CATALYSIS

It is found by experiment that some reactions can be speeded up by the presence of substances which themselves remain unchanged after the reaction has ended. Such substances are known as *catalysts,* and their effect as *catalysis.* Often only a trace of catalyst is sufficient to accelerate the reaction.* There are numerous examples of catalysis.

When $KClO_3$ is heated so that it decomposes into KCl and oxygen, it is observed that a pinch of manganese dioxide, MnO_2, considerably accelerates the reaction. At the end of the reaction the $KClO_3$ is gone, but all the MnO_2 remains. It appears as if the catalyst is not involved in the reaction, because the starting amount can be recovered. However, the catalyst must take some part in the reaction, or else it could not change the rate.

When hydrogen gas escapes from a cylinder into the air, no change is visible. If the escaping hydrogen is directed at finely divided platinum, it is observed that the platinum glows and eventually ignites the hydrogen. In the absence of platinum the rate of reaction is too small to observe. In contact with platinum, hydrogen reacts with oxygen from the air to form water. As they react, they give off energy which heats the platinum. As the platinum gets hotter, it heats the hydrogen and oxygen, so that their rate of reaction increases, until eventually ignition occurs and the reaction of hydrogen with oxygen becomes self-sustaining.

* However, there are many reactions in which the rate of reaction is proportional to some power of the concentration of catalyst. The actual dependence of rate on catalyst concentration must be determined by experiment.

Enzymes are complex substances in biological systems which act as catalysts for biochemical processes. Pepsin in the gastric juice and ptyalin in the saliva are examples. Ptyalin is the catalyst which accelerates the conversion of starch to sugar. Although starch will react with water to form sugar, it takes weeks for the conversion to occur. A trace of ptyalin is enough to make the reaction proceed at a biologically useful rate.

A special type of catalysis occasionally encountered is *autocatalysis,* or *self-catalysis.* As the name implies, this is catalysis in which one of the products of the reaction is a catalyst for the reaction. For example, in the reaction of permanganate and oxalic acid

$$2MnO_4^- + 5H_2C_2O_4 + 6H^+ \rightarrow 2Mn^{++} + 10CO_2 + 8H_2O$$

Violet   *Colorless*

the product Mn^{++} catalyzes the reaction. This can readily be observed by mixing solutions of potassium permanganate, sulfuric acid, and oxalic acid. No appreciable decolorization occurs until a tiny crystal of manganous sulfate, $MnSO_4$, is dropped into the reaction mixture. The uncatalyzed reaction is quite slow. Until some Mn^{++} is formed, the reaction does not proceed at an appreciable speed. Addition of a trace of Mn^{++} enables the reaction to start. More Mn^{++} is produced and speeds the reaction further.

Interesting catalysis is observed in the case of hydrogen peroxide. Hydrogen peroxide decomposes to water and oxygen. The reaction is rapid enough that solutions of hydrogen peroxide are difficult to keep without decomposition. It is observed that there are certain substances, such as phosphates, which can be added in trace amounts to slow down the rate of decomposition. This looks like the reverse of catalysis, and, in fact, substances which slow down the rate have been called negative catalysts. The name is misleading, since the function of the phosphate in hydrogen peroxide is probably to destroy the action of catalysts already present in the hydrogen peroxide. For example, it is found by experiment that the decomposition of hydrogen peroxide is catalyzed by traces of Fe^{+3} ion. When phosphate is added, it combines with the Fe^{+3} and prevents the Fe^{+3} from functioning as a catalyst.

12.5   COLLISION THEORY

Many of the observed facts of chemical kinetics have been interpreted in terms of the *collision theory.* This theory makes the basic assumption that, for a chemical reaction to occur, particles must collide. For substance A to react with substance B, it is necessary that the particles A, be they molecules, ions, or atoms, collide with particles B. In the collision, atoms and electrons are rearranged. There is a reshuffling of chemical bonds leading to the production of other species.

According to collision theory the rate of any step in a reaction is directly proportional to (1) the *number of collisions per second* between the reacting particles involved in that step and (2) the *fraction of these collisions that are effective*. That the rate should depend on the number of collisions per second seems obvious. For instance, in a box that contains *A* molecules and *B* molecules there is a certain frequency of collision between *A* and *B*. If more *A* molecules are placed in the box, the collision frequency between *A* molecules and *B* molecules is increased. With more collisions between reacting molecules, the reaction between *A* and *B* should go faster. However, this cannot be the full story. Calculations of the number of collisions between particles indicate that the collision frequency is very high. In a mixture containing 1 mole of *A* molecules and 1 mole of *B* molecules as gases at STP, the number of collisions is more than 10^{30} per sec. If every one of these collisions led to reaction, the reaction would be over in an instant, and all reactions would be very fast. By observation, this is not true. It must be that only some of the collisions lead to reaction.

Collisions between *A* molecules and *B* molecules may be so gentle that there is no change in the identity of the molecules after collision. The colliding particles separate to resume their original identity. The electron cloud associated with *A* and the electron cloud associated with *B* repel each other because they are similarly charged. In a gentle collision, the repulsion between the electron clouds may simply cause the molecules to bounce apart. However, if *A* or *B* or both *A* and *B* have much kinetic energy before collision, they can easily use that kinetic energy to do work against the repulsive forces. In the collision the molecules may penetrate each other far enough that electron repulsion is overcome and electron rearrangement ensues. One or more new species may be formed.

The extra amount of energy required in a collision to produce chemical reaction is known as the *energy of activation*. Its magnitude depends on the nature of the reactants. For some reactions, the energy of activation is large. Such reactions are slow, since only a small fraction of the reactant particles have enough kinetic energy to furnish the required energy of activation. Other reactions have a small energy of activation. These reactions are fast, since a greater fraction of the collisions are effective. More of the particles have sufficient kinetic energy to furnish the required energy of activation.

Qualitatively, the collision theory quite satisfactorily accounts for the four factors which influence reaction rates: (1) The rate of chemical reaction depends on the *nature of the chemical reactants*, because the energy of activation differs from one reaction to another. (2) The rate of reaction depends on the *concentration of reactants*, because the number of collisions increases as the concentration is increased. (3) The rate of reaction depends on the *temperature*, because an increase of temperature makes molecules move faster. They collide more frequently with other molecules, and, more important, the collisions are more violent and more likely to cause reaction. In any collection of molecules there is a distribution of energies. According to collision theory only the highly energetic molecules have enough energy to react. As the temperature is raised, the whole distribution curve is shifted to higher energies (see Fig. 6.12), so that a larger fraction of the molecules are highly energetic. More of the collisions are therefore effective at high temperatures than at low temperatures. (4) The rate of reaction depends on the presence of *catalysts*, because somehow, in catalysis, collisions are made more effective. This may be done by a preliminary step involving reaction between one or more of the reactants and the catalyst. New reactants may be produced which react more rapidly.

One of the trickiest aspects of chemical kinetics is to account for the quantitative dependence of rate on concentration. For simplicity, let us consider one step of a reaction. Suppose that in this step one molecule of A reacts with one molecule of B to form a molecule AB. The balanced equation for *this step* is

$$A + B \rightarrow AB$$

According to collision theory, the rate of formation of AB is proportional to the rate at which A and B collide. Let us imagine that we have a box that contains some B molecules and a single A molecule. The rate at which the A molecule collides with B molecules is directly proportional to the number of B molecules in the box. (If we should double the number of B molecules in the box, then we would have twice as many A-B collisions per second.) Suppose now we place a second A molecule in the box. We now have twice as many A molecules in the box, so that the total number of A-B collisions per second is doubled. In other words, the rate at which A and B molecules collide is directly proportional to the concentration of A and to the concentration of B. The rate of formation of AB should therefore be directly proportional to the concentration of A and to that of B. Thus, the rate law for this step is

$$\text{Rate} = k[A][B]$$

It should be noted that the exponents of $[A]$ and of $[B]$ in the rate law are unity, just as the two coefficients are in the balanced equation for the step.

What is the situation if the balanced equation for a step involves coefficients larger than one? Consider the reaction

$$2A \rightarrow A_2$$

In this step, an A molecule must collide with another A molecule to form A_2. The rate at which A_2 forms is thus proportional to the rate at which two A molecules collide. Again we imagine a box, this time containing only molecules of type A. For *any one* A molecule, the rate at which it collides with any other A molecule is proportional to the number of other A molecules in the box. If we should double the number of other A molecules in the box, then we would double the rate at which collisions occur with the one molecule under observation. Now suppose we extend our observation to all the molecules in the box. The total number of collisions per second is proportional to the number of collisions per second made by one A molecule times the total number of A molecules in the box. Another way of saying the same thing is that the rate of collisions is proportional to the number of molecules hitting multiplied by the number of molecules being hit. In any event, we can say that the rate at which two A molecules collide is proportional to the concentration of A times the concentration of A, or to the square of the concentration of A. Consequently, for the step

$$2A \rightarrow A_2$$

we can write the rate law

$$\text{Rate} = k[A]^2$$

It might be noted that the exponent of the concentration of A in the rate law is 2, just as the coefficient of A in the balanced equation for the step is 2.

For the general case of a step for which the balanced equation shows the disappearance of n molecules of A and m molecules of B, we can write the rate law

$$\text{Rate} = k[A]^n[B]^m$$

indicating that the rate of that step is proportional to the concentration of A taken to the n power times the concentration of B taken to the m power. We should note again that a net chemical change may consist of several consecutive steps, and a knowledge of only the over-all balanced equation does not permit us to predict what the experimentally observed rate law will be. For example, in the reaction between NO and H_2, discussed in Sec. 12.2, the rate law obtained experimentally states that the reaction rate is proportional to the first power of the H_2 concentration times the second power of the NO concentration. Yet the balanced equation for the reaction is

$$2H_2(g) + 2NO(g) \rightarrow N_2(g) + 2H_2O(g)$$

From collision theory, it appears that reaction could occur by a collision between two H_2 molecules and the two NO molecules. The number of such collisions per second is proportional to the molar concentration of H_2

squared times the molar concentration of NO squared. This means that doubling the H_2 concentration ought to quadruple the number of collisions per second and therefore quadruple the rate. This does not agree with experiment. The collisions that determine the rate cannot be between two H_2 molecules and two NO molecules.

To account for the observed rate law, collision theory assumes that this reaction, like many others, occurs in steps. In stepwise reactions, the slow step is the one which determines the rate. It is the bottleneck and determines the rate law for the reaction. The following example shows a two-step reaction:

$$A(g) + B(g) \rightarrow \text{[Intermediate]} \tag{1}$$

$$\text{[Intermediate]} + B(g) \rightarrow C(g) \tag{2}$$

Net reaction:

$$A(g) + 2B(g) \rightarrow C(g)$$

In step (1) a molecule of A collides with a molecule of B to form a short-lived intermediate. In step (2) the intermediate reacts with a molecule of B to form a molecule of C. If the first step is slow and if the second step is fast, the rate at which the product C forms depends only on the rate at which the intermediate forms. As soon as the intermediate appears, it is used up in the second reaction. The rate at which the intermediate is produced is determined by the collision of A and B. Thus, the rate of the slow step is proportional to the concentration of A times the concentration of B. Since the slow step is the rate-determining step in the over-all change, the rate law for the net change is

$$\text{Rate} = k[A][B]$$

The net change is determined by adding steps (1) and (2):

$$A(g) + B(g) + B(g) \rightarrow C(g)$$

The intermediate cancels out because it occurs on both sides of the equation. The coefficients which appear in the net equation are different from the exponents in the rate law.

For the specific reaction

$$2H_2(g) + 2NO(g) \rightarrow N_2(g) + 2H_2O(g)$$

the rate law is determined by experiment to be

$$\text{Rate} = k[H_2][NO]^2$$

The reaction must occur in steps. One possible set of steps is

$$H_2(g) + NO(g) + NO(g) \rightarrow N_2O(g) + H_2O(g) \tag{3}$$

$$H_2(g) + N_2O(g) \rightarrow N_2(g) + H_2O(g) \tag{4}$$

The first step [Eq. (3)] must be the slower and therefore must determine the rate law. However, many people object to this mechanism because Eq. (3) requires a simultaneous collision of three molecules. As any pool player knows, three-body collisions are quite improbable. An alternative series of steps without three-body collision is

$$2NO(g) \rightarrow N_2O_2(g) \tag{5}$$

$$N_2O_2(g) + H_2(g) \rightarrow N_2O(g) + H_2O(g) \tag{6}$$

$$N_2O(g) + H_2(g) \rightarrow N_2(g) + H_2O(g) \tag{7}$$

with Eq. (6) rate-determining. Since the N_2O_2 for Eq. (6) is formed by collision of two NO molecules, the concentration of N_2O_2 is proportional to the square of the concentration of NO. The rate of the second step thus depends on the square of the concentration of NO times the concentration of H_2. On the basis of the observed rate law it is not possible to distinguish between these two mechanisms. In fact, it may be that neither is right and that the actual mechanism is much more complicated.

12.6   ABSOLUTE-REACTION-RATE THEORY

The collision theory of chemical kinetics is the basis of the *absolute-reaction-rate theory*, which assumes that reaction rate can be calculated by applying the equations of wave mechanics (Sec. 3.10) to the colliding particles. The calculations are complicated and have been done only for a few simple cases. However, some of the basic ideas are useful and easily applied qualitatively.

For simplicity we consider the one-step reaction in which one molecule of A collides with one molecule of B to form one molecule each of C and D. The collision is assumed to consist of the approach of an A molecule to a B molecule to form some kind of a transient complex particle. This complex particle, which is called the *activated complex*, can split apart to restore the A and B molecules, or it can split in some other way to give the new particles C and D. The absolute-reaction-rate theory calculates the potential-energy change of the system as A and B molecules come together to form the activated complex and then separate to give C and D molecules. A typical potential-energy curve is shown in Fig. 12.1. On the vertical axis is plotted the potential energy of the system; on the horizontal axis is plotted a coordinate which tells how far the reaction has gone from the initial state toward the final state. In the initial state, A and B molecules are far enough apart not to affect each other. The potential energy is the sum of the potential energy of *A* by itself plus that of *B* by itself. It makes no difference what the actual value is, since potential energy is relative. As *A* and *B* come together, the forces of repulsion between the electron clouds become appreciable. Work must be done on the system to squash the particles together. This means the potential energy must increase. It increases until it reaches a maximum that corresponds to the activated complex. The activated complex then splits into *C* and *D* molecules, and the potential energy drops as *C* and *D* go apart.

The difference (shown by the arrow) between the potential energy of the initial state *A* plus *B* and the potential energy of the activated complex is a measure of the energy which must be added to the particles in order to get them to react. This is the activation energy of the reaction. It usually is supplied by converting some of the kinetic energy of the particles into potential energy. If *A* and *B* molecules do not have much kinetic energy, on collision they are able to go only part way up the side of the hump. All the kinetic energy may be converted into potential energy without getting the pair distorted into the activated complex. In such case, *A* and *B* slide back down the hump and fly apart unchanged. The situation is similar to that of a ball rolled up the side of a hill. If the ball is rolled slowly, it goes part way up, stops, and rolls back again. If the ball is rolled rapidly, it goes completely to the top of the hill and down the other side. Similarly, if *A* and *B* molecules have high enough kinetic energy, they can attain the activated complex and get over the hump from *A* and *B* to *C* and *D*. In a reaction at higher temperatures more molecules get over the potential-energy hump per unit time, and the reaction occurs faster.

Two other aspects of Fig. 12.1 are of interest. For the case represented, the final state *C* and *D* has lower potential energy than the initial state *A* and *B*. There is a net decrease in potential energy as the reaction proceeds. This energy usually shows up as heat so the particular change

$$A + B \rightarrow C + D$$

is exothermic. The amount of energy required to distort *A* and *B* into the activated complex is more than made

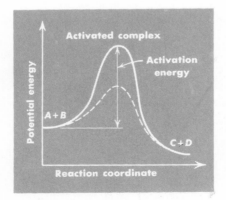

Fig. 12.1   *Potential-energy change during a reaction. (Dashed line refers to catalyzed reaction.)*

up for when the activated complex springs apart to form C and D. However, since the activation energy is large, the reaction is slow, even though the system goes to a lower potential-energy state. An example of a slow, exothermic reaction is

$$2H_2(g) + O_2(g) \rightarrow 2H_2O(g) + 116 \text{ kcal.}$$

Figure 12.1 is a potential-energy diagram for the reaction of A and B to produce C and D. It can also be read from right to left as a diagram for the reaction of C and D to produce A and B; i.e., the reaction is reversible. As can be seen from the diagram, the reaction C and D to give A and B is endothermic. Also reaction between C and D has a higher activation energy than reaction between A and B.

When a reaction is catalyzed, there is a change of path or mechanism. Since the rate is now faster, the activation energy for the new path must be lower than for the old path. The dotted curve in Fig. 12.1 shows what the potential-energy curve might look like for the new path. Since the barrier is lower, at any given temperature and concentration more particles per second can get over the hump; hence the reaction goes faster. As an example, the reaction between hydrogen and oxygen to form water is catalyzed by the presence of platinum. It has been suggested that the effect of the platinum is to react with H_2 molecules to produce H atoms. The oxygen molecules then collide with H atoms instead of with H_2 molecules. The new path has a lower activation energy in the rate-determining step.

QUESTIONS

12.1 *Change of rate.* Suppose that, in a given complex reaction in solution, the rate-determining step involves one molecule of A and one molecule of B

$$A + B \rightarrow 2C$$

Suggest four things you might do to speed up the formation of C.

12.2 *Activation energy.* (a) What is meant by "activation energy"? Draw a labeled potential-energy diagram and indicate what activation energy means on this diagram. (b) By reference to (a), account for the fact that reaction rate increases with rise in temperature.

12.3 *Change of rate.* x moles of hydrogen gas and y moles of iodine gas are injected simultaneously into a 1-liter box. The gases react at a rate directly proportional to the concentration of hydrogen and to the concentration of iodine. What effect will there be on the rate of reaction in this box if: (a) the temperature is decreased; (b) a catalyst is introduced; (c) more hydrogen is added; (d) some iodine is removed; (e) the volume of the box is increased?

12.4 *Rate theory.* The kinetics of the reaction

$$A(g) + 2B(g) + 3C(g) \rightarrow 4D(g)$$

are under investigation. The following results have been obtained: (*a*) Finely divided platinum does not affect the rate of formation of *D*, but finely divided V_2O_5 increases it. (*b*) The rate of formation of *D* is increased by a rise in temperature. (*c*) Doubling the concentration of *A* or of *B* doubles the rate of formation of *D*, but doubling the concentration of *C* has no effect on the rate. (*d*) When the volume is decreased, *D* forms faster. Account for each of these observations in terms of the theoretical picture developed in this chapter.

12.5 *Rate law.* Suppose we have the problem of preparing *C* as fast as possible from the gases *A* and *B*. Assume the rate-determining step involves

$$A(g) + 2B(g) \rightarrow$$

(*a*) Write the rate law for the reaction. (*b*) How does the rate change as each of the concentrations is doubled separately? (*c*) How does the rate change if the enclosing volume is suddenly halved?

12.6 *Heterogeneous reaction.* In terms of the molecular pictures, explain why finely powdered salt dissolves faster than coarse salt.

12.7 *Rate law.* For the reaction $A + B \rightarrow C$ the following data were obtained: In Expt. I, with $0.10 \ M$ as the initial concentrations of *A* and *B*, the observed initial rate of formation of *C* is $2.0 \times 10^{-3} \ M$ per min.; in Expt. II, with $0.20 \ M \ A$ and $0.20 \ M \ B$, the rate is $8.0 \times 10^{-3} \ M$ per min.; in Expt. III, with $0.10 \ M \ A$ and $0.20 \ M \ B$, the rate is $8.0 \times 10^{-3} \ M$ per min. (*a*) Write the rate law for this reaction and calculate the value of *k*. (*b*) What would be the initial rate of formation of *C* if the initial concentrations of *A* and *B* were each $0.50 \ M$?

Ans. (*b*) $5.0 \times 10^{-3} \ M/$min.

12.8 *Change of rate.* The burning of sugar in air requires fairly high temperatures. Yet, sugar is "burned" in the body at body temperature. Explain.

12.9 *Autocatalysis.* (*a*) What is the difference between "catalysis" and "autocatalysis"? (*b*) How could you recognize that a given reaction is autocatalytic?

12.10 *Energy of activation.* Criticize the following reasoning: "Reaction (1) is exothermic; reaction (2) is endothermic. Therefore, reaction (1) has the smaller energy of activation and goes faster than reaction (2)."

12.11 *Reaction mechanism.* For the net change

$$2A + 2B \rightarrow C + D$$

the rate law is

$$\text{Rate} = k[A][B]$$

Propose a stepwise mechanism consistent with this rate law.

12.12 *Rate calculations.* Consider the data given for Expt. I in Table 12.1. (*a*) What is the total initial pressure before any reaction has occurred? (*b*) What is the initial H_2 pressure before reaction? (*c*) What would be the total pressure after 6 sec. has elapsed, assuming that the reaction progresses at the initial rate indicated? (*d*) Noting that two moles of H_2 disappear for each 1-mole decrease of the total, what would be the H_2 pressure after 6 sec. has elapsed? (*e*) Compute the fraction of H_2 used up in the first 6 sec. of reaction. (*f*) Assuming that the same fraction of the *remaining* H_2 is used up in each succeeding 6-sec. period, compute the pressure of H_2 at 6-sec. intervals during the first minute of reaction. (*g*) Plot the pressure of H_2 as a function of time.

Ans. (*b*) 66.9 mm. Hg; (*e*) 0.060

13 Chemical Equilibrium

IT IS FOUND BY EXPERIMENT that, when reacting species are brought together so as to undergo chemical reaction, the conversion of reactants to products is often incomplete, no matter how long the reaction is allowed to continue. In the initial state, the reactants are present at a definite concentration. As the reaction proceeds, the concentrations of reactants decrease. Sooner or later, however, they level off and become constant. A state is established in which the concentrations no longer change. This state is known as the state of *chemical equilibrium*.

13.1 THE EQUILIBRIUM STATE

As an example of the attainment of equilibrium, we consider a reaction

$$A(g) + B(g) \rightarrow C(g) + D(g)$$

in which one molecule of A reacts with one molecule of B to form molecules of C and D. For simplicity, all the substances are assumed to be gases. At the start of the experiment, A and B are mixed in a box. The concentration of A and the concentration of B are measured as time passes. Results of the measurements are plotted in Fig. 13.1, where concentration is the vertical axis and time is the horizontal axis. The initial concentration of A is some definite number, depending on the number of moles of A and the volume of the box. As time goes on, the concentration of A diminishes, at first quite rapidly but later less rapidly. Eventually, the concentration of A levels off and becomes constant. The concentration of B changes in similar fashion, even though it may not start out at the same concentration as A. The initial concentrations of C and D are zero. As time goes on, C and D are produced. Their concentrations increase quite rapidly at first but then level off. At time t_e each of the concentrations becomes essentially constant. Once this equilibrium state has been established, it persists indefinitely and, if undisturbed, will last forever.

The constant state that characterizes equilibrium vapor pressure (Sec. 7.2) is due to equality of opposing reactions. Similarly, the constant state that characterizes chemical equilibrium is due to equality of opposing reactions. A and B molecules react to form C and D molecules. So long as A and B are present, this reaction continues. Reaction does not stop at time t_e. As soon as an appreciable number of C and D molecules form, they react with each other to produce A and B. After time t_e, the forward and reverse changes occur at the same rate. The equality of opposing reactions is indicated by writing

$$A(g) + B(g) \rightleftharpoons C(g) + D(g)$$

or $$A(g) + B(g) = C(g) + D(g)$$

13.2   MASS ACTION

It is found by experiment that every particular reaction has its own specific equilibrium state, in which there is a definite relation between the concentrations of the materials. To illustrate the relation, we consider the reaction between A and B to produce C and D. In a series of experiments, all done at the same temperature

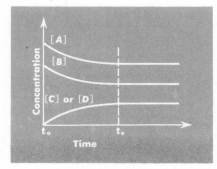

Fig. 13.1   Approach to equilibrium.

Table 13.1   Equilibrium Concentrations

(Concentrations are in moles per liter)

Experiment	Concentrations			
	A	**B**	**C**	**D**
1	3.00	2.00	1.00	1.00
2	9.60	10.0	4.00	4.00
3	0.500	3.00	0.500	0.500
4	21.9	1.22	2.11	2.11

but *differing in initial concentrations* of A and B, the results shown in Table 13.1 are obtained. The concentrations given, in moles per liter, are those in the equilibrium state and are called equilibrium concentrations. Although the equilibrium concentrations change from experiment to experiment, there is a single relationship which holds for all the experiments. If the concentration of C times the concentration of D is divided by the concentration of A times the concentration of B, the number 0.167 is obtained in every case. This number, *the equilibrium constant*, is characteristic of this specific reaction and varies only with changes in temperature. Whenever A, B, C, and D are present together in equilibrium, the concentrations must be such that they satisfy the expression

$$\frac{[C][D]}{[A][B]} = 0.167$$

The balanced general equation

$$nA(g) + mB(g) + \cdots \rightleftharpoons pC(g) + qD(g) + \cdots$$

can be read as n molecules of A plus m molecules of B react to form p molecules of C and q molecules of D. The three dots represent other reactants or products, so that this equation applies to any reaction. The letters n, m, p, and q represent numbers that are the coefficients of the chemical equation. The letters A, B, C, and D represent the formulas of the various reactants and products. If the balanced equation is written in this way, the relationship that is constant at equilibrium is

$$\frac{[C]^p[D]^q \cdots}{[A]^n[B]^m \cdots}$$

This fraction is called the *mass-action expression.** The square brackets designate concentrations in moles per liter, and the exponents are the powers to which these concentrations must be raised. By convention, in the mass-action expression concentrations of the materials on the right-hand side of the chemical equation appear in the numerator and concentrations of the materials on the left-hand side of the equation, in the denominator. At equilibrium the expression is numerically equal to the equilibrium constant K for the particular reaction.

$$\frac{[C]^p[D]^q \cdots}{[A]^n[B]^m \cdots} = K$$

This equilibrium condition is called the *law of chemical equilibrium.* The law states that, in a system at chemical equilibrium, the concentrations of the materials which participate in the reaction must satisfy the condition expressed by the constancy of the mass-action expression. There is no other restriction on the individual concentrations.

The law of chemical equilibrium is an experimental fact. It can, however, be justified by using the principles of chemical kinetics and requiring at equilibrium the equality of the rates of forward and reverse reactions. For example, in the equilibrium

$$A(g) + B(g) \rightleftharpoons C(g) + D(g)$$

reaction may proceed in a single step or in a series of steps. The mass-action expression is the same in either case and can be written without any knowledge of the kinetics of the reaction. That the mass-action expression is independent of the mechanism is shown as follows:

1. Suppose the reaction proceeds through a single reversible step.

$$A(g) + B(g) \rightleftharpoons C(g) + D(g) \tag{1}$$

---

* The term mass action derives from the original work of Cato Maximilian Guldberg and Peter Waage, Norwegian chemists, who in 1864 proposed that the reaction $A + B = C + D$ could be treated as follows: The "action force" between A and B is proportional to the "active mass" of A and that of B. This is called the law of mass action. Similarly, the action force between C and D is proportional to the active masses of C and D. At equilibrium, the action force between A and B equals the action force between C and D. Although Guldberg and Waage were not clear in what was meant by "action force" and "active mass," their work was a milestone in the development of a suitable description of chemical equilibrium.

For the forward reaction,

$$\text{Rate} = k[A][B]$$

where k is the rate constant of the forward reaction. For the reverse reaction

$$\text{Rate} = k'[C][D]$$

where k' is the rate constant of the reverse reaction. At equilibrium, the rate of the forward reaction is equal to the rate of the reverse reaction. Thus,

$$k[A][B] = k'[C][D]$$

or $$\frac{[C][D]}{[A][B]} = \frac{k}{k'}$$

This proves that in this case the mass-action expression is equal to a constant.

2. Suppose the reaction proceeds through more than one reversible step. For example, the steps

$$A(g) + A(g) \rightleftharpoons C(g) + Q(g) \tag{2}$$

$$Q(g) + B(g) \rightleftharpoons A(g) + D(g) \tag{3}$$

add up to give

$$A(g) + B(g) \rightleftharpoons C(g) + D(g)$$

which is the same net equation as Eq. (1) above. For the first step [Eq. (2)] k_1 and k_1' are the rate constants for the forward and reverse directions. For Eq. (3), k_2 and k_2' apply to the forward and reverse directions. At equilibrium, forward and reverse reactions must be equal for each step. Thus, for the first step,

$$k_1[A][A] = k_1'[C][Q]$$

For the second step

$$k_2[Q][B] = k_2'[A][D]$$

These simultaneous equations can be combined by eliminating the chemical intermediate Q to give

$$\frac{k_1}{k_1'}\frac{[A][A]}{[C]} = \frac{k_2'}{k_2}\frac{[A][D]}{[B]}$$

Rearranging and simplifying gives

$$\frac{[C][D]}{[A][B]} = \frac{k_1 k_2}{k_1' k_2'}$$

Again, the mass-action expression is shown to be equal to a constant.

13.3 EQUILIBRIUM CONSTANT

The numbers observed for equilibrium constants vary from very large numbers to extremely small numbers, depending on the specific reaction. If the equilibrium constant is small ($K < 1$), the numerator of the mass-action expression is smaller than the denominator. This means that, in the equilibrium state, the concentration of at least one of the materials on the right of the chemical equation is small. Therefore, a small equilibrium constant implies that the reaction does not proceed far from left to right. For example, if for

$$A(g) + B(g) \rightleftharpoons C(g) + D(g) \qquad K = 1.0 \times 10^{-5}$$

then the mixing of A and B does not result in the production of much C and D at equilibrium. If the equilibrium constant is large ($K > 1$), the denominator of the mass-action expression is smaller than the numerator. This means that, in the equilibrium state, the concentration of at least one of the materials on the left of the chemical equation is small. Therefore, a large equilibrium constant implies that the reaction proceeds from left to right essentially to completion. For example, if for

$$E(g) + F(g) \rightleftharpoons G(g) + H(g) \qquad K = 1.0 \times 10^{5}$$

then the mixing of E and F results in practically complete conversion of E and F to G and H.

The equilibrium constant is determined by experiment. For example, measurements have been made of the equilibrium involving hydrogen, iodine, and hydrogen iodide. The equilibrium is described by

$$H_2(g) + I_2(g) \rightleftharpoons 2HI(g)$$

In the equilibrium state all three components are present. The equilibrium condition is

$$\frac{[HI]^2}{[H_2][I_2]} = K$$

The number K can be determined by measuring all three concentrations in the equilibrium state. In an experiment at $490°$C. the following results might be obtained:

Concentration of $H_2 = 0.000862$ mole per liter

Concentration of $I_2 = 0.00263$ mole per liter

Concentration of $HI = 0.0102$ mole per liter

Since these concentrations are equilibrium concentrations, they satisfy the equilibrium condition.

$$\frac{[\text{HI}]^2}{[\text{H}_2][\text{I}_2]} = \frac{(0.0102)^2}{(0.000862)(0.00263)} = 45.9$$

For any equilibrium system at 490° C. containing H_2, I_2 and HI, the mass-action expression must be equal to 45.9. If this condition is not satisfied, the system is not at equilibrium, and changes will occur until equilibrium is established.

13.4 EQUILIBRIUM CALCULATIONS

Once the value 45.9 has been determined it can be used to describe any system containing H_2, I_2, and HI in chemical equilibrium at 490° C.

Example 1

One mole of H_2 and one mole of I_2 are introduced into a 1-liter box at a temperature of 490° C. What will be the final concentrations in the box when equilibrium has been established?

Initially, there is no HI in the box. The system is not at equilibrium, since the mass-action expression is zero instead of 45.9. In order to establish equilibrium, changes must occur to produce HI. HI can come only from the reaction

$$\text{H}_2(g) + \text{I}_2(g) \rightleftharpoons 2\text{HI}(g)$$

This reaction proceeds to produce enough HI to satisfy the equilibrium condition.

Let n equal the number of moles of hydrogen that must disappear in order to establish equilibrium. Every time 1 mole of hydrogen disappears, 1 mole of iodine also disappears. So, n also represents the number of moles of iodine that disappear in order to establish equilibrium. According to the balanced equation, if 1 mole of hydrogen disappears, 2 moles of HI must be formed. If n moles of hydrogen disappear, $2n$ moles of HI must appear. Therefore, $2n$ is equal to the number of moles of HI formed in order to establish equilibrium. The situation is summarized as follows:

Initially	At equilibrium
$[\text{H}_2] = 1.000$ mole/liter	$[\text{H}_2] = (1.000 - n)$ moles/liter
$[\text{I}_2] = 1.000$ mole/liter	$[\text{I}_2] = (1.000 - n)$ moles/liter
$[\text{HI}] = 0$	$[\text{HI}] = 2n$ moles/liter

Since the volume of the box is 1 liter, the concentration of each component is identical to the number of moles of that component in the box. The equilibrium concentrations must satisfy the condition

$$\frac{[HI]^2}{[H_2][I_2]} = 45.9$$

Substitution gives

$$\frac{(2n)^2}{(1.000 - n)(1.000 - n)} = 45.9$$

for which

$$n = 0.772^*$$

Therefore, at equilibrium

$$[H_2] = (1.000 - n) = 0.228 \text{ mole/liter}$$
$$[I_2] = (1.000 - n) = 0.228 \text{ mole/liter}$$
$$[HI] = 2n \qquad\qquad = 1.544 \text{ moles/liter}$$

That these values represent equilibrium concentrations can be checked by calculating the value of the mass-action expression

$$\frac{[HI]^2}{[H_2][I_2]} = \frac{(1.544)^2}{(0.228)(0.228)}$$

It must be 45.9 at 490°C.

To emphasize the fact that it makes no difference from which side of the equation equilibrium is approached, we consider what happens when only HI is placed in the box at 490°C. Since initially there is no hydrogen or iodine in the system, decomposition of HI must occur in order to establish equilibrium.

Example 2

Two moles of HI *are injected into a box of 1 liter volume at 490° C. What will be the concentration of each species in the box at equilibrium?*

The equilibrium is

$$H_2(g) + I_2(g) \rightleftharpoons 2HI(g)$$

Let x equal the number of moles of HI that must decompose in order to establish equilibrium. In the reverse reaction, for each 2 moles of HI that disappear, 1 mole of hydrogen and 1 mole of iodine are formed. If x moles of HI disappear, $x/2$ moles of hydrogen and $x/2$ moles of iodine appear. The initial and final concentrations are summarized:

---

*This particular equation can be solved by taking the square root of both sides of the equation. For a more general case, we can use the ordinary algebraic methods for solving quadratic equations (see Appendix 3.4). Of the two roots necessarily obtained for the quadratic equation, one can be discarded as physically impossible. In this case, the root $n = 1.42$ corresponds to more than 100 per cent reaction.

Initially	At equilibrium
$[HI] = 2.000$ moles/liter	$[HI] = (2.000 - x)$ moles/liter
$[H_2] = 0$ mole/liter	$[H_2] = (x/2)$ moles/liter
$[I_2] = 0$ mole/liter	$[I_2] = (x/2)$ moles/liter

At equilibrium

$$\frac{[HI]^2}{[H_2][I_2]} = 45.9 = \frac{(2.000 - x)^2}{(x/2)(x/2)}$$

for which

$$x = 0.456$$

Therefore, at equilibrium

$$[H_2] = x/2 \qquad = 0.228 \text{ mole/liter}$$
$$[I_2] = x/2 \qquad = 0.228 \text{ mole/liter}$$
$$[HI] = 2.000 - x = 1.544 \text{ moles/liter}$$

The two examples show that it makes no difference whether the equilibrium state is produced from the material on the left-hand side of the chemical equation or from the material on the right-hand side. Change occurs so as to produce the material that is missing in sufficient concentration to establish equilibrium. Sometimes the initial nonequilibrium system contains all the components, in which case the necessary change to establish equilibrium is not obvious. In the following example, it is not immediately clear whether the concentration of HI must increase or decrease in order to establish equilibrium.

Example 3

One mole of H_2, *two moles of* I_2, *and three moles of* HI *are injected into a 1-liter box. What will be the concentration of each species at equilibrium at* 490° C.?
The equilibrium is

$$H_2(g) + I_2(g) \rightleftharpoons 2HI(g)$$

Let x be the number of moles of H_2 that must be used up in order to establish equilibrium. (If it turns out that *more* H_2 must be formed, x will be a negative number.) According to the stoichiometry of the reaction, x is also the number of moles of I_2 that must be used up, and $2x$ is the number of moles of HI that must be formed. At equilibrium the concentration of H_2 is reduced by the amount x, the concentration of I_2 is reduced by the amount x, and the concentration of HI is increased by $2x$.

| Initially | At equilibrium |

$[H_2] = 1.000$ mole/liter

$[I_2] = 2.000$ moles/liter

$[HI] = 3.000$ moles/liter

$[H_2] = (1.000 - x)$ moles/liter

$[I_2] = (2.000 - x)$ moles/liter

$[HI] = (3.000 + 2x)$ moles/liter

At equilibrium

$$\frac{[HI]^2}{[H_2][I_2]} = 45.9 = \frac{(3.000 + 2x)^2}{(1.000 - x)(2.000 - x)}$$

for which

$$x = 0.684$$

Therefore, at equilibrium

$$[H_2] = 1.000 - x \ = 0.316 \text{ mole/liter}$$

$$[I_2] = 2.000 - x \ = 1.316 \text{ moles/liter}$$

$$[HI] = 3.000 + 2x = 4.368 \text{ moles/liter}$$

13.5   HETEROGENEOUS EQUILIBRIUM

Heterogeneous equilibria are those equilibria which involve two or more phases. For example, the equilibrium

$$2C(s) + O_2(g) \rightleftharpoons 2CO(g)$$

involves both gaseous and solid phases. The solid phase consists of pure carbon, and the gas phase of a mixture of oxygen and carbon monoxide. In mass-action expressions, the concentrations must apply to the phase specified by the equation. For example, for the above equilibrium the equilibrium condition is

$$K' = \frac{[CO(g)]^2}{[C(s)]^2[O_2(g)]}$$

where $[CO(g)]$ refers to the concentration of CO in the gas phase, $[C(s)]$ refers to the concentration of C in the solid phase, and $[O_2(g)]$ refers to the concentration of O_2 in the gas phase.

A simplification of the equilibrium condition is possible because, although the concentration of carbon monoxide and the concentration of oxygen in the gas phase are variable, the concentration of carbon in the solid cannot be changed. The concentration of carbon monoxide in the gas phase can be changed, e.g., by the addition of CO. Since the volume remains constant and more CO has been added, the concentration of CO is increased. Similarly, the concentration of O_2 can be changed, but for solid carbon this is not possible. If more solid carbon is added, the concentration is not changed, because as the number of moles of carbon increases, the volume of carbon also increases. The *number of moles per liter of solid carbon* is the same number, no matter how much carbon is present.

In the general case, at constant temperature, the concentration of any substance as a pure solid or a pure liquid cannot be changed and is a constant. The constant concentration can be combined with the original equilibrium constant to give a new equilibrium constant for which the mass-action expression does not include the pure condensed phase. Thus, for the equilibrium

$$2C(s) + O_2(g) \rightleftharpoons 2CO(g)$$

$$K'[C(s)]^2 = \frac{[CO]^2}{[O_2]}$$

where $[C(s)]$ is a constant. Therefore,

$$K'[C(s)]^2 = K$$

$$K = \frac{[CO]^2}{[O_2]}$$

The last equation expresses the requirement that a system containing $CO(g)$, $O_2(g)$, and $C(s)$ is in equilibrium no matter how much $C(s)$ is present, provided that $[CO]^2/[O_2]$ has the proper value. The simple rule is that for heterogeneous equilibria pure solids and pure liquids are omitted from the mass-action expression. Further examples are given below:

At 1000°C.: $H_2(g) + S(g) \rightleftharpoons H_2S(g)$ $\qquad K_1 = \dfrac{[H_2S]}{[H_2][S]}$

At 200°C.: $H_2(g) + S(l) \rightleftharpoons H_2S(g)$ $\qquad K_2 = \dfrac{[H_2S]}{[H_2]}$

At -100°C.: $H_2(g) + S(s) \rightleftharpoons H_2S(s)$ $\qquad K_3 = \dfrac{1}{[H_2]}$

13.6 EQUILIBRIUM CHANGES

When a system at equilibrium is disturbed, chemical reaction occurs and equilibrium is reestablished. As an example, we consider the equilibrium system consisting of H_2, I_2, and HI in a sealed box.

$$H_2(g) + I_2(g) \rightleftharpoons 2HI(g)$$

$$K = \frac{[HI]^2}{[H_2][I_2]}$$

At 490°C., K is 45.9. The concentrations of HI, H_2, and I_2 do not change until conditions are changed. Several kinds of changes are possible. (1) H_2, I_2, or HI can be injected into the box. (2) H_2, I_2, or HI can be removed from the box. (3) The volume of the box can be changed. (4) The temperature of the system can be changed. (5) A catalyst can be added. How is the equilibrium state affected by each of these changes?

  1   The concentration of one of the components is changed by addition. For example, more H_2 is added to a box which contains H_2, I_2, and HI in equilibrium at 490°C. What effect does this concentration increase have on the other components? The problem can be explored three ways:

  a. The equilibrium constant. The equilibrium condition is of the form

$$\frac{[HI]^2}{[H_2][I_2]} = 45.9$$

By increasing the concentration of hydrogen, the denominator is made bigger. If everything else stays the same, the fraction becomes less than 45.9; therefore the system is no longer at equilibrium. To reestablish equilibrium, two things could happen. There could be a decrease in the concentration of I_2, so that the denominator would be restored to its original value. Or, there could be an increase in the concentration of HI, so that the numerator would increase to compensate for the increased denominator. Since iodine atoms must exist either as I_2 or HI molecules, the decrease of I_2 and the increase of HI occur simultaneously.

  b. Le Chatelier's principle. According to the principle of Le Chatelier (Sec. 9.4), any equilibrium system subjected to a stress tends to change so as to relieve the stress. For a system in chemical equilibrium, changing the concentration of one of the components constitutes a stress. In the present case, if hydrogen is added to the box, the equilibrium system

$$H_2(g) + I_2(g) \rightleftharpoons 2HI(g)$$

adjusts itself so as to absorb the effect of the added hydrogen. The system can absorb the stress if some hydrogen molecules combine with iodine molecules to form HI. This means that the concentration of HI increases and the concentration of I_2 decreases. Le Chatelier's principle leads to the same prediction as does the equilibrium constant.

  c. Kinetics. The effect of added H_2 can be predicted from a consideration of reaction rates. The argument here is relatively simple because the reaction proceeds by one step. In the equilibrium state, collisions between H_2 and I_2 molecules form HI, and simultaneously collisions between HI molecules form H_2 and I_2. These two rates are equal. By adding H_2 to the box, the chance for collision between H_2 and I_2 molecules is increased. The more collisions there are between H_2 and I_2, the faster HI is formed. The instantaneous effect of adding hydrogen is therefore to increase the rate of HI formation. When hydrogen is added, there is no instantaneous effect on the decomposition rate of HI. For a time HI is forming faster than it is decomposing, and so its concentration increases. Eventually, the concentration of HI increases to the point that there are more collisions between HI molecules, and the reverse reaction, the decomposition of HI, begins to speed up. It speeds up until it equals the increased rate of formation. Equilibrium is reestablished with a net increase in HI and H_2 and a decrease in I_2.

2   The concentration of one of the components is changed by removal. For example, H_2 is removed from the box

  a. The equilibrium condition

$$\frac{[HI]^2}{[H_2][I_2]} = 45.9$$

predicts that a decrease in the concentration of hydrogen must be compensated for by an increase in the concentration of iodine and a decrease in the concentration of HI.

  b. Le Chatelier's principle predicts that the system will adjust to relieve the stress caused by the removal of H_2. Some HI decomposes to form H_2 to replace some of that removed. The effect is to reduce the concentration of HI and to increase the concentration of I_2.

  c. Kinetics predicts that the removal of hydrogen from the container reduces the rate at which H_2 and I_2 combine to form HI. This means that instantaneously HI is forming from H_2 and I_2 more slowly than it is decomposing to H_2 and I_2. There results a net decrease in HI concentration and a net increase in I_2 concentration.

3   The volume of the box is decreased. In cases 1 and 2 the volume of the box is kept constant, and therefore the change in concentration and the change in number of moles are parallel. When the volume of the box is decreased, the *concentration* of all species is increased. However, a detailed analysis of the specific problem is required to determine how the *number of moles* of each species changes.

  a. The equilibrium condition

$$\frac{[HI]^2}{[H_2][I_2]} = 45.9$$

is expressed in terms of concentration. For each component, the concentration is equal to the number of moles, n, of that component divided by the volume of the box, V. By substituting n/V for concentration, the equilibrium condition becomes

$$\frac{[HI]^2}{[H_2][I_2]} = \frac{(n_{HI}/V)^2}{(n_{H_2}/V)(n_{I_2}/V)} = \frac{(n_{HI})^2}{(n_{H_2})(n_{I_2})} = 45.9$$

and V cancels out. No matter what the volume of the box, the number of moles of *HI* squared divided by the number of moles of H_2 and the number of moles of I_2 must equal 45.9. Changing the volume of the box in this case cannot change the number of moles of each species. For the particular case

$$H_2(g) + I_2(g) \rightleftharpoons 2HI(g)$$

the number of gas molecules on the left-hand side of the equation is the same as the number of gas molecules on the right-hand side of the equation. If this condition is not true, the volume does not cancel out of the mass-action expression. An example of such a case is the equilibrium between nitrogen, hydrogen, and ammonia.

$$N_2(g) + 3H_2(g) \rightleftharpoons 2NH_3(g)$$

The equilibrium expression is

$$K = \frac{[NH_3]^2}{[N_2][H_2]^3}$$

Substituting n/V for concentration gives

$$K = \frac{(n_{NH_3}/V)^2}{(n_{N_2}/V)(n_{H_2}/V)^3} = \frac{(n_{NH_3})^2}{(n_{N_2})(n_{H_2})^3} V^2$$

In this case the volume does not cancel out, and a change in V must be compensated for by a change in the number of moles. Specifically, when the volume is decreased, the fraction $(n_{NH_3})^2/(n_{N_2})(n_{H_2})^3$ must increase in order to maintain K constant. There must be an increase in the number of moles of ammonia at the expense of the moles of nitrogen and hydrogen. However, the *concentrations* of NH_3, N_2, and H_2 all increase. In the case of N_2 and H_2, this can come about only because the volume decreases more than does the number of moles. In commerce, when ammonia is made from nitrogen and hydrogen, it is done in as small a volume as possible in order to get maximum conversion to ammonia.

   b. The Le Chatelier principle predicts the effect of reduced volume more simply. For the system H_2, I_2, and HI at equilibrium, the Le Chatelier principle is applied as follows: When the volume of the box is reduced, the molecules are crowded closer together. The stress can be relieved if the molecules are reduced in number. In the case

$$H_2(g) + I_2(g) \rightleftharpoons 2HI(g)$$

there is no device by which this can be accomplished. If one molecule of hydrogen and one molecule of iodine disappear, two molecules of HI are produced. There can be no change in the total number of molecules in the box. Neither the forward nor reverse reaction can absorb the stress of a decreased volume. There is no net change; the number of moles of H_2, I_2, and HI stay constant. Of course, since the volume is diminished, the *concentration* of each component is increased. In the ammonia equilibrium the situation is different. When one molecule of N_2 reacts with three molecules of H_2, two molecules of NH_3 are formed. A decrease of the volume of the box can be compensated for by forming fewer molecules, i.e., by favoring the formation of ammonia. It is a general principle that, for reactions in which there is a change in the number of gas molecules, a decrease in the volume favors the reaction which produces fewer molecules.

   c. Kinetics predicts the effect of a decrease in volume on an equilibrium system by considering the effects on the rates of the forward and reverse reactions. For example, in the equilibrium system containing H_2, I_2, and HI, a decrease of the volume forces H_2 and I_2 molecules closer together, and they collide more frequently. There is an increase in the rate of the forward reaction. At the same time, HI molecules are closer together, and they also collide more frequently. The back reaction is also increased. If the number of gas molecules is the same on the left and the right of the equation, the rate of the forward reaction is increased just as much as that of the back reaction. There is no net change in the number of molecules. If there is a change in the number of gas molecules, the situation is more complicated. For example, in the case

$$N_2(g) + 3H_2(g) \rightleftharpoons 2NH_3(g)$$

it turns out that a decrease of the volume increases the rate of ammonia formation to a greater extent than the rate of ammonia decomposition. The net effect is to increase the number of ammonia molecules present at equilibrium.

   4   The temperature of the system is changed.

   a. The equilibrium constant has a specific value at a given temperature. If the temperature is changed, K may change. For reactions which are endothermic, experiments show that raising the temperature causes K to increase. For those reactions which are exothermic, experiments show that raising the temperature causes K to decrease. The reaction

$$H_2(g) + I_2(g) \rightleftharpoons 2HI(g) + 3 \text{ kcal.}$$

is exothermic as written, and K decreases as the temperature increases. Therefore, with an increase of the temperature, the concentration of HI at equilibrium diminishes while the concentrations of H_2 and I_2 increase. This is another way of saying that HI is less stable at higher temperatures.

b. The Le Chatelier principle predicts that a rise in temperature favors the change that uses up heat. When 1 mole of H_2 and 1 mole of I_2 disappear, 2 moles of HI and 3 kcal. of heat are liberated. The reverse process absorbs heat. At equilibrium, the liberation of heat by the forward reaction is compensated for by the absorption of heat by the back reaction. If the temperature is increased, the system tries to relieve the stress by absorbing the added heat. Since the back reaction uses heat, it is favored. Favoring the back reaction causes a net decrease in the concentration of HI and a net increase in the concentration of I_2 and H_2.

c. Kinetics. It is a principle of kinetics that the rate of any reaction is increased by an increase in temperature (Sec. 12.3). Furthermore, for a given equilibrium, it is always found that the rate of the endothermic reaction is increased more than the rate of the exothermic reaction. For the HI equilibrium, the rate of HI decomposition is increased more than the rate of HI formation is. The result is a net decrease in the concentration of HI.

5   *What effect does a catalyst have on an equilibrium system?*

a. The equilibrium constant is concerned only with the materials in the net equation. There may be intermediates involved, but the net equation ignores them. Although the catalyst affects intermediates, it does not appear in the net equation nor in the equilibrium-constant expression. Insertion of a catalyst into an equilibrium system has no effect on equilibrium concentrations.

b. The Le Chatelier principle ignores the presence of a catalyst.

c. Kinetics gives the best argument for the fact that a catalyst does not affect the composition of the equilibrium system. According to reaction-rate theory, the rate of chemical reaction depends on how fast particles can get over the potential-energy barrier between the initial and final states. For example, Fig. 13.2 shows the potential energy barrier for the reaction

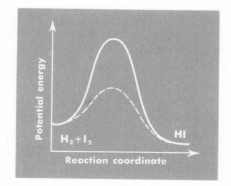

Fig. 13.2   Potential-energy diagram showing effect of catalyst.

$$H_2(g) + I_2(g) \rightleftharpoons 2HI(g)$$

The dotted line represents the path in the presence of catalyst. The rate of the forward reaction depends on the height of the barrier between the initial and final states. Since the catalyst reduces the height of the barrier, it speeds up the rate of the forward reaction. However, if the potential-energy barrier is lowered for the change in the forward direction, it is likewise lowered for the change in the reverse direction. Thus, the reverse change is also accelerated. The increase in the rates of the forward and reverse reactions is the same; hence the equilibrium concentrations are unchanged.

If a catalyst could affect equilibrium concentrations, then a perpetual-motion machine could be built, as follows: The cylinder shown in Fig. 13.3 is fitted with a sliding piston and filled with N_2, H_2, and NH_3 in chemical equilibrium. The compartment with the trap door contains catalyst, and a string is tied from the trap door to the piston. The device operates in such a way that, when the piston is up, the catalyst is exposed. Suppose the catalyst could favor the net formation of NH_3. The total number of gas molecules would decrease; hence the pressure inside the cylinder would drop. As the piston moved in, the trap door would close, and the catalyst would no longer be exposed. In returning to the initial state, some of the ammonia would revert to nitrogen and hydrogen. The total number of gas molecules would increase, and the piston would move out. The trap door would open, and the catalyst would again be exposed. The cycle could repeat itself forever. Unfortunately, this, like all perpetual-motion devices, does not work. A catalyst cannot change equilibrium concentrations. All it does is change the opposing rates, and these it changes equally.

13.7 INDUSTRIAL APPLICATION

The principles of chemical kinetics and of chemical equilibrium considered in this and the preceding chapter are of great importance in the design of industrial processes. For example, they are important factors in the production of sulfuric acid, which in the United States amounts to something like 12 million tons per year. At 10 cents per lb., this is worth 2.5 billion dollars. Sulfuric acid is easy to make. Sulfur, mined from the ground, on burning in air is oxidized to SO_2, sulfur dioxide. SO_2 in turn can be oxidized with oxygen to form sulfur trioxide, SO_3. When SO_3 is combined with water, H_2SO_4 results. The raw materials are very cheap. Economic competition rests on the efficiency with which the processes can be carried out. The bottleneck in the production is the second step, the oxidation of

SO_2 to SO_3. Even a minute advantage in this step can be decisive economically. There are two goals: to convert SO_2 to SO_3 (1) as fast as possible and (2) as completely as possible. The first is a kinetic problem, to get the maximum rate of SO_3 formation; the second is an equilibrium problem, to set the conditions so that SO_3 is favored.

What can be done to increase the rate of formation of SO_3? (1) The rate of formation is found to be proportional to the concentration of SO_2 times the concentration of O_2. To get SO_3 faster, the concentration of O_2 or SO_2 must be increased. (2) Since all reactions proceed more rapidly at high temperatures, it is advantageous to heat the mixture for rapid reaction. However, fuel costs and corrosion of reaction chambers also increase with rise in temperature. (3) If possible, it is advantageous to use a catalyst to speed up the reaction. In the reaction

$$2SO_2(g) + O_2(g) \rightarrow 2SO_3(g)$$

platinum acts as a catalyst but changes the mechanism, so that the rate law is no longer

$$\text{Rate} = k[SO_2][O_2]$$

In the presence of platinum, the observed rate is proportional to the concentration of sulfur dioxide and inversely proportional to the concentration of sulfur trioxide to the ½ power. This means that the higher the concentration of SO_3, the slower the reaction proceeds. One solution to this problem is to remove SO_3 as fast as it is formed.

To increase the yield at equilibrium, it is necessary to consider the K and how it changes with temperature. For the equilibrium

$$2SO_2(g) + O_2(g) \rightleftharpoons 2SO_3(g) + 45 \text{ kcal.}$$

the equilibrium condition is

$$K = \frac{[SO_3]^2}{[SO_2]^2[O_2]}$$

(1) To increase the concentration of SO_3 at equilibrium, high concentrations of SO_2 and O_2 should be used. Fortunately, this also speeds up the conversion. (2) Since the

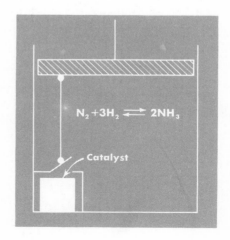

Fig. 13.3   Impossible perpetual-motion machine.

reaction is exothermic as written, K decreases with rise in temperature. Therefore, to increase the concentration of SO_3, the temperature should be decreased. This poses a dilemma. Rapid formation of SO_3 is favored by high temperature, but high temperature decreases the stability of SO_3. In practice, a compromise temperature of 400 to 450°C. is selected to ensure reasonable yields of SO_3 at reasonable rates of formation.

13.8   AQUEOUS SOLUTIONS

The discussion in this chapter has been mainly concerned with homogeneous equilibria involving gaseous solutions. The principles are directly applicable to aqueous solutions. The only modification required is to consider the fact that ions may be involved. Two important cases of equilibria in aqueous solutions are dissociation and solubility.

    1   Dissociation. In a solution of a weak electrolyte there is an equilibrium between the undissociated molecules and the ions into which the electrolyte is dissociated. A common example is the one found in solutions of acetic acid. The equilibrium is

$$HC_2H_3O_2 \rightleftharpoons H^+ + C_2H_3O_2^-$$

for which at room temperature

$$\frac{[H^+][C_2H_3O_2^-]}{[HC_2H_3O_2]} = 1.8 \times 10^{-5}$$

Such an equilibrium constant is called a *dissociation constant.*

    2   Solubility. In a saturated solution of a salt, there is an equilibrium between the ions in the solution and the excess salt. For a saturated solution of barium sulfate, the equilibrium is

$$BaSO_4(s) \rightleftharpoons Ba^{++} + SO_4^{--}$$

for which

$$[Ba^{++}][SO_4^{--}] = 1.5 \times 10^{-9}$$

Such an equilibrium constant is called a *solubility product* and is frequently designated as $K_{s.p.}$.

    The detailed consideration of these equilibria and of other related equilibria is taken up in Chap. 17 on aqueous solutions. Numerical values of some equilibrium constants in aqueous solutions can be found in Appendix 8.

QUESTIONS

13.1 *Equilibrium condition.* Write the equilibrium condition for each of the following:

(a) $COCl_2(g) \rightleftharpoons CO(g) + Cl_2(g)$

(b) $N_2O_4(g) \rightleftharpoons 2NO_2(g)$

(c) $P_4(g) + 6H_2(g) \rightleftharpoons 4PH_3(g)$

(d) $4NH_3(g) + 5O_2(g) \rightleftharpoons 4NO(g) + 6H_2O(g)$

(e) $ZnO(s) + CO(g) \rightleftharpoons Zn(g) + CO_2(g)$

(f) $FeO(s) + CO(g) \rightleftharpoons Fe(s) + CO_2(g)$

(g) $HCN \rightleftharpoons H^+ + CN^-$

(h) $AgCl(s) \rightleftharpoons Ag^+ + Cl^-$

(i) $CaF_2(s) \rightleftharpoons Ca^{++} + 2F^-$

(j) $HPO_3^{--} + I_2 + OH^- \rightleftharpoons H_2PO_4^- + 2I^-$

(k) $2NaHCO_3(s) \rightleftharpoons Na_2CO_3(s) + H_2O(g) + CO_2(g)$

(l) $P_4(s) + 5O_2(g) \rightleftharpoons P_4O_{10}(s)$

13.2 *Terms.* Distinguish clearly between each of the following: law of chemical equilibrium, mass-action expression, equilibrium constant.

13.3 *Change of temperature.* Given the equilibrium

$$CO_2(g) + H_2(g) \rightleftharpoons CO(g) + H_2O(g) - 10 \text{ kcal.}$$

What will be the effect on the equilibrium concentrations of a rise in temperature? Explain in terms of K, the principle of Le Chatelier, and kinetics.

13.4 *Rates and equilibrium.* Given the equilibrium between ozone, O_3, and oxygen:

$$2O_3(g) \rightleftharpoons 3O_2(g) + 68 \text{ kcal.}$$

(a) Is ozone more stable at high or low temperature? (b) Does ozone decompose more rapidly at high or low temperature? (c) Show that your answers to (a) and (b) are not inconsistent.

13.5 *Approach to equilibrium.* Suppose you are investigating the equilibrium

$$1A(g) + 1B(g) \rightleftharpoons 1C(g)$$

Draw graphs to show qualitatively how the concentrations of each A, B, and C change with time as equilibrium is approached in each of the following experiments: (a) One mole of A and one mole of B are simultaneously injected into an empty box. (b) One mole of C is injected into an empty box. (c) One mole of A and two moles of B are simultaneously injected into an empty box.

13.6   *Equilibrium calculation.* The equilibrium system

$$A(g) + 2B(g) + 3C(g) \rightleftharpoons 4D(g) + 5 \text{ kcal.}$$

is under investigation. At 600°C., a 7.0-liter box contains in equilibrium 1.0 mole of A, 2.0 mole of B, 3.0 mole of C, and 4.0 mole of D. (*a*) Calculate the value of K at 600°C. (*b*) How many moles of A will be in equilibrium in this 7.0-liter box at 600°C. with 1.0 mole of B, 1.0 mole of C, and 1.0 mole of D?

Ans. 1.2×10^2; 0.41 mole

13.7   *Equilibrium constant.* For which of the following cases does the reaction go farthest to completion: $K = 1$, $K = 10^{10}$, $K = 10^{-10}$?

13.8   *Heterogeneous equilibrium.* Suppose the following species occur in equilibrium systems: $CaO(s)$, $Na(g)$, $HC_2H_3O_2(soln.)$, $I_2(soln.)$, $I_2(s)$. Which can be omitted from the mass-action expression? Explain.

13.9   *Equilibrium calculation.* Given the equilibrium

$$Y(s) + 2W(g) \rightleftharpoons 2Z(g)$$

If the value of the equilibrium constant is 0.64, what concentration of Z will be in equilibrium with 0.10 mole of Y and 0.50 mole per liter of W?   *Ans.* 0.40 M

13.10   *Equilibrium changes.* Suggest four ways in which the equilibrium concentration of ammonia, NH_3, can be increased in a box in which the equilibrium can be described by the equation

$$N_2(g) + 3H_2(g) \rightleftharpoons 2NH_3(g) + 22 \text{ kcal.}$$

13.11   *Change of pressure.* It is commonly stated that an increase in pressure favors the formation of ammonia in the equilibrium

$$N_2(g) + 3H_2(g) \rightleftharpoons 2NH_3(g) + 22 \text{ kcal.}$$

Show that this is not always the case, by telling how each of the following methods for increasing pressure affects the amount of ammonia at equilibrium: (*a*) decreasing the volume of the system; (*b*) raising the temperature of the system; (*c*) adding the inert gas helium.

13.12   *Equilibrium constants.* (*a*) Calculate the value of K for $A + B \rightleftharpoons C + D$ for each experiment in Table 13.1. (*b*) Show that the value of K' for $C + D \rightleftharpoons A + B$ is the reciprocal of K in (*a*).

13.13   *Rates and equilibrium.* For the system

$$2HI(g) \rightleftharpoons H_2(g) + I_2(g)$$

the specific rate constant of the forward reaction, k, is 0.018 at 490°C. Calculate the specific rate constant of the reverse reaction, k'.

13.14 *Equilibrium changes.* Given some NO, O_2, and NO_2 gases in a box at a certain temperature.

$$2NO(g) + O_2(g) \rightleftharpoons 2NO_2(g) + 27 \text{ kcal.}$$

The number of moles of NO_2 in the box at equilibrium will be altered in what way by: (*a*) increasing the temperature; (*b*) removing NO from the box; (*c*) adding a catalyst; (*d*) adding O_2 to the box; (*e*) compressing the box to a smaller volume?

13.15 *Attainment of equilibrium.* For the reaction

$$N_2(g) + O_2(g) \rightleftharpoons 2NO(g) - 43.2 \text{ kcal.}$$

the equilibrium constant is 6.2×10^{-4} at 2000°C. Given the following situations, tell whether net reaction will occur and, if so, in which direction: (*a*) 1-liter box containing 0.010 mole of N_2, 0.010 mole of O_2, and 0.010 mole of NO at 2000°C.; (*b*) 1-liter box containing 1.0×10^{-3} mole of N_2, 2.0×10^{-1} mole of O_2, and 3.0×10^{-4} mole of NO at 2000°C.; (*c*) 50-liter box containing 0.26 mole of N_2, 0.0062 mole of O_2, and 0.0010 mole of NO at 2000°C.; (*d*) 50-liter box containing 0.26 mole of N_2, 0.0062 mole of O_2, and 0.0010 mole of NO at 2500°C.

13.16 *Amount vs. concentration.* Many students get into trouble in equilibrium calculations by not distinguishing between moles and moles per liter. In spite of this mistake, they frequently obtain correct results. In which of the following equilibria will they get the right answer? Explain.

(*a*) $H_2(g) + Cl_2(g) \rightleftharpoons 2HCl(g)$

(*b*) $2CO(g) + O_2(g) \rightleftharpoons 2CO_2(g)$

(*c*) $4H_2(g) + Fe_3O_4(s) \rightleftharpoons 3Fe(s) + 4H_2O(g)$

13.17 *Equilibrium calculations.* At 986°C., the K for

$$H_2(g) + CO_2(g) \rightleftharpoons H_2O(g) + CO(g)$$

is 1.60. In several experiments the gases were mixed in initial concentrations (in moles per liter) as indicated below. In each of the cases, calculate the final equilibrium concentration of each component at 986°C. (*a*) 0.50 *M* H_2 and 0.50 *M* CO_2; (*b*) 0.50 *M* H_2O and 0.50 *M* CO; (*c*) 0.50 *M* each of H_2, CO_2, H_2O, and CO.   *Ans.* (*c*) 0.44 *M* H_2, 0.44 *M* CO_2, 0.56 *M* H_2O, 0.56 *M* CO

13.18 *Equilibrium calculation.* At 986°C., the K for

$$H_2(g) + CO_2(g) \rightleftharpoons H_2O(g) + CO(g)$$

is 1.60. Calculate the concentration of each component in the final equilibrium system obtained from adding 1.00 mole of H_2, 2.00 moles of CO_2, 3.00 moles of H_2O, and 4.00 moles of CO to a 10.0-liter box at 986°C.   *Ans.* 0.172 *M* H_2, 0.272 *M* CO_2, 0.228 *M* H_2O, 0.328 *M* CO

13.19   *Equilibrium calculation.* Calculate the fraction of HI that decomposes at equilibrium at 490°C. into H_2 and I_2 and show that this fraction does not depend on the initial concentration of HI.

13.20   *Equilibrium calculation.* For the reaction

$$A(g) + B(g) \rightleftharpoons AB(g)$$

the equilibrium constant is 4.0×10^{-2}. Calculate the concentration of AB in a 2.0-liter box into which 0.50 mole of A and 0.60 mole of B have been injected.

Ans. 3.0×10^{-3} M

13.21   *Equilibrium constant.* When gaseous PCl_5 is heated, it decomposes to $PCl_3(g)$ and $Cl_2(g)$. At 546°K., it is observed that the equilibrium mixture of PCl_5, PCl_3, and Cl_2 has a density of 2.48 g. per liter when the pressure is 1.00 atm. Calculate the equilibrium constant for the decomposition in moles per liter.

Ans. 0.073

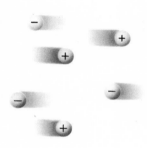

14   *Electrochemistry*

WHEN A CHEMICAL REACTION OCCURS, there is a net increase or decrease in potential energy. In most cases, the change in potential energy appears as heat evolved or absorbed from the surroundings. Occasionally, however, the change in potential energy may be made to appear as electric energy. In this chapter, the relation between chemical energy and electric energy is explored. We consider the transport of electric energy through matter, the conversion of electric energy into chemical energy, and the conversion of chemical energy into electric energy. These topics belong to the field of *electrochemistry*.

14.1   ELECTRIC CONDUCTIVITY

Electric energy may be transported through matter by the conduction of electric charge from one point to another in the form of an *electric current* (see Appendix 4.5 to 4.7 for discussion of electrical terms). In order that the electric current exist, there must be charge carriers in the matter, and there must be a force that makes the carriers move. The charge carriers can be electrons, as in the case of metals, or they can be positive and nega-

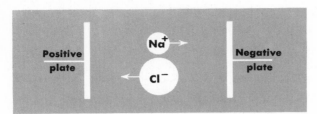

Fig. 14.1   Electric forces   on   ions   in solution.

tive ions, as in the case of electrolytic solutions and molten salts. In the former case, conduction is said to be *metallic;* in the latter, *electrolytic.* The electric force that makes charges move is usually supplied by a battery or some similar source of electrical energy. Any region of space in which there is an electric force is called an *electric field.*

As pointed out in Sec. 8.4, solid metals consist of ordered arrays of positive ions immersed in a sea of electrons. For example, silver consists of Ag^+ ions arranged in a face-centered-cubic pattern with the entire lattice permeated by a cloud of electrons equal in number to the number of Ag^+ ions in the crystal. The Ag^+ ions are more or less fixed in positions from which they do not move except under great stress. The electrons of the cloud, on the contrary, are free to roam throughout the crystal. When an electric field is impressed on the metal, the electrons migrate and thereby carry negative electric charge through the metal. In principle, it should be possible for an electric field to force all the loose electrons toward one end of a metal sample. In practice, it is extraordinarily difficult to separate positive and negative charges from each other without the expenditure of relatively enormous amounts of energy. The only way it is possible to keep a sustained flow of charge in a wire is to add electrons to one end of the wire and drain off electrons from the other end as fast as they accumulate. The metal conductor thus remains everywhere electrically neutral, since just as many electrons move into a region per unit time as move out.

Most of the electrons that make up the electron cloud of a metal are of very high kinetic energy. Metallic conductivity would therefore be extremely high were it not for a *resistance* effect. Electric resistance is believed to arise because lattice ions vibrate about their lattice points. By interfering with the migration of electrons, the ions keep the conductivity down. At higher temperatures, the thermal vibrations of the lattice increase, and therefore it is not surprising to find that, as the temperature of a metal is raised, its conductivity diminishes.

In solutions, the mechanism of conductivity is complicated by the fact that the positive carriers are also free to move. As pointed out in Sec. 10.4, solutions of electrolytes contain positive and negative ions. There are no free electrons in aqueous solutions. The ions are not fixed in position but are free to roam throughout the body of the solution. When an electric field is applied to such a solution, as shown in Fig. 14.1, the positive ions experience a force in one direction, while the negative ions experience a force in the opposite direction. The simultaneous motion of positive and negative ions in opposite directions constitutes the *electrolytic current.* The current would stop if positive ions accumulated at the negative electrode and negative ions at the positive electrode. In order that the electrolytic current continue, appropriate chemical reactions must occur at the electrodes to maintain electrical neutrality.

That ions migrate when electrolytic solutions conduct electricity can be seen from the experiment diagramed in Fig. 14.2. The U tube is initially half filled with a deep-purple aqueous solution of copper permanganate, $Cu(MnO_4)_2$. The solution contains blue hydrated Cu^{++} ions and purple MnO_4^- ions. A colorless aqueous solution of nitric acid, HNO_3, is floated on top of the $Cu(MnO_4)_2$ solution. An electric field is maintained across the solution by the two electrodes. After some time, it is observed that the blue color characteristic of hydrated Cu^{++} ions has moved into the region marked *A*, suggesting a migration toward the negative electrode. At the same time, the purple color characteristic of MnO_4^- has moved into the region marked *B*, indicating that negative ions move simultaneously toward the positive electrode.

As in the case of metallic conduction, electric neutrality must be preserved in all regions of the solution at all times. Otherwise, the current soon ceases. Figure 14.3 shows two of the possible ways by which electrical neutrality can be preserved for a given region of a NaCl solution. In (*a*), one Na^+ ion enters the region defined by the dotted line to compensate for the charge of the departing Na^+ ion. In (*b*), as one Na^+ ion leaves the region,

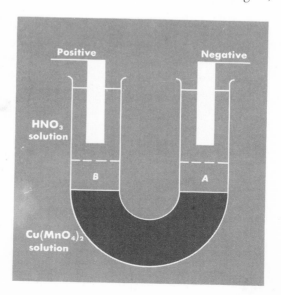

Fig. 14.2   *Migration of ions in electrolytic conductivity.*

one Cl^- ion departs in the opposite direction; hence the region shows no net change in charge. *Both* of these effects occur simultaneously, their relative importance depending on the relative mobilities of the positive and negative ions.

Unlike metallic conduction, electrolytic conduction is usually increased when the temperature of a solution is raised.* The difference arises from the fact that in metals the conducting electrons are already of such high energy that a rise in temperature does not appreciably affect their kinetic energy. In solutions, ions have average kinetic energies proportional to the absolute temperature, just as do the molecules of an ideal gas. When the temperature of a solution is raised, the average kinetic energy of the ions is increased, the ions migrate faster, and the solution becomes a better conductor of electricity.

14.2 ELECTROLYSIS

In order to maintain an electric current, it is necessary to have a complete circuit; i.e., there must be a closed loop whereby the electric charge can return to its starting point. If the complete circuit includes as one component an electrolytic conductor, chemical reaction must occur at the electrodes. Electric energy is thus used to produce chemical change, and the process is called *electrolysis.*

A typical electrolysis circuit is shown in Fig. 14.4. The two vertical lines at the top of the diagram represent a battery with the long line the positive terminal, and the short line the negative one. The curling lines represent strips of connecting wire, usually copper, that join the battery to the electrodes. The electrodes dip into the electrolytic conductor, which contains the ions M^+ and X^- that are free to move. When operating, the battery creates an electric field which pushes the electrons in the wires in the directions shown by the arrows. Elec-

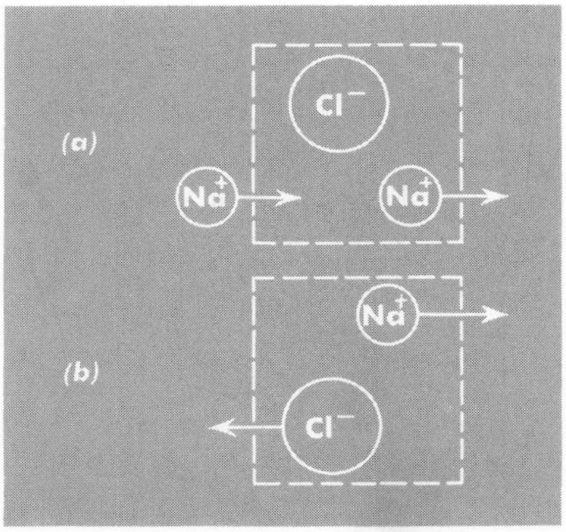

* There are exceptions to this generalization. For example, with some weak electrolytes, the per cent dissociation (Sec. 10.5) may decrease with rising temperature. The decrease in the concentration of ions may be big enough to cause a decrease in conductivity.

Fig. 14.3 *Two ways that migrating ions could maintain electric neutrality in a region of solution.*

Fig. 14.4   Electrolysis.

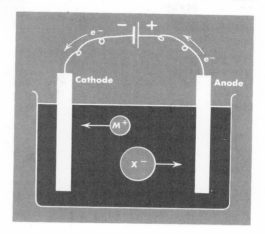

trons are crowded onto the left-hand electrode and drained away from the right-hand electrode. The circuit is not complete unless there is some way by which electrons can be used up at the left electrode and formed at the right electrode. Chemical changes must occur. At the left electrode, a *reduction* process must occur in which some ion or molecule accepts electrons and is thereby reduced. The electrode at which reduction occurs is always called a *cathode*. At the right-hand electrode, electrons must be released by an ion or molecule to the electrode. An *oxidation* process must occur. The electrode at which oxidation occurs is always called an *anode*. In order for the reduction process to continue at the cathode, ions must keep moving toward it. These ions are the positive ions and are called *cations*. Simultaneously, negative ions move to the anode and are called *anions*.

14.3   ELECTROLYSIS OF MOLTEN NaCl

Molten NaCl contains Na^+ and Cl^- ions which are free to migrate. Figure 14.5 shows a schematic diagram of the electrolysis cell. Inert electrodes of carbon or platinum dip into the molten NaCl. As diagramed, a reduction process must occur at the left-hand electrode, which therefore is the cathode. Of the two ions, Na^+ and Cl^-, only Na^+ can be reduced. On electrolysis, Na^+ is reduced and forms metallic Na. The *cathode reaction* can be written

$$Na^+ + e^- \rightarrow Na$$

indicating that at the cathode one Na^+ ion picks up an electron to form a neutral Na atom. During the change, mass and charge are conserved, so the cathode reaction is in a sense a chemical reaction expressible by a bal-

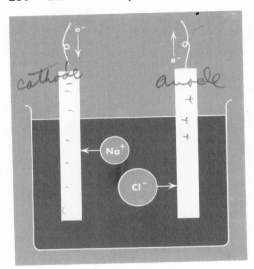

Fig. 14.5   Electrolysis of molten NaCl.

anced equation. Since the equation shows only a reduction process, it is referred to as a *half-reaction.*

At the anode, oxidation occurs. Of the two species in the cell, Na^+ and Cl^-, only the Cl^- can be oxidized. When oxidized, Cl^- releases an electron to the anode, and a neutral chlorine atom forms. Two such chlorine atoms immediately combine to produce a diatomic chlorine molecule, Cl_2. These Cl_2 molecules bubble off as a gas. The net *anode half-reaction* can be written

$$2Cl^- \rightarrow Cl_2(g) + 2e^-$$

At the cathode, electric energy has been used to convert Na^+ into Na metal; at the anode, to convert Cl^- into Cl_2. By addition, the two electrode half-reactions can be combined into a single over-all *cell reaction.* In order to keep electrons from piling up in the cell, as many must disappear at the cathode as appear at the anode. To ensure electron balance, the half-reactions are multiplied by appropriate coefficients so that, when the half-reactions are added, the electrons cancel out of the final equation. Thus, for the electrolysis of molten NaCl:

Cathode reaction: $2Na^+ + 2e^- \rightarrow 2Na$

Anode reaction: $\underline{2Cl^- \rightarrow Cl_2(g) + 2e^-}$

Over-all reaction: $2Na^+ + 2Cl^- \xrightarrow{\text{electrolysis}} 2Na + Cl_2(g)$

In order to emphasize that this reaction occurs by the consumption of electric energy, the word electrolysis is often written under the arrow.

14.4   ELECTROLYSIS OF AQUEOUS NaCl

When an aqueous NaCl solution is electrolyzed under appropriate conditions, it is observed that hydrogen gas is liberated at the cathode and that chlorine gas is liberated at the anode. How can these observations be accounted for in terms of electrode reactions? Figure 14.6 shows the electrolysis cell, which now contains, besides Na^+ and Cl^- ions, H_2O molecules and traces of H^+ and OH^- from the dissociation of water. Molecules of H_2O can be either oxidized to O_2 and H^+ by removal of electrons or reduced to H_2 and OH^- by the addition of electrons. The H_2O must thus be considered as a possible reactant at each electrode.

At the cathode, reduction must occur. Three different reactions are possible:

$$Na^+ + e^- \rightarrow Na(s) \tag{1}$$

$$2H_2O + 2e^- \rightarrow H_2(g) + 2OH^- \tag{2}$$

$$2H^+ + 2e^- \rightarrow H_2(g) \tag{3}$$

It is not easy to predict which of several possible reactions will occur at a cathode. It is necessary to consider which reactant is reduced most *easily* and which reactant is reduced most *rapidly*. The strongest oxidizing agent is not necessarily the fastest. Further complications appear when currents are very large and when concentrations of reactants are very small. The fact that hydrogen gas and not metallic sodium is formed in the electrolysis

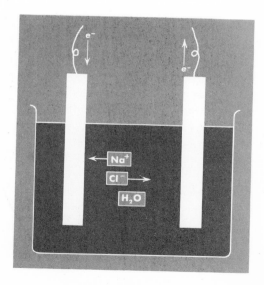

Fig. 14.6   Electrolysis of aqueous NaCl.

of aqueous NaCl indicates that reaction (2) or (3) occurs.* In NaCl solution, the concentration of H^+ is not large enough to make reaction (3) reasonable as a *net change*. Therefore, in the electrolysis of aqueous NaCl, reaction (2) is usually written for the cathode reaction. However, in acidic solutions, the concentration of H^+ may be high enough for H^+ to appear in the net electrode reaction. For example, in the electrolysis of aqueous HCl, the cathode reaction is written as Eq. (3).

In the electrolysis of NaCl solution, OH^- accumulates in the region around the cathode, and positive ions (Na^+) must move toward the cathode to preserve electric neutrality. In addition, OH^- migrates away from the cathode. Both migrations are consistent with the requirement that cations migrate toward the cathode and anions toward the anode.

At the anode, oxidation must occur. Two different reactions are possible.

$$2Cl^- \rightarrow Cl_2(g) + 2e^- \tag{4}$$

$$2H_2O \rightarrow O_2(g) + 4H^+ + 4e^- \tag{5}$$

In agreement with experiment, reaction (4) is preferred. As the chloride-ion concentration around the anode is depleted, fresh Cl^- moves into the region and Na^+ moves out.

In summary, the equations for the electrolysis of aqueous NaCl are:

Cathode reaction: $2e^- + 2H_2O \rightarrow H_2(g) + 2OH^-$

Anode reaction: $2Cl^- \rightarrow Cl_2(g) + 2e^-$

Over-all reaction: $2Cl^- + 2H_2O \xrightarrow{\text{electrolysis}} H_2(g) + Cl_2(g) + 2OH^-$

As expressed by the over-all reaction, during the electrolysis H_2 gas and Cl_2 gas are formed, the concentration of Cl^- diminishes, and the concentration of OH^- increases. Since there is always Na^+ in the solution, the solution is gradually converted, as time goes on, from aqueous NaCl to aqueous NaOH. In fact, in the commercial production of chlorine by the electrolysis of aqueous NaCl, solid NaOH is obtained as a by-product by evaporating H_2O from the residual solution left after electrolysis.

14.5   ELECTROLYSIS OF AQUEOUS Na₂SO₄

When aqueous Na_2SO_4 is electrolyzed, H_2 gas is formed at the cathode, and O_2 is formed at the anode. Changes at the electrodes can be demonstrated

---

* Years ago it was thought that the metal Na was first formed by reaction (1) and then subsequently reacted with water to liberate H_2. However, there is no evidence that any intermediate Na is ever formed in this electrolysis.

by running the electrolysis in the cell shown in Fig. 14.7. A few drops of litmus are initially added to the solution. Before electrolysis, the solution contains Na^+, SO_4^{--}, and H_2O. It is essentially neutral; therefore litmus takes the usual violet coloration. After electrolysis has proceeded for a while, the litmus in the cathode compartment becomes blue, indicating the solution to be basic; the litmus in the anode compartment becomes red, indicating the solution to be acidic. Consistent with these observations are the following electrode reactions:

Cathode: $2e^- + 2H_2O \rightarrow H_2(g) + 2OH^-$

Anode: $2H_2O \rightarrow O_2(g) + 4H^+ + 4e^-$

The OH^- from the cathode reaction turns litmus blue; the H^+ from the anode reaction turns litmus red. The over-all cell reaction is obtained by doubling the cathode reaction and adding to the anode reaction. The four electrons cancel, and the result is

$$6H_2O \xrightarrow{\text{electrolysis}} 2H_2(g) + O_2(g) + 4H^+ + 4OH^-$$

In this equation, both H^+ and OH^- appear as products. The only reason neutralization does not occur is that the H^+ is formed in the anode compartment and OH^- in the cathode compartment. If the solution is now poured from the cell in order that mixing may take place, neutralization

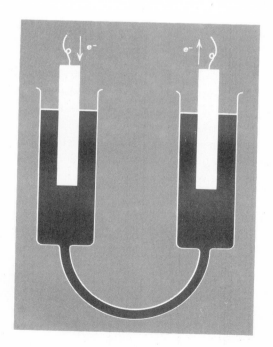

Fig. 14.7 Two-compartment electrolysis cell.

occurs, and the litmus is restored to its original purple color. Addition of the neutralization reaction

$$4H^+ + 4OH^- \rightarrow 4H_2O$$

to the above over-all cell reaction gives for the net reaction

$$2H_2O \xrightarrow[\text{electrolysis}]{} 2H_2(g) + O_2(g)$$

In this electrolysis, only water disappears. The Na^+ and SO_4^{--} initially present are also present at the conclusion of the electrolysis. Is the Na_2SO_4 necessary? Because of the requirements of electrical neutrality, some kind of electrolytic solute must be present. Positive ions must be available to move into the cathode region to counterbalance the charge of the OH^- produced. Negative ions must be available to move to the anode to counterbalance the H^+ produced.

Almost any ionic solute makes possible the electrolysis of water as described by the above equations. The only requirement is that the ions of the solute not be oxidized or reduced, as would happen, for example, when aqueous $CuSO_4$ is electrolyzed. Cu^{++} is more easily and rapidly reduced than H_2O. During electrolysis, copper plating forms on the cathode. The reactions are:

Cathode reaction: $\quad Cu^{++} + 2e^- \rightarrow Cu(s)$

Anode reaction: $\quad 2H_2O \rightarrow O_2(g) + 4H^+ + 4e^-$

Over-all reaction: $\quad 2Cu^{++} + 2H_2O \xrightarrow[\text{electrolysis}]{} 2Cu(s) + O_2(g) + 4H^+$

In some cases, the electrodes themselves may take part in the electrode reactions. In each of the above cells, the electrodes were assumed to be inert. This would almost always be the case if the electrodes were made of the inert metal platinum. If, however, the electrode material is reactive, it must be considered as a possible reactant. For example, copper anodes are frequently themselves oxidized during electrolysis when no other species present is more readily oxidized.

14.6 QUANTITATIVE ASPECTS OF ELECTROLYSIS

By experimentation, Michael Faraday, the great English chemist and physicist, established early in the nineteenth century the laws of electrolysis that bear his name (Sec. 3.1). These laws state that the weight of substance produced at an electrode is proportional to the amount of electricity transferred at the electrode and to the gram-equivalent weight of the substance. Faraday's laws can be accounted for by considering the electrode reactions. For example, in the electrolysis of molten NaCl, the cathode reaction

$$Na^+ + e^- \rightarrow Na$$

tells that one sodium atom is produced at the electrode when one sodium ion disappears and one electron is transferred. When the Avogadro number of electrons is transferred, 1 mole of Na^+ disappears, and 1 gram-atom of Na is formed. For this reaction, 1 gram-equivalent of Na is 22.991 g.; hence transfer of the Avogadro number of electrons liberates 22.991 g. of Na. Doubling the amount of electricity transferred doubles the weight of sodium produced.

The Avogadro number of electrons is such a convenient measure of the amount of electricity that it is designated by a special name, the *faraday*. In electrical units 1 faraday is equal to 96,500 coulombs of charge. As described in Appendix 4.7, a *coulomb* of charge is the amount of electricity that is transferred when a current of 1 amp. flows for 1 sec. It is useful to remember that the current in amperes multiplied by the time in seconds is equal to the number of coulombs. The electric charge in coulombs divided by 96,500 is equal to the number of faradays.

Electrode half-reactions expressed in ions, electrons, and atoms can be read in terms of moles and gram-atoms if the electricity is expressed in faradays. Thus,

$$Na^+ + e^- \rightarrow Na$$

can be read either "one sodium ion reacts with one electron to form one sodium atom" or "1 mole of sodium ions reacts with 1 faraday of electricity to form 1 gram-atom of sodium."

Example 1

How many grams of chlorine can be produced by the electrolysis of molten NaCl *at a current of 10.0 amp. for 5.00 min.?*

Coulombs $= $ amperes $\times$ seconds $= 10.0 \times 5.00 \times 60 = 3,000$

Faradays $= \dfrac{3,000}{96,500} = 0.0311$

Since $2Cl^- \rightarrow Cl_2(g) + 2e^-$,

2 faradays of electricity produce 1 mole of Cl_2

0.0311 faraday of electricity produces 0.0156 mole of Cl_2

0.0156 mole of Cl_2 weighs (0.0156)(70.9), or 1.11, g.

Example 2

A current of 0.0965 amp. is passed for 1,000 sec. through 50.0 ml. of 0.100 M NaCl. What will be the average concentration of OH^- *in the final solution?*

$$\text{Faradays} = \frac{(0.0965)(1,000)}{96,500} = 0.00100$$

At the cathode $2e^- + 2H_2O \rightarrow H_2(g) + 2OH^-$

　　2 faradays liberate 2 moles of OH^-

　　0.00100 faraday liberates 0.00100 mole of OH^-

In the final solution, assuming the volume is still 50.0 ml., the concentration of OH^- is 0.00100 mole per 50.0 ml., or 0.0200 *M*.

14.7 GALVANIC CELLS

In the above cells, electric energy in the form of a current was used to bring about oxidation-reduction reactions. It is also possible to do the reverse, i.e., use an oxidation-reduction reaction to produce electric current. The main requirement is that the oxidizing and reducing agents be kept separate from each other so that electron transfer must occur through a wire. Any device which accomplishes this is called a *galvanic*, or *voltaic*, cell after Luigi Galvani (1780) and Alessandro Volta (1800), who made the basic discoveries.

When a bar of zinc is dipped into a solution of copper sulfate, $CuSO_4$, copper plating is obtained. The net reaction is

$$Zn(s) + Cu^{++} \rightarrow Zn^{++} + Cu(s)$$

In this change, Zn is oxidized and Cu^{++} is reduced, presumably by the direct transfer of electrons from zinc atoms to copper ions. To emphasize this transfer of electrons, the net reaction can be split into two half-reactions:

$$Zn(s) \rightarrow Zn^{++} + 2e^-$$

$$Cu^{++} + 2e^- \rightarrow Cu(s)$$

The galvanic cell operates on the principle that two separated half-reactions can be made to take place simultaneously, with the electron transfer occurring through a wire. The typical galvanic cell shown in Fig. 14.8 uses the reaction

$$Zn(s) + Cu^{++} \rightarrow Zn^{++} + Cu(s)$$

Any galvanic cell that uses this reaction is called a *Daniell cell*. The dotted line represents a porous partition which separates the container into two compartments but still permits diffusion of ions between them. In the left-

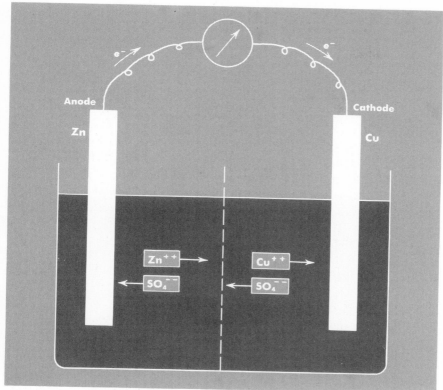

Fig. 14.8   Typical galvanic cell.

hand compartment is a solution of zinc sulfate, into which a zinc bar is dipped; in the right-hand compartment is a copper bar dipping into a solution of copper sulfate. When the two electrodes are connected by a wire, electric current flows, as shown by a meter in the circuit. As time progresses, the zinc bar is eaten away, and copper plates out on the copper bar.

The cell operates as follows: At the zinc bar, oxidation occurs, making Zn the anode. The half-reaction

$$Zn(s) \rightarrow Zn^{++} + 2e^-$$

produces Zn^{++} ions and electrons. The zinc ions migrate away from the anode into the solution, and the electrons move through the wire, as indicated in the figure. At the copper bar, reduction occurs, making Cu the cathode. The electrons come through the wire and move onto the cathode, where they are picked up and used in the reaction

$$Cu^{++} + 2e^- \rightarrow Cu(s)$$

Copper ions in the solution are depleted, and new copper ions move into the vicinity of the cathode. The circuit is complete. Consistent with previous notation, cations (Zn^{++} and Cu^{++}) in the solution move toward the cathode (the copper bar), and anions (SO_4^{--}) move toward the anode (the zinc bar). Electrons flow through the wire, and a current is obtained from an oxidation-reduction reaction. The cell runs until either the Zn or Cu^{++} is depleted.

In describing the operation of a galvanic cell, it is not necessary to specify the relative charges of the electrodes. In fact, a simple assignment of charges to the electrodes will not account for the direction of both electron and ion currents. To account for the *electron current* (from anode to cathode in the wire), the anode must be labeled *negative* with respect to the cathode. To account for the *ion current* (negative ions to the anode and positive ions to the cathode), the anode must be labeled *positive* with respect to the cathode. How can the anode be positive and negative at the same time? The discrepancy is resolved by considering the electrode in detail. For example, at the Daniell cell anode, Zn^{++} is produced. These Zn^{++} ions form a layer which makes the anode appear positive as viewed from the solution. The electrons released in forming Zn^{++} make the anode appear negative as viewed from the wire.

Actually, to get a current from a Daniell cell, the Zn^{++} ions and the Cu bar need not be initially present. Any metal support for the plating of Cu will do in place of the Cu bar. Any positive ion that does not react with Zn metal will do in place of Zn^{++}. However, as the cell reaction proceeds, Zn^{++} is necessarily produced at the anode. Furthermore, the porous partition is necessary only to keep Cu^{++} from easily getting over to the Zn metal, where direct electron transfer would short-circuit the cell. The partition must be porous in order to allow the diffusion of positive and negative ions from one compartment to the other. Otherwise the solution would soon become positively charged in the anode compartment (due to accumulation of Zn^{++}) and negatively charged in the cathode compartment (due to depletion of Cu^{++}), causing the current to cease.

In principle, any oxidation-reduction reaction is separable into two half-reactions and can be made a source of electric current as a galvanic cell. Probably the most famous example is the *lead storage battery*, or *accumulator*. As shown in Fig. 14.9, the basic features are electrodes of lead, Pb, and lead dioxide, PbO_2, dipping into aqueous H_2SO_4. When the cell operates, the reactions are:

Anode:

$$Pb(s) + HSO_4^- \rightarrow PbSO_4(s) + 2e^- + H^+$$

Cathode:

$$PbO_2(s) + HSO_4^- + 3H^+ + 2e^- \rightarrow PbSO_4(s) + 2H_2O$$

Fig. 14.9   Cell of a lead storage battery.

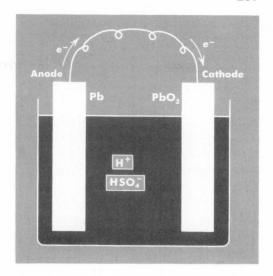

Over-all cell reaction:

$$Pb(s) + 2HSO_4^- + 2H^+ + PbO_2(s) \rightarrow 2PbSO_4(s) + 2H_2O$$

The insoluble lead sulfate, $PbSO_4$, that is formed at each electrode adheres to the electrode. During the *charging* of a battery, the electrode reactions are reversed so as to restore the cell to its original condition. In *discharge*, as shown by the over-all cell reaction, Pb and PbO_2 are depleted, and the concentration of H_2SO_4 is diminished. Since the density of the aqueous solution is chiefly dependent on the concentration of H_2SO_4, measurement of the density tells how far the cell is discharged.*

Another common galvanic cell is the Leclanché dry cell used in flashlights. The cell consists of a zinc can containing a centered graphite rod surrounded by a moist paste of manganese dioxide, MnO_2, zinc chloride, $ZnCl_2$, and ammonium chloride, NH_4Cl. The zinc can is the anode, and the graphite rod is the cathode. At the anode, Zn is oxidized; at the cathode, MnO_2 is reduced. The electrode reactions are extremely complex and seem to vary, depending on how much current is drawn from the cell. For the delivery of very small currents, the following reactions are probable:

Anode: $Zn(s) \rightarrow Zn^{++} + 2e^-$

Cathode: $2MnO_2(s) + Zn^{++} + 2e^- \rightarrow ZnMn_2O_4(s)$

Over-all cell reaction: $Zn(s) + 2MnO_2(s) \rightarrow ZnMn_2O_4(s)$

* It would seem natural to say that, when the battery is discharging, the anion HSO_4^- moves to the anode. However, as is obvious from the cathode half-reaction, some of the HSO_4^- must also move to the cathode in order to form $PbSO_4$. Thus we have the unusual but not unique situation that the anion moves toward both electrodes.

14.8 OXIDATION POTENTIALS

A voltmeter connected between the two electrodes of a galvanic cell shows a characteristic voltage which depends in magnitude on what reactants take part in the electrode reactions and on what their concentrations are. For example, in the Daniell cell, if Zn^{++} and Cu^{++} are at 1 m concentration, and the temperature is $25°C.$, the voltage measured between the Zn electrode and the Cu electrode is 1.10 volts, no matter how big the cell or how big the electrodes. This voltage is characteristic of the Daniell cell reaction

$$Zn(s) + Cu^{++} \rightarrow Zn^{++} + Cu(s)$$

The voltage measures the force with which electrons are moved around the circuit and therefore measures the tendency of this reaction to take place. Thus, galvanic cells give a quantitative measure of the relative tendency of various oxidation-reduction reactions to occur.

Figure 14.10 shows a galvanic cell set up to study the reaction

$$Zn(s) + 2H^+ \rightarrow H_2(g) + Zn^{++}$$

Fig. 14.10 *Voltage measurement of zinc-hydrogen cell.*

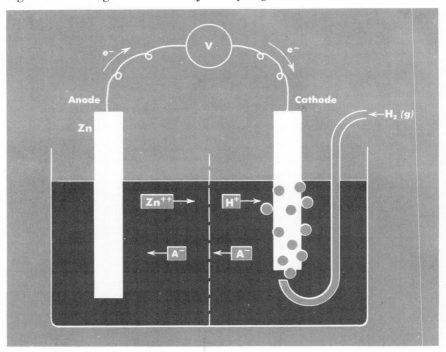

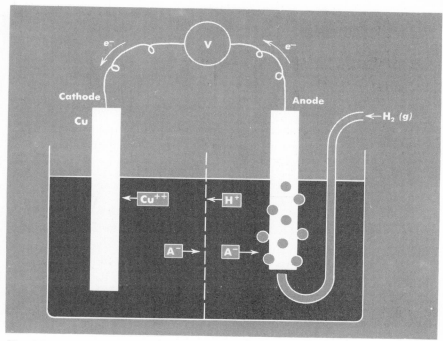

Fig. 14.11   Voltage measurement of copper-hydrogen cell.

In the anode compartment, a zinc bar dips into a solution of a zinc salt. In the cathode compartment, H_2 gas is led in through a tube so as to bubble over an inert electrode, made, for example, of Pt, dipped into an acidic solution. The anode reaction is

$$Zn(s) \rightarrow Zn^{++} + 2e^-$$

The cathode reaction is

$$2H^+ + 2e^- \rightarrow H_2(g)$$

When the concentrations of H^+ and of Zn^{++} are 1 m and when the pressure of the H_2 gas is 1 atm., the voltmeter reads 0.76 volt (at 25°C.), and the deflection is in such direction as to indicate that Zn has a greater tendency to give off electrons than has H_2. In other words, the half-reaction $Zn(s) \rightarrow Zn^{++} + 2e^-$ has a greater tendency to occur than $H_2(g) \rightarrow 2H^+ + 2e^-$ by 0.76 volt.

The galvanic cell in Fig. 14.11 makes use of the reaction

$$H_2(g) + Cu^{++} \rightarrow 2H^+ + Cu(s)$$

The anode reaction is

$$H_2(g) \rightarrow 2H^+ + 2e^-$$

and the cathode reaction is

$$Cu^{++} + 2e^- \rightarrow Cu(s)$$

When the concentrations of H^+ and Cu^{++} are 1 m and when the pressure of H_2 is 1 atm., the voltmeter reads 0.34 volt (at 25°C.), and the direction indicates that H_2 has a greater tendency to give off electrons than has Cu. In other words, the half-reaction $H_2(g) \rightarrow 2H^+ + 2e^-$ has a greater tendency to occur than $Cu(s) \rightarrow Cu^{++} + 2e^-$ by 0.34 volt.

In all cells, the voltage observed arises from two sources: a voltage at the anode and a voltage at the cathode. If either of these voltages were known, the other could be obtained by subtraction. However, it is impossible to measure the voltage of an individual electrode, since any complete circuit necessarily contains two electrodes. We are forced to assign a completely arbitrary voltage to one electrode. The voltage of the other electrode is thereby fixed. For convenience, the voltage of the standard hydrogen electrode (at 25°C., 1 atm. H_2 pressure, and 1 m H^+ concentration) is given the value zero. Consequently, in any cell which contains the hydrogen electrode, the entire measured voltage is attributed to the half-reaction at the other electrode. Voltages thus assigned are called *oxidation potentials*.

Table 14.1 lists various half-reactions with their oxidation potentials. A more extensive listing is given in Appendix 7. The double arrows indicate that under appropriate conditions the half-reaction can be made to go in either direction. The voltage given applies when the half-reaction proceeds in the forward direction. For the reverse direction, the sign of the voltage must be changed.

The forward reaction is an oxidation in which the reducing agent, shown on the left, is oxidized. The table is so arranged that the reducing agents are listed in order of decreasing strength. In other words, there is decreasing tendency of the forward half-reaction to occur from the top of the table to the bottom. For example, of the list given, lithium, Li, is the best reducing agent, since it has the highest tendency to give off electrons. Fluoride ion, F^-, is the worst reducing agent and has the least tendency to give off electrons. Such a list of reducing agents arranged in decreasing order is sometimes called the *electromotive series*.

The numerical values of the oxidation potentials given in Table 14.1 apply to aqueous solutions at 25°C. in which the concentration of dissolved species is 1 m. A positive value of the oxidation potential indicates that the reducing agent is stronger than H_2; a negative value indicates that the re-

Table 14.1   Some Half-reactions and Their Oxidation Potentials

Half-reaction		Potential, volts
Li(s)	$\rightleftharpoons$ Li$^+$ + e^-	+3.05
Na(s)	$\rightleftharpoons$ Na$^+$ + e^-	+2.71
Mg(s)	$\rightleftharpoons$ Mg^{++} + 2e^-	+2.37
Al(s)	$\rightleftharpoons$ Al^{+3} + 3e^-	+1.66
Zn(s)	$\rightleftharpoons$ Zn^{++} + 2e^-	+0.76
Fe(s)	$\rightleftharpoons$ Fe^{++} + 2e^-	+0.44
H$_2$(g)	$\rightleftharpoons$ 2H$^+$ + 2e^-	0
Cu(s)	$\rightleftharpoons$ Cu^{++} + 2e^-	−0.34
2I$^-$	$\rightleftharpoons$ I$_2$ + 2e^-	−0.54
Ag(s)	$\rightleftharpoons$ Ag$^+$ + e^-	−0.80
Hg(l)	$\rightleftharpoons$ Hg^{++} + 2e^-	−0.85
2Br$^-$	$\rightleftharpoons$ Br$_2$ + 2e^-	−1.09
2H$_2$O	$\rightleftharpoons$ O$_2$(g) + 4H$^+$ + 4e^-	−1.23
2Cl$^-$	$\rightleftharpoons$ Cl$_2$(g) + 2e^-	−1.36
4H$_2$O + Mn^{++}	$\rightleftharpoons$ MnO$_4^-$ + 8H$^+$ + 5e^-	−1.51
2F$^-$	$\rightleftharpoons$ F$_2$(g) + 2e^-	−2.87

ducing agent is weaker than H$_2$.* The magnitude of the potential is a quantitative measure of the relative tendency of the half-reaction to occur from left to right. (It should be noted that nothing is implied about whether the reaction is *fast* enough to be observed.)

Each reducing agent in Table 14.1 is coupled in its half-reaction with its oxidized form. For example, Cu is coupled with Cu^{++}. The oxidized form is capable of acting as an oxidizing agent when the half-reaction is reversed by some means. Thus, the oxidation potentials in Table 14.1 also give information about the relative tendency of oxidizing agents to pick up electrons. If a half-reaction, such as the one at the top of the table, has great tendency to go to the right, it is hard to reverse, and the oxidizing agent is a poor one. Of the oxidizing agents listed, Li$^+$ is the poorest, and fluorine, F$_2$, the best. The half-reaction

$$e^- + \text{Li}^+ \rightarrow \text{Li}(s) \qquad -3.05 \text{ volts}$$

has smaller tendency to occur than

$$2e^- + \text{F}_2(g) \rightarrow 2\text{F}^- \qquad +2.87 \text{ volts}$$

Table 14.1 lists oxidizing agents (on the right) in order of increasing strength.

---

* This assignment of "positive" and "negative" is arbitrary and could perhaps be better chosen in the opposite sense. In fact, most of the world outside America does use the opposite convention. *De gustibus non est disputandum.*

The voltage of a half-reaction is a measure of the tendency of the half-reaction to occur. This voltage is independent of the other half of the complete reaction. The voltage of any complete reaction can be obtained by addition of the voltages of its two half-reactions. The voltage so obtained gives the tendency of the complete reaction to occur and is the voltage measured for a galvanic cell which uses the reaction. For example, in the Daniell cell:

Anode:	$Zn(s) \rightarrow Zn^{++} + 2e^-$	$+0.76$ volt
Cathode:	$2e^- + Cu^{++} \rightarrow Cu(s)$	$+0.34$ volt
Complete Cell:	$Zn(s) + Cu^{++} \rightarrow Zn^{++} + Cu(s)$	$+1.10$ volts

The voltage, $+1.10$, so calculated is that observed for the Daniell cell. It is positive, which indicates that the reaction tends to go spontaneously as written. It should be noted that the value 1.10 volts applies when the concentrations of the ions are 1 m, since oxidation potentials are defined for concentrations of 1 m. If the concentrations are changed, the cell voltage changes, as can be predicted by the Le Chatelier principle. For example, an increase in Cu^{++} concentration means that the reaction has greater tendency to go to the right, and the voltage is increased. Likewise, an increase in Zn^{++} concentration decreases the voltage.*

Any oxidation-reduction reaction for which the voltage is positive has the tendency to take place as written. Whether a given reaction should take place spontaneously can be determined from the relative positions of its two half-reactions in a table of oxidation potentials. In Table 14.1, for example, any reducing agent reacts with any oxidizing agent below it. Zn reduces Fe^{++}, H^+, Cu^{++}, etc., but does not reduce Al^{+3}, Mg^{++}, Na^+, etc. Similarly, any oxidizing agent reacts with any reducing agent above it. I_2 oxidizes Cu, H_2, Fe, etc., but does not oxidize Br^-, H_2O, Cl^-, etc.

Example 3

I_2 and Br_2 are added to a solution containing I^- and Br^-. What reaction would occur if the concentration of each species were 1 m?

---

* Actually, the tendency of a reaction to occur is influenced not only by the concentrations of species but also by interionic attractions (Sec. 10.6) and other complicating factors such as the change of hydration with concentration. All of these factors as well as concentration contribute to the effectiveness of a species to take part in the chemical reaction or, in other words, contribute to the *chemical activity* of the species. For precise work, it is the *chemical activity* rather than the *concentration* of the species that must be specified. Strictly speaking, then, the oxidation potentials given in Table 14.1 are defined for all species at unit activity. For our purposes we shall assume that activity can be represented by concentration in terms of molality.

The half-reactions to be considered are

$$2I^- \rightarrow I_2 + 2e^- \qquad -0.54 \text{ volt}$$

$$2Br^- \rightarrow Br_2 + 2e^- \qquad -1.09 \text{ volts}$$

Method (a). From the positions in Table 14.1, I^- can reduce Br_2, whereas Br^- cannot reduce I_2. Therefore, the reaction is

$$2I^- + Br_2 \rightarrow I_2 + 2Br^-$$

Method (b)

$$2I^- \rightarrow I_2 + 2e^- \qquad\qquad\qquad -0.54 \text{ volt}$$

$$\underline{2e^- + Br_2 \rightarrow 2Br^- \qquad\qquad\qquad +1.09 \text{ volts}}$$

$$2I^- + Br_2 \rightarrow I_2 + 2Br^- \qquad\qquad +0.55 \text{ volt}$$

Therefore, this reaction should occur spontaneously as written, since the voltage for the reaction is positive.

$$2Br^- \rightarrow Br_2 + 2e^- \qquad\qquad\qquad -1.09 \text{ volts}$$

$$\underline{2e^- + I_2 \rightarrow 2I^- \qquad\qquad\qquad\qquad +0.54 \text{ volt}}$$

$$2Br^- + I_2 \rightarrow Br_2 + 2I^- \qquad\qquad -0.55 \text{ volt}$$

Therefore, this reaction should not occur spontaneously as written.

14.9 BALANCING EQUATIONS BY HALF-REACTIONS

An oxidation half-reaction must always be paired with a reduction half-reaction, in order that the electron balance of the world may not be disturbed. This requirement of electron balance makes possible a method of balancing equations which differs from the oxidation-number method discussed in Sec. 5.7 in that the artificially devised oxidation number is no longer necessary.

The balanced equation for the change

$$Zn(s) + Ag^+ \rightarrow Zn^{++} + Ag(s)$$

can be written by noting that the Zn must release two electrons to form Zn^{++} and that these two electrons must be picked up by two Ag^+ ions to form two Ag atoms. The principle of the method is to write the half-reactions and then match electron loss and gain. Thus,

$$Zn(s) \rightarrow Zn^{++} + 2e^-$$

$$\underline{2[e^- + Ag^+ \rightarrow Ag(s)]}$$

$$Zn(s) + 2e^- + 2Ag^+ \rightarrow Zn^{++} + 2e^- + 2Ag(s)$$

or, $\quad Zn(s) + 2Ag^+ \rightarrow Zn^{++} + 2Ag(s)$

The balanced equation for the change

$\qquad Fe^{++} + MnO_4^- \rightarrow Fe^{+3} + Mn^{++}$

in acidic solution can be written from the two half-reactions

$\qquad Fe^{++} \rightarrow Fe^{+3} + e^-$

$\qquad 5e^- + 8H^+ + MnO_4^- \rightarrow Mn^{++} + 4H_2O$

Multiplying the first by 5 and adding to the second gives

$\qquad 5Fe^{++} + 8H^+ + MnO_4^- \rightarrow 5Fe^{+3} + Mn^{++} + 4H_2O$

When given an equation to balance *in acidic solution*, the detailed steps to follow are:

    1. Separate the change into half-reactions.

    2. Balance each half-reaction separately by:

        a. Changing coefficients to account for all atoms except H and O.

        b. Add H_2O to side deficient in O.

        c. Add H^+ to side deficient in H.

        d. Add e^- to side deficient in negative charge.

    3. Multiply half-reactions by appropriate numbers needed to balance electrons, and add.

    4. Subtract any duplications on left and right.

The following example shows the stepwise procedure used to write a balanced equation for the change

$\qquad NO_2^- + Cr_2O_7^{--} \rightarrow NO_3^- + Cr^{+3}$

in acidic solution.

Step (1):

$NO_2^- \rightarrow NO_3^-$	$Cr_2O_7^{--} \rightarrow Cr^{+3}$

Step (2a):

$NO_2^- \rightarrow NO_3^-$	$Cr_2O_7^{--} \rightarrow 2Cr^{+3}$

Step (2b):

$H_2O + NO_2^- \rightarrow NO_3^-$	$Cr_2O_7^{--} \rightarrow 2Cr^{+3} + 7H_2O$

Step (2c):

$H_2O + NO_2^- \rightarrow NO_3^- + 2H^+$	$Cr_2O_7^{--} + 14H^+ \rightarrow$ $2Cr^{+3} + 7H_2O$

Step (2d):

$$H_2O + NO_2^- \rightarrow$$
$$NO_3^- + 2H^+ + 2e^-$$

[Two electrons have been added to the right side, since in step (2c) the left side has a net charge of -1 and the right side has a net charge of $+1$. The right side was deficient in negative charge by two units.]

$$Cr_2O_7^{--} + 14H^+ + 6e^- \rightarrow$$
$$2Cr^{+3} + 7H_2O$$

[Six electrons have been added to the left, since in step (2c) the left side is $+12$ while the right side is $+6$.]

Step (3):

$$3(H_2O + NO_2^- \rightarrow NO_3^- + 2H^+ + 2e^-)$$
$$Cr_2O_7^{--} + 14H^+ + 6e^- \rightarrow 2Cr^{+3} + 7H_2O$$
___
$$3H_2O + 3NO_2^- + Cr_2O_7^{--} + 14H^+ + 6e^- \rightarrow$$
$$3NO_3^- + 2Cr^{+3} + 7H_2O + 6H^+ + 6e^-$$

where $3H_2O$, $6H^+$, and $6e^-$ are duplicated on left and right.

Step (4):

$$3NO_2^- + Cr_2O_7^{--} + 8H^+ \rightarrow 3NO_3^- + 2Cr^{+3} + 4H_2O$$

If the reaction occurs in basic solution, the equation must not contain H^+. In order to add H atoms in step (2c), add H_2O molecules equal in number to the deficiency of H atoms and an equal number of OH^- ions to the opposite side. The rest of the method is the same. An example of a reaction in basic solution is the change

$$Cr(OH)_3(s) + IO_3^- \rightarrow I^- + CrO_4^{--}$$

The half-reactions are

$$Cr(OH)_3(s) + 5OH^- \rightarrow CrO_4^{--} + 4H_2O + 3e^-$$
$$IO_3^- + 3H_2O + 6e^- \rightarrow I^- + 6OH^-$$

and the final net equation is

$$2Cr(OH)_3(s) + IO_3^- + 4OH^- \rightarrow 2CrO_4^{--} + I^- + 5H_2O$$

QUESTIONS

14.1 *Electrical terms.* Distinguish between faraday, coulomb, and ampere.

14.2   *Electric conduction.* (*a*) Describe what is thought to be the mechanism of electric conduction in a copper wire and in a sodium chloride solution. (*b*) Account for the change of resistance with temperature in each.

14.3   *Electrolysis.* Draw a typical electrolysis circuit and indicate the path of moving charges in it. Why must chemical change occur at the electrodes?

14.4   *Electrolysis of HCl.* In the electrolysis of aqueous HCl, hydrogen gas is formed at one electrode and chlorine gas at the other. Diagram a cell suitable for this electrolysis. Label the anode and cathode, and write an electrode reaction for each. Indicate the direction of movement of cations, anions, and electrons in the circuit.

14.5   *Faraday's laws.* How many (*a*) faradays, (*b*) coulombs, (*c*) amperes for 1,000 min. are required to deposit, at the appropriate electrode, (1) 0.250 gram-atom of Ni from Ni^{++}, (2) 0.250 g. of Ni from Ni^{++}, (3) 0.250 gram-equivalent of Ni from Ni^{++}?   *Ans.* 0.804 amp., 0.0137 amp., 0.402 amp.

14.6   *Faraday's laws.* Calculate (*a*) moles, (*b*) grams, and (*c*) liters at STP of hydrogen gas that can be produced by the electrolysis of aqueous NaCl with a current of 1.93 amp. for 20.0 min.

14.7   *Faraday's laws.* A beaker contains 50.0 ml. of 0.500 *M* $CuSO_4$. Two platinum electrodes are placed in the solution, and it is electrolyzed with a current of 0.500 amp. Ideally, how long should it take to remove all the copper from solution? After all the copper is removed, what is the solute in the solution?
Ans. 2.68 hr.

14.8   *Lead storage battery.* The lead storage battery can be recharged by reversing the electrode reactions with an external voltage. Write half-reactions for the charging and label each as anode or cathode reaction.

14.9   *Galvanic cells.* (*a*) How does a galvanic cell differ from an electrolysis cell? (*b*) Describe the standard hydrogen electrode and tell how it can be used to compare the relative reducing ability of two metals such as zinc and copper.

14.10   *Galvanic cell.* Design a galvanic cell to make use of the reaction $Zn(s) + Cl_2(g) \rightarrow Zn^{++} + 2Cl^-$. Label the anode and cathode, write an electrode reaction for each, and indicate the direction of motion of anions, cations, and electrons in the circuit.

14.11   *Daniell cell.* A given Daniell cell has initially 65.4 g. of zinc and 75.0 ml. of 0.100 *M* $CuSO_4$. At the maximum, how long can this cell deliver current at 0.200 amp.?

14.12   *Oxidation potentials.* There are 240 possible reactions that can be written by combining pairs of half-reactions from Table 14.1. Write balanced equations for three of these that can occur spontaneously and three that cannot.

14.13   *Oxidation potentials.* Given Al(*s*), Mg^{++}, I^-, Cu(*s*), H^+, H_2O. By reference to Table 14.1, select from these six: (*a*) the best reducing agent; (*b*) the best oxidizing agent; (*c*) the poorest oxidizing agent; (*d*) the poorest reducing agent.

14.14 *Electrode charge.* Show that the designation of the cathode as the negative electrode in a circuit such as in Fig. 14.8 is ambiguous.

14.15 *Electrical units.* How many electrons per second pass a given point in a copper wire in which the current is 10.0 mamp.? *Ans.* 6.2×10^{16} electrons/sec.

14.16 *Galvanic cells.* For each of the following reactions, design a workable galvanic cell. In each case, (1) draw a diagram of the cell and indicate the materials present; (2) write the anode and cathode reactions; (3) indicate the direction of anion, cation, and electron motion when the cell is operating; and (4) by using the standard oxidation potentials, predict the measured voltage of your cell when all concentrations are unity.

(a) $Mg(s) + Cl_2(g) \rightarrow Mg^{++} + 2Cl^-$

(b) $Hg^{++} + Fe(s) \rightarrow Fe^{++} + Hg(l)$

(c) $2MnO_4^- + 5Cu(s) + 16H^+ \rightarrow 5Cu^{++} + 2Mn^{++} + 8H_2O$

Ans. 3.73 volts; 1.29 volts; 1.17 volts

14.17 *Balancing equations.* Write the two half-reactions and the net reaction for each of the following changes:

(a) $H_2S(g) + Fe^{+3} \rightarrow Fe^{++} + S(s)$ (acidic)

(b) $Cu^+ \rightarrow Cu^{++} + Cu(s)$ (acidic)

(c) $Al(s) + Cu^{++} \rightarrow Al^{+3} + Cu(s)$ (acidic)

(d) $Cr_2O_7^{--} + HNO_2 \rightarrow Cr^{+3} + NO_3^-$ (acidic)

(e) $N_2O_4(g) + Br^- \rightarrow NO_2^- + BrO_3^-$ (basic)

14.18 *Faraday's laws.* In the electrolysis of aqueous Na_2SO_4 solution with copper electrodes, the reactions are:

Cathode: $2H_2O + 2e^- \rightarrow H_2(g) + 2OH^-$
Anode: $2Cu(s) + H_2O \rightarrow Cu_2O(s) + 2H^+ + 2e^-$

If 33.6 ml. (STP) of hydrogen gas is produced at the cathode, what will be the accompanying weight increase of the anode? Assume that solid product sticks to anode.

14.19 *Faraday's laws.* Assume that, in the electrolysis of aqueous $CaCl_2$ solution with inert electrodes, hydrogen gas and chlorine gas are formed. Calculate the final concentration of Ca^{++}, OH^-, and Cl^- after 0.015 faraday has passed through 50.0 ml. of 1.0 M $CaCl_2$. Assume volume of solution does not change.

14.20 *Faraday's laws.* A solution is made by mixing 40.0 ml. of 0.10 M Ag_2SO_4 and 60.0 ml. of 0.050 M $AgNO_3$. Assume the volumes are additive. On electrolysis the electrode reactions are:

Cathode: $Ag^+ + e^- \rightarrow Ag(s)$
Anode: $2H_2O \rightarrow O_2(g) + 4H^+ + 4e^-$

Neglecting all other possible reactions, calculate the number of moles and the average concentration of Ag^+, NO_3^-, H^+, and SO_4^{--} in the final solution after 1.0 amp. has passed through the cell for 0.965 min.

Ans. 0.0104 mole of Ag^+ at 0.104 M; 0.0030 mole of NO_3^- at 0.030 M; 6.0×10^{-4} mole of H^+ at 6.0×10^{-3} M; 0.0040 mole of SO_4^{--} at 0.040 M

14.21 *Ion migration.* Given an electrolysis cell of the form shown in Fig. 14.7 filled with 0.120 liter of 0.500 M H_2SO_4. (*a*) Assuming complete dissociation by the reaction $H_2SO_4 \rightarrow H^+ + HSO_4^-$, calculate the number of moles and the concentration of H^+ and of HSO_4^- in *each* compartment. (*b*) A current of 0.386 amp. is passed through the cell for 1.00 hr. Repeat the calculation of (*a*), assuming that no H^+ migrates from one compartment to the other. (*c*) Since H^+ does migrate, how should the observed concentration compare with your calculated ones?

Ans. (*a*) 0.0300 mole of H^+ and 0.0300 mole of HSO_4^- at 0.500 M; (*b*) 0.0156 mole of H^+ and of HSO_4^- at 0.260 M in the cathode compartment and 0.0444 mole of H^+ and of HSO_4^- at 0.740 M in the anode compartment

14.22 *Oxidation potentials.* (*a*) Write balanced half-reactions for each of the following conversions in acid solution; $HAsO_2$ to H_3AsO_4; $Bi(s)$ to BiO^+; $Nb(s)$ to $Nb_2O_5(s)$; Ti^{+3} to TiO^{++}. (*b*) Experimentally it is observed that Ti^{+3} can reduce BiO^+ and H_3AsO_4 but cannot reduce Nb_2O_5. $HAsO_2$ cannot reduce BiO^+. Rank the four half-reactions in order of decreasing oxidation potential.

14.23 *Oxidation potentials.* Given three galvanic cells that use the following reactions:

$$U(s) + 3U^{+4} \rightarrow 4U^{+3}$$

$$2U^{+3} + 2H^+ \rightarrow H_2(g) + 2U^{+4}$$

$$3U^{+4} + 2H_2O \rightarrow UO_2^{++} + 2U^{+3} + 4H^+$$

The observed cell voltages (25°C., 1 m, 1 atm.) are, respectively, 1.09 volts, 0.61 volt, −0.94 volt. From these, determine the oxidation potentials for the three uranium half-reactions involved. *Ans.* 1.80 volts; 0.61 volt; −0.33 volt

Although it would be satisfying to be able to deduce all useful chemical information from first principles, in most cases this cannot be done. For one thing, theories sufficiently powerful to predict all observable behavior are not at hand. For another, it is highly questionable whether it will ever be true that chemical facts can be obtained more readily from theory than from experiment. Though we may be staggered at the prospect of the task before us, it is imperative that we provide ourselves with a knowledge of the observed behavior of the elements and their compounds. The more chemical facts we have at our immediate recall, the better equipped we shall be to evaluate the role of chemistry in natural and technological processes.

II   *Chemical Elements and Their Compounds*

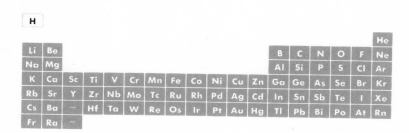

15 Hydrogen

THE FIRST ELEMENT OF THE PERIODIC TABLE, hydrogen, has but one proton in its nucleus and one orbital electron. In its lowest energy state, the H atom has the electron in a K shell, or $1s$ energy level (Sec. 3.9). Because the $1s$ level can contain but one more electron, H atoms can normally attain a lower energy state by pairing up to form H_2 molecules. H_2 molecules react with many other elements to form a large variety of compounds containing H atoms.

15.1   OCCURRENCE

In the universe, hydrogen is apparently the most abundant element. Analysis of light emitted by stars indicates that most stars are predominantly hydrogen. For example, of the sun's mass, approximately 90 per cent is hydrogen. On the earth, hydrogen is much less abundant. The earth's gravitational attraction, being much less than that of stars and larger planets, is too small to hold very light molecules. Considering only the earth's crust (atmosphere, oceans, and 10 miles of solid material), hydrogen is third in abundance on an atom basis. Of each 1,000 atoms of crust,

530 are oxygen, 160 are silicon, and 150 are hydrogen. On a weight basis, hydrogen is ninth in order and contributes only 0.88 per cent of the weight of the earth's crust.

On the earth, free, or uncombined, hydrogen is rare. It is found occasionally in volcanic gases. Also, as shown by study of the aurora borealis, it is found in traces in the upper atmosphere. On the other hand, combined hydrogen is quite common. In water, hydrogen is combined with oxygen and makes up 11.2 per cent of the total weight. The human body, two-thirds of which is water, is approximately 10 per cent H by weight. In coal and petroleum, hydrogen is combined with carbon as hydrocarbons. Clay and a few other minerals contain appreciable amounts of hydrogen, usually combined with oxygen. Finally, all plant and animal matter is composed of compounds of hydrogen with oxygen, carbon, nitrogen, sulfur, etc.

15.2 PREPARATION

In producing an element for commercial use, the primary consideration is usually cost. For laboratory use, the important consideration is convenience. For *commercial* hydrogen, the primary sources are water and hydrocarbons.

Hydrogen can be made inexpensively by passing steam over hot carbon.

$$C(s) + H_2O(g) \xrightarrow{1000°C.} CO(g) + H_2(g)$$

It is hard to get pure hydrogen from this source, because carbon monoxide, CO, is difficult to separate completely from hydrogen. The mixture of H_2 and CO is an industrial fuel, *water gas.*

Purer and still relatively inexpensive hydrogen can be made by passing steam over hot iron.

$$3Fe(s) + 4H_2O(g) \rightarrow Fe_3O_4(s) + 4H_2(g)$$

The iron can be recovered by reducing Fe_3O_4 with water gas.

The purest (99.9 per cent) but most expensive hydrogen available commercially is *electrolytic hydrogen,* made from the electrolysis of water.

$$2H_2O \xrightarrow{electrolysis} 2H_2(g) + O_2(g) - 135 \text{ kcal.}$$

The reaction is endothermic and requires energy, which must be supplied by the electric current. It is the power consumption, not the raw material, that makes electrolytic hydrogen expensive. In practice, alkaline (basic) solutions are electrolyzed with cells designed to keep anode and cathode products separate. The electrode reactions are:

Anode: $4OH^- \rightarrow O_2(g) + 2H_2O + 4e^-$

Cathode: $2e^- + 2H_2O \rightarrow H_2(g) + 2OH^-$

Net: $2H_2O \rightarrow 2H_2(g) + O_2(g)$

Considerable hydrogen is also formed as a by-product of the commercial preparation of Cl_2 and NaOH by the electrolysis of aqueous NaCl (Sec. 14.4).

In petroleum refineries, where gasoline is made by the catalytic cracking of hydrocarbons, hydrogen is a by-product. When gaseous hydrocarbons are passed over hot catalyst, decomposition occurs to form hydrogen and other hydrocarbons.

In the *laboratory*, pure hydrogen is usually made by the reaction of zinc metal with acid:

$$Zn(s) + 2H^+ \rightarrow Zn^{++} + H_2(g)$$

In principle, reaction should occur with any metal having a positive oxidation potential (Sec. 14.8). For some metals, such as iron, the reaction is quite slow, even though the voltage is favorable. In water, where the concentration of H^+ is only 1.0×10^{-7} *M*, the reduction by metals is more difficult. The voltage for the half-reaction

$$H_2(g) \rightleftharpoons 2H^+(1.0 \times 10^{-7} M) + 2e^-$$

is $+0.41$ volt. In order to liberate H_2 from water, a metal must have an oxidation potential of $+0.41$ volt or higher. Thus, the element sodium reacts with water to liberate H_2 by the reaction

$$2Na(s) + 2H_2O \rightarrow H_2(g) + 2Na^+ + 2OH^-$$

In principle, zinc should liberate H_2 from H_2O by a similar reaction, but the reaction is too slow to be useful at room temperature.

Laboratory hydrogen can also be made conveniently from the reaction of aluminum metal with base (Sec. 23.3) or from the reaction of CaH_2 with water (Sec. 15.4).

15.3   PROPERTIES AND USES

Hydrogen at room temperature is a colorless, odorless, tasteless gas. The quantitative properties are summarized in Table 15.1. The gas is diatomic and consists of nonpolar molecules containing two hydrogen atoms held together by a covalent bond. In order to rupture the bonds in 1 mole of H_2 to form H atoms, 103 kcal. of heat must be supplied. Because the dis-

Table 15.1 Properties of H_2

Molecular weight	2.016 a.m.u.
Bond length	0.749 A.
Bond energy	103 kcal./mole
Approx. molecular diameter	2 A.
Normal melting point	14.1°K.
Normal boiling point	20.4°K.
Critical temperature	33.2°K.
Density at STP	0.0899 g./liter
Density of liquid (20°K.)	0.07 g./ml.

sociation is endothermic, it increases with temperature. At 4000°K. and 1 atm. pressure, H_2 is about 60 per cent dissociated. When H_2 reacts, one of the steps is usually the breaking of the H—H bond. Because of the high energy required for this step, the activation energy is high, and H_2 reactions are slow. Most hydrogen compounds contain H covalently bound, since neither H^+ nor H^- is readily formed. The ionization potential (Sec. 3.14) is 13.60 e.v., which is about two and a half times the ionization potential of sodium; the electron affinity (Sec. 3.15) is 0.72 e.v., which is about one-fifth that of chlorine.

Molecular hydrogen is the lightest of all gases. It is one-fourteenth as heavy as air. A balloon filled with hydrogen rises in accord with Archimedes' principle that the buoyant force on an object immersed in a fluid (such as air) is equal to the weight of fluid displaced by the object. Until recently, H_2 was used extensively to lift dirigibles, but because of its combustibility, it is no longer in demand for this purpose. However, meteorologists still frequently send aloft weather balloons inflated with hydrogen.

The very low melting and boiling points of hydrogen indicate that the intermolecular attractions are quite small (Sec. 6.14). Because of the low boiling point, liquid hydrogen is used in the laboratory to produce low temperatures, but it can be kept for only a few hours, even in a Dewar flask immersed in liquid air. When the pressure above liquid H_2 in an insulated container is reduced below 54 mm. Hg (the triple-point pressure), the temperature drops and hydrogen solidifies. The critical temperature of H_2 (above which it can exist only as a gas) is 33.2°K.

Chemically, H_2 is able, under appropriate conditions, to combine directly with most elements. With oxygen, H_2 reacts to release large amounts of energy by the change

$$2H_2(g) + O_2(g) \rightarrow 2H_2O(g) + 116 \text{ kcal.}$$

which occurs at an appreciable rate only at high temperatures or in the presence of catalyst. In the oxyhydrogen torch the above reaction occurs to produce temperatures of about 2800°C., and the reaction is self-sustaining. Mixtures of H_2 and O_2 are explosive, and especially violently so when the ratio of H_2 to O_2 is approximately 2:1. With F_2, the reaction

$$H_2(g) + F_2(g) \rightarrow 2HF(g) + 130 \text{ kcal.}$$

is explosive even at liquid-hydrogen temperatures.

With metals, the reaction of H_2 is not nearly so violent and often requires elevated temperatures. For example, sodium hydride, NaH, is formed by bubbling H_2 through molten sodium at about 360°C. Hydrides of group II elements are just as difficult to form.

Hydrogen also reacts with certain compounds. In some cases, it simply adds on to the other molecule as, for instance, in forming methyl alcohol, CH_3OH, from CO:

$$CO(g) + 2H_2(g) \xrightarrow{\text{catalyst}} CH_3OH(g)$$

Such addition reactions are called *hydrogenation* reactions and account for much of the industrial consumption of hydrogen. In other cases, hydrogen removes atoms from other molecules, as in the reduction of tungsten trioxide, WO_3, to W.

15.4   COMPOUNDS

In its compounds, hydrogen is found in the three oxidation states $+1$, -1, and 0. In the first two cases, H forms compounds by losing a share of its lone electron or gaining a share of another electron. According to the rules for assigning oxidation numbers (Sec. 5.5), the relative electronegativity of H and the atom to which it is joined must be considered. In the general compound H_nX, the oxidation number of H is $+1$ if X is the more electronegative atom and -1 if X is the less electronegative atom. The oxidation state 0 for hydrogen in compounds represents a rather special case.

Oxidation state $+1$. This is the most important oxidation state of hydrogen, since it includes most of the hydrogen compounds. In these compounds, H is combined with a more electronegative element such as any element taken from the right-hand side of the periodic table. In period 2, for example, the elements more electronegative than H are C, N, O, and F. With these elements, H forms compounds such as methane, CH_4; ammonia, NH_3; water, H_2O; and hydrogen fluoride, HF. It might be noted that, even though H is thought to be the more positive in these compounds, there is no uniformity in writing H first in the formula as expected. It should be emphasized that in all these compounds the binding of hydrogen is covalent and that none of these compounds contains simple H^+ ion.

These compounds can be formed by direct union of the elements. The reactions are often slow, sometimes requiring a large amount of activation energy, and so catalysts and high temperatures may be required. For example, the reaction between N_2 and H_2 to form NH_3 is usually carried out under pressure at about 500°C. in the presence of a suitable catalyst.

In compounds containing more than two elements, the H is usually considered to be in a positive oxidation state. In most such compounds (e.g., $NaHSO_4$) the H is bonded to an atom more electronegative than itself.

Oxidation state -1. When hydrogen is combined with an atom less electronegative than itself, the compound is said to be a *hydride*. These hydrides may be predominantly ionic, as with the elements of groups I and II, or covalent, as with the lighter elements of group III.

In the hydrides of elements of groups I and II, the H occurs as the negative hydride ion, H^-. The compounds at room temperature are ionic solids forming cubic or hexagonal crystals. When melted, they conduct electric current and on electrolysis form H_2 *at the anode* by the reaction

$$2H^- \rightarrow H_2(g) + 2e^-$$

The hydride ion is unstable in water solution and is oxidized to H_2. Thus, for example, calcium hydride, CaH_2, in H_2O reacts as follows:

$$CaH_2(s) + 2H_2O \rightarrow Ca^{++} + 2OH^- + 2H_2(g)$$

The covalent hydrides such as silane, SiH_4, and arsine, AsH_3, are generally volatile liquids or gases. They are nonconductors and apparently contain no H^- ion. They are relatively mild reducing agents.

The term hydride is also applied to compounds in which H is joined to a less electronegative atom in a complex ion. Thus, for example, in the compound lithium aluminum hydride, $LiAlH_4$, the cation is Li^+ and the anion is the complex AlH_4^-. These complex hydrides are generally solids, react with water to liberate H_2, and are of great use as reducing agents.

Oxidation state 0. Hydrogen reacts with some metals such as uranium, copper, and palladium to form hard, brittle substances that conduct electricity and have typical metallic luster. In some cases, as with uranium hydride, UH_3, the number of H atoms per metal atom is fixed and is a whole number. In other cases, as with palladium hydride, PdH_n, the number of H atoms per metal atom is variable and can even be less than one. It is believed that, in these metallic hydrides, the hydrogen is dissolved as elementary hydrogen. Consequently, H is assigned a zero oxidation state. It may be that in these substances hydrogen exists as H atoms, which might even be dissociated into protons and electrons.

The dissolution of hydrogen in metals is important, because metals which dissolve hydrogen are catalysts for hydrogenation reactions. The catalyst is thought to act by dissolving the hydrogen as H atoms, which react more rapidly than H_2 molecules. The catalysis, by finely divided nickel, of the hydrogenation of oils to give fats is explainable in this way.

When hydrogen dissolves in a metal, the H atom may go into the lattice as a lattice defect (Sec. 8.5) and simply expand the lattice of the metal, or it may completely alter the type of lattice. In either case, the change may be significant enough to make the metal lose some of its desirable properties. This phenomenon, called "hydrogen embrittlement," occurs even with small amounts of dissolved hydrogen, amounts that may be unavoidable in the preparation of pure metals. Thus, the large-scale industrial use of the very valuable metal titanium was made possible only after developing preparation methods that avoided hydrogen entrapment.

15.5   HYDROGEN BOND

In some compounds a hydrogen atom is apparently bonded simultaneously to two other atoms. For example, in the compound potassium hydrogen fluoride, KHF_2, the anion HF_2^- is believed to have the structure $(FHF)^-$, in which the hydrogen acts as a bridge between the two fluorine atoms. The hydrogen bridge consists of a proton shared between two atoms and is called a *hydrogen bond*. Hydrogen bonds seem to be formed only between small electronegative atoms like F, O, and N.

Evidence in support of the existence of hydrogen bonds comes from comparing properties of hydrogen-containing substances. For example, in Fig. 15.1 are shown the normal boiling points for the hydrogen halides (lower curve) and for the hydrogen compounds of group VI elements (upper curve). It is evident that the boiling points of HF and H_2O are abnormally high compared to other members of each series. In the series HF, HCl, HBr, and HI, there is an increasing number of electrons per molecule, and, therefore, rising boiling points would be expected because of increased van der Waals attractions (Sec. 6.14). The unexpectedly high boiling point of HF is attributed to hydrogen bonds between fluorine atoms. The hydrogen bonding makes it more difficult to detach HF from the liquid. Independent evidence for hydrogen bonding in HF comes from studies of the vapor phase, which is found to contain aggregates such as $(HF)_6$, presumed to be held together by hydrogen bonds. The unexpectedly high boiling point of H_2O in the series H_2O, H_2S, H_2Se, and H_2Te is similarly attributed to hydrogen bonding. In Sec. 16.5, the importance of hydrogen bonding in the structure of water is discussed.

What is responsible for the hydrogen bond? The simplest view is that the positively charged proton is attracted by the negative electrons of two

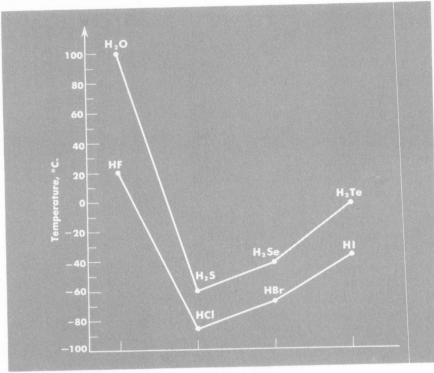

Fig. 15.1 *Boiling points of some hydrogen compounds.*

different atoms. When a hydrogen atom is bound to a very electronegative atom, the hydrogen has such a small share of the electron pair that it is almost like a bare proton. As such, it can be attracted to another electronegative atom. Because of its very tiny size, a given proton has room for only two atoms around it. This picture is consistent with the observations that hydrogen bonds are limited to compounds containing hydrogen that is bonded to very electronegative atoms and that one H can bridge between only two atoms.

Hydrogen bonds are important in biological systems. Proteins, for example, contain both >CO and >NH groups, and hydrogen bonds can be formed to bridge the space between the N and the O. The structure and hence the properties of proteins depend on the existence of hydrogen bonds.

15.6 ISOTOPES OF HYDROGEN

Natural hydrogen consists of three isotopes: protium ($_1H^1$), deuterium, or heavy hydrogen ($_1H^2$, or D), and tritium ($_1H^3$, or T). The protium nucleus consists of a lone proton; the deuterium nucleus, of a proton and a neutron;

and the tritium nucleus, of a proton and two neutrons. The protium nucleus is by far the most abundant of the three. In nature, there are 5,000 times as many protium atoms as deuterium atoms and only 0.00000000000000001 times as many tritium atoms. The scarcity of tritium atoms is due to the instability and consequent radioactivity of its nucleus.

In general, the properties of isotopes are *qualitatively* very similar. However, there may be *quantitative* differences, especially when the percentage difference in mass is appreciable. Table 15.2 shows some of the properties of protium and deuterium.

In chemical reaction, protium and deuterium show a quantitative difference both in their equilibrium and in their rate properties. Property differences arising from differences in mass are called *isotope effects.* For example, the dissociation constant of ordinary water in the equilibrium

$$H_2O \rightleftharpoons H^+ + OH^-$$

is 1.0×10^{-14} at room temperature. For the corresponding dissociation of heavy water

$$D_2O \rightleftharpoons D^+ + OD^-$$

the constant is 0.2×10^{-14}, which is significantly smaller. The isotope effect on the rates of reactions is even more marked. Thus, a bond to a protium atom can be broken as much as eighteen times faster than the bond to a deuterium atom. As an example, H_2 reacts with Cl_2 13.4 times as fast as D_2 does.

For elements heavier than hydrogen the isotope effect is much smaller. For example, $_{53}I^{127}$ reacts at most only 1.02 times faster than $_{53}I^{129}$, and the equilibrium properties are even more similar. The isotope effect becomes negligible for the heavier elements, where the percentage difference in mass between the isotopes is small.

The isotope effect in hydrogen is used as a basis for the separation of protium and deuterium. Since protium bonds are broken faster than deuterium bonds, electrolysis of water releases the light isotope faster than the

Table 15.2   Properties of Isotopes

Property	Protium	Deuterium
Mass of atom (H), a.m.u.	1.0079	2.0142
Freezing point (H_2), °K.	14.0	18.7
Boiling point (H_2), °K.	20.4	23.5
Freezing point (H_2O), °C.	0	3.8
Boiling point (H_2O), °C.	100	101.4
Density at 20°C. (H_2O), g./ml.	0.998	1.106

heavy isotope. There is an enrichment of the heavy hydrogen in the residual water. By continuing the electrolysis until the residual volume is very small, practically pure deuterium oxide can be obtained. In a typical experiment, 2,400 liters of ordinary water produces 83 ml. of D_2O that is 99 per cent pure.

QUESTIONS

15.1 *Occurrence.* Using the numerical atomic abundances given in Sec. 15.1 and assuming the remaining 160 atoms to have an average atomic weight of 25, show that the weight abundance of hydrogen is 0.88%.

15.2 *Occurrence.* If light molecules are held so feebly by the earth's gravitational attraction, how would you explain the fact that hydrogen is so abundant on the earth?

15.3 *Oxidation states.* What property of the H atom is responsible for its forming compounds in both the $+1$ and -1 oxidation states? Explain.

15.4 *Preparation.* Discuss the relative merits of the different methods of preparing hydrogen.

15.5 *Preparation.* The world's annual production of H_2 is about 300,000 tons. (*a*) How many coulombs would be required to produce this amount by the electrolysis of water? (*b*) How many tons of iron would be required instead?

15.6 *Electrolysis.* What volume of hydrogen at 25°C. and 740 mm. Hg pressure can be produced by the electrolysis of 1.00 liter of water?

Ans. 1,390 liters

15.7 *Oxidation potential.* Account for the fact that in pure water the voltage of the half-reaction

$$H_2(g) \rightarrow 2H^+ + 2e^-$$

is greater than zero.

15.8 *Heat of reaction.* In the gas-phase reaction with hydrogen, which produces more heat, 1 g. of O_2 or 1 g. of F_2?

15.9 *Isotope effect.* For

$$H_2O \rightleftharpoons H^+ + OH^- \qquad K = 1.0 \times 10^{-14}$$

$$D_2O \rightleftharpoons D^+ + OD^- \qquad K = 0.2 \times 10^{-14}$$

which has a higher concentration of positive ions, pure H_2O or pure D_2O? Justify your answer.

15.10 *Hydrogen bonds.* Show how hydrogen bonding can account for the unexpected boiling point of H_2O.

15.11 *Size.* When atoms lose electrons, there is a decrease in size. Account for the fact that if a hydrogen atom ionizes to form H^+, the decrease in size is essentially 100%.

15.12 *Isotope effects.* What are "isotope effects"? Why are they larger for hydrogen than for any other element?

15.13 *Hydride.* How can you make sodium hydride? Write anode and cathode reactions for the electrolysis of molten sodium hydride.

15.14 *Isotope effect.* In ordinary water there is one deuterium (D) atom for every 5,000 protium ($_1H^1$) atoms. When water is electrolyzed under the proper conditions, the lighter isotope is preferentially liberated, and the residual water becomes enriched in deuterium. The electrolytic enrichment is usually carried out in stages. (*a*) Assume that all D is present as D_2O molecules. Calculate the percentage of D_2O molecules, the concentration of D_2O molecules, and the number of moles of D_2O in 1 liter of H_2O. (*b*) In the first stage of the electrolysis, essentially no D is liberated. Calculate the percentage of D_2O, the concentration of D_2O, and the moles of D_2O left in the liquid after 1 liter of ordinary water is electrolyzed down to 200 ml. (*c*) In the second stage of the electrolysis, the light isotope is liberated six times as readily per mole as D. Calculate the percentage of D_2O, concentration of D_2O, and moles of D_2O left in the liquid after the 200 ml. from (*b*) is electrolyzed down to 40 ml.

Ans. (*c*) 0.44% D_2O; 0.24 *M*; 0.0096 mole

15.15 *Hydrogen preparation.* Hydrogen of 99.9% minimum purity can be purchased as a compressed gas in steel cylinders. The current price is about $16.00 for a cylinder of internal volume 1.5 cu. ft. containing hydrogen at a pressure of 130 atm. (room temperature 27°C.). Calculate the cost of this amount of hydrogen assuming it was made from the electrolytic decomposition of aqueous NaOH. Current costs: NaOH is 45 cents per pound, electrical power is 1.7 cents per kilowatthour (in this case a kilowatthour is equivalent to approximately 1.8×10^6 coulombs). Assume that the oxygen by-product pays overhead expenses.

Ans. $0.41

15.16 *Bond energies.* Given the following bond energies: H—H, 103 kcal.; X—X, 20.0 kcal.; and Y—Y, 40.0 kcal. What are the bond energies of H—X and H—Y if the following is true?

$H_2(g) + X_2(g) \rightarrow 2HX(g) + 107$ kcal.

$H_2(g) + Y_2(g) \rightarrow 2HY(g) + 117$ kcal.

16   Oxygen

THE ELEMENT OXYGEN, atomic number 8, has two $1s$, two $2s$, and four $2p$ electrons. Except for fluorine, it is more electronegative than any other element and forms compounds with all elements except the inert gases. The study of oxygen compounds has been important in unraveling the chemistry of other elements. One of these compounds, water, is the most important reaction medium in chemistry.

16.1   OCCURRENCE

Oxygen is by far the most abundant element in the earth's crust, on a basis of both weight and number of atoms. Of the weight of the earth's crust, 49.5 per cent is due to oxygen atoms. Silicon, the next most abundant, is only half as plentiful. On a number basis, oxygen atoms are more numerous than all other kinds of atoms combined.

In the free state, oxygen occurs in the atmosphere as O_2 molecules. Air is 20 per cent oxygen by volume; i.e., for every 100 molecules in air, approximately 20 are oxygen. On a weight basis, air is 21 per cent oxygen; for every 100 g. of air approximately 21 g. is oxygen.

In the combined state, oxygen occurs naturally in many minerals, plants and animals, and water. Of the oxygen-containing minerals, the most abundant are ones which contain silicon. The simplest of these is silica, SiO_2, the main constituent of sand. The most abundant mineral that does not contain silicon is limestone, $CaCO_3$. In plant and animal material, oxygen is combined with carbon, sulfur, nitrogen, or hydrogen.

16.2   PREPARATION

The industrial sources of oxygen are air and water. From air, oxygen is made by liquefaction and fractional distillation. Air, consisting of 21 per cent oxygen, 78 per cent nitrogen, and 1 per cent total of argon, neon, carbon dioxide, and water, is first freed of carbon dioxide and water, compressed, cooled, and expanded until liquefaction results to give liquid air. On partial evaporation, the N_2, being lower boiling, boils away first, leaving the residue richer in O_2. Repeated cycles of this kind give oxygen that is 99.5 per cent pure.

From water, very pure oxygen can be made by electrolysis as a by-product of hydrogen manufacture. Power consumption makes electrolytic oxygen more expensive than that obtained from air.

In the laboratory, oxygen is usually made by the thermal decomposition of potassium chlorate, $KClO_3$. The reaction

$$2KClO_3(s) \rightarrow 2KCl(s) + 3O_2(g)$$

is catalyzed by the presence of various solids such as manganese dioxide, MnO_2, ferric oxide, Fe_2O_3, fine sand, or powdered glass. It is thought that the function of the catalyst is to provide a surface on which the evolution of oxygen gas can occur.

16.3   PROPERTIES AND USES

At room temperature, oxygen is a colorless, odorless gas. The molecule is diatomic and frequently is assigned $:\overset{..}{\underset{.}{O}}:\overset{..}{\underset{.}{O}}:$ for its electronic formula. The single dots represent unpaired electrons, which must be present in the molecule to explain the observed magnetic properties of O_2. Both as a gas and as a liquid, oxygen is paramagnetic (attracted into magnetic fields). The above electronic formulation is a clear violation of the octet rule and, furthermore, does not account for the observation that the oxygen-oxygen bond is stronger than a single covalent bond. This just points up the fact, mentioned in Chap. 4, that actually all the valence electrons contribute to the bonding. When cooled to $-183°C.$, oxygen condenses to a pale blue liquid. At $-219°C.$, it solidifies to form a bluish-white solid. There is some formation of O_4 in the liquid and solid states.

Oxygen exhibits *allotropy*; i.e., it can exist as the element in more than one form. When energy is added to diatomic oxygen, the triatomic molecule ozone, O_3, is formed by the reaction

$$3O_2(g) + 68 \text{ kcal.} \rightarrow 2O_3(g)$$

At room temperature, the equilibrium constant for this reaction is calculated to be 10^{-54}. Even though it increases with temperature, the equilibrium concentration of O_3 is not appreciable at any temperature. Thus, not much O_2 can be converted to O_3 by the simple addition of heat. However, when energy is added in other forms such as electric energy or high-energy radiation, significant amounts of O_3 result. Once O_3 is obtained, it only slowly reverts to O_2. In the laboratory, ozone is easily made by passing air or oxygen between tin foil conductors that are connected to the terminals of an electric-induction coil. Under the influence of the silent electric discharge in this *ozonizer*, about 5 per cent of the oxygen is converted to ozone. Ozone is also formed in appreciable amounts by lightning bolts, ultraviolet light, and by sparking electric motors. Trace amounts found in air are apparently formed in the stratosphere by the absorption of ultraviolet sunlight. In industrial centers, the atmosphere contains reducing agents which destroy the ozone. However, minute amounts occur in unpolluted areas such as the mountains and the seashore. The ozone layer in the stratosphere makes difficult the astrophysical observations of light emitted by stars, because ozone absorbs some of the light, especially those wavelengths needed to identify nonmetallic elements.

The ozone molecule is not magnetic, so all its electrons must be paired. The three oxygen atoms are arranged in the form of an isosceles triangle in which two of the atoms are not directly bound to each other. If the octet rule is followed, it is necessary to write two contributing resonance forms for the structure:

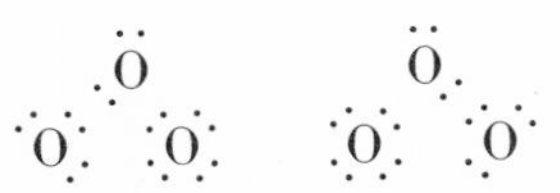

Ozone gas has a sharp, penetrating odor. Its solubility in water, in moles per liter, is about 50 per cent higher than that of oxygen, probably because O_3 is a polar molecule whereas O_2 is not. When cooled to $-111.5°C.$, ozone forms a deep blue liquid that is explosive because of the tendency of

O_3 to decompose to O_2. The decomposition is normally slow but increases rapidly as the temperature is increased or a catalyst is added.

Some of the properties of oxygen and ozone are given in Table 16.1. Both O_2 and O_3 are good oxidizing agents as shown by their oxidation potentials

$$2H_2O \rightleftharpoons O_2(g) + 4H^+ + 4e^- \qquad\qquad -1.23 \text{ volts}$$

$$H_2O + O_2(g) \rightleftharpoons O_3(g) + 2H^+ + 2e^- \qquad -2.07 \text{ volts}$$

(As pointed out in Sec. 14.8, a large negative oxidation potential indicates that the species to the right of the arrows is a strong oxidizing agent.) Of the common oxidizing agents, ozone is second only to fluorine in oxidizing strength. In most reactions, at least at room temperature, O_2 is a slow oxidizing agent, whereas O_3 is more rapid.

Because of its cheapness and ready availability, oxygen is one of the most widely used industrial oxidizing agents. For example, in the manufacture of steel it is used to burn off impurities such as carbon, phosphorus, and sulfur, which may give undesirable properties to steels. In the oxyacetylene torch, used for cutting and welding metals, temperatures in excess of 3000°C. can be obtained by the reaction

$$2C_2H_2(g) + 5O_2(g) \rightarrow 4CO_2(g) + 2H_2O(g) + 600 \text{ kcal.}$$

Liquid oxygen is mixed with alcohol, charcoal, gasoline, powdered aluminum, etc., to give powerful explosives.

The use of oxygen in respiration of plants and animals is well known. In man, oxygen, inhaled from the atmosphere, is picked up in the lungs by the hemoglobin in the blood and distributed to the various cells, which use it for tissue respiration. In tissue respiration, carbohydrates are oxidized to provide energy required for cellular activities. Since oxygen is a slow oxidizing agent, catalysts (enzymes) must be present in order that reaction

Table 16.1   Properties of Allotropic Forms of Oxygen

Property	O_2	O_3
Molecular weight, a.m.u.	32.000	48.000
Bond length, A.	1.20	1.26
Normal melting point, °K.	54.3	23.6
Normal boiling point, °K.	90.2	161.7
Critical temperature, °K.	154	268
Density of liquid (90°K.), g./ml.	1.14	1.71

may proceed at body temperature. In the treatment of heart trouble, pneumonia, and shock, air oxygen is supplemented with additional oxygen.

The uses of ozone depend on its strong oxidizing properties. For example, its germicidal use depends on its oxidation of bacteria. Inasmuch as oxidation of colored compounds often results in colorless ones, ozone is a bleaching agent for wax, starch, fats, and varnishes. When added to the air in small amounts, ozone destroys odors, but it can be used safely only in low concentration because it irritates the lungs. In the laboratory, ozone aids in certain structure studies. Since it has a specific action on carbon-carbon double bonds, it can be used to determine their position in molecules.

16.4 COMPOUNDS

Except for the oxygen fluorides, O_2F_2 and OF_2, the oxidation state of oxygen in compounds is negative. The oxidation numbers $-\frac{1}{2}$, -1, and -2 are observed.

Oxidation state $-\frac{1}{2}$. The heavier elements of group I (K, Rb, and Cs) react with oxygen to form compounds of the type MO_2, called superoxides. These are ionic solids containing the cation M^+ and the anion O_2^-. The solids are colored and paramagnetic; therefore, they must contain unpaired electrons.* The superoxide ion exists only in the solid state. When superoxides are placed in water, O_2 and H_2O_2 are formed by the reaction

$$2MO_2(s) + 2H_2O \rightarrow O_2(g) + H_2O_2 + 2M^+ + 2OH^-$$

Oxidation state -1. Compounds which contain oxygen with oxidation number -1 are called peroxides. They are characterized by a direct oxygen-oxygen bond, which usually breaks at high temperatures. Metals such as Na, Sr, and Ba form solid peroxides which contain the peroxide ion, O_2^{--}. This ion contains no unpaired electrons. Barium peroxide, BaO_2, is formed by heating solid barium with oxygen gas at a pressure of 3 atm. On further heating under reduced oxygen pressure, BaO_2 decomposes to give barium oxide, BaO.

$$2BaO_2(s) \rightarrow 2BaO(s) + O_2(g) \; -39 \text{ kcal.}$$

Since this reaction is endothermic, it reverses at lower temperature; then BaO picks up O_2. This reversible process has been used to extract O_2 from the air.

---

* The anion O_2^- has 13 valence electrons. If we assume that these electrons are divided equally, as they most certainly are, then we must assign each atom an oxidation number of $-\frac{1}{2}$. Frequently, a fractional oxidation number is explained away by assuming that the compound contains atoms of the same element in different oxidation states. In this case, such an explanation is unlikely. The odd electron belongs to the whole O_2^- ion.

When solid peroxides are added to acidic solutions, hydrogen peroxide, H_2O_2, is formed. For example,

$$BaO_2(s) + 2H^+ \rightarrow Ba^{++} + H_2O_2$$

If sulfuric acid is used, the barium ion precipitates as insoluble barium sulfate, $BaSO_4$, leaving a dilute solution of pure H_2O_2. Commercially, most H_2O_2 is prepared by the electrolysis of cold H_2SO_4 or NH_4HSO_4 solutions followed by distillation under reduced pressure. Because H_2O_2 is unstable, owing to the reaction

$$2H_2O_2 \rightarrow 2H_2O + O_2(g)$$

it is difficult to keep. The decomposition is slow but is catalyzed by impurities such as dust and dissolved compounds. It is also accelerated in the presence of light. For these reasons, solutions of H_2O_2 are stored in dark bottles with various chemicals added which destroy catalysts.

Pure anhydrous H_2O_2, obtained by distillation under reduced pressure, is a colorless liquid having a freezing point of $-0.9°C$. and an estimated boiling point of $151.4°C$. The structure corresponds to the electronic formula $:\overset{..}{O}:\overset{..}{O}:$, where the bond angle H—O—O is $97°$. All four atoms do
 H H

not lie in the same plane, but, as shown in Fig. 16.1, one H sticks out from the plane of the other three atoms at an angle of $94°$.

In aqueous solution H_2O_2 is a weak acid dissociating

$$H_2O_2 \rightleftharpoons H^+ + HO_2^-$$

with a dissociation constant of the order of 10^{-12}. Because oxygen also shows oxidation states of 0 and -2, compounds containing peroxide oxygen (-1) can gain or lose electrons; hence they can act both as oxidizing agents and as reducing agents. In fact, in the decomposition

$$2H_2O_2 \rightarrow 2H_2O + O_2(g)$$

hydrogen peroxide oxidizes and reduces itself. In the reaction

$$5H_2O_2 + 2MnO_4^- + 6H^+ \rightarrow$$
$$5O_2(g) + 2Mn^{++} + 8H_2O$$

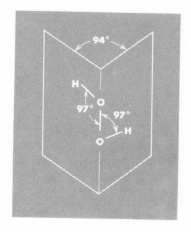

Fig. 16.1   Structure of H_2O_2 molecule.

hydrogen peroxide is a reducing agent (goes to O_2). In the reaction

$$H_2O_2 + 2I^- + 2H^+ \rightarrow I_2 + 2H_2O$$

H_2O_2 is an oxidizing agent (goes to H_2O).

Oxidation state -2. Minus two is the most common oxidation state of oxygen in compounds. These compounds include the *oxides*, such as BaO, and the *oxy compounds*, such as $BaSO_4$. In none of these is there an oxygen-oxygen bond. Instead, the oxygen atoms have completed their octets by gaining a major share of two electrons from atoms other than oxygen.

All the elements except the inert gases form oxides. Some of these oxides are ionic; others are covalent. In general, the more ionic ones are formed with the elements on the left of the periodic table. Thus, BaO contains Ba^{++} and O^{--} ions and, like all ionic substances, is a solid at room temperature. It can be heated to $2000°C$. without decomposition. When placed in water, the O^{--} ion reacts to give basic solutions.

$$O^{--} + H_2O \rightarrow 2OH^-$$

The ionic oxides are therefore called *basic oxides*, or *basic anhydrides*, or, most simply, *bases*. They have the ability to neutralize acids. Thus, for example, when CaO is placed in acidic solution, neutralization occurs according to the equation

$$CaO(s) + 2H^+ \rightarrow Ca^{++} + H_2O$$

Elements on the right of the periodic table do not form simple ionic oxides but share electrons with oxygen atoms. Many of these molecular oxides, such as sulfur dioxide, SO_2, are gases at room temperature. They dissolve in water to give acidic solutions. For example,

$$SO_2(g) + H_2O \rightarrow H_2SO_3 \rightleftharpoons H^+ + HSO_3^-$$

The molecular oxides are therefore called *acidic oxides*, or *acidic anhydrides*, or, most simply, *acids*. They have the ability to neutralize bases. As an example, when CO_2 is bubbled through a basic solution, neutralization occurs as follows:

$$CO_2(g) + OH^- \rightarrow HCO_3^-$$

It is not possible to classify all oxides sharply as either acidic or basic. Some oxides, especially those formed by elements toward the center of the periodic table, are able to *neutralize both acids and bases*. Such oxides are called *amphoteric*. An example of an amphoteric oxide is ZnO, which undergoes both the following reactions:

$$ZnO(s) + 2H^+ \rightarrow Zn^{++} + H_2O$$
$$ZnO(s) + 2OH^- + H_2O \rightarrow Zn(OH)_4^{--}$$

Further discussion of amphoteric oxides will be given later in Sec. 17.13.

When any oxide reacts with water, the resulting compound contains OH, or *hydroxyl*, groups. If the hydroxyl group exists in the compound as the OH^- ion, the compound is called a *hydroxide*. Hydroxides are formed by the reaction of ionic oxides with water; e.g.,

$$BaO(s) + H_2O \rightarrow Ba(OH)_2(s)$$

Barium hydroxide, $Ba(OH)_2$, is a solid which contains Ba^{++} and OH^- ions in its lattice. It, like all hydroxides except those of group I elements, reverts to the oxide when heated. Many hydroxides, e.g., aluminum hydroxide, $Al(OH)_3$, are insoluble in water. The soluble ones give basic solutions.

As mentioned in Sec. 10.8, some compounds contain the OH group not as an ion but covalently bound to another atom. For example, in H_2SO_3 there are two OH groups and one O joined to a central S atom. When placed in water, such compounds give acid solutions by rupture of the O—H bond. For this reason, they are called *oxyacids*. Most oxyacids can be dehydrated by heat to give oxides. They can also be neutralized to give *oxysalts* such as sodium sulfite, Na_2SO_3.

16.5 WATER

The most important of all oxides, possibly the most important of all compounds, is H_2O. The water molecule is nonlinear, with the H—O—H angle equal to $104.5°$. Because each bond is polar covalent, with the H end of the bond positive with respect to the O end, the molecule has a net dipole moment (Sec. 4.4). The attraction between the H atom of one molecule and the O atom of another leads to the association of water molecules in both the liquid and solid states. A two-dimensional representation of the association is given in Fig. 16.2. The cluster of water molecules is held together by hydrogen bonds (Sec. 15.5). The H atom, placed between two O atoms, may be considered bonded equally to both.* The result of hydrogen bonding is to form a giant molecule in which each O atom is surrounded by four H atoms. (The simplest formula is still H_2O, because, of the four H atoms

* In Fig. 16.2, the H atoms are shown midway between adjacent O atoms. Actually, a given H atom can jump back and forth from a position nearer one O atom to a position nearer the other. Thus, it is only the "average" position that is shown.

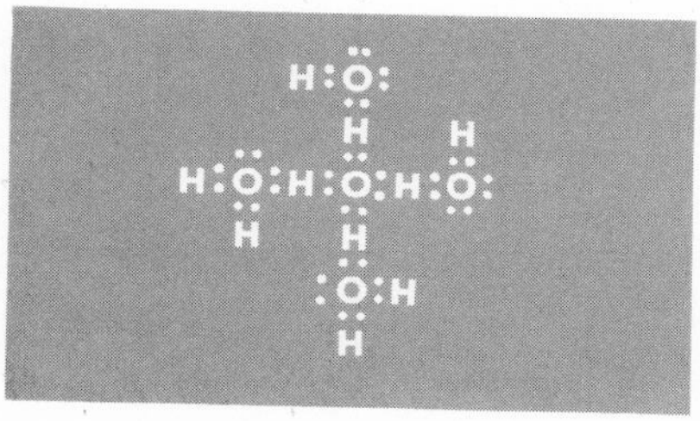

Fig. 16.2 Association of water molecules. (Hydrogen locations are the average of the two possible positions.)

Table 16.2   Density of Water at Various Temperatures

Temperature, °C.	State	Density, g./ml.
0	Solid	0.917
0	Liquid	0.9998
3.98	Liquid	1.0000
10	Liquid	0.9997
25	Liquid	0.9971
100	Liquid	0.9584

about a given O atom, only half of each H belongs to that O.) That there are four H atoms about each O is known from X-ray studies of ice. These studies do not detect the H atoms but do show that there are four oxygen atoms symmetrically placed about each oxygen. If the O atoms are joined to each other by H bonds, there must be four H atoms about each oxygen. This can be seen by considering the central atom in Fig. 16.2.

The X-ray studies indicate also that the O atoms (of neighboring H_2O molecules) about a given O are located at the corners of a regular tetrahedron, as shown in Fig. 16.3. Because of the tetrahedral arrangement, the ice structure extends in three dimensions and is not the flat, two-dimensional representation of Fig. 16.2. Figure 16.4 is a better picture of the ice structure. It shows part of the crystal lattice, which extends in three dimensions. The large circles represent oxygen atoms, each of which is tetrahedrally surrounded by four H atoms, represented by the small circles. Every other oxygen atom has its fourth H hidden beneath it. This hidden H joins to

Fig. 16.3   Tetrahedral arrangement of O atoms in ice structure. (Shaded regions occupied by H's.)

Fig. 16.4   Ice structure.

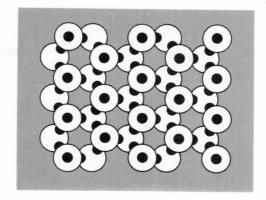

another oxygen below, and so the structure continues in three dimensions. A notable feature of the structure is that it is honeycombed with hexagonal channels. Because of these holes, ice has a relatively small density.

When ice melts, the structure becomes less orderly but is not completely destroyed. In liquid water near the melting point it is thought that the O atoms are still tetrahedrally surrounded by four H atoms as in ice. However, the over-all arrangement of tetrahedra is more random and is constantly changing. An instantaneous view might be like that shown in Fig. 16.5, where some of the hexagonal channels have collapsed to give a more dense structure. Liquid water is more dense than ice, as the data in Table 16.2 indicate.

The data in Table 16.2 also show that water has a maximum density at $3.98°C$. The maximum in the density of H_2O can be interpreted as follows: When ice is melted, the collapse of the structure leads to an increase in density. As the temperature of the liquid is raised, the collapse should continue further. However, there is an opposing effect. The higher the temperature, the greater the kinetic motion of the molecules. Hydrogen bonds

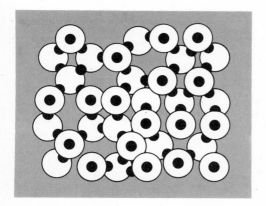

Fig. 16.5   Water structure.

are broken, and the H_2O molecules move farther apart on the average. This effect becomes dominant at temperatures above $3.98°C$. Below this temperature, collapse of structure is the more important.

16.6   WATER AS A SOLVENT

Water is the most common solvent both in nature and in the laboratory. However, it is far from being a universal solvent, since many substances are essentially insoluble in water. The factors influencing solubility are many (Sec. 10.7), and therefore predictions concerning solubility are difficult. The situation for water is especially complex, because there is strong association of H_2O molecules. For solution to occur, considerable energy is required to tear water molecules from their neighbors in order to make room for solute particles.

In general, water is a rather poor solvent for substances which exist in solution as molecules. Thus, gasoline, oxygen, and methane are practically insoluble in water. In these cases, water interacts so weakly with the molecular solute that not nearly enough energy is liberated to break down the water structure. There are, however, some molecular solutes which are highly soluble in water. Examples are ammonia, NH_3, and ethyl alcohol, C_2H_5OH. These substances apparently interact sufficiently strongly with the water to break its structure. In the case of NH_3, hydrogen bonds are established between the N of NH_3 and the O of H_2O. These hydrogen bonds can be used to justify the occasional practice of writing NH_4OH as the formula of dissolved NH_3. In aqueous solutions of ethyl alcohol, hydrogen bonds are formed between the O of C_2H_5OH and the O of H_2O. Sucrose, $C_{12}H_{22}O_{11}$, owes its appreciable solubility in large measure to hydrogen bonding, since it, like C_2H_5OH, has OH groups.

Although water is the best solvent known for substances which exist in solution as ions, many ionic solutes are practically insoluble in water. In general, the attractions between ions and polar H_2O molecules (hydration energies) are great enough to break the water structure. However, there are strong attractions between the oppositely charged ions in the solid (lattice energies), which must be overcome in order that solution may occur. Both of these attractions must be considered in explaining solubility. In sodium chloride, ion-water attractions are great enough, and NaCl is quite soluble. In $BaSO_4$, ion-water attractions are not great enough, and $BaSO_4$ is quite insoluble, despite the fact that the ion-water attraction involved is greater than that for NaCl.

In comparing NaCl with $BaSO_4$, one important factor that needs to be considered is that in NaCl the ions are singly charged, whereas in $BaSO_4$ they are doubly charged. The higher the charge of an ion, the more strongly it will attract one end of a polar H_2O molecule. But the higher charge also causes a greater attraction between the ions in the solid. Thus increase of ionic charge seems to favor both solubility and insolubility. The problem is obviously complex, and a simple, satisfactory theory has not yet been developed. It seems to be generally true that, if the charge on both anion and cation is increased, insolubility is favored. Thus, for example, $BaSO_4$ (both ions doubly charged) and $AlPO_4$ (both ions triply charged) are much less soluble than NaCl (both ions singly charged). On the other hand, if the charge of only one ion is increased, the solubility is not much changed. As an example, NaCl, $BaCl_2$, and $AlCl_3$ are all appreciably soluble. Similarly, NaCl, Na_2SO_4, and Na_3PO_4 are also soluble.

In addition to charge, there are other factors which affect solubility. One of these is size. In general, the smaller an ion, the more strongly it attracts other ions and water molecules. Another factor we have ignored is that there may be specific interactions either in the solid or in the solution. An example of specific interactions occurs in solid silver chloride, AgCl, where there are stronger van der Waals attractions between Ag^+ and Cl^- than between the ions of NaCl, thus favoring lower solubility for AgCl than for NaCl. In barium sulfide, BaS, reaction of the sulfide ion, S^{--}, with water occurs, to help make BaS more soluble than $BaSO_4$. Thus, predictions as to solubility must be made with caution since it depends on a number of factors.

16.7   HYDRATES

Analysis shows that many solids contain water molecules. These solids are called *hydrates* and are represented by formulas like that for nickel sulfate heptahydrate, $NiSO_4 \cdot 7H_2O$. The formula states that there are seven water molecules per formula unit but does not specify how the H_2O is bound in the crystal. For example, in $NiSO_4 \cdot 7H_2O$ all seven H_2O molecules are not equivalent. Six are bound to the Ni^{++} ion to give $Ni(H_2O)_6^{++}$, and the seventh is shared between $Ni(H_2O)_6^{++}$ and SO_4^{--}. The solid is better represented by the formula $Ni(H_2O)_6SO_4 \cdot H_2O$. In other hydrates, such as sodium carbonate decahydrate, $Na_2CO_3 \cdot 10H_2O$, water molecules are not bound directly to the ions, but their principal function seems to be to improve the packing of the ions in the crystal. Water of hydration can be driven off by heating to give *anhydrous* material. The loss of water is usually accompanied by a change in crystal structure. However, some substances, such as certain clay minerals called zeolites, and proteins, lose water on heating without change in crystal structure. On reexposure to water they, like sponges, take up water and swell. Apparently, water taken up this way occupies semirigid tunnels within the solid.

Actually, water of hydration is more common than not in the usual salts of the chemistry laboratory. Blue copper sulfate, for example, is $CuSO_4 \cdot 5H_2O$ or, better, $Cu(H_2O)_4SO_4 \cdot H_2O$. Even acids and bases can exist as hydrates in the solid form. Examples are barium hydroxide, $Ba(OH)_2 \cdot 8H_2O$, and oxalic acid, $H_2C_2O_4 \cdot 2H_2O$.

Frequently, oxygen- and hydrogen-containing compounds are encountered whose composition may be known but whose structure is in doubt. Such a substance is obtained, for example, from the reaction of a base with a solution of aluminum salt. Under certain conditions, the product might have the composition AlO_3H_3. The most obvious conclusion is that the compound is the hydroxide, $Al(OH)_3$. However, it could just as well be the hydrated oxide, $Al_2O_3 \cdot 3H_2O$, for which the simplest formula also is AlO_3H_3. In order to distinguish the two possibilities, structure studies are needed, but in many cases these have not been done.

QUESTIONS

16.1   *Electronic formulas.* What is the essential difference between an oxide, a superoxide, a peroxide, and a hydroxide? Write an electronic formula for an example of each.

16.2   *Preparation.* Compare the relative merits of the different ways of preparing oxygen.

16.3   *Oxidation.* When air is bubbled through an acidic solution of $MnSO_4$, no change is observed. If the air is first subjected to a silent electric discharge, the purple color characteristic of MnO_4^- is observed. Write net equations that account for these observations.

16.4   *Liquefaction.* In the preparation of liquid oxygen, why must the compressed gas be cooled before it is expanded?

16.5   *Allotropy.* What is meant by the term "allotropy"? Write the electronic formulas for the allotropic forms of oxygen. Discuss these in terms of the octet rule and the concept of resonance.

16.6   *Hydrogen peroxide.* Account for the fact that solutions of hydrogen peroxide are acid.

16.7   *Oxidation-reduction.* Why is it that H_2O_2 can act as an oxidizing agent and as a reducing agent? Diagnose each of the following changes as oxidation-reduction reactions by writing the balanced equations and the half-reactions and by indicating the oxidizing and the reducing agent in each case:

$$H_2O_2 + Cr_2O_7^{--} \rightarrow Cr^{+3} + O_2(g) \qquad \text{(acidic)}$$

$$HO_2^- + CrO_2^- \rightarrow CrO_4^{--} + OH^- \qquad \text{(basic)}$$

16.8 *Reactions.* Write net equations for each of the following changes: (*a*) an acidic oxide dissolves in water to give an acid solution; (*b*) a basic oxide dissolves in water to give a basic solution; (*c*) barium peroxide is treated with sulfuric acid; (*d*) sodium oxide, Na_2O, is treated with water; (*e*) hydrogen peroxide is exposed to sunlight; (*f*) natural gas (CH_4) is burned in a bunsen burner to give CO_2 and H_2O; (*g*) KO_2 is placed in water; (*h*) a solution of the weak acid H_2O_2 is treated with strong base.

16.9 *Density of water.* Draw a graph showing how the density of H_2O changes with temperature from -10 to $100°C$. Account for the changes.

16.10 *Water as a solvent.* Account for the fact that water is a good solvent for many ionic solutes but a poor solvent for many molecular ones.

16.11 *Solubility.* What would you predict for the solubility in water of each of the following: Na_2CO_3, $CaCO_3$, KBr, He, CH_3OH, $FePO_4$, C_2H_2?

16.12 *Hydrates.* When anhydrous $CuSO_4$ is exposed to H_2O, only 5 moles of H_2O are taken up per mole of $CuSO_4$. When anhydrous clay is exposed to H_2O, the clay swells and takes up an indefinite amount of H_2O. Account for these observations in terms of structure.

16.13 *Anhydrides.* Write the simplest formulas of the anhydrides of the following compounds: H_2CO_3, H_2SO_4, $Ba(OH)_2$, HNO_3, $Cr(OH)_3$, $NaOH$, $HClO_4$.

16.14 *Solubility.* (*a*) Why would you expect stronger van der Waals attractions in $AgCl$ than in $NaCl$? (*b*) How would you expect the solubility of AgI to compare with that of $AgCl$? Explain.

16.15 *Hydrate.* What weight of solid $CuSO_4 \cdot 5H_2O$ would be required to make 1.00 liter of each of the following: (*a*) $1.50\ M\ Cu^{++}$, (*b*) $1.50\ m\ Cu^{++}$ (density 1.22 g. per ml.)?   *Ans.* 375 g.; 369 g.

16.16 *Stoichiometry.* Given 25.0 ml. of an unknown solution of H_2O_2. When acidified, the solution requires 35.0 ml. of $0.0250\ M\ KMnO_4$ for complete reaction to form Mn^{++} and O_2. What is the molarity of the starting solution?

Ans. $0.0875\ M$

16.17 *Stoichiometry.* What volume of air at STP is required to burn 1.00 kg. of sugar, $C_{12}H_{22}O_{11}$, to CO_2 and H_2O?

16.18 *Oxidation.* In the design of a rocket engine, an important limitation may be imposed either by restricted volume or by restricted weight. How much energy would each of the following reactions produce: (*a*) if the size of the chamber holding the oxidizing agent is limited to 500 liters; (*b*) if the weight of oxidizing agent is limited to 700 kg.? Necessary data is on the next page.

$$C_2H_5OH(l) + 3O_2(l) \rightarrow 2CO_2(g) + 3H_2O(g) + 295.6 \text{ kcal.}$$

$$C_2H_5OH(l) + 2O_3(l) \rightarrow 2CO_2(g) + 3H_2O(g) + 363.4 \text{ kcal.}$$

Assume in each case you have enough fuel to consume all the oxidizing agent. The density of liquid oxygen is 1.14 g. per ml. and the density of liquid ozone is 1.71 g. per ml.

Ans. (*a*) 1.75×10^6 kcal.; 3.24×10^6 kcal.; (*b*) 2.16×10^6 kcal.; 2.65×10^6 kcal.

$$\frac{[?]}{[?][?]} = K$$

17 Aqueous Solutions

THE MOST IMPORTANT CLASSES OF REACTIONS probably are those that occur in aqueous solutions. For example, all biological reactions and a large share of laboratory reactions take place in water. In order to understand these reactions, it is necessary to appreciate the equilibria involved. Since reactions are reversible and tend toward the equilibrium state, the principles of equilibrium give the key to understanding reactions in solution. In this chapter, we consider the equilibria in aqueous solutions and how they are related to the reactions that are observed to occur. The important equilibria to be considered are of three fundamental types:

1 Dissociation, an equilibrium between a dissolved undissociated species and its component parts, e.g., acetic acid molecules in equilibrium with hydrogen ions and acetate ions.

2 Solubility, an equilibrium between a pure phase, usually a solid, and its characteristic species in solution, e.g., solid barium sulfate in equilibrium with barium ions and sulfate ions.

3 Oxidation-reduction, an equilibrium between an oxidizing agent and a reducing agent and their reaction products, e.g., dichromate ion and ferrous ion in equilibrium in acidic solution with ferric ion and chromic ion.

Besides these three simple types, various combinations of them are possible.

17.1   DISSOCIATION

When a substance in aqueous solution can dissociate into simpler fragments, an equilibrium is established between the undissociated species and the component parts. Thus, for example, when the weak acid HX is placed in water, some of it dissociates to give H^+ and X^-. When equilibrium is established, the association of H^+ with X^- to form HX occurs at a rate just sufficient to balance the dissociation. The equilibrium can be represented by the reversible equation

$$HX \rightleftharpoons H^+ + X^-$$

and the equilibrium condition can be expressed as

$$\frac{[H^+][X^-]}{[HX]} = K$$

(Recall that square brackets indicate concentration in moles per liter.) This equilibrium constant is called a *dissociation constant* and is often designated as K_{diss} or K_{HX}. The mass-action expression is constant only in quite dilute solutions. In more concentrated solutions, interionic attraction must be considered; because of their complexity, we shall, however, ignore such considerations.* Typical experimental values of the dissociation constants of various weak acids are given in Table 17.1. Others may be found in Appendix 8. Values are quoted for 25°C. The smaller the value of K_{diss}, the weaker the acid. Thus, HCN is a weaker acid than HF, and much less dissociated for a given concentration. When K_{diss} is 1 or greater, the acid is extensively dissociated, even in 1 M solution, and is classified as moderately strong. When K_{diss} is 10 or greater, the acid is essentially 100 per cent dissociated in all except very concentrated solutions. For example, perchloric acid, $HClO_4$, is one of our strongest acids and has K_{diss} greater than 10. Similarly, HNO_3, HCl, and H_2SO_4 are common acids with high dissociation constants.

Strictly speaking, the dissociation of an acid, as explained in Sec. 10.4, is better written as

$$H_2O + HX \rightleftharpoons H_3O^+ + X^-$$

---

* The mass-action expression is strictly constant only if we use the chemical activity of the various species in the expression. Just as was true for oxidation potentials (footnote, page 294), the true chemical activity of a species in the mass-action expression is frequently approximated by its concentration.

Table 17.1 Dissociation of Weak Acids

Acid	Reaction	K_{diss} (25°C.)
Acetic	$HC_2H_3O_2 \rightleftharpoons H^+ + C_2H_3O_2^-$	1.8×10^{-5}
Nitrous	$HNO_2 \rightleftharpoons H^+ + NO_2^-$	4.5×10^{-4}
Hydrofluoric	$HF \rightleftharpoons H^+ + F^-$	6.7×10^{-4}
Hydrocyanic	$HCN \rightleftharpoons H^+ + CN^-$	4.0×10^{-10}
Sulfurous	$H_2SO_3 \rightleftharpoons H^+ + HSO_3^-$	1.3×10^{-2}

However, this leads to the same equilibrium condition as above, as can be seen from the following: The equilibrium condition for the reaction that includes water is

$$\frac{[H_3O^+][X^-]}{[H_2O][HX]} = K'$$

but, in those dilute solutions for which K' applies without correction for interionic attractions, the concentration of H_2O is essentially constant. (In dilute solutions the concentration of H_2O is so great that it changes little as the concentration of other species changes.) Therefore, the equilibrium condition is

$$\frac{[H_3O^+][X^-]}{[HX]} = K'[H_2O] = K$$

By ignoring the water of hydration, $[H_3O^+]$ can be replaced by $[H^+]$, giving the same equilibrium condition as that for the reaction written without water.

The dissociation constant can also be applied to ions which dissociate as acids. For example, the hydrogen sulfate ion, HSO_4^-, can dissociate into H^+ and SO_4^{--} and must be in equilibrium with these ions.

$$HSO_4^- \rightleftharpoons H^+ + SO_4^{--}$$

$$K_{HSO_4^-} = \frac{[H^+][SO_4^{--}]}{[HSO_4^-]} = 1.3 \times 10^{-2}$$

This dissociation constant of HSO_4^- can be considered the second dissociation constant of H_2SO_4, since it applies to the second step of its dissociation.

$$H_2SO_4 \rightleftharpoons H^+ + HSO_4^- \qquad K_I > 10$$
$$HSO_4^- \rightleftharpoons H^+ + SO_4^{--} \qquad K_{II} = 1.3 \times 10^{-2}$$

K_I and K_{II} are, respectively, the first and second dissociation constants of sulfuric acid. The large value of K_I means that H_2SO_4 is essentially com-

Table 17.2 *Dissociation of Weak Bases*

Base	Reaction	K_{diss} (25°C.)
Ammonium hydroxide	$NH_4OH \rightleftharpoons NH_4^+ + OH^-$	1.8×10^{-5}
Hydrazine hydroxide	$N_2H_5OH \rightleftharpoons N_2H_5^+ + OH^-$	1×10^{-6}
Phenylammonium hydroxide	$C_6H_5NH_3OH \rightleftharpoons C_6H_5NH_3^+ + OH^-$	5×10^{-10}
Hydroxyaluminum ion	$AlOH^{++} \rightleftharpoons Al^{+3} + OH^-$	7.1×10^{-10}

pletely dissociated into H^+ and HSO_4^-. The moderate value of K_{II} means that a modest amount of the HSO_4^- (about 10 per cent in 0.1 M H_2SO_4) is in turn dissociated into H^+ and SO_4^{--}. In a given solution of H_2SO_4, both equilibria exist simultaneously, and both constants must be satisfied by the concentration of undissociated H_2SO_4, H^+, HSO_4^-, and SO_4^{--}.

For weak bases the dissociation equilibria are treated in the same way. For example, aqueous solutions of ammonia are frequently considered as containing ammonium hydroxide, NH_4OH, a weak base which in water sets up the following equilibrium:

$$NH_4OH \rightleftharpoons NH_4^+ + OH^-$$

The equilibrium condition is

$$\frac{[NH_4^+][OH^-]}{[NH_4OH]} = K_{diss} = 1.8 \times 10^{-5}$$

Some values found for the dissociation constants of other weak bases are listed in Table 17.2. Besides acids and bases there are in chemistry a few salts that are weak electrolytes, i.e., they are only slightly dissociated in solution. An example is mercuric chloride, $HgCl_2$, which dissociates

$$HgCl_2 \rightleftharpoons HgCl^+ + Cl^-$$

for which

$$\frac{[HgCl^+][Cl^-]}{[HgCl_2]} = K_{diss} = 3.3 \times 10^{-7}$$

The second dissociation is

$$HgCl^+ \rightleftharpoons Hg^{++} + Cl^-$$

for which

$$\frac{[Hg^{++}][Cl^-]}{[HgCl^+]} = K_{II} = 1.8 \times 10^{-7}$$

Mercuric chloride is an exception to the usual rule that salts are 100 per cent dissociated in solution. However, $HgCl_2$ is not unique. For instance, cadmium sulfate, $CdSO_4$, has a dissociation constant of 5×10^{-3}.

As pointed out in Sec. 13.4, it makes no difference whether an equilibrium state is produced from the material on the left-hand side of the chemical equation or from the material on the right-hand side. Change occurs to form material in sufficient concentration to establish equilibrium. This means that the same equilibrium state is produced by having a weak electrolyte dissociate as is produced by having the ions associate. Specifically, the same final solution results from placing either 1 mole of acetic acid or 1 mole of H^+ plus 1 mole of $C_2H_3O_2^-$ in a liter of water. In either case, the condition for equilibrium is

$$\frac{[H^+][C_2H_3O_2^-]}{[HC_2H_3O_2]} = 1.8 \times 10^{-5}$$

Since $HC_2H_3O_2$ is a weak acid, the concentration of H^+ and of $C_2H_3O_2^-$ in the final solutions must be small.

When ions are mixed and association occurs, a chemical equation can be written to stress the direction of the net reaction. For example, when solutions of HCl and $NaC_2H_3O_2$ are mixed, the equation can be written

$$H^+ + C_2H_3O_2^- \rightleftharpoons HC_2H_3O_2$$

for which

$$\frac{[HC_2H_3O_2]}{[H^+][C_2H_3O_2^-]} = K_{\text{assoc}}$$

The numerical value of K_{assoc} is 5.6×10^4, which is the reciprocal of K_{diss} for acetic acid.

Association occurs whenever the constituent parts of a weak electrolyte are mixed. Thus, when solutions of NH_4Cl and $NaOH$ are mixed, NH_4^+ ions associate with OH^- ions to form NH_4OH. Likewise, when solutions of $Hg(NO_3)_2$ and $NaCl$ are mixed, Hg^{++} ions associate with Cl^- ions to form $HgCl_2$.

17.2   CALCULATIONS USING K_{diss}

The methods of equilibrium calculation described in Sec. 13.4 apply to dissociation equilibria in aqueous solution. Like any equilibrium constant, K_{diss} must be experimentally determined. Once its value is known at a given temperature, it can be used for all calculations involving that equilibrium at the same temperature.

Example 1

What is the concentration of all solute species in a solution labeled 1.00 M $HC_2H_3O_2$?
What per cent of the acid is dissociated?

$$HC_2H_3O_2 \rightleftharpoons H^+ + C_2H_3O_2^- \qquad K_{diss} = 1.8 \times 10^{-5}$$

Let x equal the moles per liter of $HC_2H_3O_2$ that dissociate to establish equilibrium. According to the dissociation equation, each mole of $HC_2H_3O_2$ that dissociates produces 1 mole of H^+ and 1 mole of $C_2H_3O_2^-$. If x moles of $HC_2H_3O_2$ dissociate, then x moles of H^+ and x moles of $C_2H_3O_2^-$ must be formed. The initial and equilibrium concentrations are summarized as follows:

Initially	**At equilibrium**
$[HC_2H_3O_2] = 1.00$ mole/liter	$[HC_2H_3O_2] = (1.00 - x)$ moles/liter
$[H^+] = 0$ mole/liter	$[H^+] = x$ moles/liter
$[C_2H_3O_2^-] = 0$ mole/liter	$[C_2H_3O_2^-] = x$ moles/liter

At equilibrium

$$\frac{[H^+][C_2H_3O_2^-]}{[HC_2H_3O_2]} = 1.8 \times 10^{-5} = \frac{(x)(x)}{(1.00 - x)}$$

Solving this equation by use of the quadratic formula (Appendix 3.4) gives $x = 0.0042$. Therefore, at equilibrium (with due regard for significant figures)

$$[HC_2H_3O_2] = 1.00 - x = 1.00 \; M$$
$$[H^+] = x = 0.0042 \; M$$
$$[C_2H_3O_2^-] = x = 0.0042 \; M$$

The percentage dissociation is defined as 100 times the number of moles of $HC_2H_3O_2$ dissociated divided by the number of moles of $HC_2H_3O_2$ originally available.

$$\text{Percentage dissociation} = \frac{0.0042 \times 100}{1.00} = 0.42\%$$

It might be noted here that much of the algebraic work involved in solving equilibrium problems can be avoided by judicious attention to chemical facts which may suggest laborsaving approximations. Thus, in Example 1, since $HC_2H_3O_2$ is a weak acid, it cannot be much dissociated. In other words, x must be small compared to 1.00 and may be neglected when added to or subtracted from 1.00. Thus, instead of solving the exact equation

$$1.8 \times 10^{-5} = \frac{(x)(x)}{(1.00 - x)}$$

we can solve the approximate equation

$$1.8 \times 10^{-5} \cong \frac{(x)(x)}{(1.00)}$$

obtained by assuming that $1.00 - x \cong 1.00$. From

$$1.8 \times 10^{-5} \cong x^2$$

we get

$$x \cong \sqrt{1.8 \times 10^{-5}} = \sqrt{18 \times 10^{-6}} = 4.2 \times 10^{-3}$$

Checking the approximation and paying due attention to significant figures, we find that $1.00 - x = 1.00 - (4.2 \times 10^{-3}) = 1.00$, as assumed.

Example 2

Suppose that 1.00 mole of HCl and 1.00 mole of $NaC_2H_3O_2$ are mixed in enough water to make a liter of solution. What will be the concentration of H^+ in the final solution?

Since HCl and $NaC_2H_3O_2$ are strong electrolytes, they are 100% dissociated in solution. The Na^+ and Cl^- do not associate and so can be ignored. The problem is thus one of associating H^+ and $C_2H_3O_2^-$ to form $HC_2H_3O_2$ in sufficient concentration to satisfy the equilibrium

$$HC_2H_3O_2 \rightleftharpoons H^+ + C_2H_3O_2^-$$

which is described by $K_{diss} = 1.8 \times 10^{-5}$. The initial and equilibrium concentrations can be summarized as follows, where y is the moles of H^+ and of $C_2H_3O_2^-$ that associate per liter to form y moles of $HC_2H_3O_2$:

Initially	**At equilibrium**
$[H^+] = 1.00 \ M$	$[H^+] = (1.00 - y) \ M$
$[C_2H_3O_2^-] = 1.00 \ M$	$[C_2H_3O_2^-] = (1.00 - y) \ M$
$[HC_2H_3O_2] = 0 \ M$	$[HC_2H_3O_2] = y \ M$

At equilibrium

$$\frac{[H^+][C_2H_3O_2^-]}{[HC_2H_3O_2]} = 1.8 \times 10^{-5} = \frac{(1.00 - y)(1.00 - y)}{(y)}$$

This equation can be solved by applying the quadratic formula (see Appendix 3.4), giving $y = 0.996$. Since y is not small compared to 1.00, the approximation made in solving Example 1 cannot be used.

A better way to solve this problem is to note that, when 1.00 mole of H^+ and 1.00 mole of $C_2H_3O_2^-$ are mixed, the resulting system is exactly the same as if H^+ and $C_2H_3O_2^-$ first completely react to form 1.00 mole of $HC_2H_3O_2$, which then dissociates to establish equilibrium. If x is defined as the moles per liter that dissociate of this hypothetical 1.00 mole of $HC_2H_3O_2$, the problem becomes identical with Example 1. We can therefore write down directly the equilibrium concentrations:

$[H^+] = 4.2 \times 10^{-3} \ M$

$[C_2H_3O_2^-] = 4.2 \times 10^{-3} \ M$

$[HC_2H_3O_2] = 1.00 \ M$

$[Na^+] = 1.00 \ M$

$[Cl^-] = 1.00 \ M$

Example 3

What are the concentrations of species and the percentage dissociation in 0.10 M $HC_2H_3O_2$?

Let x = moles of $HC_2H_3O_2$ that dissociate per liter.

Then x = final concentration of H^+

x = final concentration of $C_2H_3O_2^-$

$0.10 - x$ = final concentration of $HC_2H_3O_2$

At equilibrium

$$\frac{[H^+][C_2H_3O_2^-]}{[HC_2H_3O_2]} = 1.8 \times 10^{-5} = \frac{(x)(x)}{(0.10 - x)}$$

Assuming that x is small compared to 0.10,

$$\frac{x^2}{0.10} \cong 1.8 \times 10^{-5}$$

$$x^2 \cong 1.8 \times 10^{-6}$$

$$x \cong 1.3 \times 10^{-3}$$

Therefore, at equilibrium

$$[H^+] = x = 1.3 \times 10^{-3} \ M$$

$$[C_2H_3O_2^-] = x = 1.3 \times 10^{-3} \ M$$

$$[HC_2H_3O_2] = 0.10 - x = 0.10 \ M$$

$$\text{Percentage dissociation} = \frac{1.3 \times 10^{-3}}{0.10} 100 = 1.3\%$$

Comparison of Examples 1 and 3 indicates the general fact that, when a solution of a weak electrolyte is diluted, the concentration of each species *decreases* and the percentage dissociation *increases*. It should be noted that, although there is a tenfold dilution in going from 1.00 M $HC_2H_3O_2$ to 0.10 M $HC_2H_3O_2$, the concentration of H^+ does not decrease tenfold but only from $4.2 \times 10^{-3} \ M$ to $1.3 \times 10^{-3} \ M$. This, of course, is consistent with the fact that in the more dilute solution a greater percentage of the acid is dissociated to counterbalance partially the tenfold dilution.

17.3   DISSOCIATION OF WATER

In the preceding section, we have ignored the fact that water is a weak electrolyte and is dissociated according to the equation

$$H_2O \rightleftharpoons H^+ + OH^-$$

In pure water and in all aqueous solutions, this equilibrium exists and must satisfy the condition

$$\frac{[H^+][OH^-]}{[H_2O]} = K$$

In all dilute solutions the concentration of H_2O can be considered constant and combined with the constant K to give K_w as follows:

$$K[H_2O] = K_w = [H^+][OH^-]$$

K_w is usually called the dissociation constant, or *ion product*, of water. It has the value of 1.0×10^{-14} at $25°C$.

In pure water, all the H^+ and the OH^- must come from the dissociation of water molecules. If x moles of H^+ are produced per liter, x moles of OH^- must be simultaneously produced.

$$[H^+][OH^-] = 1.0 \times 10^{-14}$$

$$(x)(x) = 1.0 \times 10^{-14}$$

$$x^2 = 1.0 \times 10^{-14}$$

$$x = 1.0 \times 10^{-7}$$

Thus, in pure H_2O, the concentrations of H^+ and OH^- are each 1.0×10^{-7} *M*. This very small concentration is to be compared with H_2O concentration of approximately 55.4 moles per liter. (A liter of H_2O at $25°C$. weighs 997 g., and a mole of H_2O weighs 18.0 g., therefore 1 liter contains 997/18.0, or 55.4, moles.) This means that on the average there is one H^+ ion and one OH^- ion for every 554 million H_2O molecules.

If an acid is added to water, the hydrogen-ion concentration increases above 1.0×10^{-7} *M*. The ion product must remain equal to 1.0×10^{-14}; consequently the hydroxide-ion concentration decreases below 1.0×10^{-7} *M*. Similarly, when a base is added to water, the concentration of OH^- increases above 1.0×10^{-7} *M*, and the concentration of H^+ decreases below 1.0×10^{-7} *M*.

17.4   pH

As a convenience for working with small concentrations, the pH scale has been devised to express the concentration of H^+. By definition,

$$pH = -\log[H^+] \quad \text{or} \quad [H^+] = 10^{-pH}$$

For example, in pure water, where the concentration of H^+ is 1.0×10^{-7}

M, the pH is 7. All neutral solutions have a pH of 7. Acid solutions have pH less than 7; basic solutions have pH greater than 7. (For a review of logarithms, see Appendix 3.3.)

Example 4

What is the pH of 0.10 M HCl?

In 0.10 M HCl, practically all the H^+ comes from the 100% dissociation of the strong electrolyte HCl. H_2O is such a weak electrolyte in comparison that it contributes a negligible amount of H^+.

$$[H^+] = 0.10 \ M = 1.0 \times 10^{-1} \ M$$
$$pH = -\log (1.0 \times 10^{-1}) = 1$$

Note that the logarithm of a product is equal to the sum of the logs. The log of 1.0 is zero and the log of 10^{-1} is -1.

Example 5

What is the pH of 0.10 M NaOH?

NaOH is a strong electrolyte and accounts for essentially all the OH^- in the solution.

$$[OH^-] = 0.10 \ M$$
$$[H^+] = \frac{K_w}{[OH^-]} = \frac{1.0 \times 10^{-14}}{0.10} = 1.0 \times 10^{-13} \ M$$
$$pH = -\log (1.0 \times 10^{-13}) = 13$$

In Examples 4 and 5, the contributions from H_2O dissociation to $[H^+]$ in the acidic solution and to $[OH^-]$ in the basic solution are negligible. This is true because acids and bases repress the dissociation of water. To illustrate, in Example 5, the added OH^- represses the dissociation of H_2O so that only 1.0×10^{-13} mole of H^+ per liter is produced. This means that only 1.0×10^{-13} mole of OH^- per liter comes from the H_2O dissociation, an amount that is indeed negligible compared to that from 0.10 M NaOH.

17.5 TITRATION

So far, we have emphasized the dissociation of water to give ions. However, since equilibrium may be approached from the left or the right side of an equation, the same equilibrium constant that describes the dissociation of water also describes the association of H^+ and OH^- to form water. Such association occurs in neutralization reactions, as discussed in Sec. 10.9,

Table 17.3   Progressive Addition of Solid NaOH to 1 Liter of 0.010 M HCl

Moles of NaOH added	[H⁺]	[OH⁻]	pH
None	0.010	1.0×10^{-12}	2.00
0.001	0.009	1.1×10^{-12}	2.04
0.002	0.008	1.3×10^{-12}	2.10
0.003	0.007	1.4×10^{-12}	2.15
0.004	0.006	1.7×10^{-12}	2.23
0.005	0.005	2.0×10^{-12}	2.30
0.006	0.004	2.5×10^{-12}	2.40
0.007	0.003	3.3×10^{-12}	2.52
0.008	0.002	5.0×10^{-12}	2.70
0.009	0.001	1.0×10^{-11}	3.00
0.010	1.0×10^{-7}	1.0×10^{-7}	7.00
0.011	1.0×10^{-11}	0.001	11.00
0.012	5.0×10^{-12}	0.002	11.30
0.013	3.3×10^{-12}	0.003	11.48
0.014	2.5×10^{-12}	0.004	11.60
0.015	2.0×10^{-12}	0.005	11.70
0.016	1.7×10^{-12}	0.006	11.77
0.017	1.4×10^{-12}	0.007	11.85
0.018	1.3×10^{-12}	0.008	11.90
0.019	1.1×10^{-12}	0.009	11.96
0.020	1.0×10^{-12}	0.010	12.00

and is the basis of the process of *titration*, the progressive addition of an acid to a base or vice versa. At each step in the titration, the expression $[H^+][OH^-] = 1.0 \times 10^{-14}$ must be satisfied in the solution. Table 17.3 represents what happens to the concentration of H⁺ and OH⁻ as solid NaOH is added stepwise to 0.010 mole of HCl in 1 liter of water. As NaOH is progressively added, the original solution changes from acid (pH less than 7) to basic (pH greater than 7). The titration can be represented graphically by plotting the concentration of H⁺ against the moles of added NaOH. However, since the H⁺ concentration changes by a factor of 10 billion during the experiment, it is hard to get all the values on the same scale. Not so with the pH. It changes only by a factor of 6 and is a convenient representation of what happens to the solution during the titration. Figure 17.1 represents the change of pH as solid NaOH is added to 1 liter of 0.010 *M* HCl. The pH first rises very slowly, then rapidly through the neutral point, and finally very slowly as the solution gets more basic. Such a pH curve is typical of the titration of any strong acid with any strong base. The impor-

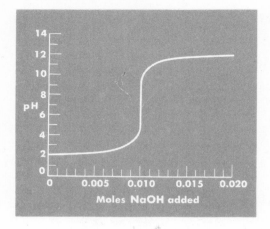

Fig. 17.1 Titration curve of 1 liter of 0.01 M HCl.

tant thing to note is that, as the neutral point is approached, there is a sharp rise in pH. At this point even a trace of NaOH adds enough moles of base to increase the pH greatly. Thus, any method which locates the point at which the pH changes rapidly can be used to detect the *equivalence point* of a titration, i.e., the point at which equivalent amounts of base and acid have been mixed.

One method for determining the equivalence point makes use of the fact that many dyes have colors that are sensitive to hydrogen-ion concentration. Such dyes can be used as *indicators* to give information about the pH of a solution. Indicators can be considered to be weak acids, H*In*, which dissociate to give H$^+$ and *In*$^-$. As weak acids, they must satisfy the condition

$$\frac{[\text{H}^+][In^-]}{[\text{H}In]} = K \quad \text{or} \quad \frac{[In^-]}{[\text{H}In]} = \frac{K}{[\text{H}^+]}$$

from which it is evident that the ratio $[In^-]/[\text{H}In]$ is inversely proportional to the hydrogen-ion concentration of the solution. If the species *In*$^-$ and H*In* have different colors, the color of the solution depends on which species is predominant. For phenolphthalein, H*In* is colorless, but *In*$^-$ is red. In solutions of high hydrogen-ion concentration, the ratio $[In^-]/[\text{H}In]$ is small, and the colorless species H*In* is dominant. Conversely, when [H$^+$] is small, the red species *In*$^-$ is dominant. Table 17.4 lists the characteristic colors of some common indicators.

In Fig. 17.1, the pH rises so sharply at the equivalence point that any one of the indicators of Table 17.4, except possibly alizarin yellow, could be used to tell when enough NaOH has been added to neutralize 1 liter of 0.010 *M* HCl.

The titration curve of Fig. 17.1 is general for strong acids and strong bases but does not apply when a strong acid is titrated with a weak base, when a strong base is titrated with a weak acid, or when a weak acid is titrated with a weak base. In the latter cases the shapes of the titration curves are quite different and require individual consideration before an indicator is chosen. It turns out that, in titrating acetic acid with NaOH, phenolphthalein is satisfactory but methyl orange is not.

17.6   BUFFER SOLUTIONS

In practically all biological processes as well as in many other chemical processes, it is important that the pH not deviate very much from a fixed value. For example, the proper functioning of human blood in carrying oxygen to the cells from the lungs is dependent on maintaining a pH very near to 7.4. In fact, for a particular individual, there is a difference of but 0.02 pH unit between venous and arterial blood in spite of numerous acid and base-producing reactions in the cells.

The near constancy of pH in a system to which acid or base is added is due to a buffering action of an acid-base equilibrium. Let us consider, for example, a solution that contains acetic acid molecules and acetate ions (plus other ions, of course). The principal equilibrium in this solution can be written

$$HC_2H_3O_2 \rightleftharpoons H^+ + C_2H_3O_2^-$$

for which

$$\frac{[H^+][C_2H_3O_2^-]}{[HC_2H_3O_2]} = K$$

Solving this expression for $[H^+]$, we get

Table 17.4   *Indicator Colors*

Indicator	pH at which color changes	Color at lower pH	Color at higher pH
Methyl orange	4	Red	Yellow
Methyl red	5	Red	Yellow
Litmus	7	Red	Blue
Bromthymol blue	7	Yellow	Blue
Phenolphthalein	9	Colorless	Red
Alizarin yellow	11	Yellow	Red

$$[H^+] = K\frac{[HC_2H_3O_2]}{[C_2H_3O_2{}^-]}$$

which indicates that the hydrogen-ion concentration of the solution depends on K and on the ratio of the concentrations of undissociated acetic acid to acetate ion. Taking the negative logarithm of both sides we get

$$pH = -\log K - \log\frac{[HC_2H_3O_2]}{[C_2H_3O_2{}^-]}$$

In a particular solution (made by dissolving equal moles of $HC_2H_3O_2$ and $NaC_2H_3O_2$) where the ratio $[HC_2H_3O_2]/[C_2H_3O_2{}^-]$ is equal to unity, pH is just equal to $-\log K$ since $\log 1$ equals zero. In any solution where the ratio $[HC_2H_3O_2]/[C_2H_3O_2{}^-]$ is not far from unity, the pH will not differ much from $-\log K$ (sometimes called pK). Thus, a mixture of acetic acid and acetate ion is said to be a *buffer* for pH of $-\log(1.8 \times 10^{-5})$, or 4.74. If a small amount of strong acid is added to such a solution, some of the acetate ion is converted to acetic acid; if base is added, some of the acetic acid is converted to acetate ion. In either case the ratio $[HC_2H_3O_2]/[C_2H_3O_2{}^-]$ changes slightly from unity and the pH changes even less—not nearly so much as in the absence of the buffer.

Example 6

Calculate the pH of a solution made by adding 0.0010 mole of NaOH *to 100 ml. of 0.50 M* $HC_2H_3O_2$ *and 0.50 M* $NaC_2H_3O_2$*.*

Assume that in the 100 ml. there are originally 0.050 mole $HC_2H_3O_2$ and 0.050 mole of $C_2H_3O_2{}^-$, and that the added 0.0010 mole of OH^- converts an equivalent amount of $HC_2H_3O_2$ into $C_2H_3O_2{}^-$. This gives 0.049 mole $HC_2H_3O_2$ and 0.051 mole $C_2H_3O_2{}^-$ in the final solution. Since the volume of the solution is 0.100 liter, the respective concentrations are 0.49 M and 0.51 M, and the pH is

$$pH = -\log(1.8 \times 10^{-5}) - \log\frac{(0.49)}{(0.51)} = +4.74 + 0.017 = +4.76$$

In contrast, when 0.0010 mole of NaOH is added to 100 ml. of water, the pH becomes 10.0.

In general, any solution of a weak acid which also contains a salt of that acid can function as a buffer. The buffer region—that is, the region in which the pH changes most slowly—is centered about the pK of the acid. In a similar way, a solution of a weak base plus a salt of that base can function as a buffer to keep the OH^- concentration equal to $K[MOH]/[M^+]$.

$$MOH \rightleftharpoons M^+ + OH^-$$

$$\frac{[M^+][OH^-]}{[MOH]} = K$$

$$[OH^-] = \frac{K[MOH]}{[M^+]}$$

$$[H^+] = \frac{K_w}{[OH^-]} = \frac{K_w}{K}\frac{[M^+]}{[MOH]}$$

$$pH = -\log\frac{K_w}{K} - \log\frac{[M^+]}{[MOH]}$$

Thus, there are as many possible buffers as there are weak acids and weak bases. In human blood there are a number of buffers acting simultaneously. These include (1) dissolved CO_2 and HCO_3^-, (2) $H_2PO_4^-$ and HPO_4^{--}, and (3) the various proteins which can accept hydrogen ions.

17.7   COMPLEX IONS

The term *complex ion* refers to charged particles which contain more than one atom. Certain of these, such as sulfate, SO_4^{--}, are little different from simple ions in that for all practical purposes they do not dissociate into smaller fragments. Others, however, may dissociate to establish an equilibrium between the complex ion and its component pieces. Thus, for example, in a solution containing the silver-ammonia complex ion, $Ag(NH_3)_2^+$, there is an equilibrium between the complex ion, silver ion, and ammonia molecules. For

$$Ag(NH_3)_2^+ \rightleftharpoons Ag^+ + 2NH_3$$

the equilibrium condition is

$$\frac{[Ag^+][NH_3]^2}{[Ag(NH_3)_2^+]} = 6 \times 10^{-8}$$

When silver nitrate, $AgNO_3$, and aqueous ammonia are mixed, enough silver-ammonia complex ion is formed to satisfy this equilibrium condition. Furthermore, as the concentration of NH_3 in the solution is increased by addition of more NH_3, the concentration of Ag^+ decreases, as required by constancy of the mass-action expression.

Table 17.5 lists some common complex ions and their equilibrium constants. The dissociation constant of a complex ion gives a measure of its stability with respect to dissociation. Of the three complex ions of silver in Table 17.5, the silver-cyanide complex is least dissociated and is said to

Table 17.5   Dissociation of Complex Ions

Complex ion	Reaction	K_{diss}
Copper-ammonia	$Cu(NH_3)_4^{++} \rightleftharpoons Cu^{++} + 4NH_3$	5×10^{-15}
Cobaltous-ammonia	$Co(NH_3)_6^{++} \rightleftharpoons Co^{++} + 6NH_3$	1.3×10^{-5}
Cobaltic-ammonia	$Co(NH_3)_6^{+3} \rightleftharpoons Co^{+3} + 6NH_3$	2.2×10^{-34}
Silver-ammonia	$Ag(NH_3)_2^{+} \rightleftharpoons Ag^+ + 2NH_3$	6×10^{-8}
Silver-thiosulfate	$Ag(S_2O_3)_2^{-3} \rightleftharpoons Ag^+ + 2S_2O_3^{--}$	6×10^{-14}
Silver-cyanide	$Ag(CN)_2^{-} \rightleftharpoons Ag^+ + 2CN^-$	1.8×10^{-19}
Ferric-thiocyanate	$FeSCN^{++} \rightleftharpoons Fe^{+3} + SCN^-$	1×10^{-3}
Mercuric-cyanide	$Hg(CN)_4^{--} \rightleftharpoons Hg^{++} + 4CN^-$	4×10^{-42}

be most stable. For example, in a solution containing silver ion, cyanide ion, thiosulfate ion, and ammonia, the silver-cyanide complex is preferentially formed, since it is the least dissociated, i.e., since it is the most stable.

17.8   SOLUBILITY OF IONIC SOLIDS

When an ionic solid is placed in water, an equilibrium is established between the ions in the saturated solution and the excess solid phase. For example, with excess solid silver chloride in contact with a saturated solution of silver chloride, the equilibrium is

$$AgCl(s) \rightleftharpoons Ag^+ + Cl^-$$

for which

$$\frac{[Ag^+][Cl^-]}{[AgCl(s)]} = K$$

As pointed out in Sec. 13.5, the concentration of a pure solid is a constant number. Thus, the concentration of silver chloride *in the solid phase* is fixed and cannot change, no matter how much solid there is in contact with the solution. It follows that

$$[Ag^+][Cl^-] = K[AgCl(s)] = K_{s.p.}$$

The constant $K_{s.p.}$ is called the *solubility product*, and the expression $[Ag^+][Cl^-]$ the *ion product*. The equation states that the ion product must equal $K_{s.p.}$ when the saturated solution is in equilibrium with excess solid. It should be noted that there is no separate restriction on what the concentrations of Ag^+ and Cl^- must be. The concentration of Ag^+ can have any value, so long as the concentration of Cl^- is such that the product of Ag^+ concentration and Cl^- concentration is equal to $K_{s.p.}$.

The numerical value of $K_{s.p.}$, as of any equilibrium constant, must be determined by experiment. Once determined, it can be tabulated for future use. (Appendix 8 contains some typical values.) The kind of experiment that can be done is illustrated as follows, for the case of barium sulfate: A weighed amount of solid $BaSO_4$ is ground up and thoroughly agitated with a liter of water at $25°C$. until the saturated solution is formed. The saturated solution is then filtered, and the residual solid $BaSO_4$ is dried and weighed. The loss in weight corresponds to the amount dissolved in a liter of H_2O at $25°C$. The solubility of $BaSO_4$ thus determined is 3.9×10^{-5} mole per liter.

Like practically all salts, $BaSO_4$ is a strong electrolyte and so is 100 per cent dissociated into ions. Therefore, when 3.9×10^{-5} mole of $BaSO_4$ dissolves, it forms 3.9×10^{-5} mole of Ba^{++} and 3.9×10^{-5} mole of SO_4^{--}. In the saturated solution, the concentration of Ba^{++} is 3.9×10^{-5} M, and the concentration of SO_4^{--} is 3.9×10^{-5} M. Therefore, for the equilibrium

$$BaSO_4(s) \rightleftharpoons Ba^{++} + SO_4^{--}$$

we have the condition

$$K_{s.p.} = [Ba^{++}][SO_4^{--}] = (3.9 \times 10^{-5})(3.9 \times 10^{-5}) = 1.5 \times 10^{-9}$$

This means that, in any solution containing Ba^{++} and SO_4^{--} in equilibrium with solid $BaSO_4$, the product of the concentrations of Ba^{++} and SO_4^{--} is equal to 1.5×10^{-9}. Since $K_{s.p.}$ is a very small number, $BaSO_4$ may be called an insoluble salt. If $[Ba^{++}]$ multiplied by $[SO_4^{--}]$ is less than 1.5×10^{-9}, the solution is unsaturated, and $BaSO_4$ must dissolve to increase the concentrations of Ba^{++} and SO_4^{--}. If the product of $[Ba^{++}]$ times $[SO_4^{--}]$ is greater than 1.5×10^{-9}, the system is not at equilibrium. $BaSO_4$ precipitates in order to decrease the concentrations of Ba^{++} and SO_4^{--}.

When $BaSO_4$ is placed in pure water, the concentrations of Ba^{++} and SO_4^{--} must be equal. On the other hand, it is possible to prepare a solution in which unequal concentrations of Ba^{++} and SO_4^{--} are in equilibrium with solid $BaSO_4$. As illustration, unequal amounts of barium chloride and sodium sulfate might be added to water. A precipitate of $BaSO_4$ forms if $K_{s.p.}$ of $BaSO_4$ is exceeded. However, there is no requirement that $[Ba^{++}] = [SO_4^{--}]$, since the two ions come from different salts. Alternatively, barium sulfate solid might be added to a Na_2SO_4 solution. Some barium sulfate dissolves, but in the final solution the concentration of SO_4^{--} is greater than the concentration of Ba^{++}.

Example 7

Given that the $K_{s.p.}$ of radium sulfate, $RaSO_4$, is 4×10^{-11}. Calculate its solubility in (a) pure water and (b) 0.10 M Na_2SO_4.

(a) Let x = moles of $RaSO_4$ that dissolve per liter of water. Then, in the saturated solution,

$[Ra^{++}] = x$ moles/liter

$[SO_4^{--}] = x$ moles/liter

$RaSO_4(s) \rightleftharpoons Ra^{++} + SO_4^{--}$

$[Ra^{++}][SO_4^{--}] = K_{s.p.} = 4 \times 10^{-11}$

$(x)(x) = 4 \times 10^{-11}$

$x = 6 \times 10^{-6}$ mole/liter

Thus, the solubility of $RaSO_4$ is 6×10^{-6} mole per liter of water, giving a solution containing 6×10^{-6} M Ra^{++} and 6×10^{-6} M SO_4^{--}.

(b) Let y = moles of $RaSO_4$ that dissolve per liter of 0.10 M Na_2SO_4. This dissolving produces y moles of Ra^{++} and y moles of SO_4^{--}. The solution already contains 0.10 M SO_4^{--}. Thus, in the final saturated solution,

$[Ra^{++}] = y$ moles/liter

$[SO_4^{--}] = (y + 0.10)$ moles/liter

where

$[Ra^{++}][SO_4^{--}] = (y)(y + 0.10) = K_{s.p.} = 4 \times 10^{-11}$

Since $K_{s.p.}$ is very small, not much $RaSO_4$ dissolves, and y is so small that it is negligible compared to 0.10.

$(y + 0.10) \cong 0.10$

$[Ra^{++}][SO_4^{--}] \cong (y)(0.10) \cong 4 \times 10^{-11}$

$y \cong \dfrac{4 \times 10^{-11}}{0.10} = 4 \times 10^{-10}$ mole/liter

Thus, the solubility of $RaSO_4$ in 0.10 M Na_2SO_4 is 4×10^{-10} mole per liter, giving a solution in which the concentration of Ra^{++} is 4×10^{-10} M and that of SO_4^{--} is 0.10 M.

It is interesting to note that $RaSO_4$ is less soluble in a Na_2SO_4 solution than in pure water. This is an example of the common-ion effect, by which the solubility of an ionic salt is generally decreased by the presence of another solute that furnishes one of its ions. Thus, radium sulfate is less soluble in any solution containing either radium ion or sulfate ion than it is in water. The greater the concentration of the common ion, the less radium sulfate can dissolve. Of course, if the common ion is present in negligible concentration, it has no appreciable effect on the solubility. This is illustrated in the following example.

Example 8

Given that magnesium hydroxide, $Mg(OH)_2$, is a strong electrolyte and has a solubility product of 8.9×10^{-12}, calculate the solubility of $Mg(OH)_2$ in water.

Let $x = $ moles of $Mg(OH)_2$ that dissolve per liter. According to the equation

$$Mg(OH)_2(s) \rightleftharpoons Mg^{++} + 2OH^-$$

x moles of $Mg(OH)_2$ dissolve to give x moles of Mg^{++} and $2x$ moles of OH^-. Some hydroxide ion is also furnished by the dissociation of water. Since H_2O is a very weak electrolyte, we assume as in Example 5 that it contributes only a negligible amount of OH^- compared to that furnished by the dissolving of $Mg(OH)_2$. Thus at equilibrium

$$[Mg^{++}] = x \text{ moles/liter}$$

$$[OH^-] \cong 2x \text{ moles/liter}$$

For the saturated solution the equilibrium is

$$Mg(OH)_2(s) \rightleftharpoons Mg^{++} + 2OH^-$$

and $K_{s.p.} = 8.9 \times 10^{-12} = [Mg^{++}][OH^-]^2$

Substituting, we get

$$(x)(2x)^2 = 8.9 \times 10^{-12}$$

$$4x^3 = 8.9 \times 10^{-12}$$

$$x = \sqrt[3]{2.2 \times 10^{-12}} = 1.3 \times 10^{-4} \text{ mole/liter}$$

Thus, 1.3×10^{-4} mole of $Mg(OH)_2$ dissolve per liter of water. The saturated solution contains 1.3×10^{-4} M Mg^{++} and 2.6×10^{-4} M OH^-.

As noted in Sec. 13.2, the mass-action expression for a given reaction contains concentrations raised to powers that correspond to the coefficients in the chemical equation. Since the ion product is a mass-action expression, it must be formed by raising the concentrations of ions to powers that correspond to the coefficients in the solubility equation. An exponent applies to the concentration of the specified ion, no matter where that ion comes from. For example, in the following problem, essentially all the OH^- comes from NaOH, but its concentration still must be squared.

Example 9

Calculate the solubility of $Mg(OH)_2$ in 0.050 M NaOH.

Let $x = $ moles of $Mg(OH)_2$ that dissolve per liter. This forms x moles of Mg^{++} and $2x$ moles of OH^-. Since the solution already contains 0.050 mole of OH^-, equilibrium concentrations are

$$[Mg^{++}] = x \text{ moles/liter}$$

$$[OH^-] = (2x + 0.050) \text{ moles/liter}$$

$$[Mg^{++}][OH^-]^2 = (x)(2x + 0.050)^2 = K_{s.p.}$$

$$(x)(2x + 0.050)^2 = 8.9 \times 10^{-12}$$

Assuming that x is a very small number and that $2x$ can be neglected when added to 0.050, we have approximately

$$(x)(0.050)^2 \cong 8.9 \times 10^{-12}$$

$$x = 3.6 \times 10^{-9} \text{ mole/liter}$$

Since x is small compared to 0.050, the assumption is valid. The calculation indicates that 3.6×10^{-9} mole of $Mg(OH)_2$ can dissolve in 1 liter of 0.050 M NaOH to give a saturated solution containing 3.6×10^{-9} M Mg^{++} and 0.050 M OH^-.

17.9   PRECIPITATION

One of the most useful applications of the solubility product is to predict whether precipitation will occur when two solutions are mixed. In the saturated solution of a salt, the ion product equals $K_{\text{s.p.}}$. If two solutions containing the ions of a salt are mixed and if the ion product then exceeds $K_{\text{s.p.}}$, precipitation should occur.

Example 10

Should precipitation occur when 50 ml. of 5.0×10^{-4} M Ca(NO₃)₂ is mixed with 50 ml. of 2.0×10^{-4} M NaF to give 100 ml. of solution? The $K_{\text{s.p.}}$ of CaF₂ is 1.7×10^{-10}.

In order to solve such a problem, it is convenient to calculate first the concentration of the ions in the mixture, assuming that no precipitation occurs. Thus, the Ca^{++} from the 5.0×10^{-4} M $Ca(NO_3)_2$ solution is made 2.5×10^{-4} M in the final mixture because of the twofold dilution. Likewise, the F^- is diluted to 1.0×10^{-4} M in the final mixture. Therefore, if no precipitation occurs, the final solution would have

$$[Ca^{++}] = 2.5 \times 10^{-4} \ M \qquad \text{and} \qquad [F^-] = 1.0 \times 10^{-4} \ M$$

To determine whether precipitation should occur, it is necessary to see whether the ion product exceeds the solubility product. For a saturated solution of CaF_2 the equilibrium would be

$$CaF_2(s) \rightleftharpoons Ca^{++} + 2F^-$$

for which the ion product is $[Ca^{++}][F^-]^2$. In the present mixture the ion product has the numerical value

$$[Ca^{++}][F^-]^2 = (2.5 \times 10^{-4})(1.0 \times 10^{-4})^2 = 2.5 \times 10^{-12}$$

Since this number does not exceed 1.7×10^{-10}, the $K_{\text{s.p.}}$ of CaF_2, precipitation does not occur. The solution obtained as the final mixture is unsaturated with respect to precipitation of CaF_2.

In order to precipitate a salt, the ion product must be made to exceed the $K_{s.p.}$ of that salt. This gives a method for driving ions out of solution. For example, given a solution of $RaCl_2$, the Ra^{++} can be made to precipitate as $RaSO_4$ by addition of Na_2SO_4. The more the concentration of SO_4^{--} is increased in the solution, the lower the concentration of Ra^{++} becomes. Essentially all the valuable Ra^{++} can be recovered from the solution in this way by adding a large excess of SO_4^{--} ions.

17.10   SIMULTANEOUS EQUILIBRIA

In the preceding discussion only one equilibrium has been considered at a time. This is an idealized situation, since usually aqueous solutions have two or more equilibria which must be satisfied simultaneously. For example, in a solution containing the weak acid $HC_2H_3O_2$ there are two dissociation equilibria:

$$HC_2H_3O_2 \rightleftharpoons H^+ + C_2H_3O_2^- \qquad \frac{[H^+][C_2H_3O_2^-]}{[HC_2H_3O_2]} = K_{diss}$$

$$\text{and } H_2O \rightleftharpoons H^+ + OH^- \qquad [H^+][OH^-] = K_w$$

The solution of acetic acid has a characteristic concentration of H^+ which simultaneously satisfies K_{diss} and K_w. Strictly speaking, this H^+ comes partly from the dissociation of $HC_2H_3O_2$ and partly from the dissociation of H_2O. However, H_2O is so slightly dissociated compared to $HC_2H_3O_2$ that it is justified to consider the H^+ as coming entirely from the $HC_2H_3O_2$. This assumption was implicitly made in the calculations of Sec. 17.2. The H^+ concentration of $1M$ $HC_2H_3O_2$ was calculated assuming that negligible H^+ is contributed by dissociation of H_2O. Since the OH^- comes exclusively from H_2O dissociation, its concentration is calculated by using K_w.

Example 11

Calculate the concentrations of H^+ *and* OH^- *in a solution made by mixing 0.50 mole of* $HC_2H_3O_2$ *and 0.50 mole of* HCN *with enough water to make a liter of solution.*

There are three simultaneous equilibria in the final solution:

$$HC_2H_3O_2 \rightleftharpoons H^+ + C_2H_3O_2^- \qquad K_{HC_2H_3O_2} = 1.8 \times 10^{-5} \qquad (1)$$

$$HCN \rightleftharpoons H^+ + CN^- \qquad K_{HCN} = 4 \times 10^{-10} \qquad (2)$$

$$H_2O \rightleftharpoons H^+ + OH^- \qquad K_w = 1.0 \times 10^{-14} \qquad (3)$$

Only acetic acid contributes an appreciable concentration of H^+, because it has much the largest dissociation constant. Ignoring the other dissociations, let x = moles of $HC_2H_3O_2$ that dissociate per liter. Then, at equilibrium

$[HC_2H_3O_2] = (0.50 - x)$ moles/liter

$[H^+] = x$ moles/liter

$[C_2H_3O_2^-] = x$ moles/liter

$\dfrac{[H^+][C_2H_3O_2^-]}{[HC_2H_3O_2]} = \dfrac{(x)(x)}{(0.50 - x)} = 1.8 \times 10^{-5}$

$x = 3.0 \times 10^{-3} \, M$

Thus, the final solution has a hydrogen-ion concentration of $3.0 \times 10^{-3} \, M$. Substituting this value in the equilibrium condition for equilibrium (3),

$K_w = [H^+][OH^-] = 1.0 \times 10^{-14}$

$(3.0 \times 10^{-3})[OH^-] = 1.0 \times 10^{-14}$

$[OH^-] = 3.3 \times 10^{-12} \, M$

Another common example of simultaneous equilibrium occurs in solutions of polyprotic acids (Sec. 10.10). For example, in a solution of hydrogen sulfide, besides the water equilibrium, there are the two equilibria that correspond to the stepwise dissociation of H_2S.*

$H_2S \rightleftharpoons H^+ + HS^- \qquad K_I = 1.1 \times 10^{-7}$

$HS^- \rightleftharpoons H^+ + S^{--} \qquad K_{II} = 1 \times 10^{-14}$

Since H_2S is a weak acid, a solution of H_2S is slightly acidic. In order to calculate the acidity of the solution, is it necessary to consider both steps of the dissociation? The case is exactly analogous to that of acetic acid in water, where the H_2O dissociation contributes a negligible concentration of H^+. In H_2S, the dissociation of HS^- contributes a negligible concentration of H^+. Using only K_I, we can calculate that the concentration of H^+ in 0.10 M H_2S is approximately 1×10^{-4} M and the HS^- concentration is 1×10^{-4} M.

Because of the second step of the dissociation of H_2S, there is a small trace of sulfide ion, S^{--}, in the solution. Its numerical magnitude can be calculated by using K_{II}.

$K_{II} = \dfrac{[H^+][S^{--}]}{[HS^-]} = 1 \times 10^{-14}$

* There is considerable disagreement as to the value of the second dissociation constant of H_2S. The old accepted value was 1×10^{-15}; more recent values range as high as 1×10^{-12}. It is not very probable that HS^- is becoming a stronger acid with the years. We have chosen the intermediate value 1×10^{-14}, as given by W. M. Latimer in *Oxidation Potentials*, 2d ed., Prentice-Hall, Inc., Englewood Cliffs, N.J., 1952.

If, as is the case in 0.10 M H_2S, the concentrations of H^+ and HS^- are 1×10^{-4} M, they cancel each other out of the expression, and $[S^{--}] = 1 \times 10^{-14}$ M.

In any solution of H_2S, both K_I and K_{II} must be simultaneously satisfied and give rise to the two simultaneous equations

$$\frac{[H^+][HS^-]}{[H_2S]} = 1.1 \times 10^{-7} \tag{1}$$

$$\frac{[H^+][S^{--}]}{[HS^-]} = 1 \times 10^{-14} \tag{2}$$

According to the rules of algebra, any two simultaneous equations can be combined into a single equation. Solving Eqs. (1) and (2) for $[HS^-]$, we get

$$[HS^-] = 1.1 \times 10^{-7} \frac{[H_2S]}{[H^+]} \tag{3}$$

$$[HS^-] = \frac{[H^+][S^{--}]}{1 \times 10^{-14}} \tag{4}$$

and equating (3) and (4) gives

$$\frac{1.1 \times 10^{-7} [H_2S]}{[H^+]} = \frac{[H^+][S^{--}]}{1 \times 10^{-14}} \tag{5}$$

Rearranging the terms in Eq. (5), we get the condition for any H_2S solution that

$$(1.1 \times 10^{-7})(1 \times 10^{-14}) = \frac{[H^+]^2[S^{--}]}{[H_2S]}$$

For a saturated solution of H_2S at atmospheric pressure and room temperature, the concentration of H_2S in solution is constant at 0.10 M. This means that, for a saturated solution of H_2S,

$$[H^+]^2[S^{--}] = (1.1 \times 10^{-7})(1 \times 10^{-14})(0.10)$$

$$[H^+]^2[S^{--}] = 1 \times 10^{-22} \tag{6}$$

Equation (6) is useful because it states that the sulfide-ion concentration of a saturated H_2S solution can be changed by changing the concentration of H^+. For example, if enough HCl is added to a saturated H_2S solution to make the H^+ concentration 1 M, the S^{--} concentration becomes 1×10^{-22} M. This possibility of changing the S^{--} concentration by juggling the concentration of H^+ is the basis of the classic method of ion separation, in qualitative analysis, by sulfide precipitation.

Example 12

A solution contains Zn^{++} and Cu^{++}, each at 0.02 M. The $K_{s.p.}$ of ZnS is 1×10^{-22}; that of CuS, 8×10^{-37}. If the solution is made 1 M in H^+, and H_2S gas is bubbled in until the solution is saturated, should a precipitate form?

In a saturated H_2S solution $[H^+]^2[S^{--}] = 1 \times 10^{-22}$

If $[H^+] = 1\ M$, $[S^{--}] = 1 \times 10^{-22}\ M$

For ZnS, the ion product is

$$[Zn^{++}][S^{--}] = (0.02)(1 \times 10^{-22}), \text{ or } 2 \times 10^{-24}$$

For CuS, the ion product is

$$[Cu^{++}][S^{--}] = (0.02)(1 \times 10^{-22}), \text{ or } 2 \times 10^{-24}$$

Since the ion product of ZnS does not exceed 1×10^{-22}, the $K_{s.p.}$ of ZnS, ZnS does not precipitate. Since the ion product of CuS does exceed 8×10^{-37}, the $K_{s.p.}$ of CuS, CuS does precipitate.

The principles of simultaneous equilibrium can also be applied to dissolving solids by introducing appropriate secondary equilibria. For example, although ZnS is essentially insoluble in water, it can be made to dissolve by the addition of acid. The qualitative argument is as follows: If solid ZnS is added to pure water, the equilibrium is

$$ZnS(s) \rightleftharpoons Zn^{++} + S^{--} \tag{7}$$

When acid is added, the additional equilibria

$$H^+ + S^{--} \rightleftharpoons HS^- \tag{8}$$

$$H^+ + HS^- \rightleftharpoons H_2S \tag{9}$$

become important. The added H^+ ties up S^{--} in the form of HS^- and H_2S. As the concentration of S^{--} is reduced, more ZnS can dissolve. The net reaction for the dissolving is the sum of Eqs. (7), (8), and (9), or

$$ZnS(s) + 2H^+ \rightleftharpoons Zn^{++} + H_2S$$

Similarly, although AgCl is insoluble in water, it can be dissolved by addition of sodium thiosulfate, $Na_2S_2O_3$. In water the equilibrium is

$$AgCl(s) \rightleftharpoons Ag^+ + Cl^-$$

Added thiosulfate ion, $S_2O_3^{--}$, combines with Ag^+ to form the complex ion $Ag(S_2O_3)_2^{-3}$ by the equation

$$Ag^+ + 2S_2O_3^{--} \rightleftharpoons Ag(S_2O_3)_2^{-3}$$

Since the concentration of Ag^+ is thereby reduced, more AgCl can dissolve. The net reaction for the dissolving is

$$AgCl(s) + 2S_2O_3^{--} \rightleftharpoons Ag(S_2O_3)_2^{-3} + Cl^-$$

The last reaction is of practical value in photographic developing. An insoluble silver salt such as AgCl is the active ingredient in photographic emulsions and must be removed in order to fix the picture. Dissolution is accomplished through the use of hypo, a solution of $Na_2S_2O_3$.

17.11   HYDROLYSIS

When the salt NaCl is placed in water, the resulting solution is observed to be neutral; i.e., the concentrations of H^+ and OH^- are 1×10^{-7} M just as in pure H_2O. However, when the salt $NaC_2H_3O_2$ is dissolved in H_2O, the resulting solution is observed to be slightly basic. Other salts such as ammonium chloride, NH_4Cl, or aluminum chloride, $AlCl_3$, give slightly acid solutions. These interactions between salts and water are called *hydrolysis.*

The explanation of hydrolysis is that the water dissociation equilibrium is affected by addition of certain salts. Again the problem is one of simultaneous equilibria. In pure water, the equilibrium is $H_2O \rightleftharpoons H^+ + OH^-$. If a species is added which associates either with H^+ or OH^-, the water equilibrium is perturbed so as to produce a predominance of either OH^- or H^+.

If solid NaCl is added to water, there is no hydrolysis. The Na^+ and Cl^- ions do not appreciably affect the water equilibrium, since there is no possibility of forming an associated species. Na^+ and OH^- do not associate, because NaOH is a strong electrolyte; Cl^- and H^+ do not associate, because HCl is a strong electrolyte.

If solid $NaC_2H_3O_2$ is added to water, hydrolysis occurs. Although the Na^+ does not hydrolyze, $C_2H_3O_2^-$ can combine with H^+ to form the associated species $HC_2H_3O_2$. There are now two equilibria in the solution:

$$H_2O \rightleftharpoons H^+ + OH^- \tag{1}$$

$$H^+ + C_2H_3O_2^- \rightleftharpoons HC_2H_3O_2 \tag{2}$$

Both of these equilibria must be satisfied simultaneously. In order to set up equilibrium (2), some H^+ must combine with the added $C_2H_3O_2^-$. The H^+ concentration is thus diminished. But this upsets equilibrium (1). According to the principle of Le Chatelier, H_2O must dissociate to reestablish equilibrium. The concentration of OH^- increases, and the solution becomes basic. The net effect is the sum of the two reactions. Adding Eqs. (1) and (2) gives the net equation

$$H_2O + C_2H_3O_2^- \rightleftharpoons HC_2H_3O_2 + OH^-$$

which describes the fact that, in the hydrolysis of acetate ion, some H_2O molecules and acetate ions disappear and some $HC_2H_3O_2$ molecules and OH^- ions appear. A solution of sodium acetate is basic because of the formation of OH^-; the molecules of acetic acid do not affect the pH.

If solid aluminum chloride is added to water, hydrolysis occurs. Although Cl^- does not hydrolyze, Al^{+3} ion combines with OH^- to form $AlOH^{++}$. Adding the following two equations:

$$Al^{+3} + OH^- \rightleftharpoons AlOH^{++}$$

$$H_2O \rightleftharpoons H^+ + OH^-$$

gives the net hydrolysis reaction

$$Al^{+3} + H_2O \rightleftharpoons H^+ + AlOH^{++}$$

Thus, solutions of aluminum chloride are slightly acid.

In the broadest sense, hydrolysis has been defined as the reaction of any substance with water. We shall use the term in the more restricted sense of the two examples just given. *Hydrolysis is thus the reaction of an ion with water to form an associated species plus* H^+ *or* OH^-. For cation hydrolysis, the general equation is

$$M^+ + H_2O \rightleftharpoons MOH + H^+$$

whereas, for anion hydrolysis, it is

$$X^- + H_2O \rightleftharpoons HX + OH^-$$

It might be noted that, in general, hydrolysis is usually a small effect, and the concentration of H^+ or OH^- so produced is generally quite small. However, even a slight amount of hydrolysis may appreciably change the concentrations of H^+ and OH^- from their small values in pure water. In some cases the extent of hydrolysis may be quite large as, for example, with oxide ion. The hydrolysis

$$O^{--} + H_2O \rightarrow OH^- + OH^-$$

is essentially complete.

The extent of hydrolysis is governed by the affinity of the hydrolyzing ion for H^+ or OH^-. In the hydrolysis $X^- + H_2O \rightleftharpoons HX + OH^-$, the extent of conversion from X^- to HX depends on the affinity of X^- for H^+;

i.e., it depends on how tightly HX hangs together. The weaker an electrolyte HX is, the greater the extent of hydrolysis of X^-. Thus, in comparable concentration, cyanide ion, CN^-, is more extensively hydrolyzed than acetate ion, $C_2H_3O_2^-$. HCN is a weaker electrolyte than $HC_2H_3O_2$; i.e., CN^- has a higher affinity for H^+ than does $C_2H_3O_2^-$.

The quantitative treatment of hydrolysis can be approached as follows. For the hydrolysis of X^- ion, the equilibria are

$$H_2O \rightleftharpoons H^+ + OH^- \qquad\qquad [H^+][OH^-] = K_w$$

$$X^- + H^+ \rightleftharpoons HX \qquad\qquad \frac{[HX]}{[H^+][X^-]} = \frac{1}{K_{diss}}$$

These two equilibrium conditions must be satisfied simultaneously and so can be combined into one. This is done by solving for $[H^+]$ and equating to eliminate $[H^+]$.

$$[H^+] = \frac{K_w}{[OH^-]} = \frac{[HX]}{[X^-]}\,K_{diss}$$

$$\frac{[HX][OH^-]}{[X^-]} = \frac{K_w}{K_{diss}} \qquad\qquad (3)$$

This final expression represents a condition that must be satisfied by the hydrolysis. The net reaction for hydrolysis can be written

$$X^- + H_2O \rightleftharpoons HX + OH^-$$

The equilibrium condition is

$$\frac{[HX][OH^-]}{[X^-]} = K_h \qquad\qquad (4)$$

where H_2O is omitted because it is constant. K_h is called the hydrolysis constant. As seen from comparison of Eqs. (3) and (4), K_h is equal to K_w divided by K_{diss}.

Once the numerical value of K_h has been obtained, it can be used for equilibrium calculations in the usual way. The following problems illustrate specific cases.

Example 13

Calculate the pH of 0.10 M $NaC_2H_3O_2$, *and the percentage hydrolysis.*

The net hydrolysis reaction is

$$C_2H_3O_2^- + H_2O \rightleftharpoons HC_2H_3O_2 + OH^-$$

for which

$$\frac{[HC_2H_3O_2][OH^-]}{[C_2H_3O_2^-]} = \frac{K_w}{K_{diss}} = \frac{1.0 \times 10^{-14}}{1.8 \times 10^{-5}} = 5.6 \times 10^{-10}$$

Let x = moles of $C_2H_3O_2^-$ that hydrolyze per liter. This forms x moles of $HC_2H_3O_2$ and x moles of OH^- and leaves $(0.10 - x)$ moles of $C_2H_3O_2^-$. At equilibrium

$[HC_2H_3O_2] = x$ moles/liter

$[OH^-] = x$ moles/liter

$[C_2H_3O_2^-] = (0.10 - x)$ moles/liter

Substituting in the mass-action expression gives

$$\frac{(x)(x)}{(0.10 - x)} = 5.6 \times 10^{-10}$$

Assuming that x is small compared to 0.10

$$\frac{x^2}{0.10} \cong 5.6 \times 10^{-10}$$

$$x = 7.5 \times 10^{-6} \; M$$

Since x represents the concentration of OH^-,

$$[H^+] = \frac{K_w}{[OH^-]} = \frac{1.0 \times 10^{-14}}{x} = \frac{1.0 \times 10^{-14}}{7.5 \times 10^{-6}} = 1.3 \times 10^{-9} \; M$$

$$pH = -\log[H^+] = -\log 1.3 \times 10^{-9} = 8.89$$

The percentage hydrolysis of acetate ion in this solution is given as follows:

$$\frac{\text{Moles } C_2H_3O_2^- \text{ hydrolyzed} \times 100}{\text{Moles } C_2H_3O_2^- \text{ available}} = \frac{7.5 \times 10^{-6} \times 100}{0.10} = 0.0075\%$$

Example 14

What is the concentration of H^+ *in 0.10 M* $AlCl_3$? *The dissociation constant of* $AlOH^{++}$ *is* 7.1×10^{-10}.

$$Al^{+3} + H_2O \rightleftharpoons AlOH^{++} + H^+$$

$$\frac{[AlOH^{++}][H^+]}{[Al^{+3}]} = \frac{K_w}{K_{diss}} = \frac{1.0 \times 10^{-14}}{7.1 \times 10^{-10}} = 1.4 \times 10^{-5}$$

Let x = moles of Al^{+3} that hydrolyze. At equilibrium

$[Al^{+3}] = (0.10 - x)$ moles/liter

$[AlOH^{++}] = x$ moles/liter

$[H^+] = x$ moles/liter

$$\frac{(x)(x)}{(0.10 - x)} = 1.4 \times 10^{-5}$$

$$x = 1.2 \times 10^{-3} \; M$$

Table 17.6   Extent of Hydrolysis

Not hydrolyzed	Moderately hydrolyzed	Extensively hydrolyzed
Na^+, K^+, Ca^{++}, Ba^{++}, Cl^-, NO_3^-, HSO_4^-	NH_4^+, Zn^{++}, Cu^{++}, Al^{+3}, Fe^{+3}, Cr^{+3}, $C_2H_3O_2^-$, CO_3^{--}, CN^-	Sn^{+4}, O^{--}, S^{--}, PO_4^{-3}

The concentration of H^+ in 0.10 M $AlCl_3$ should be 1.2×10^{-3} M, according to this calculation. (For comparison, the concentration of H^+ in 0.10 M $HC_2H_3O_2$ is 1.3×10^{-3} M.)

Although in principle the extent of hydrolysis can always be calculated if the appropriate dissociation constant is known, it is convenient to keep in mind the qualitative differences between various ions. Table 17.6 separates the common ions into three classes according to their extent of hydrolysis in 1 M solution.

17.12   DISSOCIATION THEORY OF HYDROLYSIS

An alternate picture has been proposed to account for the facts of hydrolysis. This picture makes possible the correlation of a large body of experimental material. It is most useful for highly charged cations, though it can be extended to any ion. Instead of considering hydrolysis as being due to the formation of an associated species, it considers hydrolysis as the dissociation of a hydrated ion. For example, the acid nature of solutions of aluminum salts is attributed to splitting off a proton from a hydrated aluminum ion. Although the configuration of hydrated aluminum ion is not known, it is usually assumed to be octahedral; i.e., the aluminum ion is thought to be attached to six H_2O molecules at the corners of an octahedron. The first drawing in Fig. 17.2 represents an octahedron having eight faces and six corners. In the hydrated aluminum ion, shown in the second drawing, the oxygen atoms (large circles) are located so that their centers describe an octahedron. The dissociation of a proton from hydrated aluminum ion can be written

$$Al(H_2O)_6^{+3} \rightleftharpoons Al(H_2O)_5OH^{++} + H^+$$

The dissociation leaves a doubly charged complex ion. Structurally, the dissociation is represented by Fig. 17.3. The hydrated-ion picture of hydrolysis is not much different from that given in Sec. 17.11. Omitting five water molecules of hydration from the equation just written gives

$$Al(H_2O)^{+3} \rightleftharpoons AlOH^{++} + H^+$$

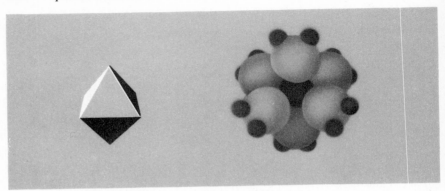

Fig. 17.2   Octahedral Al(H₂O)₆⁺³. *(Central black spot is* Al; *outer black spots are* H *atoms attached to* O *atoms.)*

This equation compares with the one given in Sec. 17.11

$$Al^{+3} + H_2O \rightleftharpoons AlOH^{++} + H^+$$

The two equations are equivalent and differ only in that the first shows the dissociating water molecule to be a water of hydration.

The extent of dissociation of protons from hydrated ions depends on how tightly the protons are held to the oxygen atoms. The effect of the aluminum ion is to pull electrons toward itself away from the water molecule, as shown in Fig. 17.4. The bond between the hydrogen and the oxygen is thereby weakened, and the proton may dissociate. The higher the charge of the cation, the more pull exerted on the electrons and the more easily the protons dissociate.

In the case of very strong interaction between cations and waters of hydration, all the protons from the attached waters may dissociate. The formation of oxanions, such as SO_4^{--}, can be explained in this way. The argument is as follows: In SO_4^{--}, the sulfur is assigned an oxidation state

Fig. 17.3   Dissociation of hydrated aluminum ion.

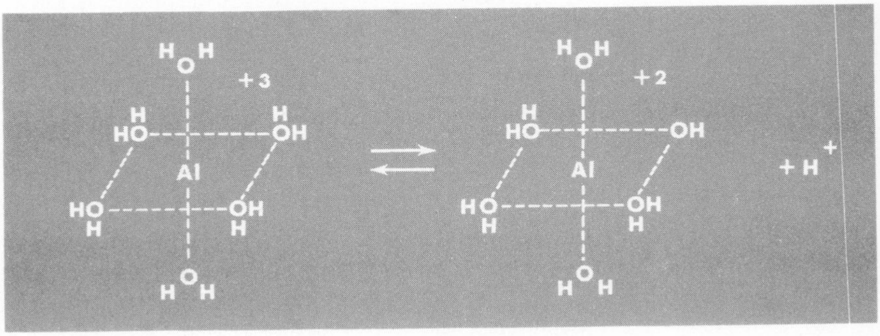

of $+6$. Except under extreme conditions of high temperature, S^{+6} is not encountered as a chemical species. However, let us imagine having an S^{+6} ion, which is then placed in water. Molecules of H_2O cluster about it in the usual process of hydration, but S^{+6} has such a high positive charge that electrons are strongly attracted to it. The hydrogen-oxygen bonds in the H_2O are so weakened that the protons split off to leave the oxygen associated with the sulfur. Thus, the formation of SO_4^{--} can be described by the hypothetical reaction

$$S^{+6} + 4H_2O \xrightarrow{\ 100\%\ } SO_4^{--} + 8H^+$$

Of the eight dissociating protons, the last one is weakly held, thus accounting for hydrogen sulfate ion, HSO_4^-. The formation of nitrate ion, NO_3^-, can be similarly explained as resulting from the 100 per cent hydrolysis of hypothetical N^{+5}.

17.13 AMPHOTERISM

If a solution of sodium hydroxide is added dropwise to a solution of aluminum nitrate, it is observed that a white precipitate, aluminum hydroxide, is formed. On further addition of base or on addition of acid, the precipitate dissolves. The net equations for the dissolving processes can be written

$$Al(OH)_3(s) + OH^- \rightarrow AlO_2^- + 2H_2O$$

$$Al(OH)_3(s) + 3H^+ \rightarrow Al^{+3} + 3H_2O$$

These two equations indicate that $Al(OH)_3$ is able to neutralize bases and acids; i.e., aluminum hydroxide is able to act as an acid and also as a base. Such substances are said to be *amphoteric*. Zinc hydroxide, $Zn(OH)_2$, lead hydroxide, $Pb(OH)_2$, and chromium hydroxide, $Cr(OH)_3$, are examples of other common amphoteric hydroxides. Oxides may also be classified as amphoteric if they react with water to form amphoteric hydroxides.

How can amphoterism be explained? The answer lies in the relative ease of breaking the bonds in the hydroxide. In aluminum hydroxide, for example, the bonds of interest are the Al-to-O bonds and the O-to-H bonds. In order that a hydroxide be amphoteric, it must be possible to break the two kinds of bonds with nearly equal

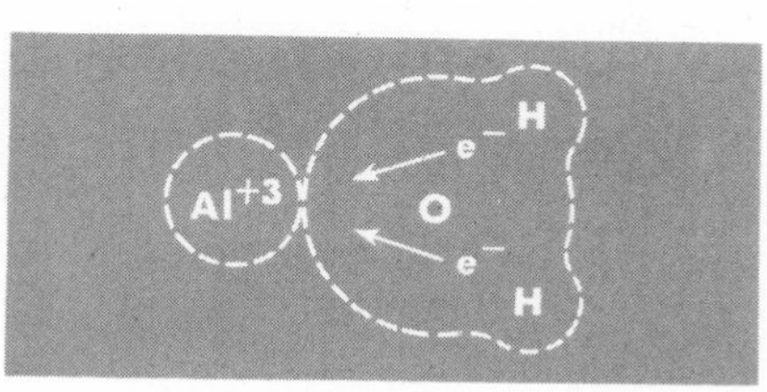

Fig. 17.4   Effect of Al^{+3} on H_2O.

ease. If acid is added, the H^+ pulls OH^- away from the aluminum, thus breaking the Al-to-O bond.

$$Al(OH)_3(s) + H^+ \rightarrow Al(OH)_2{}^+ + H_2O$$

After the first OH^- has been removed, further addition of H^+ successively pulls off the second and third OH^-. The net reaction is

$$Al(OH)_3(s) + 3H^+ \rightarrow Al^{+3} + 3H_2O$$

which shows that all three of the Al-to-O bonds can be broken. If base is added, the OH^- pulls H^+ away from $Al(OH)_3$, thus breaking the O-to-H bond in aluminum hydroxide.

$$Al(OH)_3(s) + OH^- \rightarrow Al(OH)_2O^- + H_2O$$

In principle, it should be possible to remove successively the other two protons from $Al(OH)_2O^-$. However, there is no clear evidence that any one has been able to achieve this in aqueous solution. The complex ion $Al(OH)_2O^-$ is usually more simply written as $AlO_2{}^-$. The two formulations differ only by a water molecule of hydration. It is probable that neither $Al(OH)_2O^-$ nor $AlO_2{}^-$ represents the actual species in the final solution but that the situation is more complicated.

As in the case of hydrolysis, it is also possible to consider amphoterism in terms of hydrated cations, e.g., $Al(H_2O)_6{}^{+3}$. As base is progressively added, protons are successively neutralized, as shown by the following equations:

$$Al(H_2O)_6{}^{+3} + OH^- \rightarrow Al(H_2O)_5OH^{++} + H_2O$$

$$Al(H_2O)_5OH^{++} + OH^- \rightarrow Al(H_2O)_4(OH)_2{}^+ + H_2O$$

$$Al(H_2O)_4(OH)_2{}^+ + OH^- \rightarrow Al(H_2O)_3(OH)_3(s) + H_2O$$

$$Al(H_2O)_3(OH)_3(s) + OH^- \rightarrow Al(H_2O)_2(OH)_4{}^- + H_2O$$

In each of these steps, OH^- removes one hydrogen ion from an attached H_2O molecule. It should be noted that in every step the aluminum remains associated with six oxygen atoms, some of which have two protons on them and some of which have but one. If, as previously, all waters of hydration are omitted, the four equations given above become

$$Al^{+3} + OH^- \rightarrow AlOH^{++}$$

$$AlOH^{++} + OH^- \rightarrow Al(OH)_2{}^+$$

$$Al(OH)_2{}^+ + OH^- \rightarrow Al(OH)_3(s)$$

$$Al(OH)_3(s) + OH^- \rightarrow Al(OH)_4{}^-$$

The final ion shown, $Al(OH)_4{}^-$, is equivalent to $AlO_2{}^-$ and $Al(OH)_2O^-$. By simply counting up the atoms, we see that $Al(OH)_2O^-$ is equivalent to $AlO_2{}^-$ plus one H_2O and that $Al(OH)_4{}^-$ is equivalent to $AlO_2{}^-$ plus two H_2O.

The preceding discussion leaves unanswered the question why certain ions form amphoteric hydroxides whereas others do not. As already mentioned, in an amphoteric hydroxide the O-to-H and X-to-O bonds can be broken with about equal ease, where X is the element whose hydroxide is being considered. In order for this to be true, X must draw electrons to itself (see Fig. 17.4) sufficiently to weaken the O-to-H bond. However, if X is an ion that attracts electrons too strongly, the X-to-O bond becomes much stronger than the O-to-H bond. Thus, there should be a relation between the extent of hydrolysis of an ion and the amphoterism of its hydroxide, since both depend on the ability of the ion to attract electrons. For example, an ion that is strongly hydrolyzed, e.g., S^{+6}, does not form an amphoteric hydroxide, because the S-to-O bond is too strong to be broken by addition of acid. An ion that is hydrolyzed weakly or not at all, such as Na^+, also does not form an amphoteric hydroxide. Na^+ does not draw electrons to itself sufficiently to weaken the O-to-H bond, and therefore the bond cannot be broken by addition of base. However, those ions which show moderate hydrolysis, such as Al^{+3}, do form amphoteric hydroxides. The Al-to-O and the O-to-H bonds can both be broken, the former by adding H^+, and the latter by adding OH^-. It is useful to remember that, in general, elements falling in the center of the periodic table show amphoterism, especially in the $+2$, $+3$, and $+4$ oxidation states. Some elements, such as chromium, show amphoterism in one oxidation state but not in another.

In conclusion, the following are different definitions of amphoterism, all of which are equivalent.

1. The hydroxide (or oxide) neutralizes acids and bases.

Example: $Cr(OH)_3(s) + 3H^+ \rightarrow Cr^{+3} + 3H_2O$

$Cr(OH)_3(s) + OH^- \rightarrow CrO_2{}^- + 2H_2O$

2. The hydroxide dissociates as an acid (in basic solution) and as a base (in acidic solution).

Example:

In basic: $Cr(OH)_3(s) \rightleftharpoons H^+ + CrO_2{}^- + H_2O$

In acidic: $Cr(OH)_3(s) \rightleftharpoons Cr^{+3} + 3OH^-$

3. For a given oxidation state, the element can exist as a positive ion (in acidic solution) and a negative ion (in basic solution).

Example:

In basic: CrO_2^- or $Cr(OH)_4^-$

In acidic: Cr^{+3} or $Cr(H_2O)_6^{+3}$

17.14   OXIDATION-REDUCTION

In aqueous solutions, we have available about 100 common oxidizing agents and about 100 common reducing agents. By various combinations of oxidizing and reducing agents, it is possible to have 10,000 oxidation-reduction reactions. This large number of reactions is systematized by considering each of them as consisting of two half-reactions, an oxidation and a reduction.

As discussed in Sec. 14.8, the tendency of a half-reaction to occur is expressed by its oxidation potential. Combining the oxidation potentials of the half-reactions gives a voltage which expresses the tendency of the complete reaction to occur. Since the equilibrium constant K also expresses this tendency, there should be a relation between the voltage of an oxidation-reduction reaction and its equilibrium constant.

If we let E represent the voltage (calculated by combining the two oxidation potentials) that is characteristic of an oxidation-reduction reaction and let n be the number of electrons transferred in the balanced chemical equation for the reaction, then the relationship between E and K is

$$\log K = 16.9nE$$

This relation is derived by considering how the chemical energy of a reaction is converted into electrical energy. We need not go into the details of this derivation but should note that the constant 16.9 changes with temperature and applies only at 25°C.

For the Daniell cell reaction

$$Zn(s) + Cu^{++} \rightleftharpoons Zn^{++} + Cu(s)$$

the voltage, as found in Sec. 14.8, is 1.10. The number of electrons transferred is 2.

$$\log K = (16.9)(2)(1.10)$$
$$K = 1.5 \times 10^{37}$$

The mass-action expression for the Daniell cell reaction is

$$\frac{[Zn^{++}]}{[Cu^{++}]} = K = 1.5 \times 10^{37}$$

This means that, at equilibrium, the concentration of Zn^{++} is 1.5×10^{37} times the concentration of Cu^{++}. It is no wonder then that the addition of zinc metal to a solution of copper ion results in essentially complete reduction of Cu^{++} to Cu.

For the reaction

$$Cr_2O_7^{--} + 6Fe^{++} + 14H^+ \rightleftharpoons 2Cr^{+3} + 6Fe^{+3} + 7H_2O$$

the voltage is 0.46 and n is 6. The equilibrium constant calculated as above has a value of 4.4×10^{46}.

The extremely large equilibrium constants often encountered for oxidation-reduction equilibria simply indicate that these reactions essentially go to completion.

QUESTIONS

17.1 *Dissociation.* Suppose that the acid HX is a weak electrolyte. What happens to the H^+ concentration of an HX solution if: (*a*) water is added; (*b*) gaseous HCl is added; (*c*) solid NaX is added?

17.2 *Polyprotic acids.* Although H_2SO_4 is a strong electrolyte, the concentration of H^+ in an H_2SO_4 solution is not equal to two times the concentration of SO_4^{--}. Explain.

17.3 *Dissociation.* Given $K_{HX} = 1.0 \times 10^{-6}$, $K_{HY} = 1.0 \times 10^{-8}$, $K_{HZ} = 1.0 \times 10^{-10}$. Which solution has the highest H^+ concentration, $1\,M$ HX, $1\,M$ HY, or $1\,M$ HZ? What is its value?   *Ans.* $1 \times 10^{-3}\,M$

17.4 *Association.* Account for the fact that the final solution made by adding 1 mole of $NaC_2H_3O_2$ and 1 mole of HCl to 1 liter of water has the same pH as a solution made by adding 1 mole of $HC_2H_3O_2$ to 1 liter of water.

17.5 *Dissociation.* What is the concentration of H^+ in each of the following: pure water, 0.050 M HCl, 0.010 M NaOH?

17.6 *pH.* What is the pH of each of the following: pure water, $1.0 \times 10^{-3}\,M$ $HClO_4$, $1.0 \times 10^{-3}\,M$ NaOH, $1.0 \times 10^{-3}\,M$ NaCl?

17.7 *Dissociation.* Given that the dissociation constant of nitrous acid, HNO_2, is 6.0×10^{-4} at $30°C$. Calculate the concentration of H^+ and the per cent dissociation of HNO_2 in 0.667 M HNO_2.   *Ans.* 0.020 M; 3.0%

17.8 *Dissociation and pH.* Hypochlorous acid, HOCl, is a weak acid that dissociates as follows:

$$HOCl \rightleftharpoons H^+ + OCl^- \qquad K_{diss} = 3.2 \times 10^{-8}$$

Calculate the concentrations of H^+ and of OH^- in a solution that is 0.0125 M HOCl. What is the pH of this solution?

17.9   *Dissociation.* Acetic acid, $HC_2H_3O_2$, and deutero-acetic acid dissociate as follows:

$$HC_2H_3O_2 \rightleftharpoons H^+ + C_2H_3O_2^- \qquad K = 1.84 \times 10^{-5}$$

$$DC_2H_3O_2 \rightleftharpoons D^+ + C_2H_3O_2^- \qquad K = 0.59 \times 10^{-5}$$

What is the relative concentration of D^+ to H^+ in a solution that is simultaneously 1.0 M $HC_2H_3O_2$ and 1.0 M $DC_2H_3O_2$?   *Ans.* 0.32

17.10   *Titration.* With the aid of Fig. 17.1, explain why either phenolphthalein or litmus can be used to determine the equivalence point in the titration of HCl with NaOH.

17.11   *Dissociation.* A given solution contains H^+ at 4.0×10^{-4} M, X^- at 2.0×10^{-6} M, Cl^- at 4.0×10^{-4} M, and HX at 0.40 M. Calculate the dissociation constant of HX.

17.12   *pH.* Given a solution that contains H^+, CN^-, and HCN in equilibrium. What effect would each of the following have on the pH of the solution? (*a*) addition of water; (*b*) addition of HCN; (*c*) addition of HCl; (*d*) addition of NaCN.

17.13   *Hydrolysis.* A solution of NH_4Cl is slightly acidic, owing to hydrolysis. What happens to the pH of the solution when: (*a*) solid NH_4Cl is added; (*b*) water is added; (*c*) HCl is added; (*d*) Ag^+ is added? (AgCl is insoluble.)

17.14   *Association.* Hydrazine hydroxide, N_2H_5OH, has a dissociation constant of 1.0×10^{-6}. What would be the concentration of OH^- in each of the following solutions: (*a*) a solution made by mixing 0.50 mole of $N_2H_5^+$ and 0.50 mole of OH^- with enough water to make 0.500 liter of solution? (*b*) a solution made by mixing 0.75 mole of $N_2H_5^+$ and 0.25 mole of OH^- with enough water to make 0.500 liter of solution?   *Ans.* 1.0×10^{-3} M; 5.0×10^{-7} M

17.15   *Common ion.* Tell what is meant by the "common-ion effect"? Give an example that does not involve a solubility equilibrium.

17.16   *Solubility.* How is the solubility of silver acetate affected by addition of: (*a*) $AgNO_3$; (*b*) $NaC_2H_3O_2$; (*c*) HNO_3; (*d*) $Na_2S_2O_3$?

17.17   *Hydrolysis.* Arrange the following solutions in order of increasing H^+ concentration: NaCl, $NaC_2H_3O_2$, NH_4Cl. Justify your order.

17.18   *Amphoterism.* (*a*) What is meant by an amphoteric hydroxide? (*b*) Which of the following is amphoteric: NaOH, $Ba(OH)_2$, $Al(OH)_3$, $SO_2(OH)_2$, ClOH? Illustrate your answer with net equations.

17.19   *Hydrolysis.* What relationship exists between amphoterism and hydrolysis of a positive ion? Account for this in terms of an atomic picture.

17.20   *Amphoterism.* Arsenic trihydroxide is insoluble in water. How could you show experimentally that it is amphoteric?

17.21 *Solubility.* Given a saturated solution of the slightly soluble strong base $X(OH)_2$. The pH of the saturated solution is 9.70. The equilibrium is $X(OH)_2(s) \rightleftharpoons X^{++} + 2OH^-$. (a) What is the concentration of OH^- in the solution? (b) What is the concentration of X^{++} in the solution? (c) Calculate the solubility product of $X(OH)_2$.

17.22 *Hydrolysis.* Hydrogen cyanide, HCN, is a weak acid with a dissociation constant of 4.0×10^{-10}. Because of this, a solution of NaCN is slightly basic by hydrolysis. (a) Neglecting hydrolysis, calculate the concentration of Na^+ and of CN^- in a solution made by mixing 0.49 g. of NaCN with enough water to make 0.25 liter of solution. (b) Calculate the hydrolysis constant for

$$CN^- + H_2O \rightleftharpoons HCN + OH^-$$

(c) Using the constant from (b), calculate the concentration of HCN in the above solution (a). (d) Calculate the percentage of CN^- that is hydrolyzed. (e) Calculate the pH of the solution.

Ans. $0.040\ M\ Na^+$ and $0.040\ M\ CN^-$; 2.5×10^{-5}; $1.0 \times 10^{-3}\ M$; 2.5%; 11.0

17.23 *Solubility products.* Suppose that *AZ, BZ,* and *CZ* are three slightly soluble salts. The corresponding formula weights are 120, 130, and 140. If the respective solubilities are 0.1080, 0.1040, and 0.0980 g. per liter, what are the solubility products of the three salts, assuming formation of a $(+1)$ cation and a (-1) anion in each case?

17.24 *Solubility product.* For the equilibrium $RQ_2(s) \rightleftharpoons R^{++} + 2Q^-$ the $K_{s.p.}$ is 3.2×10^{-11}. Calculate how many moles of RQ_2 can dissolve in: (a) 50.0 ml. of pure water; (b) 50.0 ml. of a solution in which the concentration of R^{++} is already 0.020 M; (c) 50.0 ml. of a solution in which the concentration of Q^- is already 0.020 M.

Ans. 1.0×10^{-5} mole; 1.0×10^{-6} mole; 4.0×10^{-9} mole

17.25 *Solubility.* (a) It is found that 1.3×10^{-6} mole of $PbSO_4$ is all that can be dissolved in 0.100 liter of $1.0 \times 10^{-3}\ M\ Na_2SO_4$. Calculate the $K_{s.p.}$ for $PbSO_4$. (b) Should a precipitate be formed if 20.0 ml. of $2.0 \times 10^{-4}\ M$ $Pb(NO_3)_2$ is mixed with 80.0 ml. of $1.0 \times 10^{-4}\ M\ Na_2SO_4$? Justify your answer.

Ans. (a) 1.3×10^{-8}

17.26 *Solubility.* For MgF_2, $K_{s.p.}$ is 8×10^{-8}. Calculate the number of moles of MgF_2 that can be dissolved per liter of: (a) pure water; (b) 0.020 M NaF, (c) 0.020 M BaF_2.

17.27 *Solubility.* (a) If 1.0×10^{-4} mole of relatively insoluble salt MX_2 dissolves in 2.0 liters of water, what is the $K_{s.p.}$ of MX_2? (Assume dissolved MX_2 is completely dissociated into M^{++} and X^- ions.) (b) How many moles of MX_2 can be dissolved in 2.0 liters of 0.010 M NaX?

Ans. 5.0×10^{-13}; 1.0×10^{-8} mole

17.28   *Dissociation and hydrolysis.* Given weak acid HX such that 0.10 M HX has a pH of 4.00: (*a*) Calculate the value of K_{diss} for HX. (*b*) What would be the concentration of OH$^-$ in 0.40 M HX? (*c*) What would be the pH of 0.10 M NaX?

17.29   *Dissociation.* A solution of 0.40 M XOH shows an OH$^-$ concentration that is 1.4×10^{-5} M. (*a*) Calculate the dissociation constant of the weak base XOH. (*b*) What is the H$^+$ concentration of 0.40 M XOH? (*c*) What is the pH of 0.40 M XOH? (*d*) What is the OH$^-$ concentration of a solution that is 0.10 M XOH?   *Ans.* 4.9×10^{-10}; 7.1×10^{-10} M; 9.15; 7.0×10^{-6} M

17.30   *Dissociation.* A solution of 0.20 M YOH shows a pH of 9.00. (*a*) What is the K_{diss} of YOH? (*b*) What is the per cent dissociation of YOH in 0.20 M YOH? (*c*) What would be the pH of 0.020 M YOH?

17.31   *Dissociation.* Given 1.00 liter of 1.00 M XOH ($K_{diss} = 4.9 \times 10^{-10}$) and 1.00 liter of water. What is the maximum volume of pH = 9.00 solution that can be made, assuming no other starting material is available?
   Ans. 1.26 liters

17.32   *Dissociation.* Select from each of the following lists the one item that most closely satisfies the condition given. Needed constants are given in the chapter.

(*a*) strongest acid	HNO$_2$	HC$_2$H$_3$O$_2$	HF
(*b*) weakest base	NH$_4$OH	N$_2$H$_5$OH	NaOH
(*c*) present at highest concentration in 0.10 M H$_2$SO$_4$	H$^+$	HSO$_4^-$	SO$_4^{--}$
(*d*) present at lowest concentration in 0.10 M H$_2$SO$_4$	H$^+$	HSO$_4^-$	SO$_4^{--}$
(*e*) highest per cent dissociation	0.5 M HCN	1.0 M HCN	0.5 M HNO$_2$
(*f*) would have pH 2.8	0.20 M HC$_2$H$_3$O$_2$	0.0076 M HNO$_2$	80 M HOCl

17.33   *pH.* Given that K_{diss} equals 4.0×10^{-9} for HX and 9.0×10^{-9} for HY. Which of the following solutions has the highest pH: (*a*) a solution made by dissolving 0.10 mole of NaX in 0.50 liter of solution; (*b*) a solution made by dissolving 0.10 mole of NaY in 0.50 liter of solution; (*c*) a solution made by mixing 0.10 mole of HX with 0.10 mole of NaOH in 0.20 liter of solution; (*d*) a solution made by mixing 0.10 mole of HY with 0.10 mole of NaOH in 0.20 liter of solution?

17.34   *Mixing problem.* Suppose you have a liter of 1.0000 M HC$_2$H$_3$O$_2$ ($K_{diss} = 1.8 \times 10^{-5}$) and a liter of 1.0000 M NaOH. How would you go about using only these reagents to make up 1.0000 liter of a solution of pH $= 7.00$?

Ans. 498.6 ml. and 501.4 ml.

17.35 *Solubility.* (a) The solubility product of MnS is 7×10^{-16}. Will MnS precipitate if $0.0050\ M$ Mn^{++} solution is saturated with H_2S? Explain. (b) Show that MnS can be made to precipitate by adding NaOH to the above solution. To what concentration must OH^- be raised before precipitation can occur? (c) The solubility product of $Mn(OH)_2$ is 2×10^{-13}. Will $Mn(OH)_2$ precipitate if OH^- is added as in (b)? Explain. *Ans.* (b) $4 \times 10^{-10}\ M$

17.36 *Hydrolysis.* When 0.10 mole of NH_4OH is "neutralized" with 0.10 mole of HCl in 0.500 liter of water, the resulting solution has a pH of 4.98. Account quantitatively for this slight acidity. The dissociation constant of NH_4OH is 1.8×10^{-5}.

17.37 *Buffer.* (a) Calculate the concentration of H^+ in the solution made by adding 0.50 mole of $NaC_2H_3O_2$ to 1.0 liter of $0.50\ M$ $HC_2H_3O_2$. This solution is a buffer solution. (b) Calculate the H^+ concentration after 0.050 mole of HCl has been added to 1.0 liter of the buffer in (a). (c) Calculate the H^+ concentration after 0.050 mole of NaOH has been added to 1.0 liter of the buffer in (a). (d) Repeat the calculations of (b) and (c) for the addition to 1.0 liter of water to see what effect the buffering process has on the change of $[H^+]$.

17.38 *Mixing problem.* Calculate the weight of solid formed and the concentration of each ion in the final solution when all the following are mixed: 20.0 ml. of $0.10\ M$ K_2SO_4, 20.0 ml. of $0.20\ M$ Na_2SO_4, 30.0 ml. of $0.30\ M$ $BaCl_2$, and 30.0 ml. of $0.40\ M$ $Ba(NO_3)_2$. Assume the final volume to be 100.0 ml.

Ans. 1.4 g. of $BaSO_4$; $0.040\ M$ K^+; $1.0 \times 10^{-8}\ M$ SO_4^{--}; $0.080\ M$ Na^+; $0.15\ M$ Ba^{++}; $0.18\ M$ Cl^-; $0.24\ M$ NO_3^-

17.39 *Buffer.* From the equilibrium constants

$$CO_2 + H_2O \rightleftharpoons H^+ + HCO_3^- \qquad K = 4.2 \times 10^{-7}$$

$$H_2PO_4^- \rightleftharpoons H^+ + HPO_4^{--} \qquad K = 6.2 \times 10^{-8}$$

and the fact that the observed pH of human blood is 7.40, calculate what fraction of the CO_2—HCO_3^- buffer in human blood is in the HCO_3^- form and what fraction of the $H_2PO_4^-$—HPO_4^{--} buffer is in the HPO_4^{--} form.

Ans. 0.91; 0.61

17.40 *Hydrolysis.* Sulfide ion hydrolyzes quite extensively by the reaction

$$S^{--} + H_2O \rightleftharpoons HS^- + OH^-$$

(a) Show that the hydrolysis constant for this equilibrium is equal to K_w/K_{II} of H_2S. (b) Calculate the concentration of Na^+, S^{--}, HS^-, and OH^- in a solution labeled $0.050\ M$ Na_2S. What per cent of the original S^{--} has hydrolyzed?

17.41 *General.* (a) How many grams of Na can be obtained by passing 1.61 amp. through molten NaCl for 20.0 min.? *Ans.* 0.460 g.

(b) If the sodium from (a) is dumped into 0.400 liter of water, what will be the concentration of each ion in the resulting solution?

Ans. 0.0500 M Na$^+$, 0.0500 M OH$^-$, 2.0 $\times$ 10^{-13} M H$^+$

(c) If the solution from (b) is mixed with 0.600 liter of 0.15 M HCl, what will be the concentration of each ion in the resulting solution?

Ans. 0.0200 M Na$^+$, 0.070 M H$^+$, 0.090 M Cl$^-$, 1.4 $\times$ 10^{-13} M OH$^-$

(d) If to the final solution of (c) is added 0.090 mole of sodium acetate, what will be the concentration of each species in the resulting solution?

Ans. 0.110 M Na$^+$, 0.090 M Cl$^-$, 0.020 M C$_2$H$_3$O$_2^-$, 0.070 M HC$_2$H$_3$O$_2$, 6.3 $\times$ 10^{-5} M H$^+$, 1.6 $\times$ 10^{-10} M OH$^-$

(e) Suppose 0.010 faraday is passed through the residual solution of (d). What will be the concentration of H$^+$ in the final solution?

Anode reaction: $\qquad$ $2\text{Cl}^- \rightarrow \text{Cl}_2(g) + 2e^-$

Cathode reaction: $\qquad$ $2\text{HC}_2\text{H}_3\text{O}_2 + 2e^- \rightarrow \text{H}_2(g) + 2\text{C}_2\text{H}_3\text{O}_2^-$

Ans. 2.3 $\times$ 10^{-5} M

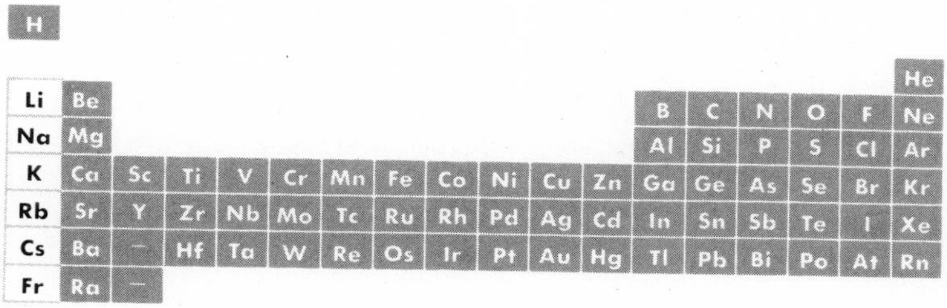

H																	
Li	Be											B	C	N	O	F	He
Na	Mg											Al	Si	P	S	Cl	Ne
K	Ca	Sc	Ti	V	Cr	Mn	Fe	Co	Ni	Cu	Zn	Ga	Ge	As	Se	Br	Ar
Rb	Sr	Y	Zr	Nb	Mo	Tc	Ru	Rh	Pd	Ag	Cd	In	Sn	Sb	Te	I	Kr
Cs	Ba	–	Hf	Ta	W	Re	Os	Ir	Pt	Au	Hg	Tl	Pb	Bi	Po	At	Xe
Fr	Ra	–															Rn

18   *The Alkali Metals*

HAVING DISCUSSED THE FUNDAMENTAL PRINCIPLES OF CHEMISTRY and the characteristic behavior of hydrogen, oxygen, and water, we can now consider the detailed descriptive chemistry of the other elements. We shall begin with group I and proceed from left to right across the periodic table. The chemistry of group I elements is relatively simple, since but one valence electron is involved.

The elements of group I are lithium ($Z = 3$), sodium ($Z = 11$), potassium ($Z = 19$), rubidium ($Z = 37$), cesium ($Z = 55$), and francium ($Z = 87$). They are usually referred to as the alkali metals, after the Arabic word *al-qili*, meaning plant ashes, since the ashes of plants are particularly rich in sodium and potassium carbonate. The term alkali is also applied to any substance with marked basic properties. In addition to forming hydroxides which are strongly basic, the elements of group I show metallic behavior to a high degree and are very good reducing agents.

18.1   METALLIC PROPERTIES

The term metal is applied to any substance which has a silvery luster and good conductivity of electricity and heat. Some metals, of which the alkali metals are examples, also are relatively soft, malleable (can be beaten into sheets), and ductile (can be drawn into wires). All of these properties can be accounted for in terms of the metallic structure mentioned in Sec. 8.4.

The alkali elements crystallize with a body-centered-cubic lattice in which the lattice points are occupied by $+1$ ions. The valence electrons (one from each atom) make up a sea of negative charges, which permeates the whole lattice. Since they are not fixed in position, these electrons can wander at will throughout the metal and thus produce high electric conductivity (see Sec. 14.1). Furthermore, it is almost invariably observed that high conductivity of electricity is accompanied by high conductivity of heat. This is not surprising, because thermal energy is transported rapidly from one part of a metal to another by the conduction electrons.

The high luster observed in the alkali metals is also explained by the highly mobile electrons of the metallic lattice. When a light beam strikes the surface of a metal, electric fields associated with the light wave set the electrons in the metal surface into back-and-forth oscillation. This is easy to do, because the valence electrons are not bound to specific atoms. However, like any moving electric charge, oscillating electrons give off electromagnetic energy as light. The net effect is that the beam of light is "reflected." In this respect, the electrons in metals act like tiny radio stations which receive a light signal and send it out again. Actually, nonmetals, even paper, also show high reflectivity, but only when looked at from very low angles. For nonmetals there is a critical angle beyond which the reflectivity disappears. The unusual thing about metals is that they show high reflectivity of light at all angles.

The softness, malleability, and ductility that also characterize the alkali metals are accounted for by the nature of the forces holding the lattice together. For example, in metallic sodium the principal force holding the lattice together is the attraction between Na^+ ions and the valence-electron cloud. Since this attraction is uniform in all directions, there are no strongly preferred positions for the Na^+ ions. The result is that Na^+ ions can easily be moved from one lattice site to another. Under pounding, the crystal can be flattened out like a pancake with but little expenditure of energy. Also it can be cut with a knife like soft processed cheese. All this behavior is in contrast to the case of iron, where there are strong, directed forces between adjacent positive ions which are due to covalent binding (Sec. 20.2).

The above discussion interprets metallic properties in terms of the metallic lattice, but a more fundamental question is, Why do the alkali elements prefer to form a crystal consisting of $+1$ ions and electrons? The question is complex but can be at least partly answered by considering the properties of the individual atoms. Table 18.1 shows some of these properties. The column headed Electronic configuration indicates the population according to the principal quantum number in the undisturbed neutral atom.

Table 18.1   Properties of Alkali Atoms

Element	Atomic number	Electronic configuration	Ionization potential, e.v.		Ionic radius, A. (M^+)
			First	Second	
Lithium	3	2, 1	5.39	75.6	0.68
Sodium	11	2, 8, 1	5.14	47.3	0.98
Potassium	19	2, 8, 8, 1	4.34	31.8	1.33
Rubidium	37	2, 8, 18, 8, 1	4.18	27.4	1.48
Cesium	55	2, 8, 18, 18, 8, 1	3.89	23.4	1.67
Francium	87	2, 8, 18, 32, 18, 8, 1	—	—	(1.75)

As indicated, each of the atoms has one electron in the outermost energy level. The energy required to pull off this valence electron is given in the column headed First ionization potential. As ionization potentials go, these are relatively small values, indicating that it is relatively easy to pull this one electron off a neutral alkali atom. However, the second ionization potential, the energy required to pull off a second electron, is many times higher than the first ionization potential. This means that, although it is relatively easy to form the M^+ ion, it is practically impossible under ordinary conditions to form the M^{++} ion of the alkali metals. All of this is consistent with the notion that the closed shell of electrons is difficult to break up. The result is that, when alkali atoms come together to form liquid or solid, M^+ ions are formed. The valence electrons are so weakly held that they can move throughout the lattice.

The properties of the alkali metal atoms shown in Table 18.1 are well illustrative of the general changes expected in going through a group of the periodic table. For example, the radius of the $+1$ cation* increases progressively from lithium down. This is expected because of the increasing number of electronic shells populated. Similarly, the ionization potential shows progressive decrease in going down the group. This is consistent with increased size and resulting smaller attraction for the valence electron, as discussed in Sec. 3.14. Actually, the change in properties in group I is so regular as to give a false sense of confidence about how well periodic-table trends can be predicted. There are traps for the unwary in later groups.

* From X-ray studies of ionic solids it is possible to determine the radius of an ion. There is a problem, however, in that X-ray investigations give only the distance between centers of adjacent atoms. How should this distance be apportioned? The usual procedure is to adopt one ion as a standard and to assume that it has a definite radius in all its compounds. Other radii are then assigned so that the sum of radii equals the observed spacing. A standard may be obtained from a salt like LiI, where Li$^+$ is so small that the spacing can be assumed to be due to large I$^-$ ions in contact.

18.2   REDUCING PROPERTIES

The alkali metals are the most reactive metals known. Practically any oxidizing agent, no matter how weak, can be reduced by the alkali metals. Quantitatively, reducing strength (at least for aqueous solutions) is measured by the oxidation potential. Table 18.2 lists the oxidation potentials of the alkali metals, along with other properties that characterize the behavior of these elements. As mentioned in Sec. 14.8, the oxidation potential measures the tendency of a substance, compared to that of hydrogen, to act as a reducing agent. For the alkali metals, the oxidation potential is characteristic of the reaction

$$M(s) \rightarrow M^+ + e^-$$

in which the solid metal gives off electrons and forms ions in aqueous solution. The high values indicate that these elements are all excellent reducing agents and that lithium is the best of the lot.

At first sight there seems to be a discrepancy between the implications of Tables 18.1 and 18.2. The ionization potentials of Table 18.1 indicate that lithium holds its electron most tightly. The oxidation potentials of Table 18.2 indicate that lithium gives off its electron most readily. The apparent discrepancy is resolved by noting that the ionization potential is a property of the *isolated atom*, whereas the oxidation potential describes the *metal* as it goes into *solution*. The difference between ionization potential and oxidation potential may be clarified by the following consideration: The process

$$M(s) \rightarrow M^+ + e^-$$

can be thought of as consisting of three consecutive steps:

$$M(s) \rightarrow M(g) \tag{1}$$

Table 18.2   Properties of Alkali Metals

Element	Oxidation potential, volts	Density, g./cc.	Melting point, °C.	Boiling point, °C.
Lithium	+3.05	0.53	186	1336
Sodium	+2.71	0.97	97.5	880
Potassium	+2.93	0.86	62.3	760
Rubidium	+2.93	1.53	38.5	700
Cesium	+2.92	1.87	28.5	670

$$M(g) \rightarrow M^+(g) + e^- \tag{2}$$

$$M^+(g) + H_2O \rightarrow M^+(aq.) \tag{3}$$

In step (1), the metal is evaporated; i.e., the atoms are converted to the gaseous state, in which they are independent of each other. The energy required to do this (called the *sublimation energy*) is approximately the same for all the metals of group I. In step (2), an electron is pulled off the neutral atom to give a gaseous ion. The energy required (the ionization potential) is largest for lithium. In step (3), the gaseous ion is placed in water, i.e., hydrated. Energy (hydration energy) is liberated. The tendency of the over-all change to occur (the oxidation potential) depends on the net effect of all three of these steps. The fact that for lithium the tendency of the over-all change to occur is greatest suggests that the relative difficulty of step (2) has been more than compensated for by step (3). Apparently, the hydration energy of the tiny Li^+ ion is so great that it makes up for the higher energy required to pull the electron off. In other words, the stabilizing effect of water on lithium ion makes the reaction

$$Li(s) \rightarrow Li^+ + e^-$$

have a greater tendency to occur than the corresponding reaction for the other alkali elements.

The great reactivity of the alkali metals poses a special problem in their handling. For example, water, although a relatively poor oxidizing agent, has great tendency to attack them. The tarnishing of freshly cut sodium is partially due to this oxidation by moisture in the air. To avoid such problems, alkali metals are usually stored under kerosene or other inert hydrocarbon compounds.

As shown in Table 18.2, the melting points of the alkali metals are quite low, in which respect they are unlike many other metals such as iron. The explanation for the low melting points lies in the ease of moving the positive ions, the feature that also accounts for malleability and ductility. However, the boiling points are fairly high, showing that it is hard to remove atoms from the metal. This indicates that metallic forces are appreciable.

18.3 OCCURRENCE

The alkali metals occur in nature only as $+1$ ions. Sodium and potassium are most abundant, ranking sixth and seventh of all the elements in the earth's crust. Lithium is moderately rare but is found in small amounts in practically all rocks. Rubidium and cesium are rare. Francium is essentially nonexistent, since it has an unstable nucleus and is radioactive. Trace amounts of it have been prepared by nuclear reactions.

Since most of the compounds of the alkali metals are soluble in water, they are generally found in sea water and in brine wells. However, there are many clays which are insoluble complex compounds of the alkali metals combined with Si, O, and Al. Presumably as the result of evaporation of ancient seas, there are also large salt deposits which serve as convenient sources of the alkali metals and their compounds.

Sodium ion and potassium ion are among the indispensable constituents of animal and plant tissue. Na^+ is the principal cation of the fluids outside the cells, whereas K^+ is the principal cation inside the cells. Besides filling general physiological roles, such as aiding water retention, these ions have specific functions. For example, Na^+ depresses the activity of muscle enzymes and is required for contraction of all animal muscle. In plants, K^+, but not Na^+, is a primary requirement. As a result, more than 90 per cent of the alkali content of ashes is due to potassium. Plants have such a high demand for potassium that, even in soils where the sodium content predominates manyfold, the potassium is taken up preferentially. Since an average crop extracts from the soil about 50 lb. of potassium per acre, the necessity of potassium fertilizers is obvious.

18.4   PREPARATION

To prepare the alkali elements, it is necessary to reduce the $+1$ ion. This can be done chemically or electrolytically. Purely chemical methods would seem impossible, since they require a reducing agent stronger than the alkali metals. However, chemical reduction can be carried out in special cases, as in the reaction of rubidium chloride with calcium at high temperature.

$$Ca(s) + 2RbCl(s) \rightarrow CaCl_2(s) + 2Rb(g)$$

The reaction occurs in the direction indicated only because the rubidium escapes as a gas out of the reacting mixture, thus preventing the attainment of equilibrium. In the equilibrium state, the concentration of rubidium would be very small.

In practice, the alkali metals are generally prepared by electrolysis of molten alkali compounds. For example, sodium is made commercially in ton quantities by the electrolysis of a fused mixture of $NaCl$ and $CaCl_2$ at about $600°C$. ($CaCl_2$ is added to reduce the melting point of the bath.) Sodium metal is formed at the iron or copper cathodes, and chlorine at the carbon anodes. To prevent oxidation of the Na by the chlorine, the electrode compartments are separated by a wire-gauze partition.

18.5   PROPERTIES AND USES

As mentioned, the alkali metals exhibit to a high degree typically metallic properties. Although too expensive and too chemically reactive to be used for their metallic properties, they do find special application. For example, liquid alkali metal is used to solve the difficult engineering problem of conducting heat energy from the center of a nuclear reactor to the exterior, where it can be converted into useful work (Chap. 29). The expense and difficulty involved in working with alkali metal is partially compensated for by its excellence as a heat conductor.

Cesium has the distinction of being the metal from which electrons are ejected most easily by light; such light-induced emission is termed the *photoelectric effect.* For this reason, cesium finds use in the *photocell,* a device for converting a light signal to an electric signal. The basic principle of the photocell is illustrated in Fig. 18.1. An evacuated tube contains two electrodes, one of which is coated with cesium metal, cesium oxide, or an alloy of cesium, antimony, and silver. In the absence of light, the tube does not conduct electricity, since there is nothing to carry the charge from one electrode to the other. When struck by light, the cesium-coated electrode emits electrons, which are attracted to the positive electrode, and thus the circuit is completed. Television pickup devices such as the iconoscope and the image orthicon use the photocell principle. Color effects are made possible because the cesium metal has a high response to red light and a low response to blue light, whereas cesium oxide is most sensitive to the blue.

Though all the alkali metals are very good reducing agents, only sodium finds extensive use for this purpose. It is used to make other metals by reducing their chlorides and also in the production of various compounds of carbon. For this latter purpose, sodium is frequently used in the form of its solution in liquid ammonia. It is a remarkable fact that sodium and the other alkali metals dissolve in the waterlike solvent NH_3 to give colored solutions which can be evaporated to give the alkali metal unchanged. In the blue solutions it is assumed

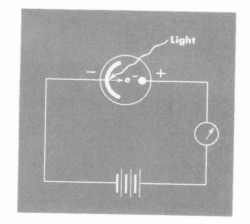

Fig. 18.1   Photocell circuit.

that the alkali metal is dissociated into $+1$ ions and electrons. The electrons are associated with NH_3 molecules; therefore the anions in these solutions can be considered as solvated electrons. More concentrated solutions have a metallic, bronzelike appearance and have very high electric conductivity, indicating that the electrons are extremely mobile. Reducing properties are somewhat toned down in all these solutions compared to the pure alkali metals.

18.6 COMPOUNDS

The alkali metals readily form compounds by reacting with other substances. For example, sodium metal on standing in air becomes covered with sodium peroxide, Na_2O_2. Furthermore, water vigorously attacks any of the alkali metals to liberate hydrogen

$$2M(s) + 2H_2O \rightarrow 2M^+ + 2OH^- + H_2(g)$$

Thus, the problem with the alkali metals is not to get them to form compounds but to keep them from doing so.

All the compounds of the alkali metals are ionic, even the hydrides, and all contain the alkali metal as a $+1$ ion. Most of the compounds are quite soluble in water; hence a convenient way to get a desired anion in solution is to use its sodium salt. The alkali-metal ions do not hydrolyze appreciably and do not form complex ions to any appreciable extent. Since the alkali-metal ions are colorless, any color of alkali metal compounds must be due to the anion.

The hydrides (Sec. 15.4) of the alkali metals are white solids prepared by heating alkali metal in hydrogen. The simple oxides, M_2O, are not so easily formed. Of the alkali metals, only lithium reacts directly with oxygen to form Li_2O. When sodium reacts with oxygen, the peroxide Na_2O_2 is formed instead. Potassium, rubidium, and cesium under similar conditions form superoxides of the type MO_2. In order to get the simple oxides, it is necessary to reduce some alkali-metal compound such as the nitrate. For example,

$$2KNO_3(s) + 10K(s) \rightarrow 6K_2O(s) + N_2(g)$$

The oxides are all basic oxides and react with water to form hydroxides. However, commercially, the hydroxides of the alkali metals are made by electrolysis of aqueous alkali-chloride solutions. For example, as discussed in Sec. 14.4, sodium hydroxide, or *caustic soda*, as it is often called, is made by electrolysis of aqueous NaCl.

Other important compounds of the alkali metals, such as *washing soda*, Na_2CO_3, and *baking soda*, $NaHCO_3$, are discussed in later chapters in connection with the corresponding anions.

18.7   SPECTRA

As described in Sec. 3.8, an electron which changes from a higher energy level of an atom to a lower energy level must give up the excess energy to the surroundings. If the energy is emitted as light, as is often the case, the light will be made up of one or more energies, each of which corresponds to a definite energy jump in the atom. This distribution of energies, or spectrum of the atom, is characteristic of the atom in question.

For the alkali metals, it is particularly easy to excite electrons to higher energy states and thus produce their spectra. Even a bunsen burner flame can do it. For this reason, alkali-metal compounds impart characteristic colors to flames. Lithium salts produce red flames; sodium, yellow; potassium, violet; rubidium, reddish violet; and cesium, reddish violet. These colors serve as the basis of the well-known flame tests for these elements.

18.8   QUALITATIVE ANALYSIS

Because the alkali metals do not form many insoluble compounds and because the alkali ions are colorless, it is difficult to detect the presence of these elements by chemical methods. Instead, their presence is usually shown by running flame tests on the sample in question. The simplest way to run a flame test is to shape a piece of fine platinum wire into a loop, dip the loop in HCl solution and heat to remove volatile impurities, and then use the loop to heat the sample in a burner flame. The sodium yellow is extremely intense, so that even traces of it can mask other flame colors. The main reason for cleaning the platinum loop by the HCl treatment is to help expel sodium as the relatively volatile chloride. (In general, chlorides are more volatile than most other solids.) The potassium flame is colored a delicate violet and can be observed in many cases only through cobalt glass, which filters out interfering colors such as sodium yellow. The flames of K, Rb, and Cs are so similar that definite identification requires examination of the line spectrum with a spectroscope.

QUESTIONS

18.1   *Group properties.* Account for the observed trends in ionization potential and ionic size within the alkali-metal group.

18.2   *Metals.* What are the typical properties of a metal, and how can each be accounted for in terms of structure?

18.3   *Properties.* Account for the following facts: (*a*) sodium forms $+1$ ions but not $+2$ ions; (*b*) potassium forms a metallic lattice; (*c*) iron is hard and high-melting, but cesium is soft and low-melting; (*d*) lithium has the highest oxidation potential of the alkali metals.

18.4   *Francium.* How would you expect the following properties of francium to compare with those of the other alkali metals: (*a*) ionic radius; (*b*) ionization potential; (*c*) oxidation potential; (*d*) melting point; (*e*) density?

18.5   *Oxidation potentials.* Given:

$$Li(s) \rightleftharpoons Li^+ + e^- \qquad +3.05 \text{ volts}$$
$$Na(s) \rightleftharpoons Na^+ + e^- \qquad +2.71 \text{ volts}$$
$$K(s) \rightleftharpoons K^+ + e^- \qquad +2.93 \text{ volts}$$

From this list pick out (*a*) the best reducing agent, (*b*) the best oxidizing agent, (*c*) the poorest reducing agent, and (*d*) the poorest oxidizing agent.

18.6   *Potassium cycle.* Account for the use of wood ashes as fertilizer.

18.7   *Equations.* Write balanced equations for the following: (*a*) potassium is "dissolved" in water; (*b*) cesium is exposed to air; (*c*) preparation of NaOH from NaCl; (*d*) preparation of Rb_2O.

18.8   *Strong bases.* Show that the following two statements are consistent: "Alkali metals form hydroxides that are strong bases," and "alkali ions do not hydrolyze."

18.9   *Percentage composition.* A given fertilizer is described as 5-10-5, indicating, respectively, the per cent nitrogen, phosphorus pentoxide, and potassium oxide. Most fertilizers do not contain potassium oxide as such but have the potassium as KCl. What per cent of 5-10-5 fertilizer is KCl?

18.10   *Electrolysis.* If 0.75 liter of 0.60 M NaCl is electrolyzed for 12 min. at 0.50 amp., what should be the pH of the residual solution?   *Ans.* 11.70

18.11   *Stoichiometry.* Given an old piece of sodium which is covered with a coating of Na_2O_2. When this piece, total weight 0.269 g., is dropped into water, 112 ml. (STP) of hydrogen gas is evolved. If the final volume of solution is 20.0 ml., what would be the OH^- concentration in it? Assume that on reaction with water, $Na_2O_2(s)$ forms HO_2^-.   *Ans.* 0.525 M

18.12   *Ionic radii.* The crystal structure of lithium iodide is the same as that of NaCl. Using the observed unit-cell-edge length of 6.050 A. and assuming anion-anion contact, calculate the apparent radius of iodide ion. Show that the radius of Li^+ (Table 18.1) is small enough to allow anion contact.

19 The Alkaline-earth Metals

GROUP II OF THE PERIODIC TABLE contains the elements beryllium ($Z = 4$), magnesium ($Z = 12$), calcium ($Z = 20$), strontium ($Z = 38$), barium ($Z = 56$), and radium ($Z = 88$). They are called the *alkaline-earth metals*, because the old alchemists referred to any nonmetallic substance insoluble in water and unchanged by fire as an "earth" and because the "earths" of this group, e.g., lime (CaO) and magnesia (MgO), give decidedly alkaline reactions.

Probably the most characteristic features of the group II elements are their good metallic properties, their strength as reducing agents, and their formation of compounds in which they show oxidation state $+2$. Many of these compounds are of low solubility. Compared to group I elements, the alkaline-earth elements are both less metallic and poorer reducing agents.

19.1 PROPERTIES

Electronic configurations and some related properties of the alkaline-earth-metal atoms are shown in Table 19.1. It should also be noted that radium atoms are radioactive and undergo spontaneous nuclear disintegration. In

Table 19.1   Properties of Alkaline-earth Atoms

Element	Atomic number	Electronic configuration	Ionization potential, e.v.			Ionic radius, A. (M^{++})
			First	Second	Third	
Beryllium	4	2, 2	9.32	18.2	153.9	0.30
Magnesium	12	2, 8, 2	7.64	15.0	80.1	0.65
Calcium	20	2, 8, 8, 2	6.11	11.9	51.2	0.94
Strontium	38	2, 8, 18, 8, 2	5.69	11.0	(43)	1.10
Barium	56	2, 8, 18, 18, 8, 2	5.21	10.0	(36)	1.29
Radium	88	2, 8, 18, 32, 18, 8, 2	5.28	10.1	—	1.52

each of the alkaline-earth-metal atoms there are two electrons in the outermost energy level. With the exception of beryllium, the next lower principal quantum level contains eight electrons. The chief difference in going down the group is the stepwise inclusion of sets of 8, 18, and 32 electrons. As expected, there is a corresponding increase in size from Be to Ra. This is illustrated in the last column, which gives experimentally determined values of the M^{++} cation radius in crystals. The values need to be considered as approximate, since ionic sizes depend on environment, but they do show the expected trend as more levels are populated.

As expected, with increasing size we find a decreasing ionization potential in going down the group. The first ionization potential is the energy required to pull one electron off the neutral, isolated atom. As mentioned in Sec. 3.14, the larger atoms hold their outer electrons less tightly than do small atoms, hence the decreasing ionization potential from Be to Ba. The anomaly for radium is not explained. The second ionization potential measures the energy required to pull one electron off the $+1$ ion to form a $+2$ ion. Because the electron is pulled off a positively charged ion rather than a neutral atom, the second ionization potential of an atom is always greater than the first. The third ionization potential indicates the energy to pull one electron off a $+2$ ion to form a $+3$ ion and, for a given element, is greater than the second ionization potential.

Inspection of the ionization potentials in Table 19.1 shows that removal of the third electron from alkaline-earth elements requires very high energies. Such high energies are usually not available in chemical reactions, and therefore $+3$ ions of the alkaline-earth elements are not encountered except in some hot stars. In practice, only the $+2$ ions of these elements are observed. How can this be justified in the light of the fact that the second ionization potentials are almost twice as great as the first? It would seem that these elements, like group I elements, should prefer to form $+1$ ions rather than $+2$. If only the ionization potentials were involved, such would indeed be the case. With magnesium, for example, it requires 7.64 e.v. to pull off the first electron and 15.0 e.v. to pull off the second. This means that return of one electron to Mg^{++} liberates 15.0 e.v. of energy. As a consequence, magnesium gas and doubly charged magnesium ions are unstable with respect to conversion to singly charged magnesium ions.

$$Mg(g) \rightarrow Mg^+(g) + e^- \qquad \text{Requires 7.64 e.v.}$$

$$\underline{e^- + Mg^{++}(g) \rightarrow Mg^+(g)} \qquad \text{Liberates 15.0 e.v.}$$

$$Net: \quad Mg(g) + Mg^{++}(g) \rightarrow 2Mg^+(g) \qquad \text{Liberates 7.4 e.v.}$$

The net energy release is enormous (7.4 e.v. = 170 kcal.); hence Mg^+ should be formed in the gas phase. It has, in fact, been detected at high temperatures. However, normally we work with solid magnesium and hydrated ions. In water, Mg^+ would react as follows:

$$2Mg^+(aq.) \xrightarrow[100\%]{} Mg(s) + Mg^{++}(aq.)$$

That is, Mg^+ *disproportionates* (*oxidizes and reduces itself*) completely into solid Mg and hydrated Mg^{++}. The reason for this disproportionation is the stability of solid magnesium and the much greater hydration energy of the more highly charged Mg^{++}. For similar reasons, all the other alkaline-earth elements form only a $+2$ ion under usual conditions.

Table 19.2 shows some of the properties of the group II elements in the solid state, as distinguished from the properties of the isolated atoms. In the solid state the elements have typically metallic properties: high luster and good conductivity. They are harder than the group I elements but still can be cut with a hard steel knife. The fairly high melting points are in line with this greater hardness. The boiling points (many of which have not been accurately determined) are higher than those of the alkali metals and

Table 19.2   *Properties of Alkaline-earth Metals*

Element	Oxidation potential, volts	Density, g./cc.	Melting point, °C.	Boiling point, °C.
Beryllium	$+1.85$	1.86	1280	1500(?)
Magnesium	$+2.37$	1.74	650	1100
Calcium	$+2.87$	1.55	810	1300(?)
Strontium	$+2.89$	2.6	800	1300(?)
Barium	$+2.90$	3.6	850	1500(?)
Radium	$+2.92$	5(?)	960(?)	1100(?)

suggest that the forces of attraction between the electron cloud and M^{++} ions are greater than those between the electron cloud and M^+ ions.

The oxidation potentials, shown in the second column, are relatively high. They correspond to the reaction

$$M(s) \rightarrow M^{++} + 2e^-$$

and indicate that in aqueous solutions these elements are good reducing agents. For example, all the alkaline-earth metals have the ability to react with water to release hydrogen by the reaction

$$M(s) + 2H_2O \rightarrow M^{++} + H_2(g) + 2OH^-$$

19.2   COMPARISON WITH ALKALI METALS

It is interesting to compare the properties of group I and group II elements and attempt to account for any differences. We first consider size, which is fundamental for many properties. Examination of Tables 18.1 and 19.1 shows that the ionic radius of any group II element is smaller than that of the group I element of the same period. For example, Mg^{++} has an ionic radius of 0.65 A. compared to 0.98 A. for Na^+. Both of these elements fall in the third period of the periodic table. Why the difference in size? Sodium ion has a nuclear charge of $+11$ and has two electrons in the K shell and eight electrons in the L shell; magnesium ion has a nuclear charge of $+12$ and also has two electrons in the K shell and eight electrons in the L shell. These two ions are *isoelectronic*; i.e., they have identical electronic configurations. The difference between Na^+ and Mg^{++} is that the latter has a higher nuclear charge. Increased nuclear charge means increased attraction for electrons, which in turn means a smaller K shell and a smaller L shell. In any isoelectronic sequence, ionic size decreases with increased nuclear charge.

Just as the ionic size decreases in going from group I to group II, the apparent atomic size (Sec. 3.13) also decreases. This smaller atomic size of the group II neutral atoms accounts for the difference between the first ionization potentials of groups I and II. Tables 18.1 and 19.1 show that, in going from group I to group II, there is a rather large increase in the energy required to pull off one electron (e.g., 5.14 e.v. for Na and 7.64 e.v. for Mg). This, of course, is in line with the smaller size of group II atoms and their consequent tighter hold on electrons.

The most puzzling comparison between groups I and II is in the oxidation potentials. For the lighter elements at the top of the group, there is a distinct difference, and it is in the direction that group I elements have higher oxidation potentials and are, therefore, better reducing agents. For example, the oxidation potential of beryllium is $+1.85$ volts compared to that of lithium, $+3.05$ volts. However, for the heavier elements at the bottom of the group, there is little difference between groups I and II. Barium, for instance, has an oxidation potential of $+2.90$, whereas cesium, of the same period, has $+2.92$ volts.

Actually, it is not surprising that group I elements are stronger reducing agents than corresponding group II elements. After all, the ionization potentials of group I elements are much lower. The surprising thing is that group II elements are as good reducing agents as they are. The key to the explanation apparently lies in the hydration energy. Although it takes a fair amount of energy to pull two electrons off a group II atom, the net process $M(s) \rightarrow M^{++}(aq.) + 2e^-$ nevertheless has a great tendency to occur, because the doubly charged ion interacts strongly with water in forming the hydrated ion.

19.3   OCCURRENCE

In nature, the alkaline-earth elements are found only in compounds as $+2$ ions. As discussed in Sec. 16.6, $+2$ ions combine with -2 ions to form compounds less soluble than those of $+1$ ions. Consequently, many alkaline-earth compounds are insoluble and, unlike alkali-metal compounds, are found as insoluble deposits in the earth's crust. Most important of these deposits are the silicates, carbonates, sulfates, and phosphates.

Beryllium on a weight basis makes up only 0.0006 per cent of the earth's crust. It is very widespread, but only in trace amounts. The only important beryllium mineral found in any quantity is a silicate, beryl, or $Be_3Al_2Si_6O_{18}$. Enormous single crystals of beryl weighing many tons have been found. The gem stone emerald is beryl, colored deep green by trace amounts of chromium.

Magnesium is the eighth most abundant element in the earth's crust, making up about 2 per cent of its weight. It is widely distributed, principally as the silicate minerals such as asbestos ($CaMg_3Si_4O_{12}$) and the carbonate, oxide, and chloride. Magnesite ($MgCO_3$) and dolomite ($MgCO_3 \cdot CaCO_3$) are the principal sources of magnesium in addition to sea water and deep salt wells.

Calcium is the most abundant of the group I and group II elements on a weight basis (3.6 per cent of the earth's crust) but is outnumbered 6 to 5 on an atom basis by sodium. The principal minerals of calcium are the silicates, carbonate, sulfate, phosphate, and fluoride. Calcium carbonate ($CaCO_3$) appears in such diverse minerals as limestone, marble, and chalk. Most of these appear to be derived from the skeletons of marine animals which have been laid down on sea-beds and consolidated. The mineral gypsum ($CaSO_4 \cdot 2H_2O$) is also very common. It apparently owes its origin in many cases to limestone beds which have been acted on by sulfuric acid produced from the oxidation of sulfide minerals. Phosphate rock is essentially $Ca_3(PO_4)_2$, an important ingredient of bones, teeth, and sea shells.

Strontium is relatively rare and ranks twentieth in order of abundance; barium, which makes up 0.05 per cent of the earth's crust, is about 2.5 times as abundant. The principal mineral of strontium is strontianite ($SrCO_3$); of barium, barite ($BaSO_4$).

Radium is very rare, but its presence is easily detected by its radioactivity. Because its nucleus spontaneously disintegrates, all the radium found is due to the nuclear breakdown of heavier elements, particularly uranium. For this reason, uranium ores such as pitchblende (impure U_3O_8) are principal sources of radium. It has been estimated that the average abundance of radium in the earth's crust is less than 1 part per million million. This makes a uranium mineral which contains ¼ g. of radium per ton of ore a relatively rich source of radium.

19.4 PREPARATION

Since the alkaline-earth elements occur only as the $+2$ ions, preparation of the metals requires a reduction process. Reduction can be accomplished by electrolysis of the molten halides or hydroxides or by chemical reduction with appropriate reducing agents. Beryllium, for example, is made by heating beryllium fluoride, BeF_2, with Mg and also by electrolyzing a mixture of beryllium chloride, $BeCl_2$, and NaCl.

The extraction of magnesium from sea water accounts for the bulk of U.S. production. In the process, the magnesium ion in sea water (about 0.13 per cent) is precipitated as $Mg(OH)_2$ by the addition of lime, CaO. The hydroxide is filtered off and converted to $MgCl_2$ by reaction with HCl. The dried $MgCl_2$ is mixed with other salts to lower the melting point and then electrolyzed at about 700°C. to give metal of 99.9 per cent purity.

Magnesium can also be prepared by a chemical reduction process in which magnesium oxide, obtained by heating dolomite, is reduced at high temperatures by iron and silicon. Since the reaction is carried out above 1100°C., the boiling point of magnesium, the process produces gaseous magnesium, which escapes from the reaction mixture to condense as a very high purity product.

19.5   PROPERTIES AND USES

All the alkaline-earth metals are good conductors of heat and electricity, but of them only magnesium finds any considerable use. Surprisingly, this use is based on the structural qualities of magnesium rather than on its electrical properties. Lightest of all the commercially important structural metals, magnesium has relatively low structural strength, but this can be increased by alloying with other elements. The principal elements added are aluminum, zinc, and manganese. The aluminum helps increase the tensile strength; the zinc improves the working properties (machining); and the manganese reduces corrosion. The use of magnesium alloys is ever increasing because of modern emphasis on weight reduction in such things as aircraft, railroad equipment, and household goods.

Too rare and costly for most large-scale uses, beryllium is important as a trace addition for hardening other metals such as copper. In the finely powdered form, beryllium (and its compounds) must be handled carefully, since it is extremely toxic.

Calcium, strontium, and barium are more reactive than beryllium and magnesium. The situation is complicated further by the fact that, when exposed to air, they form oxides which flake off to expose fresh surface. The great affinity for oxygen makes these elements useful as deoxidizers in steel production and as getters in the production of low-cost electron tubes. Most radio tubes, for example, have a thin deposit of barium metal on the inner wall of the glass or metal envelope. The purpose is to pick up any gases such as oxygen in the tube.

Finely divided magnesium burns rather vigorously to emit very intense light which is particularly rich in the higher energies. For this reason, magnesium is used as one of the important light sources for photography. Flash bulbs contain wire or foil of magnesium (or aluminum) packed in an oxygen atmosphere. When the bulb is fired, an electric current heats the metal and initiates the oxidation reaction.

The flame spectra of strontium salts are characteristically red, and those of barium are yellowish green. Strontium and barium salts are frequently used for color effect in pyrotechnics.

19.6   COMPOUNDS

At ordinary temperatures, the alkaline-earth elements form compounds only in the $+2$ oxidation state. With the exception of beryllium, all such compounds are essentially ionic. The alkaline-earth ions are colorless and, except for Be^{++}, do not hydrolyze appreciably in aqueous solution. Beryllium salts hydrolyze to give acid solutions. Unlike the compounds of group I, many group II compounds are not soluble in water.

1   Hydrides. When heated in hydrogen gas, Ca, Sr, and Ba form hydrides. These are white powders which react with H_2O to liberate H_2. Calcium hydride, CaH_2, is used as a convenient, portable hydrogen supply.

$$CaH_2(s) + 2H_2O \rightarrow Ca^{++} + 2OH^- + 2H_2(g)$$

2   Oxides. The oxides of these elements are characteristically very high melting (*refractory*). They can be made by heating the metals in oxygen or thermally decomposing the carbonates or hydroxides. For example, lime (CaO) is made from limestone ($CaCO_3$) by the reaction

$$CaCO_3(s) \rightarrow CaO(s) + CO_2(g)$$

Except for beryllium oxide, BeO, which is amphoteric, the oxides of group II are basic. Both lime and magnesia (MgO) are used as linings in furnaces, sometimes specifically to counteract acidic impurities, as in steel production.

3   Hydroxides. The hydroxides of group II are made by adding water to the oxides in a process called *slaking*. For example, the slaking of lime produces calcium hydroxide, $Ca(OH)_2$, sometimes called slaked lime. The reaction

$$CaO(s) + H_2O \rightarrow Ca(OH)_2(s) + 16 \text{ kcal}.$$

is accompanied by a threefold expansion in volume, sometimes to the consternation of building contractors whose lime supplies accidentally get wet. Lime is an important constituent of cement and is also used as an important industrial base, since it is cheaper than NaOH.

The hydroxides of the alkaline-earth elements are only slightly soluble in water; however, the solubility increases with increasing ionic size. The solubility products are given in Table 19.3. With the exception of $Be(OH)_2$, which is amphoteric, the other hydroxides are completely dissociated in water to give basic solutions.

Table 19.3 $K_{s.p.}$ for Alkaline-earth Hydroxides

$Be(OH)_2$	Less than 10^{-19}
$Mg(OH)_2$	8.9×10^{-12}
$Ca(OH)_2$	1.3×10^{-6}
$Sr(OH)_2$	3.2×10^{-4}
$Ba(OH)_2$	5.0×10^{-3}

4   *Sulfates.* The sulfates of group II range from the very soluble beryllium sulfate to the practically insoluble radium sulfate. Going down the group, the solubilities decrease in regular order; for $BeSO_4$, $K_{s.p.}$ is very large; $MgSO_4$, about 10; $CaSO_4$, 2.4×10^{-5}; $SrSO_4$, 7.6×10^{-7}; $BaSO_4$, 1.5×10^{-9}; and $RaSO_4$, 4×10^{-11}. This decreasing order is opposite to that observed for the hydroxides. To account for the alteration of trend, two factors need to be considered: As discussed in Sec. 16.6, solubility depends on lattice energy and on hydration energy. For the alkaline-earth sulfates, the lattice energies are all about the same, apparently because the sulfate ion is so large (about 3 A. radius) that changing the size of the much smaller cation makes little difference. The difference in solubility must therefore be due to differences in hydration energy. From Be^{++} to Ba^{++}, size increases, hydration energy decreases, and the sulfates become less soluble. For the alkaline-earth hydroxides, the lattice energies are not the same but decrease with increasing cation size. Apparently for these hydroxides this is a larger effect than the change in hydration energy. Thus, the hydroxides increase in solubility down the group.

Magnesium sulfate is well known as the heptahydrate, $MgSO_4 \cdot 7H_2O$, or epsom salt. In medicine it is useful as a purgative, apparently because magnesium ions in the alimentary canal favor passage of water from other body fluids into the bowel to dilute the salt.

Calcium sulfate has already been mentioned as the mineral gypsum, $CaSO_4 \cdot 2H_2O$. When gypsum is partially dehydrated

$$CaSO_4 \cdot 2H_2O(s) \rightleftharpoons CaSO_4 \cdot \tfrac{1}{2}H_2O(s) + \tfrac{3}{2}H_2O(g)$$

it forms plaster of paris, sometimes written $2CaSO_4 \cdot H_2O$. The use of plaster of paris in making casts and molds arises from the reversibility of the above reaction. On water uptake, plaster of paris sets to gypsum, and the expansion of volume results in remarkably faithful reproductions.

Barium sulfate and its insolubility have been repeatedly mentioned. Although Ba^{++}, like most heavy metals, is poisonous, the solubility of $BaSO_4$ is so low that $BaSO_4$ can safely be ingested into the stomach. The use of $BaSO_4$ in taking X-ray pictures of the digestive tract depends on the great scattering of X rays by the Ba^{++} ion.* Actually, $BaSO_4$ is more important as a white pigment.

5   *Chlorides and fluorides.* Beryllium chloride and fluoride, $BeCl_2$ and BeF_2, are unusual in that they do not conduct electricity in the molten state. For this reason, they are usually considered to be molecular rather than ionic salts. The chlorides and fluorides of the other group II elements are

---

* The scattering of X rays by atoms is proportional to the electron density of the atom. Ba^{++} contains 54 electrons in a relatively small volume and, hence, scatters X rays more efficiently than ions of lighter elements.

all typical ionic solids. Calcium fluoride, CaF_2, occurring in nature as the mineral fluorspar, is quite insoluble in water. The chloride, $CaCl_2$, is very soluble in water and, in fact, has such great affinity for water that it is used as a dehydrating agent.

6   *Carbonates.* All the carbonates of group II are quite insoluble and therefore are found as solid minerals in nature. Calcium carbonate, $CaCO_3$, or limestone, is the most common nonsilicate mineral. The existence of large natural beds of $CaCO_3$ poses a special problem for water supplies, since $CaCO_3$, though essentially insoluble in water, is soluble in water containing carbon dioxide. Since our atmosphere contains an average of 0.04 per cent CO_2 at all times, essentially all ground waters are solutions of CO_2 in H_2O. These ground waters dissolve limestone by the reaction

$$CaCO_3(s) + CO_2 + H_2O \rightleftharpoons Ca^{++} + 2HCO_3^-$$

which produces a weathering action on limestone deposits and results in contamination of most ground waters with calcium ion and bicarbonate ion, HCO_3^-. The dissolving action of CO_2-containing water explains the many caves found in limestone regions. These caves abound in weird formations produced partly by the dissolving action and partly by reprecipitation of $CaCO_3$. The optimum conditions for $CaCO_3$ deposition are slow seepage of ground water, steady evaporation, and no disturbing air currents. In limestone caves, these conditions are ideally met. Ground water containing Ca^{++} and HCO_3^- may seep through a fissure in the roof and hang as a drop from the ceiling. As the water evaporates along with the carbon dioxide, the above reaction reverses to deposit a bit of limestone. Later, another drop of ground water seeps on to the limestone speck, and the process repeats. In time a long shaft reaching down from the roof may be built up in the form of a limestone stalactite. Occasionally drops of ground water may drip off the stalactite to the cave floor, where they evaporate to form a spire, or stalagmite, of $CaCO_3$. The whole process of dissolving and reprecipitation of limestone is very slow and may take hundreds of years.

19.7   HARD WATER

Because limestone is such a widespread mineral, most ground water contains small but appreciable concentrations of calcium ion. The presence of this Ca^{++} (or of Mg^{++} or Fe^{++}) is objectionable because of the formation of insoluble precipitates when such water is boiled or when soap is added. Water that behaves in this way is called "hard" water. It represents an industrial and household problem of the first magnitude.

Hardness in water is always due to the presence of calcium, magnesium, or ferrous (Fe^{++}) ion. The hardness may be of two types: (*a*) *tempo-rary*, or *carbonate, hardness*, in which HCO_3^- ions are present in the water in addition to the aforementioned metal ions; (*b*) *permanent*, or *noncarbonate, hardness*, in which the dipositive ions but no HCO_3^- ions are in the water. In either case, the hardness manifests itself by a reaction with soap (but not with detergents) to produce a scum. Soap, as discussed in Sec. 24.4, is a sodium salt of a complicated hydrocarbon acid. The usual soap is sodium stearate, $NaC_{18}H_{35}O_2$, and consists of Na^+ ions and negative stearate ions. When stearate ions are added to water containing Ca^{++}, insoluble calcium stearate forms.

$$Ca^{++} + 2C_{18}H_{35}O_2^- \rightarrow Ca(C_{18}H_{35}O_2)_2(s)$$

This insoluble calcium stearate is the familiar scum or bathtub ring.

Hardness in water is also objectionable because boiling a solution containing Ca^{++} and HCO_3^- results in the deposition of $CaCO_3$, as in cave formation. In industrial boilers the deposition of $CaCO_3$ is an economic headache, since, like most salts, $CaCO_3$ is a poor heat conductor. Fuel effi-ciency is drastically cut, and boilers have been put completely out of action by local overheating due to boiler scale.

The major question then is how to soften hard water effectively and economically. The most direct way to soften water (as is done in many households) is simply to add huge quantities of soap. Eventually, enough stearate ion can be added to precipitate all the objectionable Ca^{++} as scum, leaving the excess soap to carry on the cleansing action.

Another way to soften water (this works only for temporary hardness) is to boil the water. The reaction

$$Ca^{++} + 2HCO_3^- \rightleftharpoons CaCO_3(s) + H_2O + CO_2(g)$$

is reversible, but the forward reaction can be made dominant by boiling off the CO_2. Boiling is not practical for large-scale softening.

The third way to soften water is to precipitate the Ca^{++} out of solu-tion. This can be done by adding washing soda, Na_2CO_3. The added car-bonate ion, CO_3^{--}, reacts with Ca^{++} to give insoluble $CaCO_3$. If bicarbon-ate ion is present, the water may be softened by adding a base such as ammonia. The base neutralizes HCO_3^- to produce CO_3^{--}, which then precipitates the Ca^{++}. On a large scale, temporary hardness is removed by adding limewater. The added OH^- neutralizes HCO_3^- and precipitates $CaCO_3$ by the process

$$Ca^{++} + HCO_3^- + OH^- \rightarrow CaCO_3(s) + H_2O$$

It might seem odd that limewater, which itself contains Ca^{++}, can be added to hard water to remove Ca^{++}. Yet it should be noted that, when $Ca(OH)_2$

is added, there are 2 moles of OH^- per mole of Ca^{++}. Two moles of OH^- neutralize two moles of HCO_3^- and liberate two moles of CO_3^{--}, thus precipitating two moles of Ca^{++}—one that was added and one that was originally in the hard water.

A fourth method to soften water is to tie up the Ca^{++} so that it becomes harmless. One way to do this is to form a complex containing Ca^{++}. Certain phosphates, such as $(NaPO_3)_n$, sodium polyphosphate, presumably form such complexes in which the Ca^{++} is trapped by the phosphate.

The fifth and most clever method of softening water is to replace the offending calcium ion by a harmless one such as Na^+. This is done by the process called *ion exchange*.

19.8   ION EXCHANGE

An *ion exchanger* is a special type of giant molecule, which is pictured in part in Fig. 19.1. The open circles represent atoms which are covalently bound to each other in the form of a three-dimensional, cross-linked network. The negatively marked circles represent covalently bound atoms which carry an excess of negative charge. The molecule is thus a negatively charged network with a very porous structure. The pores are filled with water molecules (not shown) and enough positive ions to give an electrically neutral structure. The identity of the positive ions is not very important, since their only function is to preserve electrical neutrality. Consequently, one type of cation such as Ca^{++} can take the place of another type such as Na^+ without much change in structure. It is this kind of ion exchange which is used in water softening. Hard water containing Ca^{++} is placed in contact with an ion exchanger whose mobile ion is Na^+. Exchange occurs which can be represented by the equilibrium

$$Ca^{++} + 2Na^+_\ominus \rightleftharpoons 2Na^+ + {_\ominus}Ca^{++}{_\ominus}$$

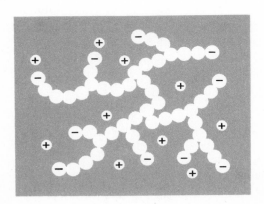

Fig. 19.1   *An ion exchanger.*

where the negative circle represents a negative site on the exchanger. The equilibrium constant for this reaction is usually of the order of 10 or less, and therefore, in order to remove all the Ca^{++}, it is necessary to run the hard water through a large amount of ion exchanger. This is most conveniently done by pouring the water through a tube, a foot or more high, filled with ion exchanger. Once the exchanger has given up its supply of Na^+, it cannot soften water further. However, it can be regenerated by exposure to concentrated solutions of NaCl, which reverses the above reaction.

The ion exchangers originally used for softening water were naturally occurring silicate minerals called *zeolites*. The giant network of a zeolite is negatively charged and is composed of covalently bound silicon, oxygen, and aluminum atoms. Mobile Na^+ ions in the pores can be readily exchanged for Ca^{++} ions. Zeolites are very closely related in structure to the clays, which also show ion exchange. Such ion exchange is important for plant nutrition, since many plants receive nourishment from the soil in this fashion.

Just before World War II, chemists were able to synthesize ion exchangers superior to the zeolites. The most common synthetic exchanger consists of a giant hydrocarbon framework having a negative charge due to covalently bound SO_3^- groups. It has also been possible to prepare ion exchangers in which the giant network is positively charged, the charge being due to covalently bound groups of the type $N(CH_3)_3^+$. Such positively charged networks can function as *anion* exchangers; i.e., they have mobile negative ions which can be displaced by other anions.

Combination of synthetic anion exchangers with cation exchangers has made possible the removal of all ions from a salt solution. If a salt solution containing M^+ and A^- is first run through a cation exchanger whose exchangeable ions are H^+, the salt solution is completely converted to a solution of an acid containing H^+ and A^-. If now the acid solution is run through an anion exchanger whose exchangeable ions are OH^-, the anions A^- in the solution are replaced by OH^-. Since in the original solution the number of negative charges is exactly equal to the number of positive charges, equal amounts of H^+ and OH^- are exchanged into the solution. Neutralization occurs, and pure water results. Water thus "deionized" contains fewer ions than the most carefully distilled water.

19.9   QUALITATIVE ANALYSIS

As a group, the alkaline-earth cations (excluding beryllium) can be distinguished from other common cations by taking advantage of the fact that, like group I elements, they form soluble sulfides but, unlike group I elements, they form insoluble carbonates.

Given a solution containing alkaline-earth cations, the barium can be precipitated as yellow $BaCrO_4$ by addition of K_2CrO_4 in the presence of an acetic acid buffer. From the residual solution (containing Sr^{++}, Ca^{++}, Mg^{++}), light yellow $SrCrO_4$ can be precipitated by subsequent addition of NH_3 and alcohol. The $BaCrO_4$ precipitates in the first step and $SrCrO_4$ in the second because $BaCrO_4$ ($K_{s.p.} = 8.5 \times 10^{-11}$) is less soluble than $SrCrO_4$ ($K_{s.p.} = 3.6 \times 10^{-5}$). The point of using an acetic acid buffer (Sec. 17.6) is to keep the H^+ concentration around 10^{-5}, where the chromate concentration, governed by the equilibrium

$$2CrO_4^{--} + 2H^+ \rightleftharpoons Cr_2O_7^{--} + H_2O$$

is too low to precipitate Sr^{++} but high enough to precipitate Ba^{++}. Subsequent addition of NH_3 reduces the H^+ concentration, thereby increasing the CrO_4^{--} concentration sufficiently to precipitate $SrCrO_4$, especially in the presence of alcohol which lowers its solubility.

Calcium ion can be separated from magnesium ion by addition of ammonium oxalate to form white, insoluble calcium oxalate, CaC_2O_4. (The $K_{s.p.}$ of CaC_2O_4 is 1.3×10^{-9}, compared to 8.6×10^{-5} for MgC_2O_4.) Finally, the presence of Mg^{++} can be shown by adding more NH_3 and Na_2HPO_4, which precipitates white magnesium ammonium phosphate, $MgNH_4PO_4$.

QUESTIONS

19.1   *Comparison of groups I and II.* Compare a typical alkali element and a typical alkaline-earth element with respect to first and second ionization potential, oxidation potential, ionic size, melting point, boiling point, and hardness. Account for similarities and differences.

19.2   *Group properties.* Account for the observed trends in oxidation potential, ionic size, and solubility of sulfates within the alkaline-earth group.

19.3   *Hydrolysis.* On the basis of the theory given in Sec. 17.12, account for the fact that, of all the group II ions, only Be^{++} hydrolyzes.

19.4   *Equations.* Write balanced equations for the following: (*a*) formation of barium hydride; (*b*) reaction of barium hydride with water; (*c*) electrolysis of molten magnesium chloride; (*d*) thermal decomposition of dolomite; (*e*) reaction of calcium with water; (*f*) softening of temporarily hard water by boiling; (*g*) softening of temporarily hard water by ammonia; (*h*) dissolving of beryllium hydroxide in NaOH.

19.5   *Hard water.* (*a*) How could you prepare some permanently hard water in the laboratory? (*b*) How could you show that it is both hard and permanently so? (*c*) How could you soften it without use of any chemical (including ion exchangers)?

19.6   *Solubility.* Tell how each of the following affects solubility: high lattice energy, high hydration energy, low lattice energy, low hydration energy. Explain.

19.7   *Ion exchange.* Show how solutions containing one doubly charged cation for each two singly charged anions (e.g., $CaCl_2$ solution) can be deionized.

19.8 *Solubility*. Account for the facts that (a) $BaSO_4$ is insoluble, but Na_2SO_4 is soluble; (b) $BeSO_4$ is soluble, but $BaSO_4$ is insoluble; (c) $Be(OH)_2$ is insoluble, but $Ba(OH)_2$ is soluble.

19.9 *Ion stability*. By reasoning analogous to that used in this chapter, account for the fact that the usual alkaline-earth salts *in the solid state* contain M^{++} and not M^+.

19.10 *Concentrations*. Calculate the concentration of each ion in each of the following mixtures: (a) 15.0 ml. of 0.16 M $CaCl_2$ plus 45.0 ml. of 0.20 M $Ca(NO_3)_2$; (b) 25.0 ml. of 0.030 M HCl plus 50.0 ml. of 0.010 M $Ba(OH)_2$; (c) 20.0 ml. of 0.10 M H_2SO_4 plus 60.0 ml. of 0.050 M $Ba(OH)_2$.

19.11 *Solubility*. Calculate the pH of a saturated $Sr(OH)_2$ solution.

Ans. 12.63

19.12 *Solubility*. How many moles of $Mg(OH)_2$ can be dissolved in 1.00 liter of each of the following: (a) pure water; (b) 0.050 M NaOH; (c) solution maintained at pH 9.0?

19.13 *Stoichiometry*. Given 1.8500 g. of dolomite, which consists of $CaCO_3$, $MgCO_3$, and inert material. When exactly half of this sample is treated with nitric acid, 0.0079 g. of inert residue remains undissolved. When the other half of the sample is heated to expel all the CO_2, the weight of residue is 0.4871 g. What is the molar ratio of $MgCO_3$ to $CaCO_3$ in the sample? *Ans.* 1.010

19.14 *Simultaneous equilibria*. Consider the precipitation of $BaCrO_4$ as discussed in Sec. 19.9. The equilibrium constant for $2CrO_4^{--} + 2H^+ \rightleftharpoons H_2O + Cr_2O_7^{--}$ is 4.3×10^{14}. Assume you have an acetic acid–sodium acetate buffer in which the concentrations of $HC_2H_3O_2$ and $C_2H_3O_2^-$ are equal and the concentration of $Cr_2O_7^{--}$ is 0.020 M. (a) Show that in this solution 0.020 M Ba^{++} would result in precipitation of $BaCrO_4$ but 0.020 M Sr^{++} would produce no precipitate. (b) To what pH would the solution have to be adjusted to start precipitating $SrCrO_4$ from 0.020 M Sr^{++}? *Ans.* (b) 5.43

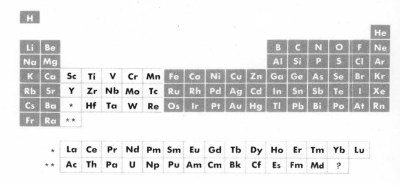

20 *Transition Elements* I
Sc, Ti, V, Cr, and Mn Subgroups

INTERVENING BETWEEN GROUPS II AND III IN THE PERIODIC TABLE are subgroups of elements collectively referred to as the transition elements. The precise definition of "transition element" is a matter of taste, and frequently there is ambiguity on the question whether a given element is included in the classification or not. Using the form of the periodic table shown in Table 3.2, we shall find it is most convenient to include all 10 of the intervening subgroups. Thus, in the fourth period the transition elements are scandium ($Z = 21$), titanium (22), vanadium (23), chromium (24), manganese (25), iron (26), cobalt (27), nickel (28), copper (29), and zinc (30). Each of these elements heads a subgroup named after itself. Thus, the titanium subgroup, for instance, includes the elements titanium ($Z = 22$), zirconium (40), and hafnium (72). In this and two succeeding chapters, we consider the properties characteristic of the transition elements. Since the first-row transition elements are most abundant and therefore most important, they are considered in greater detail than the heavier elements. First, we examine the general properties of transition elements.

20.1   ELECTRONIC CONFIGURATION

Transition elements owe their separate classification to belated filling of the next-to-outermost energy level of the atoms (Sec. 3.9). In Table 20.1 are given the detailed electronic configurations of the first-row transition elements. The significant difference in these configurations is that the third principal quantum level is gradually built up to 18 electrons by progressive addition to the $3d$ subshell. With the exception of chromium and copper, there are two electrons in the fourth shell (the $4s$ subshell). The apparent anomaly of Cr and Cu is due to the fact that the $3d$ and $4s$ subshells are very close in energy and that half-filled and filled subshells have extra stability. Thus, Cr gains stability by moving an electron from the $4s$ to the $3d$ level to give a half-filled $3d$ subshell (five out of ten maximum) and a half-filled $4s$ subshell (one out of two maximum). In Cu, the dropping of a $4s$ electron to the $3d$ subshell gives a filled $3d$ subshell and a half-filled $4s$ subshell. Actually these minor deviations in electron configuration are of little more than academic interest, since the configurations have been determined for the gaseous atoms and do not necessarily hold for other states.

In the second- and third-row transition elements, the electronic expansion is much like that just described. The detailed configurations are given in Table 3.6.

20.2   PROPERTIES

Because the electron expansion occurs in a shell other than the outermost, there is considerable similarity of the transition elements within a horizontal sequence. In fact, in some cases the horizontal similarity through a period is greater than the vertical resemblance down a subgroup.

The most characteristic property of the transition elements is that they are all metals. This is not surprising, since the outermost shell contains so few electrons. However, unlike the metals of groups I and II, the transition metals are likely to be hard, brittle, and fairly high melting. The difference is partly due to the extremely small size of the atoms (Table 3.10 shows that the atomic volumes are consistently very small) and partly to the existence of some covalent binding between the ions. There are exceptions to this general hardness, as in the case of mercury ($Z = 80$), which is a liquid and is about as soft as a metal can be.

Another characteristic property of the transition elements is that in forming compounds they exhibit many oxidation states, presumably because

Table 20.1 *Electronic Configurations*

Element	Symbol	Atomic number	Electronic configuration						
			1s	2s	2p	3s	3p	3d	4s
Scandium	Sc	21	2	2	6	2	6	1	2
Titanium	Ti	22	2	2	6	2	6	2	2
Vanadium	V	23	2	2	6	2	6	3	2
Chromium	Cr	24	2	2	6	2	6	5	1
Manganese	Mn	25	2	2	6	2	6	5	2
Iron	Fe	26	2	2	6	2	6	6	2
Cobalt	Co	27	2	2	6	2	6	7	2
Nickel	Ni	28	2	2	6	2	6	8	2
Copper	Cu	29	2	2	6	2	6	10	1
Zinc	Zn	30	2	2	6	2	6	10	2

some or all of the $3d$ electrons can also be used with $4s$ electrons in chemical bonding. Manganese ($Z = 25$), for example, has oxidation numbers of $+2$, $+3$, $+4$, $+6$, and $+7$, corresponding to use of none, one, two, four, and five of the $3d$ electrons, respectively.

Many of the compounds of the transition elements are *paramagnetic*, i.e., are attracted into a magnetic field. Such paramagnetism suggests the existence of unpaired electrons in the compounds.

Most of the compounds of the transition elements are colored, both as solid salts and in solution. This coloring suggests that in these compounds there are electronic energy levels close enough together so that electrons can easily absorb light.

Finally, it is characteristic of the transition elements that they have great ability to form many complex ions. Also the simple ions show extensive hydrolysis.

In order to account for most of the above properties, it is necessary to consider the detailed electronic configurations of the transition elements. As illustration, we consider the specific case of manganese, the electronic configuration of which is given in Table 20.1. Closed shells (shells that are fully populated) are not of interest here; hence we need consider only the third and fourth shells. The third shell consists of the three subshells $3s$, $3p$, and $3d$. The $3s$ subshell consists of but one orbital (Sec. 3.10) and can accommodate one pair of electrons; the three orbitals of the $3p$ subshell can accommodate three pairs of electrons; the five orbitals of the $3d$ subshell can accommodate five pairs of electrons. Since only the number of orbitals in a subshell is usually of interest, it is convenient to represent orbitals as dashes and to show their population by arrows pointing up or down to show the two possible spin states (Sec. 3.11). In this picture, the electronic configuration of manganese becomes

$$\underset{1s}{\uparrow\downarrow} \quad \underset{2s}{\uparrow\downarrow} \quad \underset{2p}{\uparrow\downarrow\ \uparrow\downarrow\ \uparrow\downarrow} \quad \underset{3s}{\uparrow\downarrow} \quad \underset{3p}{\uparrow\downarrow\ \uparrow\downarrow\ \uparrow\downarrow} \quad \underset{3d}{\uparrow\ \uparrow\ \uparrow\ \uparrow\ \uparrow} \quad \underset{4s}{\uparrow\downarrow}$$

Each pair of arrows represents an electron pair occupying that particular orbital; a lone arrow represents an unpaired electron in an orbital. In an isolated atom all the orbitals of a given subshell, e.g., the five orbitals of the $3d$ subshell, are of the same energy. It is also true that, whenever several orbitals of equal energy are available, electrons spread out to occupy as many orbitals (orientations in space) as possible, so as not to interfere with each other. This is the reason why the five electrons in the $3d$ subshell of manganese are shown spread out over the five orbitals instead of bunched in pairs.

With this model, it is now possible to account for the properties of manganese. For example, in solid manganese, there are Mn^{++} ions, the two $4s$ electrons having been donated to the electron cloud of the metal. In each Mn^{++} ion (as seen from the above picture) there is room for five more electrons in the five $3d$ orbitals. In other words, electrons of neighboring Mn^{++} ions can occupy these orbitals, and thus there can be electron sharing between adjacent Mn^{++} ions. Thus, with covalent bonds between Mn^{++} ions, the observed hardness, brittleness, and high melting point ($1260°C.$) of manganese are not surprising.

When manganese takes part in chemical reaction, it can do so by losing the two $4s$ electrons to form Mn^{++} ion; in addition, one or more of the five $3d$ electrons can be used for chemical bonding. It is possible to visualize the various oxidation states of manganese as corresponding to the representations shown in Table 20.2. Actually, the picture is complicated by the fact that, in the higher oxidation states, the compounds are covalent; therefore some electrons from other bound atoms may occupy these orbitals. Such additional electrons are not shown in Table 20.2.

As mentioned, unpaired electrons lead to paramagnetism. From Table 20.2, it is evident that all manganese compounds except those of manganese in the $+7$ oxidation state should be paramagnetic. Thus, Ag_2MnO_4 is strongly attracted into a magnetic field, whereas $AgMnO_4$ is not.

The color of transition-metal compounds may also be explained by the presence of $3d$ electrons. White light consists of all colors, each of which corresponds to a definite energy. When light interacts with an atom, the energy of the light can be transferred to the atom only if the amount of energy

Table 20.2 *Apparent Orbital Population of Manganese*

(Shared electron pairs not shown)

Oxidation state	3d	4s
+2	↑ ↑ ↑ ↑ ↑	
+3	↑ ↑ ↑ ↑ __	__
+4	↑ ↑ ↑ __ __	__
+6	↑ __ __ __ __	__
+7	__ __ __ __ __	__

corresponds exactly to that needed to raise an electron to a higher energy level. In transition elements, the energy needed to raise $3d$ electrons to a higher level happens to equal exactly the energy found in certain colors of visible light. Therefore, when white light is shone on a transition-element compound, some of the color components are absorbed in this excitation of $3d$ electrons. The remaining light now lacks some of its color components and no longer appears white. As a specific example, some cobalt compounds absorb red light, which, when subtracted from white light, leaves blue. For this reason, blue glass is often made by addition of cobalt compounds to glass.

The complex-ion formation so characteristic of transition elements is due to vacant orbitals. For example, when chromium ion, Cr^{+3}, forms an ammonia complex by the reaction

$$Cr^{+3} + 6:\overset{\overset{\displaystyle H}{|}}{\underset{\underset{\displaystyle H}{|}}{N}}:H \rightleftharpoons Cr(NH_3)_6{}^{+3}$$

six NH_3 molecules share their extra electron pairs with the Cr^{+3} ion. The electron configuration of Cr^{+3}

$$\underset{3d}{\underline{↑}\ \underline{↑}\ \underline{↑}\ \underline{\ }\ \underline{\ }}\qquad \underset{4s}{\underline{\ }}\qquad \underset{4p}{\underline{\ }\ \underline{\ }\ \underline{\ }}$$

indicates that there are two $3d$, one $4s$, and three $4p$ orbitals completely empty and able to accept a share of six pairs of electrons.

The rather extensive hydrolysis of transition-metal ions can be explained by the general cation-hydrolysis picture discussed in Sec. 17.12. In agreement with the above tendency to form complexes, H_2O molecules partially share their electrons with the transition-metal cation. This pulls electrons away from the H—O bond, making it easier to split off hydrogen ions.

Bearing these general properties in mind, we turn now to specific consideration of the transition elements.

20.3   SCANDIUM SUBGROUP; LANTHANIDES AND ACTINIDES

The scandium subgroup contains the elements scandium ($Z = 21$), yttrium ($Z = 39$), lanthanum through lutetium ($Z = 57$ through 71), and actinium through element 102 ($Z = 89$ through 102). The fourteen elements following lanthanum ($Z = 58$ through 71) are called the *lanthanides*, or *rare-earth elements*. The elements following actinium are called the *actinides*. As usually displayed in the periodic table (Table 3.2), the lanthanides all occupy the same position in the sixth period, below yttrium. The actinides occupy a corresponding position in the seventh period. Table 20.3 indicates the electron configurations characteristic of the scandium-subgroup elements.

The lanthanide elements correspond to belated filling of the $4f$ subshell. Since in these elements the $4f$ subshell is third outermost, changes in its electronic population are well screened from neighboring atoms by the second-outermost and outermost shells. Consequently, all the lanthanides have properties remarkably alike. Similar belated filling of the $5f$ subshell occurs in the actinide series (see Table 3.6).

The scandium-subgroup elements including the lanthanides and actinides are all typically metallic with high luster and good conductivity. They are all quite reactive, with oxidation potentials of about 2 volts. Many of their compounds such as hydroxides, carbonates, and phosphates are of low solubility. There is some slight tendency for the $+3$ ions to hydrolyze in aqueous solution to give slightly acid solutions. All these elements are quite rare in nature.

1   Scandium. Scandium occurs in nature only in the combined form in minerals such as monazite (a complex phosphate) and gadolinite (a complex silicate). Not much is known

Table 20.3   Electronic Configurations of Scandium Subgroup

Element	Z	Electron population
Scandium	21	2, 8, 9, 2
Yttrium	39	2, 8, 18, 9, 2
Lanthanum	57	2, 8, 18, 18, 9, 2
↓	↓	↓
Lutetium	71	2, 8, 18, 32, 9, 2
Actinium	89	2, 8, 18, 32, 18, 9, 2
↓	↓	↓
Element 102	102	2, 8, 18, 32, 32, 8, 2(?)

about the element except that it reacts vigorously with water to liberate hydrogen, has a melting point of about 1300°C. and a boiling point of about 2500°C., and forms compounds only in the $+3$ oxidation state. All of these compounds are colorless, and none is paramagnetic.

2   *Yttrium.* Like scandium, yttrium is quite rare. It occurs in the combined form in a few rare minerals, such as gadolinite. The metal is quite vigorously reactive but only to give compounds in which its oxidation state is $+3$. As expected, these compounds are colorless and are not paramagnetic. The oxide, Y_2O_3, or yttria, is a pure white powder. There are no commercial uses of the element or its compounds.

3   *Lanthanum and the lanthanides.* Lanthanum is the third most common element of the scandium subgroup, but its natural abundance is only 0.00007 per cent of the earth's crust. It is a rather soft, gray metal that has an oxidation potential of about $+2.4$ volts (for $La(s) \rightarrow La^{+3} + 3e^-$). Only $+3$ compounds are known. As expected, these are colorless and nonmagnetic. The oxide, La_2O_3, is the most basic oxide of the scandium subgroup.

The lanthanides include cerium (58), praseodymium (59), neodymium (60), promethium (61), samarium (62), europium (63), gadolinium (64), terbium (65), dysprosium (66), holmium (67), erbium (68), thulium (69), ytterbium (70), and lutetium (71). Except for promethium, which is radioactive and has an unstable nucleus, they always occur together in combined form. The richest source is the mineral monazite. Cerium is the most abundant (0.00031 per cent) with neodymium next (0.00018 per cent). Because of the great similarity in chemical properties, it is difficult to isolate one of the rare-earth elements from contamination by the others. Many of the properties given in the older literature are not those of the pure elements but of solid solutions.

The gradual filling of the $4f$ subshell in the lanthanides is accompanied by a slight shrinkage in atomic radius, since the nuclear charge increases through the sequence. This decrease in size, called the *lanthanide contraction*, leads to subtle differences in the properties of the elements. These slight differences have been exploited in the development of a tedious ion-exchange procedure which allows separation of the elements.

The lanthanide elements are quite vigorously reactive but can be prepared by electrolysis of the molten salts. The metals react with moist air to give oxides. Unlike Sc, Y, and La, most of the compounds of the lanthanides are colored and paramagnetic. Since the $4f$ subshell contains seven orbitals, there is good opportunity to get unpaired electrons. In addition to showing the common $+3$ oxidation states, cerium also forms Ce^{+4} and europium also forms Eu^{++}.

4   *Actinium and the actinides.* All of these elements are radioactive in that they have unstable nuclei. The elements include actinium (89), thorium (90), protactinium (91), uranium (92), neptunium (93), plutonium (94), americium (95), curium (96), berkelium (97), californium (98), einsteinium (99), fermium (100), mendelevium (101), and (102).* All of these are active metals forming compounds in several oxidation states (except only $+3$ for actinium), although the higher-numbered elements have been obtained only in trace amounts. The use of thorium, uranium, and plutonium for nuclear energy and the production of transuranium elements is discussed in Chap. 29.

---

* Element 102, prematurely "discovered" in Sweden as "nobelium," has since been definitely prepared in the United States. Its name is not yet officially chosen. Element 103, which may conclude the $5f$ electron expansion, has not yet been produced.

Experiments to determine the electronic configurations of the actinides are not conclusive, and the assignment of electrons to various energy levels as given in Table 3.6 is in doubt. In general, the elements are not nearly so similar in behavior as are the lanthanides.

20.4 TITANIUM SUBGROUP

The elements of the titanium subgroup are titanium ($Z = 22$), zirconium ($Z = 40$), and hafnium ($Z = 72$). They are more common than the elements of the scandium subgroup, and their chemistry is more complicated because of the additional oxidation state, $+4$. As Table 20.4 indicates, each of these elements has two electrons in the outermost shell and two d electrons in the second-outermost shell. Removal of the outermost electrons would give the $+2$ oxidation state; further removal of one or two electrons from the second-outermost shell would give the $+3$ and the $+4$ states. Only in the case of Ti are all three of these states observed. For Zr, there are some $+3$ compounds, but the $+4$ state is the more common. Hafnium forms compounds only in the $+4$ state. This trend of favoring the higher oxidation states in going down the group is typical of the transition subgroups.

Other characteristic properties of the titanium subgroup elements are that the elements are metallic, have very high melting and boiling points, and are quite reactive to most oxidizing agents. Although it does not show up in the physical properties, there is an extraordinary similarity in the chemical properties of Zr and Hf. This similarity is attributed to the lanthanide contraction, which just intervenes between these two elements and makes their atoms identical in size.

1   Titanium. In the earth's crust, titanium is tenth most abundant (0.58 per cent by weight) and ranks ahead of such familiar elements as

Table 20.4   Elements of Titanium Subgroup

Symbol	Z	Electronic configuration	Melting point, °C.	Boiling point, °C.	Ionization potential, e.v.	Oxidation potential, volts
Ti	22	2, 8, 10, 2	1660	>3000	6.83	+1.6 (to Ti^{++})
Zr	40	2, 8, 18, 10, 2	1860	>3000	6.95	+1.5 (to ZrO^{++})
Hf	72	2, 8, 18, 32, 10, 2	2200	>3000	5.5	+1.7 (to HfO^{++})

chlorine, carbon, and sulfur. However, it is distributed very widely, and commercially useful deposits are scarce. The principal sources are rutile (TiO_2), ilmenite ($FeTiO_3$), and iron ores. It is very difficult to prepare the pure metal, because it has great affinity for carbon, nitrogen, oxygen, and hydrogen. The usual method for getting Ti is to convert the oxides with chlorine to $TiCl_4$, which is then reduced with Mg.

Pure titanium which has low carbon impurity and is free from hydrogen embrittlement (Sec. 15.4) is extremely strong (stronger than iron). Because it also has a high melting point and is resistant to corrosion (because of surface coatings of oxide and nitride), the metal is in great demand as a structural material, for example, in jet engines. Until recently, the principal use of titanium had been for hardening and toughening steel.

In its compounds, titanium exhibits oxidation states of $+2$, $+3$, and $+4$. Compounds of the first two are colored and paramagnetic because of the presence of unpaired d electrons. They are also good reducing agents. For the half-reaction $Ti^{++} \rightleftharpoons Ti^{+3} + e^-$, the oxidation potential is $+0.37$ volt, indicating that Ti^{++} is a better reducing agent than H_2 and that Ti^{++} added to H^+ solutions liberates H_2.

Titanous ion, Ti^{+3}, is a violet ion which also is a convenient reducing agent. When oxidized in aqueous solution, it does not form titanic ion, Ti^{+4}, as expected, but appears in a hydrolyzed form usually written TiO^{++} and called titanyl ion. From this are derived ionic salts such as $TiOSO_4$, titanyl sulfate. Like most of the $+3$ ions of the transition elements, Ti^{+3} forms an insoluble trihydroxide when base is added to its solutions. This black $Ti(OH)_3$ turns white and evolves H_2 when allowed to stand, indicating decomposition:

$$2Ti(OH)_3(s) \rightarrow 2TiO_2(s) + 2H_2O + H_2(g)$$

The most important oxidation state of titanium is the $+4$, and probably the most important compound is TiO_2, titanium dioxide, or titania. This compound is quite inert and has good covering power; it is used extensively as a pigment in both the paint industry and the cosmetic industry. In crystalline form, it is used as a semiprecious, artificial gem. With a higher refractive index than diamond (Sec. 24.2), it has more sparkle than diamond, but, unfortunately, it is not very hard and becomes scratched. When TiO_2 is heated with carbon in a stream of chlorine, titanium tetrachloride ($TiCl_4$) is formed. This is a colorless, fuming liquid which is used for making smoke screens. The smoke is thought to be $TiCl_4 \cdot 4H_2O$.

2   Zirconium and hafnium. These two elements are remarkable because they have essentially identical chemical properties. The atomic radii of Zr and Hf are 1.454 A. and 1.442 A., respectively. Since their outer-electron configurations are the same, it is not surprising that the two elements resemble each other chemically. The resemblance is so marked that hafnium atoms replace zirconium atoms in crystals with ease. For this reason, all naturally occurring zirconium minerals are contaminated with hafnium. Zirconium is about fifty times as abundant as hafnium, which makes up only 4.5×10^{-4} per cent of the earth's crust. The principal minerals of Zr are baddeleyite (ZrO_2) and zircon ($ZrSiO_4$). In its transparent form, especially when colored, zircon finds use as a gem stone.

Zr and Hf metals are extremely difficult to prepare in the pure state, because, like Ti, they have such great affinity for hydrogen, carbon, oxygen, and nitrogen. One method for getting the pure metals is the thermal decomposition of the tetraiodide (MI_4) on a hot tungsten wire.

Practically all the known compounds of Zr and Hf correspond to the $+4$ oxidation state. Of these, the oxides zirconia (ZrO_2) and hafnia (HfO_2) are refractory and are used for high-temperature insulation. In the Nernst glow lamp, used in scientific work as a concentrated light source, the incandescent body is chiefly ZrO_2. The other $+4$ compounds readily hydrolyze to form the zirconyl (ZrO^{++}) or hafnyl (HfO^{++}) ions, which can also be written as $M(OH)_2{}^{++}$. The actual species present in solution is not known. It may even be $M(OH)_3{}^+$.

Like titanium, both zirconium and hafnium form complex ions, especially with fluorine. Examples of these are $ZrF_6{}^{--}$ and $ZrF_7{}^{-3}$. The latter is a rather rare illustration of seven neighbors about a central atom. The complex salts K_2ZrF_6 and K_2HfF_6 differ in solubility, and this is the basis of the separation of Zr from Hf by fractional crystallization.

At this point, it might be appropriate to note that the naming of complex ions is rather complicated. For example, $ZrF_6{}^{--}$ is often called "fluorozirconate" ion, but to distinguish it from $ZrF_7{}^{-3}$, it should more properly be called "hexafluorozirconate" ion. To reduce ambiguity, the modern trend of nomenclature is to indicate also the oxidation number. Thus, K_3HfF_7 is called "tripotassium heptafluorohafniate (IV)" where IV indicates the oxidation state $+4$. Since nomenclature is not standardized, it is necessary to be cautious and ingenious in looking up information about complex compounds in the scientific literature.

20.5   VANADIUM SUBGROUP

The elements of the vanadium subgroup are vanadium ($Z = 23$), niobium ($Z = 41$), and tantalum ($Z = 73$). The name columbium has also been used instead of niobium. These elements are considerably less abundant than those of the titanium subgroup, and their chemistry is more complicated because of the formation of a $+5$ oxidation state. Properties are summarized in Table 20.5. Of these elements, vanadium shows compounds corresponding to oxidation states $+2$, $+3$, $+4$, and $+5$. Niobium shows $+5$ and possibly $+3$; tantalum shows only $+5$. Again because of the intervening lanthanide contraction, the last two elements of the subgroup are very similar in chemical properties.

1   Vanadium. The principal minerals of vanadium are patronite (V_2S_5) and vanadinite ($Pb_5V_3O_{12}Cl$), but it is also obtained as a valuable

Table 20.5   *Elements of Vanadium Subgroup*

Sym-bol	z	Electronic configuration	Melting point, °C.	Boiling point, °C.	Ioni-zation poten-tial, e.v.	Oxidation potential, volts
V	23	2, 8, 11, 2	1710	3000(?)	6.74	$+1.2$(to V^{++})
Nb	41	2, 8, 18, 12, 1	1950	3000(?)	6.77	$+0.65$(to Nb_2O_5)
Ta	73	2, 8, 18, 32, 11, 2	>3000	>4100	6	$+0.81$(to Ta_2O_5)

by-product from the uranium mineral carnotite ($KUVO_6$). The name vanadium comes from Vanadis, the Scandinavian goddess of beauty, and recalls the beautiful colors of the various vanadium compounds. The pure metal is very hard to prepare, and since the main use of V is as an additive to steel alloys, it is usually made as ferrovanadium (solid solution of Fe and V). When added to steel, the V combines with the oxygen and nitrogen, and also dissolves in the molten iron, to increase the tensile strength, toughness, and elasticity of the resulting steel.

In its compounds, vanadium shows oxidation states of $+2$, $+3$, $+4$, and $+5$. These correspond to at least partial removal of the two $4s$ electrons plus none, one, two, or all of the three $3d$ electrons. Many of the compounds are characteristically colored. Those in the lower oxidation states are good reducing agents.

Probably the most important compound of vanadium is the pentoxide, V_2O_5. This is a red or orange solid made by thermal decomposition of ammonium vanadate (NH_4VO_3). It is used as a catalyst in various oxidation reactions where O_2 is the oxidizing agent, e.g., in the conversion of SO_2 to SO_3 for making sulfuric acid. Vanadium pentoxide is amphoteric. It dissolves in highly acid solutions to give an ion variously described as VO^{+3}, $V(OH)_2^{+3}$, VO_2^+, or $V(OH)_4^+$; in basic solution, V_2O_5 dissolves to give vanadate anions such as VO_4^{-3}. When acid is gradually added to these vanadate solutions, anions are formed which contain more than one V atom per ion (such as $V_2O_7^{-4}$). Eventually V_2O_5 precipitates.

Acid solutions containing vanadium in the $+5$ oxidation state go through a series of color changes when a reducing agent such as zinc is added. The solutions first turn blue, then green, and then violet, corresponding to stepwise reduction to the $+4$, $+3$, and $+2$ states. The characteristic ions are $V(OH)_2^{++}$, V^{+3} (vanadic), and V^{++} (vanadous). The oxidation potentials relating these species are:

$$V(s) \rightleftharpoons V^{++} + 2e^- \qquad\qquad +1.2 \text{ volts}$$

$$V^{++} \rightleftharpoons V^{+3} + e^- \qquad\qquad +0.25 \text{ volt}$$

$$2H_2O + V^{+3} \rightleftharpoons V(OH)_2^{++} + 2H^+ + e^- \qquad -0.36 \text{ volt}$$

$$2H_2O + V(OH)_2^{++} \rightleftharpoons V(OH)_4^+ + 2H^+ + e^- \qquad -1.0 \text{ volt}$$

Since the oxidation potential of $Zn(s) \rightleftharpoons Zn^{++} + 2e^-$ is $+0.76$ volt, zinc can reverse each of the above half-reactions except the first.

2   Niobium and tantalum. Both niobium and tantalum are rather rare elements, and almost always they are found together in nature. The principal minerals are columbite and tantalite, which are mixed oxides of the two metals along with those of iron and manganese. Although Ta is rare in nature (0.00021 per cent, an abundance about one-tenth that of Nb), its desirable properties have led to rather extensive use. The problem of preparation is a difficult one, and, in fact, the name tantalum reflects the frustrations in its first recovery. In Greek mythology Tantalus was sent to Hell, where, plagued by hunger and thirst, he was placed near food and drink which always stayed out of reach. The close relationship of Nb to Ta is indicated by the name niobium, after Niobe, the tragic daughter of Tantalus. In order to separate the two elements, the mixed oxides are converted by HF and KF to K_2TaF_7 (fluorotantalate) and K_2NbOF_5 (oxyfluoroniobate), which differ in solubility and can be concentrated by fractional crystallization.

Tantalum has very high ductility and for a time preceded tungsten as filament material in electric-light bulbs and electron tubes. It is also used in one kind of electrolytic *rectifier*, a device for converting alternating current into direct current. This rectifier consists of an aqueous solution with two electrodes, one of which is Ta. When the Ta acts as an anode, it immediately forms an oxide coat, which cuts off the current. Ta can, however, act as a cathode and so permits flow of current in only one direction. Since tantalum is very resistant to corrosion, it is used extensively for constructing apparatus in chemical plants, especially in apparatus designed for handling acids.

The most common compounds of Nb and Ta are the pentoxides, Nb_2O_5 and Ta_2O_5. These are rather inert, stable solids which can be formed by heating the finely divided metals in air or oxygen. They dissolve in concentrated bases to form niobate and tantalate anions. Little is known of these anions except that they are quite complex and can have varying numbers of metal atoms per ion. Tantalum carbide, TaC, made by heating the oxide with carbon, is extremely hard and finds use in making tools for high-speed machining of metals and wiredrawing dies.

20.6   CHROMIUM SUBGROUP

The chromium subgroup contains the elements chromium $(Z = 24)$, molybdenum $(Z = 42)$, and tungsten $(Z = 74)$. They are all metals of small atomic volume, extremely high melting point, great hardness, and excellent resistance to corrosion. Their chemistry is complicated by the existence of several oxidation states ranging from $+2$ to $+6$ and by the formation of many complex ions, including oxyanions. Some properties are given in Table 20.6. All of these elements form compounds in which they show the $+6$ oxidation state. In addition, chromium commonly shows $+2$ and $+3$ states, and molybdenum $+3$ and $+4$ states.

1   Chromium. Chromium is one of the less abundant metals (0.037 per cent of the earth's crust), but still it is approximately fifty times as abundant as Mo and W. Its principal mineral is chromite ($FeCr_2O_4$), some of which is reduced directly by heating with carbon in order to provide ferrochromium (solid solution of Cr in Fe) for addition to alloy steels. Low-chrome steels (up to 1 per cent Cr) are quite hard and strong; high-chrome steels (up to 30 per cent Cr), or stainless steels, are very resistant to corrosion. Most of the remaining chromite is converted to sodium chromate (Na_2CrO_4) by heating it with Na_2CO_3 in air.

$$8Na_2CO_3(s) + 4FeCr_2O_4(s) + 7O_2(g) \rightarrow$$
$$2Fe_2O_3(s) + 8Na_2CrO_4(s) + 8CO_2(g)$$

The sodium chromate is leached out with acid to form $Na_2Cr_2O_7$, an important oxidizing agent.

Chromium metal is very hard and, although quite reactive in the powdered form, in the massive form is quite resistant to corrosion. Furthermore, it takes a high polish, which lasts because of formation of an invisible, self-protective oxide coat. Consequently, chromium finds much use as a plating material, both for its decorative effect (0.00005 cm. thick) and for its protective effect (0.0075 cm. thick). The plate is usually put on by electrolyzing the object in a bath made by dissolving $Na_2Cr_2O_7$ and H_2SO_4 in water. Since plating will not occur unless the sulfate is present, the sulfate must be involved in some intermediate formed during the electrolysis.

Table 20.6   Elements of Chromium Subgroup

Symbol	z	Electronic configuration	Melting point, °C.	Boiling point, °C.	Ionization potential, e.v.	Oxidation potential, volts
Cr	24	2, 8, 13, 1	1600	2500(?)	6.76	$+0.91$ (to Cr^{++})
Mo	42	2, 8, 18, 13, 1	2620	>3700	7.18	$+0.2$ (to Mo^{+3})
W	74	2, 8, 18, 32, 12, 2	3370	5900	7.98	$+0.12$ (to WO_2)

The compounds of chromium are all colored, a fact which suggested the name chromium, from the Greek word for color, *chrōma*. The characteristic oxidation states are $+2$, $+3$, and $+6$, represented in acid solution by Cr^{++} (chromous), Cr^{+3} (chromic), and $Cr_2O_7^{--}$ (dichromate) and in basic media by $Cr(OH)_2$, CrO_2^- (chromite), and CrO_4^{--} (chromate).

The chromous ion, Cr^{++}, is a beautiful blue ion obtained by reducing either Cr^{+3} or $Cr_2O_7^{--}$ with zinc metal. However, it is rapidly oxidized in aqueous solution by air. The oxidation potential for $Cr^{++} \rightleftharpoons Cr^{+3} + e^-$ is $+0.41$ volt, which means that Cr^{++} should also be oxidized by H^+, but the latter reaction is very slow. When base is added to solutions of chromous salts, chromous hydroxide precipitates. On exposure to air, $Cr(OH)_2$ is oxidized by O_2 to give $Cr(OH)_3$ (also written $Cr_2O_3 \cdot xH_2O$).

Many chromic salts, such as chromic nitrate, $Cr(NO_3)_3$, and chromic perchlorate, $Cr(ClO_4)_3$, dissolve in water to give violet solutions, in which the violet color is due to the hydrated chromic ion, $Cr(H_2O)_6^{+3}$. If high concentrations of chloride ion are added, some of the hydrate water is replaced, and the solution slowly turns green because of formation of a chloro complex. Solutions of chromic salts can be kept indefinitely, exposed to the air, without oxidation or reduction. In general, they are slightly acid because of hydrolysis of the chromic ion. This reaction can be written in either of the following ways:

$$Cr^{+3} + H_2O \rightleftharpoons CrOH^{++} + H^+$$

$$Cr(H_2O)_6^{+3} \rightleftharpoons Cr(H_2O)_5OH^{++} + H^+$$

When base is gradually added to chromic solutions, a green slimy precipitate, which is either $Cr(OH)_3 \cdot xH_2O$ or $Cr_2O_3 \cdot xH_2O$, first forms but then disappears as excess OH^- is added. A deep green color characteristic of chromite ion, written as CrO_2^- or $Cr(OH)_4^-$, is produced. The precipitation and redissolving associated with this amphoteric behavior can be described as follows:

$$Cr^{+3} + 3OH^- \rightarrow Cr(OH)_3(s)$$

$$Cr(OH)_3(s) + OH^- \rightarrow CrO_2^- + 2H_2O$$

The green species in the final solution is certainly more complicated than CrO_2^- and probably contains more than one Cr atom per ion. When filtered off and heated, the insoluble hydroxide loses water to form Cr_2O_3, chromic oxide or chromium sesquioxide. This is an inert green powder much used as the pigment chrome green.

Chromic ion forms a great number of complex ions. In all of these the chromium atom is surrounded by six other atoms arranged at the corners of an octahedron. A typical octahedral complex, CrF_6^{-3}, is shown in Fig.

20.1. The easiest way to visualize the three-dimensional nature of this complex is to imagine four F atoms at the corners of a square in the middle of which sits the Cr atom. Directly above and below the Cr atom are the fifth and sixth F atoms. All six octahedral positions are equivalent. Other octahedral complexes of chromic ion are $Cr(NH_3)_6^{+3}$, $Cr(H_2O)_6^{+3}$, $Cr(H_2O)_5Cl^{++}$, $Cr(NH_3)_4Cl_2^+$, etc. It is characteristic of all these complexes that they form and dissociate very slowly. In potassium chrome alum, $KCr(SO_4)_2 \cdot 12H_2O$, the $Cr(H_2O)_6^{+3}$ complex occurs as a unit in occupying some of the crystal lattice sites.

In the $+6$ oxidation state, chromium is known principally as the chromates and dichromates. The chromate ion, CrO_4^{--}, can be made quite easily by oxidizing chromite ion, CrO_2^-, in basic solution with a moderately good oxidizing agent such as hydrogen peroxide. The reaction is

$$2CrO_2^- + 3HO_2^- \rightarrow 2CrO_4^{--} + H_2O + OH^-$$

where the peroxide is written as HO_2^-, because H_2O_2 is an acid and does not exist in basic solution. The chromate ion is yellow and has a tetrahedral structure with four oxygen atoms bound to a central chromium atom.

When solutions of chromate salts are acidified, the yellow color is replaced by a characteristic orange, the result of formation of $Cr_2O_7^{--}$, dichromate ion.

$$2CrO_4^{--} + 2H^+ \rightleftharpoons Cr_2O_7^{--} + H_2O$$

The change is reversed by adding base. The structure of the dichromate ion is shown in Fig. 20.2 and consists of two tetrahedra sharing an oxygen atom. Each of the two chromium atoms at the centers of the tetrahedra is bound to four oxygen atoms at the corners. The dichromate ion is a very good oxidizing agent, especially in acid solution. The half-reaction

$$2Cr^{+3} + 7H_2O \rightleftharpoons Cr_2O_7^{--} + 14H^+ + 6e^-$$

Fig. 20.1 *Octahedral chromium complex.*

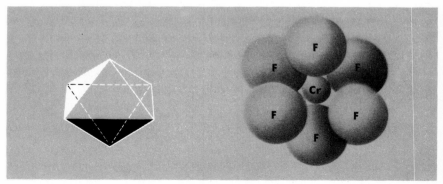

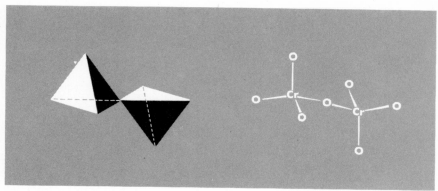

Fig. 20.2   Dichromate ion.

has an oxidation potential of -1.33 volts; therefore $Cr_2O_7^{--}$ is able to oxidize all but the very poorest reducing agents. It will, for example, oxidize hydrogen peroxide to form O_2:

$$Cr_2O_7^{--} + 3H_2O_2 + 8H^+ \rightarrow 3O_2(g) + 2Cr^{+3} + 7H_2O$$

It might seem strange that in basic solution hydrogen peroxide oxidizes chromium, whereas in acid solution chromium oxidizes hydrogen peroxide. The reason for this is that, in going from the $+3$ to the $+6$ state of chromium (Cr^{+3} to $Cr_2O_7^{--}$), oxygen atoms have to be added, whereas, in going from the $+6$ to the $+3$ state ($Cr_2O_7^{--}$ to Cr^{+3}), oxygen is removed. In acid solution, H^+ helps in removing oxygen by forming water; in basic solution, the scarcity of H^+ allows addition of oxygen. In the general case of preparing compounds, the change to compounds of higher oxidation state is usually most easily done in basic solution; to go to compounds of lower oxidation state, it is best to work in acid solution.

When solutions of dichromate ion are made very acid, especially in the presence of a dehydrating agent such as concentrated H_2SO_4, the uncharged species, CrO_3, is formed. This deep red solid is chromium trioxide, or, as it is sometimes called, chromic anhydride. It is a very powerful oxidizing agent and is used extensively in preparing organic compounds (see Chap. 24). Solutions of CrO_3 in concentrated H_2SO_4 are used as "cleaning solution" for glass equipment in laboratories. The cleaning action is due to the oxidation of grease.

2   Molybdenum. Molybdenum is found in nature as the mineral molybdenite, MoS_2, a beautiful blue-gray material of metallic luster, frequently confused with graphite. When heated in air, MoS_2 is oxidized to the trioxide, MoO_3, which is then reduced to the metal by heating with hydrogen. Because of its very high melting point ($2620°C$.), Mo is obtained as a powder. This is pressed into bars and heated, so as to sinter the particles together to give sheet or wire for use as supports in X-ray tubes, electron tubes, electric furnaces, etc., where high temperatures may develop locally.

The major part of the Mo metal produced goes into iron alloys, where it acts as a toughening agent, favoring fine-grained structure. The molybdenum is added as ferromolybdenum (55 to 75 per cent Mo in Fe), made by reducing mixed oxides of Mo and Fe.

The most important oxidation state of molybdenum is $+6$, as, for example, in molybdenum trioxide, MoO_3. This trioxide is acidic and dissolves in basic solutions to form a complicated series of oxyanions called the molybdates, the simplest of which is MoO_4^{--}. More complicated molybdates, having Mo-O-Mo bridges and containing up to 24 Mo atoms per ion, are known. These are called polymolybdates but are not well characterized. Neither MoO_3 nor the molybdates are particularly good oxidizing agents. When reduced, MoO_3 can form a deep blue oxide of variable composition $MoO_{2.5-3.0}$, which is apparently some sort of defect structure (Sec. 8.5). Further reduction of MoO_3 or the molybdates usually forms the metal, but under appropriate conditions Mo^{+3} can be formed in aqueous solution. Its properties have not been well determined.

3   Tungsten. The element tungsten is frequently also called wolfram, whence the symbol W. It occurs in nature principally as the tungstates, e.g., as a calcium tungstate, $CaWO_4$, or scheelite, and as a mixture of iron and manganese tungstates, $(Fe,Mn)WO_4$, or wolframite. In order to get the metal, tungstates are treated with acid to precipitate insoluble tungstic acid, H_2WO_4, which is then dehydrated by ignition to tungstic oxide, WO_3. Hydrogen reduction of WO_3 produces W.

Since W has such a high melting point,* it, like Mo, is obtained as a fine powder, which is sintered into workable form. Fine tungsten wire for lamp filaments can be produced by heating the sintered powder in H_2 and subjecting the specimen to prolonged, vigorous pounding in a swaging machine (a machine for beating wire from large cross section down to small). Finally, an electric current through the wire heats it to a very high temperature, at which the microparticles coalesce.

The metal is rather inert to common oxidizing agents such as oxygen and nitric acid. However, it can be dissolved in a mixture of concentrated HNO_3 and HF. Most W goes into steel production, especially to make "high-speed steel" for cutting tools. Addition of W increases the ability to hold hardness at high temperatures and slows down the tearing off of small particles that causes the dulling of fast finishing tools.

In its compounds, tungsten usually occurs as the $+6$ oxidation state. The oxide WO_3 is acidic and dissolves in basic solutions or in molten basic oxides to form tungstates and polytungstates. Like the molybdates, the tungstates are not particularly good oxidizing agents.

20.7   MANGANESE SUBGROUP

The elements of the manganese subgroup are manganese ($Z = 25$), technetium ($Z = 43$), and rhenium ($Z = 75$). Manganese is by far the most important of the group; technetium is radioactive and does not occur in nature;

---

* At room temperature, tungsten has an extremely small vapor pressure. It has been calculated to correspond to one W atom per universe.

rhenium is so rare as to constitute a chemical curiosity. Some of the properties of the subgroup are given in Table 20.7.

1   Manganese. Manganese is not a very common element (abundance, 0.08 per cent), but in the earth's crust it is as abundant as carbon and more so than sulfur. The most important minerals are the oxides: MnO_2 or pyrolusite, Mn_2O_3 or braunite (usually contaminated with iron oxide), and Mn_3O_4 or hausmannite. Probably the best way to prepare the metal is by reduction with powdered aluminum. However, since most metallic manganese goes into steel production, alloys of manganese are used instead. Two such alloys are ferromanganese (about 80 per cent Mn in Fe) and spiegeleisen (about 20 to 30 per cent Mn and about 5 per cent C in Fe); they are made by reducing mixed oxides of iron and manganese in a blast furnace with carbon or carbon monoxide acting as reducing agent. When added to steel, Mn has two functions. In low amounts, it acts as a scavenger by combining with O and S in the molten iron to form easily removable substances. In high amounts (up to 14 per cent), it imparts special hardness and toughness such as is needed for resistance to battering abrasion.

In its chemical compounds, manganese shows oxidation states of $+2$, $+3$, $+4$, $+6$, and $+7$. Most of these compounds are colored and paramagnetic. In the $+2$ state, manganese exists as the manganous ion, Mn^{++}. This is one of the few pink ions in chemistry, and many manganous salts, such as manganous sulfate, $MnSO_4$, and manganous chloride, $MnCl_2$, have pink coloration. Unlike Cr^{++}, Mn^{++} is a very poor reducing agent, and neutral or acid solutions of manganous salts can be kept indefinitely exposed to oxygen or other oxidizing agents. When base is added to Mn^{++}, a white precipitate of $Mn(OH)_2$ is formed. This solid, unlike manganous salts, is promptly oxidized by air to the $+3$ state.

In the $+3$ state, manganese can exist as the manganic ion, Mn^{+3}, but only in solids and complex ions. Unlike Cr^{+3}, Mn^{+3} is a very powerful

Table 20.7   Elements of Manganese Subgroup

Symbol	z	Electronic configuration	Melting point, °C.	Boiling point, °C.	Ionization potential, e.v.	Oxidation potential, volts
Mn	25	2, 8, 13, 2	1260	1900	7.43	$+1.18$(to Mn^{++})
Tc	43	2, 8, 18, 14, 1(?)	—	—	—	-0.4(?)(to Tc^{++})
Re	75	2, 8, 18, 32, 13, 2	3200	—	7.87	-0.25(to ReO_2)

oxidizing agent and can even oxidize H_2O to liberate oxygen. The oxidation potential of $Mn^{++} \rightleftharpoons Mn^{+3} + e^-$ is -1.51 volts, high enough so that manganic ion can oxidize itself to the $+4$ state:

$$2Mn^{+3} + 2H_2O \rightarrow Mn^{++} + MnO_2(s) + 4H^+$$

This disproportionation can be prevented and the $+3$ state stabilized by (1) complexing the manganese, e.g., with cyanide, CN^-, to give $Mn(CN)_6^{-3}$ or with oxalate, $C_2O_4^{--}$, to give $Mn(C_2O_4)_3^{-3}$, or by (2) forming an insoluble salt, such as $MnPO_4$, manganic phosphate, or the hydroxide, written as $Mn(OH)_3$ or $MnOOH$ or even Mn_2O_3.

In the $+4$ state the principal compound of manganese is manganese dioxide, MnO_2. It is not a simple compound, because no matter how careful the preparation, the product always contains less than two oxygen atoms per manganese atom. As mentioned in Sec. 14.7, MnO_2 is the oxidizing agent in the dry cell.

When MnO_2 is heated with basic substances in air, it is oxidized from its original black color to a deep green, the result of conversion to manganate ion, MnO_4^{--}. Though stable in alkaline solution, this ion (which represents Mn in the $+6$ state) disproportionates when the solution is acidified.

$$3MnO_4^{--} + 4H^+ \rightarrow MnO_2(s) + 2MnO_4^- + 2H_2O$$

The MnO_4^- ion is the permanganate ion and shows manganese in its highest oxidation state. It is a very good oxidizing agent, especially in acid solution, where it is usually reduced all the way to manganous ion. For the half-reaction

$$Mn^{++} + 4H_2O \rightleftharpoons MnO_4^- + 8H^+ + 5e^-$$

the oxidation potential is -1.51 volts. This means that MnO_4^- is one of the strongest common oxidizing agents. Solutions of permanganate salts are frequently used in analytical chemistry to determine amounts of reducing agents by titration. Titration is simplified by using the disappearance of the deep violet color of MnO_4^- as the end-point indicator. The usual procedure is to make the solutions acid, so as to get complete reduction to Mn^{++}. With neutral or alkaline solutions, MnO_2 is formed; in very basic solutions, MnO_4^{--}. When $KMnO_4$ is treated with concentrated H_2SO_4, a violently explosive oil, Mn_2O_7, or manganese heptoxide, is formed.

The chemistry of manganese illustrates well how the characteristics of compounds change in going from low oxidation state to high. In the low oxidation states, manganese exists as a cation which forms basic oxides and hydroxides. In the higher oxidation states, it exists as anions derived from acidic oxides.

2 *Technetium.* Since the technetium nucleus is very unstable and rapidly undergoes radioactive decay, it does not occur in nature. The name is derived from the Greek *technetos,* for artificial, and draws attention to the fact that it is made synthetically by bombardment of molybdenum with neutrons. Tc does not resemble manganese nearly so much as it does the following element rhenium.

3 *Rhenium.* Rhenium is a very rare element (abundance, 10^{-7} per cent by weight) occurring in trace amounts in molybdenite, columbite, and pyrolusite. The element is extracted by oxidizing to perrhenic acid, $HReO_4$, and precipitating as slightly soluble potassium perrhenate, $KReO_4$. In many of its properties, Re is much like tungsten. It has a high melting point (about 3200°C.) and a high density (21 g./cc.), and is not particularly reactive. When heated in air, it gives off clouds of pale yellow rhenium heptoxide, a volatile solid which, unlike Mn_2O_7, is not explosive. Like WO_3, Re_2O_7 is an acidic oxide and not especially reactive. Compounds of lower oxidation states (including a surprising -1 state) have been reported. Rhenium is too scarce to be much used, but it does have remarkable catalytic properties for hydrogenation reactions.

20.8   QUALITATIVE ANALYSIS

Of the elements discussed in this chapter, only manganese and chromium are included in the common schemes of qualitative analysis. The confirming tests depend on the characteristic colors of compounds of these elements.

If the chromium and manganese are present in the original unknown mixture as chromate or dichromate and permanganate, they will be reduced by H_2S in acid solution to Cr^{+3} and Mn^{++}, forming finely divided sulfur in the process. When the solution, still containing sulfide, is made basic $Cr(OH)_3$ and MnS precipitate. Treatment with acid and an oxidizing agent serves to remove the sulfide and subsequent addition of excess NaOH precipitates manganese as a hydroxide and converts the chromium to soluble chromite ion. The appearance of a green color in the solution at this point is strong indication of the presence of chromium. It can be confirmed by treating the green, basic solution with H_2O_2 to oxidize chromite to yellow chromate which can be precipitated as yellow $BaCrO_4$ by the addition of barium ion in an acetic acid buffer.

The hydroxide precipitate suspected of containing manganese, on treatment with acid and a very strong oxidizing agent such as sodium bismuthate, $NaBiO_3$, or sodium periodate, $NaIO_4$, produces the characteristic violet color of MnO_4^- if manganese is present.

QUESTIONS

20.1 *Electronic configuration.* What are "transition elements"? What is characteristic about their electronic configurations?

20.2 *Properties.* Account for each of the characteristic properties usually shown by the transition elements.

20.3 *Terms.* Identify each of the following: lanthanide elements, actinide elements, orbital, lanthanide contraction, spiegeleisen, chromium subgroup, paramagnetism, pyrolusite.

20.4 *Cr and Mn.* Make tables for chromium and manganese, showing the characteristic species for each oxidation state in acid and basic solutions. If there is no soluble species, indicate the solid.

20.5 *Equations.* Write balanced equations for each of the following changes: (a) hydrolysis of a transition-metal ion; (b) formation of a complex ion; (c) scandium dissolving in acid; (d) reduction of $TiCl_4$ with Mg; (e) three steps in the reduction of $V(OH)_4^+$ by Zn; (f) air oxidation of Cr^{++} in acid solution; (g) reduction of $Cr_2O_7^{--}$ by Cr^{++}; (h) reaction between Ce^{+4} and Eu^{++}; (i) $Mo^{+3} + MnO_4^- \rightarrow MoO_3(s) + Mn^{++}$; (j) amphoterism of $Cr(OH)_3$ (two equations needed).

20.6 *Oxidation states.* (a) How does the maximum oxidation state change from scandium through manganese? (b) In going down a subgroup, the higher oxidation states become more stable. Illustrate by reference to the oxidizing ability of compounds in the maximum oxidation state.

20.7 *Oxidation.* In preparing compounds of high oxidation state, it is preferable to use alkaline conditions rather than acid. Explain.

20.8 *Structures.* Sketch spatial configurations for the following complexes:

$$CrO_4^{--}, \quad MoO_4^{--}, \quad Cr(NH_3)_6^{+3}, \quad Cr(NH_3)_4Cl_2^+$$

20.9 *Technetium.* Predict the properties (including chemical behavior) of technetium.

20.10 *Electronic configurations.* Assign the $3d$ and $4s$ electrons to orbitals in each of the following, tell which of the gaseous species should be paramagnetic, and indicate which ions might be colored: V, Cr, V^{++}, Sc^{+3}, Cu^{++}, Zn^{++}.

20.11 *Hydrolysis.* For the equilibrium $Cr^{+3} + H_2O \rightleftharpoons H^+ + CrOH^{++}$, the constant K is 2×10^{-4}. (a) Calculate the values of the equilibrium constants for each of the following:

$$CrOH^{++} \rightleftharpoons Cr^{+3} + OH^-$$
$$Cr^{+3} + OH^- \rightleftharpoons CrOH^{++}$$
$$Cr(H_2O)_6^{+3} \rightleftharpoons Cr(H_2O)_5OH^{++} + H^+$$

(b) What should be the pH of a solution which contains 1.0 g. of $KCr(SO_4)_2 \cdot 12H_2O$ per 5.0 ml. of solution?   *Ans.* (b) 2.0

20.12 *Oxidation potentials.* Calculate the voltage for the cell (all concentrations at 1 m) that uses the reaction

$$2Mn^{+3} + 2H_2O \rightarrow MnO_2(s) + Mn^{++} + 4H^+$$

from the oxidation potentials

$$Mn^{++} \rightarrow Mn^{+3} + e^- \qquad\qquad -1.51 \text{ volts}$$

$$Mn^{+3} + 2H_2O \rightarrow MnO_2(s) + 4H^+ + e^- \qquad -0.95 \text{ volt}$$

What does your answer imply about Mn^{+3}? Show that the fact that $Mn(CN)_6^{-3}$ does not disproportionate is not necessarily inconsistent with your result.

20.13 *Stoichiometry.* (*a*) Write a balanced net equation for the following change in acidic solution:

$$Mn^{++} + S_2O_8^{--} \rightarrow MnO_4^- + SO_4^{--}$$

(*b*) What will be the concentration of MnO_4^- in a solution made by mixing 20.0 ml. of 0.016 M Mn^{++} with 40.0 ml. of 0.040 M $S_2O_8^{--}$, if reaction proceeds as in (*a*)?

20.14 *Stoichiometry.* The concentration of an unknown solution of $KMnO_4$ can be determined by allowing the unknown solution to react with H_2O_2 and measuring the oxygen evolved. (*a*) Balance the equation for the following in acid solution

$$MnO_4^- + H_2O_2 \rightarrow Mn^{++} + O_2(g)$$

(*b*) If 24.0 ml. of x M $KMnO_4$ solution liberates 0.100 liter of O_2 gas at STP, what is the molarity of the $KMnO_4$ solution?
Ans. 0.0744 M

20.15 *Stoichiometry.* A bottle containing a $KMnO_4$ solution used for oxidizing Fe^{++} to Fe^{+3} in acidic solution bears the label "0.100 N." How many milliliters of this solution would be needed if it were to be added to 20.0 ml. of 0.016 M Na_2SO_3 and 30.0 ml. of 3 M $NaOH$ with the idea of converting all the SO_3^{--} to SO_4^{--}?
Ans. 32 ml.

20.16 *Solubility product.* Given a solution that is saturated with respect to $Mn(OH)_2$, assumed to be a strong base. If the saturated solution shows a pH of 9.87, what is the numerical value of $K_{s.p.}$ for $Mn(OH)_2$?   *Ans.* 2.0×10^{-13}

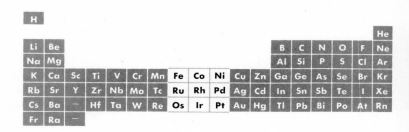

21   *Transition Elements* II
Iron Triad and Platinum Metals

THE FIRST FIVE SUBGROUPS OF THE TRANSITION ELEMENTS were discussed as individual subgroups in Chap. 20. In the next three subgroups, the chemical resemblance along the horizontal sequence is more pronounced than the chemical resemblance down the subgroup. For this reason, it is convenient to consider the next three subgroups in terms of horizontal triads. In the top transition period, the elements iron ($Z = 26$), cobalt ($Z = 27$), and nickel ($Z = 28$) make up the *iron triad;* in the middle period, ruthenium ($Z = 44$), rhodium ($Z = 45$), and palladium ($Z = 46$) are the *light platinum triad;* in the bottom period, osmium ($Z = 76$), iridium ($Z = 77$), and platinum ($Z = 78$) are the *heavy platinum triad.* All of these elements are metals of low atomic volume with high melting points and high densities. The elements of the first triad are moderately reactive; those of the platinum triads are fairly inert. In the original Mendeleev periodic table all of these elements were lumped into what was called group VIII. The platinum elements (together with gold and silver) are sometimes referred to as the *noble* metals.

21.1   IRON TRIAD

In progressing from left to right in the first transition period, there is a progressive rise in the maximum oxidation state from $+3$ for Sc to $+7$ for Mn. The surprising thing about the following iron-triad elements is that their maximum oxidation states are less than those of the preceding elements. Furthermore, compounds containing these maximum oxidation states are such strong oxidizing agents that they are not usually encountered. Specifically, iron shows a maximum oxidation state of $+6$, but only the $+2$ and $+3$ states are common; cobalt shows only $+2$ and $+3$; nickel, usually only $+2$. The reason for this return to lower oxidation states is apparently associated with the fact that, at manganese, the $3d$ sublevel has become half filled. With increasing nuclear charge, it gets progressively harder to break into this half-filled subshell; therefore effectively five of the $3d$ electrons are not available for forming compounds. Table 21.1 indicates schematically the electron population of the neutral atoms. Removal of the two $4s$ electrons is relatively easy in each case; hence a $+2$ state is formed. Additional removal of a $3d$ electron would give a $+3$ state. In the case of iron, this happens easily because a half-filled $3d$ level is left; in cobalt and nickel, it does not happen so readily. For cobalt, the $+3$ state must be stabilized as by formation of a complex ion; for nickel, the $+3$ state is very rare, and compounds of $+3$ nickel are powerful oxidizing agents.

The properties of the iron-triad elements are very similar, as shown in Table 21.2. The melting points and boiling points are uniformly high; the energies required to pull an electron off the gas atom are nearly the same for the three elements; and the oxidation potentials are all moderately more positive than that of hydrogen. In addition to the properties listed, these elements are alike in that all are *ferromagnetic*; i.e., they are strongly

Table 21.1   Electron Population of Iron Triad

Sublevel	Iron	Cobalt	Nickel
1s	2	2	2
2s and 2p	8	8	8
3s and 3p	8	8	8
3d	↑↓ ↑ ↑ ↑ ↑	↑↓ ↑↓ ↑ ↑ ↑	↑↓ ↑↓ ↑↓ ↑ ↑
4s	↑↓	↑↓	↑↓

Table 21.2   Elements of the Iron Triad

Property	Fe	Co	Ni
Melting point, °C.	1535	1490	1450
Boiling point, °C.	2700	2900	2700
Ionization potential, e.v.	7.90	7.86	7.63
Oxidation potential (to M^{++}), volts	+0.44	+0.28	+0.25
Density, g./cc.	7.9	8.7	8.9

attracted into a magnetic field and show permanent magnetization when removed from such a field. That these elements are magnetic is not surprising. The electronic configurations in Table 21.1 would lead us to expect that there would be unpaired electrons in the +2 ions such as might exist in the metal lattice. However, it is surprising that the magnetization is so large and so persistent. The explanation is that in these metals there are *domains* of magnetization, regions of a million or so ions, all of which cooperatively direct their individual magnetic effects the same way. In an unmagnetized piece of metal, these domains point randomly in all directions in such a way that, in sum, the magnetic effect cancels. When placed in a magnetic field, the domains are turned so that all point in the same direction, giving rise to a large magnetic effect. If the metal is now removed from the field, it remains permanently magnetized unless the domain orientation is disorganized, as by heating or pounding. Of all the elements, only iron, cobalt, and nickel show this kind of magnetism at room temperature. Apparently they are the only ones that satisfy the conditions necessary for domain formation. These conditions are that the ions contain unpaired electrons and that the distance between ions be just exactly right in order that the interaction for lining up all the ions to form a domain may be effective. Manganese metal has most of the properties needed to be ferromagnetic, but the ions of the metal are too close; addition of copper to manganese increases this average spacing, and the resulting alloy is ferromagnetic.

In their compounds, the iron-triad elements behave like typical transition elements. Many of the compounds are colored and paramagnetic and frequently they contain complex ions.

21.2   IRON

The element iron has an industrial importance which exceeds that of any other element. It is very abundant, ranking fourth in the earth's crust (after O, Si, and Al); it is very common, being an essential constituent of several hundred minerals; it is easy to make by simply heating some of its minerals with carbon; it has many desirable properties, especially when impure. For all these reasons, iron has become such a distinctive feature of civilization that it marks one of the ages in archaeological chronology.

About 5 per cent of the earth's crust is iron. Some of this iron is meteoric in origin and occurs in the uncombined, metallic state. However, most of it is combined, with oxygen, silicon, or sulfur. The important source minerals are hematite (Fe_2O_3), limonite ($Fe_2O_3 \cdot H_2O$), magnetite (Fe_3O_4), and siderite ($FeCO_3$), usually contaminated with complex iron silicates from which these minerals are produced by weathering. Iron sulfides, such as iron pyrites (FeS_2) or fool's gold, are also quite abundant, but they cannot be used as sources of iron because sulfur is an objectionable impurity in the final product.

Besides the earth's crust, there is a possibility that the center of the earth may be iron. Indirect evidence based on the study of earthquake waves and tidal action indicates that the core of the earth is liquid and has a density corresponding to that of liquid iron at high pressure.

Iron is practically never produced in a pure state, since it is difficult to make and is too expensive for most purposes. Furthermore, impure iron (steel) has desirable properties, especially when the specific impurity is carbon in carefully controlled amounts. The industrial production of impure iron is carried out on a massive scale in the well-known blast furnace, in which complicated high-temperature reactions occur involving iron ore, limestone, and carbon. As shown in Fig. 21.1, the blast furnace is designed for continuous operation. Iron ore, limestone, and coke are added at the top; preheated air or oxygen is blown in at the bottom. As the molten iron forms, it trickles down to a pit at the bottom, from which it is periodically drawn off. All told, it takes about 12 hr. for material to pass through the furnace. The actual chemical processes which occur in such a furnace are still obscure. It is generally agreed, however, that the active reducing agent is not carbon, but carbon monoxide. As the charge settles through the furnace, the coke is oxidized by the incoming oxygen by the reaction

$$2C(s) + O_2(g) \rightarrow 2CO(g) + 53.7 \text{ kcal.}$$

thus forming the reducing agent CO and liberating large amounts of heat. As the carbon monoxide moves up the furnace, it encounters oxides of iron in various stages of reduction, depending on the temperature of the particular zone. At the top of the furnace, where the temperature is lowest (250°C.), the iron ore (mostly Fe_2O_3) is reduced to Fe_3O_4 by the reaction

$$3Fe_2O_3(s) + CO(g) \rightarrow 2Fe_3O_4(s) + CO_2(g)$$

As the Fe_3O_4 settles, it gets reduced further to FeO

$$Fe_3O_4(s) + CO(g) \rightarrow 3FeO(s) + CO_2(g)$$

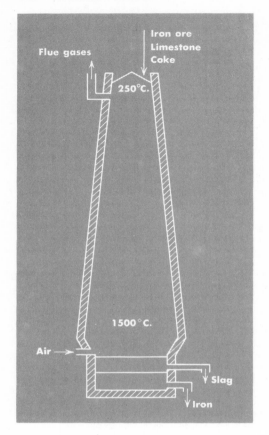

Fig. 21.1   Blast furnace.

Finally, toward the bottom of the furnace, FeO is eventually reduced to iron

$$FeO(s) + CO(g) \rightarrow Fe(s) + CO_2(g)$$

Since the temperature at the lowest part of the furnace is above the melting point of the impure iron, the solid melts and drips down into the hearth at the very bottom. The net equation for the reduction of Fe_2O_3 can be written as the sum of the last three equations.

$$Fe_2O_3(s) + 3CO(g) \rightarrow 2Fe(l) + 3CO_2(g)$$

In addition to the foregoing reactions, there occurs the combination of CO_2 with hot carbon,

$$C(s) + CO_2(g) \rightarrow 2CO(g)$$

and the thermal decomposition of limestone by the reaction

$$CaCO_3(s) \rightarrow CaO(s) + CO_2(g)$$

Both of these reactions are helpful: the former raises the concentration of the reducing agent CO, and the latter facilitates the removal of silica-containing contaminants present in the original ore. Lime (CaO), being a basic oxide, reacts with the acidic oxide SiO_2 to form calcium silicate ($CaSiO_3$). In the form of a lava-like *slag*, calcium silicate collects at the bottom of the furnace, where it floats on the molten iron and protects it from oxidation by incoming oxygen.

Four times a day the liquid iron and molten slag are drawn off through tapholes in the bottom of the furnace. About 1,000 tons of impure iron can be produced per day from one furnace. For each ton of iron, there is also produced approximately half a ton of slag. Since slag is essentially calcium aluminum silicate, some of it is put to good use in making cement (Sec. 24.5).

The crude product of the blast furnace (called pig iron) contains about 4 per cent C, 2 per cent Si, a trace of sulfur, up to 1 per cent of phosphorus and manganese, and the rest iron. Sulfur is probably the worst impurity (making steel break when worked) and must be avoided, since it is hard to remove in refining operations. The refining operations are technical and of great variety. Only a few of the basic ideas will be discussed.

When pig iron is remelted with scrap iron and cast into molds, it forms *cast iron*. This can be either gray or white, depending on the rate of cooling. When cooled slowly (as in sand molds, where heat loss is slow), the carbon separates out almost completely in the form of tiny flakes of graphite (Sec. 24.2), giving gray cast iron that is relatively soft and tough. When cooled rapidly (as in water-cooled molds), the carbon does not have a chance to separate out but remains combined in the form of the compound iron carbide, Fe_3C. Such white cast iron is extremely hard and brittle.

Most pig iron is refined into steel by burning out the impurities to leave small controlled amounts of carbon. In the *open-hearth* process (which accounts for most of the U.S. production), carbon is removed by oxidation with air and iron oxide, the latter being added as hematite and rusted scrap iron. The process is usually carried out on a shallow hearth arranged so that a hot air blast can play over the surface. In the *basic* open-hearth process, limestone is added to provide CaO for converting oxidation products, such as acidic P_2O_5, into slag. Since it takes about 8 hr. to refine a batch of steel by this process, there is ample time for continuous testing to maintain quality control. The *Bessemer process* is much more rapid (10 to 15 min.) but gives a less uniform product. In this process, molten pig iron taken directly from the blast furnace is poured into a large pot, and a blast of air is swept through the liquid mix to burn off most of the carbon and silicon. Frequently, the Bessemer and open-hearth processes are combined to take advantage of the good points of each. In the duplex process, a preliminary blowing in the Bessemer converter gets rid of most of the C and Si, with a following burn-off in an open-hearth furnace to get rid of P. Elements such as Cr, V, or Mn can be added to produce steels with desired properties. In order to prevent the formation of blowholes (as in Swiss cheese) when the molten steel is poured into ingots, it is necessary for the finished steel to contain some Mn. The function of this Mn is apparently to combine with the oxygen so as to keep it from bubbling out as the steel solidifies.

The properties of iron in the form of steel are very much dependent on the percentage composition of the impurities present, on the heat-treatment of the specimen, and even on the working to which the sample has been subjected. For these reasons, the following comments about iron properties do not necessarily apply to every given sample of iron. Compared to most metals, iron is a fairly good reducing agent, but it is not so good as the preceding transition elements. With nonoxidizing acids, it reacts to liberate H_2 by the reaction $Fe(s) + 2H^+ \rightarrow Fe^{++} + H_2(g)$. It also has the ability to replace less active metals in their solutions. For example, a bar of iron placed in a solution of $CuSO_4$ immediately is covered with a reddish deposit of copper formed by the reaction $Fe(s) + Cu^{++} \rightarrow Fe^{++} + Cu(s)$. In concentrated nitric acid, iron, like many other metals (Cr, Mo, Co, Ni, etc.), becomes *passive*; i.e., it loses the ability to react with H^+ and Cu^{++} as above and appears to be inert. When scratched or subjected to shock, reactivity is restored. It may be that passivity is due to the formation of a thin surface coating of oxide which slows down the rates of oxidation below the limits of detectability. When the film is broken, reactivity is restored. Passivity is important in some methods of preventing corrosion of iron.

21.3   COMPOUNDS OF IRON

The two common oxidation states of iron are $+2$ (ferrous) and $+3$ (ferric). Under vigorous oxidizing conditions it is also possible to get compounds such as $BaFeO_4$, barium ferrate, but in general the $+6$ state is rare. Compounds in which the oxidation state is fractional, as in Fe_3O_4, can be thought of as mixtures of two oxidation states. Thus, it is frequently convenient to consider Fe_3O_4 as a ferroso-ferric oxide which can be written $FeO \cdot Fe_2O_3$.

In the $+2$ state, iron exists essentially as ferrous ion, Fe^{++}. This is a pale green, almost colorless ion which, except in acid solutions, is rather hard to keep, since it is easily oxidized to the $+3$ state by oxygen in the air. However, since the rate of oxidation by O_2 is inversely proportional to

H^+ concentration, acid solutions of ferrous salts can be kept for long periods. When base is added to ferrous solutions, a nearly white precipitate of ferrous hydroxide, $Fe(OH)_2$, is formed. On exposure to air, $Fe(OH)_2$ turns brown, owing to oxidation to hydrated ferric oxide, $Fe_2O_3 \cdot xH_2O$. For convenience, the latter is often written as $Fe(OH)_3$, ferric hydroxide, and the oxidation can be written

$$4Fe(OH)_2(s) + O_2(g) + 2H_2O \rightarrow 4Fe(OH)_3(s)$$

However, pure ferric hydroxide has never been prepared.

In the $+3$ state, iron exists as the colorless ferric ion, Fe^{+3}. Since solutions of ferric salts are acid, appreciable hydrolysis must take place. This can be written as

$$Fe^{+3} + H_2O \rightleftharpoons FeOH^{++} + H^+$$

Apparently, the yellow-brown color so characteristic of ferric solutions is mainly due to $FeOH^{++}$. By addition of an acid such as HNO_3, the color can be made to disappear.* On addition of base, a slimy, red-brown, gelatinous precipitate forms, which may be written as $Fe(OH)_3$. This can be dehydrated to form yellow or red Fe_2O_3.

In both the $+2$ and $+3$ states, iron shows a great tendency to form complex ions. For example, ferric ion combines with thiocyanate ion, SCN^-, to form $FeSCN^{++}$, which has such a deep red color that it can be detected at concentrations of 10^{-5} M. The formation of this complex is the basis of one of the most sensitive qualitative tests for the presence of Fe^{+3}. With cyanide ion, CN^-, both Fe^{++} and Fe^{+3} form complexes; these are so stable to dissociation that they can be thought of as single units like SO_4^{--} ion. As shown in Fig. 21.2 both ferrocyanide, $Fe(CN)_6^{-4}$, and ferricyanide, $Fe(CN)_6^{-3}$, are octahedral with six CN groups joined through carbon to the central iron. Since, in assigning oxidation states, cyanide is usually given a -1 charge, Fe is assigned a $+2$ charge in ferrocyanide and a $+3$ charge in ferricyanide. Though simple in structure, these ions take part in some very complicated reactions, among which are the formation of prussian blue and Turnbull's blue.

Prussian blue is a deep blue precipitate obtained by mixing a solution of a ferric salt with a solution of potassium ferrocyanide, $K_4Fe(CN)_6$. It is used extensively as a dye for blueprint paper, for ink, and for bluing, in the last case because its color counteracts the yellow color of fabrics and makes them appear white. Turnbull's blue is a similar deep blue precipitate obtained by mixing a solution of a ferrous salt with a solution of potassium ferricyanide, $K_3Fe(CN)_6$. The surprising thing about prussian blue and

---

* The color will not disappear on the addition of HCl because $FeCl^{++}$, which is yellow, forms.

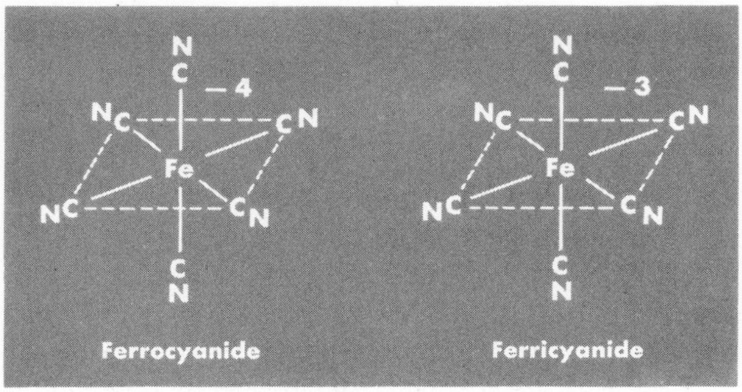

Fig. 21.2   Octahedral complex ions of iron and cyanide.

Turnbull's blue is that apparently they have identical over-all compositions, corresponding to $KFeFe(CN)_6$. However, no one has yet been able to carry out a definitive experiment to prove that they are the same or, for that matter, that they are different.

Another unusual iron complex is that formed between ferric ion and oxalate ion, $C_2O_4^{--}$. The complex has the composition $Fe(C_2O_4)_3^{-3}$, which indicates three oxalate ions joined to a single iron atom. As shown in Fig. 21.3, the iron is still surrounded by six oxygen atoms, each of which is at a corner of an octahedron. The unusual feature of this structure is that adjoining oxygen atoms are bridged together by the rest of the oxalate-ion structure. The complex ferrioxalate ion is of more than academic interest. Because it is so stable to dissociation, it is formed when many iron compounds are treated with oxalate salts. The removal of ink stains and of rust spots by oxalic acid ($H_2C_2O_4$) or potassium oxalate ($K_2C_2O_4$) depends on this reaction.

21.4   CORROSION OF IRON

Corrosion is a general term applied to the process in which uncombined metals change over to compounds. In the special case of iron, the corrosion process is called *rusting*. Economically, rusting is a serious problem, and it has been estimated that 20 per cent of the annual production of iron goes simply to replace that lost by rusting. Still, despite much study, corrosion is a mysterious process, and its chemistry not well understood.

Rust appears to be a hydrated ferric oxide with a chemical composition corresponding approximately to $2Fe_2O_3 \cdot 3H_2O$, that is, 3 moles of water per 2 moles of ferric oxide. However, since the water content is not always the same, it is preferable to write $Fe_2O_3 \cdot xH_2O$. Because iron will not rust in dry air or in water than is completely free of air, it would seem that both

O_2 and H_2O are required for rust formation. Furthermore, it is observed that rusting is speeded up by the presence of acids, strains in the metal, contact with less active metals, and the presence of rust itself (autocatalysis).

In order to account for the observed facts, the following steps have been proposed as the mechanism by which rusting occurs:

$$Fe(s) \rightarrow Fe^{++} + 2e^- \tag{1}$$

$$e^- + H^+ \rightarrow H \tag{2}$$

$$4H + O_2(g) \rightarrow 2H_2O \tag{3}$$

$$4Fe^{++} + O_2(g) + (4 + 2x)H_2O \rightarrow 2(Fe_2O_3 \cdot xH_2O)(s) + 8H^+ \tag{4}$$

In step (1), ferrous ions are produced by loss of electrons from neutral Fe atoms. However, this process cannot go very far unless there is some way of getting rid of the electrons which accumulate on the residual iron. One way to do this is by step (2), where H^+ ions, either from the water or from acid substances in the water, pick up the electrons to form neutral H atoms. (Normally we would expect these H atoms to pair up to form H_2 molecules; however, H_2 gas is usually not observed in rust formation.) Since iron is a good catalyst for hydrogenation reactions, step (3) now occurs to use up the H atoms. In the meantime, the ferrous ion reacts with oxygen gas by step (4) to form the rust and restore H^+ required for step (2). The net reaction, obtained by adding these steps, is

$$4Fe(s) + 3O_2(g) + 2xH_2O \rightarrow 2(Fe_2O_3 \cdot xH_2O)(s)$$

Since H^+ accelerates step (2) and is replenished in step (4), it is a true catalyst for the reaction and explains the observation that acids speed up the rate of rust formation. (A remarkable example of this is observed when iron pipes are located so as to be in contact with cinders. Such pipes corrode much more rapidly than they normally do, apparently because weathering of sulfur compounds in the cinders forms sulfuric acid.)

The above mechanism also accounts for many other observations and, in particular, for the process often called electrolytic corrosion. For example, when iron pipes are connected to copper pipes, the iron corrodes much faster than normally. The explanation lies in step (1). Residual electrons accumulating from the dissolution of Fe flow from the iron to the copper, where their energy is lower. This removes the excess negative charge from the iron and allows more Fe^{++} to leave the metal. A complicating feature which also accelerates the reaction is that H atoms, which now form on the negative copper surface instead of the iron, detach themselves more readily from copper than from iron, thus accelerating step (3).

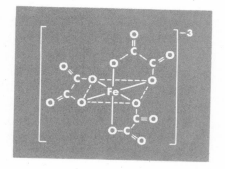

Fig. 21.3   *Complex between* Fe^{+3} *and oxalate ions.*

One of the strongest supports for the stepwise rusting mechanism comes from the observation that the most serious pitting of a rusting iron bar occurs in that part of the bar where the oxygen supply is restricted. The reason for this is that, where the oxygen supply is unrestricted, step (4) promptly occurs to deposit rust before the Fe^{++} formed by step (1) can move away. This, of course, makes it more difficult for more Fe to dissolve, and the reaction is self-stopping. However, if the oxygen supply is restricted, Fe^{++} may have a chance to diffuse away before encountering enough oxygen to form rust. This means that the rust may deposit some distance away from the point where pitting occurs. Common examples of this are observed at the edges of overlapping plates or around rivet heads. In the latter case, the rivet shank, although protected from air, is eaten away, but the rust forms where the rivet head overlaps the plate. Apparently, moisture that seeps in allows Fe^{++} to diffuse out to the surface, where it can react with O_2. Another slightly different example is found in the well-known water-line deposition of rust on partially immersed steel posts. When a new post is placed in water, pitting usually starts where there are strains in the metal, but the rust forms near the water line, where oxygen is plentiful. This makes the situation go from bad to worse, since the water-line rust now acts as a screen to keep O_2 from reaching the iron. Self-protection is no longer possible, and severe pitting can now occur where the O_2 supply is restricted.

Although there are still many unanswered questions about rusting, it is clear what must be done to prevent it. The most direct approach is to shut off the reactants O_2 and H_2O. This can be done by smearing grease over the iron to be protected, painting it either with an ordinary paint or better with an oxidizing paint so as to make the iron passive, or plating the iron with some other metal. All these methods are used to some extent. Painting or greasing is probably the cheapest, but it must be done thoroughly; otherwise, rusting may only be accelerated by partial exclusion of oxygen. Plating with another metal is more common when appearance is a factor. Chrome plating, for example, is usually chosen because of its dressy look. Zinc plating, or galvanizing, is actually more permanent. Tin plating looks good and is extremely cheap, but it is not reliable.

The relative merits of metals used for plating depend on the activity of the metal relative to iron and the ability of the metal to form a self-protective coat. Zinc, for example, is a self-protecting metal which reacts with O_2 and CO_2 in the air to form an adherent coating which prevents further corrosion. Furthermore, it has a higher oxidation potential than iron, so that, if a hole is punched in a zinc plating so that Zn and Fe are both exposed to oxidation, it is the Zn that is preferentially oxidized. The Zn compound forms a plug to seal the hole. Tin also forms a self-protective coat, but tin has a smaller oxidation potential than iron, and iron is preferentially oxidized when a tin coating is punctured.

One of the most elegant ways to protect iron from corrosion is by "cathodic protection." In this method, iron is charged to a negative voltage compared to its surroundings. This forces the iron to act as a cathode instead of as the anode required for oxidation and effectively stops corrosion. Actually, zinc plating is a method of cathodic protection, since zinc has a higher oxidation potential than iron and forces electrons onto the iron. In practice, for pipelines and standpipes, cathodic protection is obtained by driving stakes of zinc or magnesium, for example, into the ground and connecting them to the object to be protected. In salt water, where rusting is unusually severe, the steel plates of ships have been protected by strapping blocks of magnesium to the hulls. These preferentially corrode (since they are acting as anodes) but can easily be replaced, while the iron is essentially untouched.

Cathodic protection also explains why tin plating (as in the ordinary tin can) is so unlasting. So long as the tin coating is unpunctured, there is no corrosion, since tin is a rather inert metal and can be exposed indefinitely to the atmosphere. Once the coating is punctured (and this happens very easily, because it is very thin), there is real trouble, and the iron is worse off than if the tin plating were not there. The reason for this is that iron, being more active than tin, acts as anode in setting up cathodic protection for the tin. This, of course, accelerates the dissolving of iron and the formation of rust; hence the rust spreads very rapidly.

21.5   COBALT AND NICKEL

The other elements of the iron triad, cobalt and nickel, although less important than iron, do have some interesting aspects. They are both much less abundant than iron (Co at 0.002 per cent and Ni at 0.008 per cent) and are harder to extract from their minerals. The name cobalt reflects this difficulty since it comes from the German word *Kobold*, meaning goblin. Cobalt minerals look very much like copper minerals and were occasionally worked by mistake as sources of copper. Furthermore, since arsenic is usually present with cobalt, poisonous fumes were inevitably present, all obviously due to black magic. Similar troubles with nickel minerals led to their being named after "Old Nick" and his devilish assistants. Cobalt minerals and nickel minerals frequently occur together, associated with those of iron and copper. The principal compounds in these minerals are oxides, sulfides, and arsenides.

1   Cobalt. The more important minerals of cobalt are cobalt glance ($CoAsS$), linnaeite (Co_3S_4), and smaltite, or cobalt speiss, ($CoAs_2$). The extraction is very complex and involves roasting in a blast furnace, dissolving with sulfuric acid, and precipitating by addition of sodium carbonate. The hydroxide so produced is dehydrated to the oxide, which can then be reduced with hydrogen.

The properties of the metal have been given in Table 21.2. The oxidation potential of $+0.28$ volt for the reaction $Co(s) \rightleftharpoons Co^{++} + 2e^-$ indicates that cobalt should dissolve in acids with the liberation of hydrogen. The reaction is slow and does not occur at all in concentrated nitric acid, where Co becomes passive. The ferromagnetism of Co is actually higher than that of iron and accounts for its extensive use in magnets, especially in alloys such as the Alnico alloys (Co, Ni, Al, and Cu). Other alloys such as stellite (55 per cent Co, 15 per cent W, 25 per cent Cr, 5 per cent Mo) are important for their extreme hardness and resistance to corrosion. They are used, for example, in high-speed tools and surgical instruments.

In its compounds, cobalt shows oxidation states of $+2$ (cobaltous) and $+3$ (cobaltic). Unlike ferrous ion, the cobaltous ion is quite stable to oxidation, and solutions of cobaltous salts can be kept indefinitely exposed to the air. Most cobaltous solutions are pink and presumably contain the hydrated ion $Co(H_2O)_6^{++}$. Addition of base precipitates dark blue insoluble hydroxide, which in the absence of oxygen can be dehydrated to give yellow-green cobaltous oxide, CoO. This is a basic oxide much used to produce blue color in pottery and enamel. When heated in the presence of air, cobaltous hydroxide dehydrates to give Co_3O_4, cobaltocobaltic oxide, reminiscent of Fe_3O_4. Cobaltous forms many complex ions, which, however, are easily oxidized.

In aqueous solution, the cobaltic ion Co^{+3} is a very powerful oxidizing agent. The oxidation potential of $Co^{++} \rightleftharpoons Co^{+3} + e^-$ is -1.84 volts, which means that Co^{+3} is strong enough to oxidize water to form O_2. Only a few simple cobaltic salts such as CoF_3 and $Co_2(SO_4)_3 \cdot 18H_2O$ have been made, and these decompose in aqueous solution.

$$4Co^{+3} + 2H_2O \rightarrow 4Co^{+2} + O_2(g) + 4H^+$$

Unlike the simple ion, the complex ions of cobalt $+3$ are quite stable to reduction. There are a tremendous number of these, ranging from the simple $Co(CN)_6^{-3}$ and $Co(NH_3)_6^{+3}$ to complicated *polynuclear* complexes, in which several cobalt atoms are bridged together by shared complexing groups.

2   Nickel. The principal minerals of nickel are pentlandite and nickeliferous pyrrhotite (mixed sulfides of iron and nickel) and garnierite (a mixed silicate of magnesium and nickel). Since most ores are very poor in nickel content, they are concentrated before smelting, usually by *flotation*. In this process the ore is ground up and then agitated briskly with water to which wetting agents have been added. Earthy particles (*gangue*) are wet by the water and hence sink, whereas the fine particles of mineral are not wet and get carried off with the froth. The concentrate is then roasted in air to get rid of some of the sulfur as SO_2, burned in a furnace (smelted) to form oxide, and finally reduced with carbon. To get pure nickel, the final product must be refined, either electrolytically or by taking advantage of the instability of volatile nickel carbonyl. In the Mond process, carbon monoxide at 80°C. is passed over impure nickel to form volatile $Ni(CO)_4$, nickel tetracarbonyl. This is then heated to about 200°C., where it decomposes into Ni and CO.

The properties of nickel metal are much like those of cobalt, except that Ni is less ferromagnetic and more inert to chemical oxidation. More than 65 per cent of nickel production goes into iron alloys to increase their strength and corrosion resistance. The rest of it goes into nickel-copper alloys, e.g., into nickel coinage (from 10 to 100 per cent Ni), or is used as the pure metal. In the latter case it is used for plating steel and as a catalyst for hydrogenation reactions.

The chemistry of nickel compounds is essentially that of the $+2$ state. In aqueous solution, it exists either as the green nickelous ion, Ni^{++}, or as a complex ion. On treatment with base, nickelous ion precipitates as the light green nickelous hydroxide, $Ni(OH)_2$, which can be dehydrated thermally to black NiO. The complex ions of nickel are almost as numerous as those of cobalt. However, unlike cobaltous complexes, they are quite stable to air oxidation. Furthermore, not all of them are octahedral (as is the blue $Ni(NH_3)_6^{++}$) but may be planar ($Ni(CN)_4^{--}$). Figure 21.4 shows the different arrangements possible.

In basic solution, nickelous hydroxide can be oxidized by the powerful oxidizing agent hypochlorite, ClO^-. The product is a dark-colored oxide of indefinite composition variously described as NiO_2, Ni_2O_3, or Ni_3O_4. No matter what it is, it is a very good oxidizing agent and contains nickel in an oxidation state higher than $+2$. As such, it forms the cathode material in the Edison storage battery. On discharge, the cathode reaction can be written as

$$Ni_2O_3(s) + 2e^- + 3H_2O \rightarrow 2Ni(OH)_2(s) + 2OH^-$$

Fig. 21.4   *Complex nickel ions.*

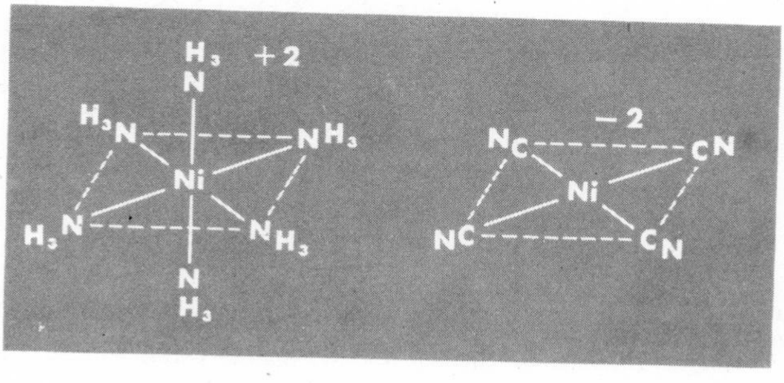

Since $Ni(OH)_2$ sticks to the cathode and since the reaction is reversible, the discharged cell can be recharged by the application of an external voltage. The anode in the Edison cell is usually of iron, with NaOH as electrolyte. The anode reaction is probably

$$Fe(s) + 2OH^- \rightarrow Fe(OH)_2(s) + 2e^-$$

The Edison cell has an advantage over the lead storage battery because the OH^- produced at the cathode is used up at the anode; hence there is no concentration change in the electrolyte. Consequently, as the battery runs down, there is no change in its output voltage. Also, the materials are less dense and stronger than those of the lead storage battery, and hence the Edison battery is more easily portable and more rugged. Unfortunately, the chemical components are too expensive to make it of general usefulness.

21.6 LIGHT PLATINUM TRIAD

In the second transition period, the three elements following technetium are ruthenium ($Z = 44$), rhodium ($Z = 45$), and palladium ($Z = 46$). Since these elements chemically resemble platinum but have only about half the density of platinum, they are called the light platinum elements. Their properties are summarized in Table 21.3. As can be seen, these elements are high-melting and high-boiling with rather high densities. They are not very reactive, and their oxidation potentials indicate that, unlike the iron-triad elements, they are much poorer reducing agents than hydrogen. For this reason they are difficult to oxidize and, in fact, occur in nature as the uncombined elements. Because of great similarity in chemical properties, they usually occur together.

1 Ruthenium. Ruthenium occurs as a natural alloy of ruthenium, osmium, and iridium. To prepare the pure metal, the alloy is heated with alkaline oxidizing agents (e.g.,

Table 21.3 Light Platinum Elements

Property	Ru	Rh	Pd
Atomic number	44	45	46
Electronic configuration	2, 8, 18, 15, 1	2, 8, 18, 16, 1	2, 8, 18, 18
Melting point, °C.	2450	1970	1550
Boiling point, °C.	>2700	>2500	2200(?)
Ionization potential, e.v.	7.5	7.7	8.3
Oxidation potential (to M^{++}), volts	−0.5	−0.6	−1.2
Density, g./cc.	12.4	12.4	12.0

a mixture of KOH and KNO_3) to form potassium ruthenate (K_2RuO_4). After being dissolved and acidified, the mixture is boiled to eliminate osmium as osmium tetroxide (OsO_4), and then, after the solution has been made basic, Ru is distilled off as ruthenium tetroxide, RuO_4. Reduction with hydrogen gives the metal. It is quite inert and thus far has found use only as a hardening agent for platinum and for making other hard, inert alloys required for fountain-pen tips and phonograph needles.

In its principal compounds, ruthenium shows oxidation states corresponding to $+3$, $+4$, $+6$, and $+8$. Some of these compounds are simple, like the volatile, toxic ruthenium tetroxide (RuO_4); others, like $K_3Ru(C_2O_4)_3$, are complex. In general, they are rarely encountered.

2   Rhodium. Rhodium is a rather rare element, amounting to only 10^{-7} per cent of the earth's crust. It occurs principally with platinum, from which it can be separated by fusion with $KHSO_4$. Rhodium dissolves to give $KRh(SO_4)_2$, a rose-colored salt, which can be leached out and recrystallized from water. The metal is rather inert and finds use for plating scientific instruments. An alloy of rhodium and platinum is used to make high-temperature scientific apparatus such as crucibles and thermocouples. The principal oxidation state is $+3$ and is represented by many simple salts, such as $RhCl_3$, as well as by complex ones like K_3RhCl_6.

3   Palladium. Palladium is the most abundant (10^{-6} per cent) of the platinum elements. Since it alone of the platinum elements forms an insoluble cyanide, it can be separated from the others by precipitation of $Pd(CN)_2$. On ignition, this decomposes to give pure metal. Like the other platinum elements, Pd is inert, but not so much so that it cannot dissolve in concentrated nitric acid. One of its most remarkable properties is that it has the ability to absorb hydrogen. At dull-red heat, a piece of palladium can absorb about 1,000 times its own volume of hydrogen. When the temperature is raised further, the hydrogen is expelled. Apparently in this absorption process the H_2 molecule is ripped apart into H atoms, which can then fit into the Pd lattice. It may be that this dissociation $H_2 \rightarrow 2H$ also explains the powerful catalytic effect of Pd on hydrogenation reactions. Because it is not corroded in air and is capable of taking a high polish, palladium finds use for making optical mirrors and for jewelry. The compounds, both simple and complex, are essentially those of the $+2$ oxidation state.

21.7   HEAVY PLATINUM TRIAD

The elements of the heavy platinum triad, osmium ($Z = 76$), iridium ($Z = 77$), and platinum ($Z = 78$), resemble very closely the elements just above them. Their properties are shown in Table 21.4. They are all very high melting, of extraordinarily high density, and generally quite unreactive.

1   Osmium. The chief source of osmium is naturally occurring osmiridium, an alloy of Os and Ir which is usually contaminated with ruthenium. As discussed in Sec. 21.6, this alloy can be dissolved by strong, alkaline oxidizing agents and osmium tetroxide driven off as a volatile material from the acidified product. Metallic osmium forms when OsO_4 is reduced with almost any reducing agent, since the half-reaction

$$Os(s) + 4H_2O \rightleftharpoons OsO_4(s) + 8H^+ + 8e^- \qquad -0.85 \text{ volt}$$

Table 21.4   *Heavy Platinum Elements*

Property	Os	Ir	Pt
Atomic number	76	77	78
Electronic configuration	2, 8, 18, 32, 14, 2	2, 8, 18, 32, 15, 2	2, 8, 18, 32, 17, 1
Melting point, °C.	2700	2450	1774
Boiling point, °C.	>5300	>4800	4100
Ionization potential, e.v.	8.7	9.2	8.96
Oxidation potential (to M^{++}), volts	−0.9	−1	−1.2
Density, g./cc.	22.7	22.6	21.5

is easily reversed. In the massive state, the metal is quite inert, even to aqua regia (a mixture of concentrated nitric and hydrochloric acids). It is very hard, especially when alloyed with iridium, and is used as the alloy for the tips of fountain pens.

Compounds of osmium are known in the +2, +3, +4, +6, and +8 oxidation states. The most important of these is OsO_4, osmium tetroxide, sometimes called osmic acid. Though solid at room temperature (its melting point is 40°C., and its boiling point 100°C.), it is very volatile and hence very dangerous, since it is corrosive to animal tissue, especially the eyes. It finds some use in staining tissue for microscopic study. Apparently the tissue reduces OsO_4 to metallic osmium, which in the finely divided state appears black. It is also of increasing importance in synthetic chemistry, since OsO_4 is a specific catalyst for the addition of OH to carbon-carbon double bonds by hydrogen peroxide.

2   Iridium. Iridium is obtained from natural osmiridium by driving off the osmium and ruthenium as mentioned above. The iridium is usually separated as the slightly soluble ammonium iridium chloride, $(NH_4)_2IrCl_6$. Thermal decomposition produces the metal, which in the massive state is quite inert. The chief use of iridium metal is for additive hardening of platinum. Compounds, corresponding principally to the +3 and +4 states, are known but are not commonly encountered.

3   Platinum. Of all the platinum elements, platinum is the most useful. Although not very abundant (5×10^{-7} per cent), it occurs in concentrated deposits, a fact which makes its separation feasible. In order to isolate it from the other platinum metals, the naturally occurring alloys are treated with aqua regia. Pt and Pd dissolve, and, from the resulting solution, Pt is precipitated as insoluble ammonium hexachloroplatinate (IV), $(NH_4)_2PtCl_6$. Thermal decomposition produces the metal.

The metal is quite inert to many kinds of chemical attack, and for this reason, especially when hardened with a few per cent of iridium, it is used in making jewelry and laboratory equipment. In using platinum ware (e.g., crucibles), fused alkalis, such as NaOH, must be avoided, because Pt dissolves in molten bases to form platinates. Also to be avoided are phosphorus, silicon, arsenic, antimony, lead, etc., with which Pt forms alloys. Industrially, probably the most important use of platinum is as a catalyst. For example, it catalyzes the oxidation of ammonia in the manufacture of nitric acid (Sec. 25.2). It has been estimated that at present half the platinum in the United States is used as a catalyst in making gasoline.

Although rather inert, platinum occurs in many chemical combinations, principally in the $+2$ and $+4$ oxidation states. Many of these compounds contain complex ions, and practically all of them are unstable with respect to thermal decomposition.

21.8 QUALITATIVE ANALYSIS

All three iron triad elements precipitate as black sulfides insoluble in basic solution. (If ferric ion were present, it would be reduced by H_2S in acid solution to ferrous ion.) FeS can be separated from CoS and NiS because it dissolves fairly quickly in a Na_2SO_4-$NaHSO_4$ buffer whereas CoS and NiS are slow to dissolve. Separation of iron from cobalt and nickel can also be achieved by making use of the fact that Fe^{++} plus an excess of NH_3 forms in air insoluble ferric hydroxide while Co^{++} and Ni^{++} form soluble ammonia complexes. The presence of iron can be confirmed by adding thiocyanate after oxidation of Fe^{++} to Fe^{+3} with H_2O_2, if necessary. The deep red color of $FeSCN^{++}$ shows that iron is present.

To distinguish cobalt from nickel, the sulfides CoS and NiS can be dissolved in acid solution, boiled with bromine water to destroy H_2S, and the solution treated with potassium nitrite. The appearance of insoluble, yellow potassium cobaltinitrite, $K_3Co(NO_2)_6$, shows the presence of cobalt. Nickel can be identified by adding a special reagent, dimethylglyoxime, which from basic solution precipitates the reddish-orange, voluminous solid, nickel dimethylglyoxime.

QUESTIONS

21.1 *Oxidation states.* Account for the scarcity of high-oxidation-state compounds in the iron triad.

21.2 *Terms.* Identify each of the following: slag, gray cast iron, polynuclear complexes, hematite, passivity, cathode protection, Mond process.

21.3 *Magnetism.* Single atoms can be paramagnetic but only solids can be ferromagnetic. Explain.

21.4 *Blast furnace.* There are at least five carbon-containing substances in an operating blast furnace. What are they?

21.5 *Steel.* Trace the conversion of hematite to a high-vanadium steel, assuming that a duplex process is used. State the function of each step.

21.6 *Preparations.* Tell how each of the following can be prepared: Fe^{++}, Fe^{+3}, $Fe(OH)_2$, $Fe(OH)_3$, $Fe(C_2O_4)_3{}^{-3}$.

21.7 *Rusting.* Show how the mechanism proposed in this chapter for the rusting of iron accounts for each of the following: (*a*) H^+ is a true catalyst for the process; (*b*) corrosion of iron pipes is accelerated by direct coupling to copper pipes; (*c*) rivets are usually sealed over with paint.

21.8 *Fe, Co, Ni.* Contrast iron, cobalt, and nickel with respect to oxidation states shown, use of compounds as oxidizing and reducing agents, configuration of complex ions, ferromagnetism.

21.9 *Pt elements.* (*a*) Which of the platinum elements is most abundant? (*b*) Which ones form volatile oxides? (*c*) Which show oxidation state $+3$? (*d*) Which one dissolves in concentrated nitric acid? (*e*) Which is a catalyst for making nitric acid?

21.10 *Iron.* Trace the path of iron atoms (using equations where possible) through the following typical "life cycle": from natural occurrence as hematite to white cast iron, to low-carbon steel, and finally the corrosive return to hematite-like rust.

21.11 *Association.* For $FeSCN^{++}$, K_{diss} is 1×10^{-3}. In a solution of 1.0×10^{-4} M $Fe(NO_3)_3$ and 0.1 M KSCN, what fraction of the total ferric iron is not complexed?

21.12 *Color.* Suggest a reason why Fe^{+3} might be expected to be colorless.

21.13 *Stoichiometry.* Assuming that the Fe gets oxidized to Fe_2O_3, calculate the increase in weight undergone by 1.00 g. of iron when heated in air.

Ans. 0.429 g.

21.14 *Stoichiometry.* Assuming that the FeS_2 gets oxidized to Fe_2O_3 and gaseous SO_2, calculate the change in weight undergone by 1.00 g. of iron pyrites when heated in air.

21.15 *Stoichiometry.* Suppose you are given a 1.000-g. sample that contains only FeO and Fe_2O_3. When this sample is dissolved in acid and all the iron reduced to the ferrous state, it takes 54.0 ml. of acidified 0.0500 M $KMnO_4$ to oxidize all the Fe^{++} back to Fe^{+3}. Calculate the weight per cent of FeO in the original sample.

Ans. 70%

21.16 *Equilibrium.* Solutions of ferric ion are usually colored, owing to formation of $FeOH^{++}$ by hydrolysis as follows:

$$Fe^{+3} + H_2O \rightleftharpoons FeOH^{++} + H^+$$

$$K_{hyd} = 4.0 \times 10^{-3}$$

In order to be visible to the naked eye, the concentration of $FeOH^{++}$ would have to be at least 10^{-4} M. How concentrated would the H^+ have to be in order to suppress completely any color in 0.010 M $Fe_2(SO_4)_3$?

21.17 *Mixing problem.* A solution is made by mixing 0.012 mole of $FeSO_4$, 0.14 mole of H_2SO_4, and 0.0060 mole of $K_2Cr_2O_7$ in enough water to make 0.200 liter of solution. The principal reaction is the oxidation of Fe^{++} to Fe^{+3} in acidic solution by $Cr_2O_7^{--}$. Calculate the concentration of Cr^{+3} in the final solution.

H

Li Be · · · · · · · · · · · · · · · B C N O F Ne
Na Mg · · · · · · · · · · · · · · · Al Si P S Cl Ar
K Ca Sc Ti V Cr Mn Fe Co Ni **Cu Zn** Ga Ge As Se Br Kr
Rb Sr Y Zr Nb Mo Tc Ru Rh Pd **Ag Cd** In Sn Sb Te I Xe
Cs Ba — Hf Ta W Re Os Ir Pt **Au Hg** Tl Pb Bi Po At Rn
Fr Ra —

22 *Transition Elements* III

Copper and Zinc Subgroups

THE CHEMICAL SIMILARITY between the members of the iron triad (Fe, Co, Ni) is more pronounced along the period than down the subgroup, as indicated in Chap. 21. With the elements of the next two subgroups the situation is reversed, and it is more convenient to compare them vertically than horizontally. The head elements of the next subgroups are copper ($Z = 29$) and zinc ($Z = 30$). The copper subgroup also includes silver ($Z = 47$) and gold ($Z = 79$); the zinc subgroup, cadmium ($Z = 48$) and mercury ($Z = 80$). With these elements, the sequence we have referred to as the transition elements is completed.

22.1   COPPER SUBGROUP

The elements of the copper subgroup, copper, silver, and gold, have been known to man since antiquity, for, unlike most of the preceding elements discussed, they are sometimes found in nature in the uncombined, or native, state. Originally decorative in function, they soon were adapted to use in coins because of their relative scarcity and resistance to corrosion. Originally, only silver and gold were used as coins, but then someone discovered the happy coincidence that copper could be added, not only to make the coins cost less but also to increase their life in circulation because of increased hardness. Since then, copper, silver, and gold have been called the coinage metals, even though their principal uses are quite different.

Some of the important properties of these elements are shown in Table 22.1. They are all typically metallic with rather high melting points and rather high boiling points. The low oxidation potentials indicate that they are not very reactive. According to the electronic configurations, there is, in the ground state of these atoms, one electron in the outermost energy level. When this electron is removed, the $+1$ ion results. This is all that we expect, since the second-outermost shell is filled and presumably is hard to break into. In this respect, these elements resemble the alkali metals (Chap. 18) and consequently are sometimes classified as a group IB. However, the d electrons in the second-outermost shell are close in energy to the outermost electrons and can be removed with little additional energy, especially if there is some way to stabilize the resulting $+2$ or $+3$ ions. Apparently, this is exactly what happens. Copper forms $+1$ and $+2$ compounds; silver forms $+1$ and $+2$ (although the $+2$ state is rare); and gold forms $+1$ and $+3$ compounds. However, even with such a variable oxidation state, the chemistry of these elements is simpler than that of the preceding transition elements.

22.2   COPPER

Considering its usefulness and familiarity, it is surprising that copper is such a small fraction (0.0001 per cent) of the earth's crust. Fortunately, its deposits are concentrated and easily worked. Besides native copper, which is 99.9 per cent pure, the element occurs as two principal classes of minerals:

Table 22.1   Elements of Copper Subgroup

Symbol	Z	Electronic configuration	Melting point, °C.	Boiling point, °C.	Ionization potential, e.v.	Oxidation potential (to M^+), volts
Cu	29	2, 8, 18, 1	1083	2300	7.72	−0.52
Ag	47	2, 8, 18, 18, 1	961	1950	7.57	−0.799
Au	79	2, 8, 18, 32, 18, 1	1063	2600	9.22	−1.7

*Fig. 22.1   Electrorefining of
copper.*

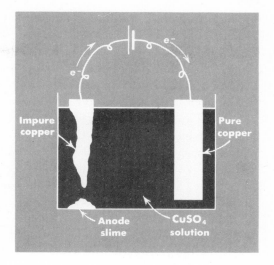

sulfide ores and oxide ores. The principal sulfide ores are chalcocite (Cu_2S),
chalcopyrite, or copper pyrites ($CuFeS_2$), and covellite (CuS); the principal
oxides ores are cuprite (Cu_2O), malachite [$CuCO_3 \cdot Cu(OH)_2$], and tenorite
(CuO). About 80 per cent of present copper production is from the sulfide
ores. In order to make the metal, the minerals are first concentrated by
flotation (Sec. 21.5), roasted in air, and then smelted. The roasting and
smelting process, represented, for example, by the simplified over-all
equation

$$2CuFeS_2(s) + 5O_2(g) \rightarrow 2Cu(s) + 2FeO(s) + 4SO_2(g)$$

produces tremendous quantities of sulfur dioxide, which are converted on
the spot into sulfuric acid.

The copper product is about 97 to 99 per cent pure and must be refined
(purified) for most uses. This can be done best in a $CuSO_4$ electrolysis cell,
like that sketched in Fig. 22.1. In the electrolysis cell, the impure copper
is made the anode, and pure copper the cathode. By careful control of the
electrolysis voltage, the copper can be transferred from the anode to the
cathode. The principle of operation can be seen from the following example,
in which we consider the purification of a typical bar of copper containing
iron and silver as impurities: The iron represents an impurity that is more
easily oxidized than copper; the silver, an impurity that is less easily oxidized
than copper. The pertinent half-reactions and their oxidation potentials are

$$Fe(s) \rightarrow Fe^{++} + 2e^- \qquad +0.44 \text{ volt}$$

$$Cu(s) \rightarrow Cu^{++} + 2e^- \qquad -0.34$$

$$Ag(s) \rightarrow Ag^+ + e^- \qquad -0.80$$

By keeping the cell voltage at an appropriate value, only the Fe and Cu are oxidized and go into the solution as ions. The more difficultly oxidized Ag simply drops off to the bottom of the cell as the anode dissolves away. At the cathode, where reduction must occur, the high concentration of Cu^{++} and the fact that Cu^{++} is more readily reduced than Fe^{++} lead to deposition of pure copper. The Fe^{++} remains in solution, and the solid silver stays at the bottom of the cell. Some common impurities in crude copper are iron, nickel, arsenic, antimony, bismuth (all of which, like iron, are oxidized and remain oxidized) and silver, gold, and traces of platinum metals (all of which, like silver, are not oxidized and collect at the bottom of the cell). The residue at the bottom of the cell beneath the anode is called the *anode slime*. With efficient operation, the recovery of noble metals from the anode slime can pay for the whole refinery operation, leaving the copper as profit.

Metallic copper is malleable and ductile and a very good conductor of heat and electricity. Except for silver, it has the lowest electric resistance of any metal and is used extensively in wires and switches that carry current. It is a poorer reducing agent than hydrogen and does not dissolve in acids unless they contain oxidizing anions. When exposed to the air, it slowly tarnishes with the formation of a green hydroxy carbonate, but this adheres to the metal and protects it from further corrosion.

World production of copper is of the order of 3 million tons per year. Most of this goes into the electrical industry, with the remainder used to make alloys. There are over a thousand of these alloys ranging from simple *brasses* (copper plus zinc) and *bronzes* (copper plus tin) to the more complex and specialized, such as monel metal (copper, nickel, iron, and manganese).

The compounds of copper correspond to oxidation states of $+1$ (*cuprous*) and $+2$ (*cupric*). The $+1$ state is easily oxidized and is stable only in very insoluble compounds or in complex ions. The $+2$ state is the one commonly observed in most copper compounds. The simple cuprous ion, Cu^+, cannot exist in aqueous solution, since it oxidizes and reduces itself by the reaction

$$2Cu^+ \rightarrow Cu^{++} + Cu(s)$$

A comparison of the oxidation potentials

$$Cu^+ \rightarrow Cu^{++} + e^- \qquad -0.15 \text{ volt}$$

$$Cu(s) \rightarrow Cu^+ + e^- \qquad -0.52 \text{ volt}$$

indicates that Cu^+ is a better reducing agent than Cu. This means that, when Cu^+ ions are placed in aqueous solutions, some of the Cu^+ ions transfer electrons to other Cu^+ ions. Disproportionation (self-oxidation-reduction) occurs, with the formation of solid copper and cupric ion. This reaction takes place, for example, when cuprous oxide, Cu_2O, is placed in a solution of sulfuric acid. The net reaction

$$Cu_2O(s) + 2H^+ \rightarrow Cu(s) + Cu^{++} + H_2O$$

can be considered to be the sum of two steps:

$$Cu_2O(s) + 2H^+ \rightarrow 2Cu^+ + H_2O$$

$$2Cu^+ \rightarrow Cu(s) + Cu^{++}$$

However, the cuprous condition can be stabilized by formation of insoluble substances or complex ions. For instance, in the presence of chloride ion, cuprous ion can form insoluble cuprous chloride.

$$CuCl(s) \rightleftharpoons Cu^+ + Cl^- \qquad K_{s.p.} = 3.2 \times 10^{-7}$$

The oxidation potentials then become

$$CuCl(s) \rightarrow Cu^{++} + Cl^- + e^- \qquad -0.54 \text{ volt}$$

$$Cu(s) + Cl^- \rightarrow CuCl(s) + e^- \qquad -0.14 \text{ volt}$$

which indicates that CuCl is not a good enough reducing agent to reduce itself (i.e., reverse the second half-reaction). Thus, cuprous chloride can be obtained as a stable white solid in contact with aqueous solutions. If there is a high concentration of chloride ion in the aqueous phase, then an additional complication appears in the formation of complex ions such as $CuCl_2^-$, called dichlorocuprate(I). The cuprous complex can be prepared by boiling $CuCl_2$ with copper turnings in concentrated hydrochloric acid. The deep brown color first formed is believed to be due to a complex containing both cuprous and cupric copper. As all the cupric state becomes reduced, the solution turns colorless. If the chloride-ion concentration of the colorless solution is decreased, as by dilution, white CuCl precipitates.

The cuprous state is also found in cuprous oxide, Cu_2O, a reddish, insoluble solid. It can be formed by addition of base to a solution of a cuprous complex (e.g., $CuCl_2^-$), followed by dehydration. The reddish color observed on metallic copper that has been heated in air is apparently due to a surface coating of Cu_2O. In the classic test for reducing sugars (e.g., glucose, which, unlike sucrose, acts as a mild reducing agent), Cu_2O is formed as a red precipitate when a reducing sugar is heated with an alkaline solution of a cupric salt.

The simple cupric ion, Cu^{++}, is apparently colorless, since many anhydrous cupric salts are white. However, hydrated cupric salts and their aqueous solutions are blue, owing to the presence of hydrated cupric ion. In general, aqueous solutions of cupric salts are acidic because of hydrolysis

$$Cu^{++} + H_2O \rightleftharpoons CuOH^+ + H^+$$

but the hydrolysis is not very extensive ($K_h = 1 \times 10^{-6}$). When base is added to these solutions, light blue cupric hydroxide, $Cu(OH)_2$, is formed. The hydroxide is slightly soluble in excess base, and so it might be called slightly amphoteric. When treated with aqueous ammonia solution, $Cu(OH)_2$ dissolves to give a deep blue solution, in which the color is usually attributed to a copper-ammonia complex ion, $Cu(NH_3)_4{}^{++}$.

$$Cu(OH)_2(s) + 4NH_3 \rightarrow Cu(NH_3)_4{}^{++} + 2OH^-$$

Like many other complexes of cupric ion, $Cu(NH_3)_4{}^{++}$ is paramagnetic owing to an unpaired electron. It has a planar structure and can be destroyed by heat or by addition of acid. Heat is effective, because it boils the NH_3 out of the solution

$$Cu(NH_3)_4{}^{++} \rightarrow Cu^{++} + 4NH_3(g)$$

and thus favors dissociation of the complex. Addition of acids results in neutralization of the NH_3 and similarly favors breakup of the complex.

$$Cu(NH_3)_4{}^{++} + 4H^+ \rightarrow Cu^{++} + 4NH_4{}^+$$

It is interesting to note that addition of an acid to a basic solution containing $Cu(NH_3)_4{}^{++}$ can produce $Cu(OH)_2$ precipitation. As acid is added, the concentration of Cu^{++} rises to compensate for the gradual neutralization of NH_3, until eventually the $K_{s.p.}$ of $Cu(OH)_2$, 1.6×10^{-19}, is exceeded.

One of the least soluble of cupric compounds is cupric sulfide, CuS. This is the black precipitate which is easily prepared by bubbling hydrogen sulfide through a solution of cupric salt. The very low $K_{s.p.}$ of CuS (8×10^{-37}) indicates that not even very concentrated H^+ can dissolve appreciable amounts of it. For instance, in 10 M H^+ the relation $[H^+]^2[S^{--}] = 1 \times 10^{-22}$, derived in Sec. 17.10, indicates that the S^{--} concentration is $1 \times 10^{-22}/(10)^2$, or 1×10^{-24} M. From the $K_{s.p.}$ of CuS, the copper concentration would be $8 \times 10^{-37}/1 \times 10^{-24}$, or 8×10^{-13} M. Thus, not any appreciable amount of CuS can dissolve in this fashion. It is possible, however, to dissolve appreciable amounts of CuS by heating it with nitric acid. Dissolving occurs, not because H^+ reacts with the S^{--}, but because hot nitrate ion (especially in acid solution) is a very good oxidizing agent and oxidizes the sulfide ion to elementary sulfur. The net reaction is

$$3CuS(s) + 2NO_3{}^- + 8H^+ \rightarrow 3Cu^{++} + 3S(s) + 2NO(g) + 4H_2O$$

Probably the best known cupric compound is copper sulfate pentahydrate, $Cu(H_2O)_4SO_4 \cdot H_2O$. In this material, each cupric ion is surrounded by a distorted octahedron of oxygen atoms; four of these lie in a square and belong to four H_2O molecules, while the other two belong to neighboring sulfate groups. The odd H_2O molecule, the fifth one, is not directly bound to the cupric ion but forms a bridge between SO_4^{--} and other H_2O groups. The pentahydrate, or blue vitriol, as it is sometimes called, is used extensively as a germicide and fungicide, since the cupric ion is toxic to lower organisms. Its application to water supplies for controlling algae depends on this toxicity.

22.3   SILVER

Silver is a rather rare element (10^{-8} per cent of the earth's crust), occurring principally as native silver, argentite (Ag_2S), and horn silver (AgCl). Only about one-fifth of current silver production comes from silver ores; the rest is mainly a by-product of copper and lead production. The main problem in extracting silver from its ores is to get the rather inert silver (or the very insoluble silver compounds) to go into solution. This can be accomplished by blowing air for a week or two through a suspension of the ore in dilute aqueous sodium cyanide (NaCN) solution. With native silver, the reaction can be written

$$4Ag(s) + 8CN^- + 2H_2O + O_2(g) \rightarrow 4Ag(CN)_2^- + 4OH^-$$

Were it not for the presence of cyanide ion, the oxygen would not oxidize the silver to a higher oxidation state. This can be seen from a comparison of the following oxidation potentials

$$Ag(s) \rightarrow Ag^+ + e^- \qquad\qquad -0.799 \text{ volt}$$

$$Ag(s) + 2CN^- \rightarrow Ag(CN)_2^- + e^- \qquad +0.31 \text{ volt}$$

In the absence of cyanide ion, metallic silver is a rather poor reducing agent, and hence it is difficult to oxidize it to Ag^+. In the presence of cyanide ion, Ag^+ forms a strongly associated complex ion and is thus stabilized. What this means is that, when silver reacts to form the silver-cyanide complex ion, it acts as a fair reducing agent and is rather easily oxidized. Similar reasoning applies to the dissolving of argentite (Ag_2S). This sulfide is very insoluble ($K_{s.p.} = 5.5 \times 10^{-51}$), and air oxidation by itself is not sufficient to get it into solution. However, in the presence of cyanide ion, solution does occur. In fact, the stability of the complex $Ag(CN)_2^-$ is so great that with high concentrations of cyanide ion the reaction

$$Ag_2S(s) + 4CN^- \rightarrow 2Ag(CN)_2^- + S^{--}$$

can be made to proceed to a useful extent without invoking air oxidation to oxidize the S^{--}. To recover the silver from the residual solutions, it is necessary to use a rather strong reducing agent, such as aluminum metal or zinc metal in basic solution. A possible reaction is

$$Zn(s) + 2Ag(CN)_2^- + 3OH^- \rightarrow 2Ag(s) + 4CN^- + Zn(OH)_3^-$$

where some of the zinc in the final solution is also present as a cyanide complex, $Zn(CN)_4^{--}$.

Massive silver appears almost white because of its high luster. It is too soft to be used pure in jewelry and coinage and is usually alloyed with copper for these purposes. Because of expense it cannot be used much for its best property, its electric and thermal conductivity, which is second to none. In the finely divided state, silver appears black, because the haphazard arrangement of tiny crystalline faces reflects light in all directions with very little probability of sending it back to the eye of the observer. Also with smaller particles (of colloidal dimensions), metallic reflection of the type discussed in Sec. 18.1 cannot occur.

The compounds of silver are essentially all of the $+1$ state, although $+2$ and $+3$ compounds have been prepared under extreme oxidizing conditions. For example, an oxide believed to be AgO is formed when ozone is passed over elementary silver. The compound is not very stable toward decomposition to Ag and O_2 and, in general, behaves as a very strong oxidizing agent. In the $+1$ state silver forms the ion Ag^+, sometimes called argentous ion after the Latin word for silver, *argentum*. It does not hydrolyze appreciably in aqueous solution, is a good oxidizing agent, and forms many complex ions [e.g., $Ag(NH_3)_2^+$, $Ag(CN)_2^-$, $AgCl_2^-$, all of which are linear]. When base is added to solutions of silver salts, a brown oxide is formed, which shows little sign of being amphoteric:

$$2Ag^+ + 2OH^- \rightarrow Ag_2O(s) + H_2O$$

However, the oxide does dissolve in an aqueous solution of ammonia because of formation of the colorless silver-ammonia complex ion, $Ag(NH_3)_2^+$.

$$Ag_2O(s) + 4NH_3 + H_2O \rightarrow 2Ag(NH_3)_2^+ + 2OH^-$$

Solutions containing $Ag(NH_3)_2^+$ are frequently used as sources of silver for silver plating. They have the advantage of providing low concentrations of Ag^+, so that reduction by mild reducing agents, such as glucose, slowly deposits a compact silver plate. Evaporation of these solutions leaves dangerous solid residues which are violently explosive. Their composition is not known but has been described both as silver amide, $AgNH_2$, and as silver nitride, Ag_3N.

Probably the most interesting of all the silver compounds are the silver halides, AgF, AgCl, AgBr, and AgI. Except for silver fluoride, which is very soluble in water (up to 14.3 moles per 1,000 g. of H_2O), these halides are quite insoluble. The solubility products, 1.7×10^{-10} for AgCl, 5.0×10^{-13} for AgBr, and 8.5×10^{-17} for AgI, indicate a decrease in solubility from AgCl to AgI. The low solubility is rather surprising, because in general salts of $+1$ cations and -1 anions are usually soluble. In this respect AgF is normal; it dissolves much like NaF or KF. The abnormal insolubility of the other silver halides is attributed to the fact that their lattice energies (Sec. 16.6) are higher than expected. The principal reason for this is that there are strong van der Waals attractions between Ag^+ ions and the halide ions, and these attractions are superposed on the ordinary ionic attractions. Suppose we compare AgCl with KCl. Since Ag^+ (ionic radius, 1.26 A.) and K^+ (ionic radius, 1.33 A.) have about the same size, we would expect the ionic attractions in the solid to be about the same. However, the Ag^+ has 46 electrons, whereas K^+ has only 18. In general, the more electrons an atom has, the more easily it is deformed electrically, and hence the stronger its van der Waals attraction to neighboring atoms (Sec. 6.14). Consequently, the lattice of AgCl should be held together more strongly than that of KCl. In fact, the lattice energy of AgCl is 214 kcal.; that of KCl, 168 kcal. Since more energy is required to break up the AgCl lattice than the KCl, AgCl should be less soluble. In support of this picture is the observed decrease in solubility from AgF to AgCl to AgBr to AgI. As the anion contains more electrons, the van der Waals attraction increases, and the lattice energy gets bigger.

Except for AgF, the silver halides are sensitive to light. For this reason, they find use in making photographic emulsions. The chemistry of the photographic process is not well understood and is complicated, because it apparently involves defect structures (see Sec. 8.5). However, the basic steps are usually described as follows: When photographic film, consisting essentially of a dispersion of silver bromide in gelatin, is exposed to light, grains of silver bromide are activated, depending on the intensity of the incident light. This is not a visible change and, according to one theory, simply involves migration of electrons in the silver bromide emulsion. Whatever the cause, the activated grains are more susceptible to chemical reduction by mild reducing agents (developers) than nonactivated grains. When the exposed photographic emulsion is developed, black metallic silver forms by the preferential reduction of exposed silver bromide grains. The result is that black areas appear on the film where the light was strongest. Since AgBr slowly turns black when exposed to light, the whole film would turn black eventually. However, the photographic image can be fixed by washing out unexposed AgBr grains. Although very insoluble ($K_{s.p.} = 5.0 \times 10^{-13}$), AgBr will dissolve in solutions containing high concentrations of thiosulfate ion, $S_2O_3^{--}$, by the reaction

$$AgBr(s) + 2S_2O_3^{--} \rightarrow Ag(S_2O_3)_2^{-3} + Br^-$$

Thus, the final step involves soaking the film in a fixing bath, the essential component of which is $Na_2S_2O_3$, or hypo. The result is a fixed negative image of the exposure. By shining light through the negative on another emulsion, developing, and then fixing it, the light and dark areas are inverted to produce a positive image.

In color photography the processes are much more involved. Fundamentally, they depend on having film coated with three emulsion layers, each of which is sensitive to one of the primary colors. On exposure and development, images are formed in each of the three layers. By appropriate choice of dyes and other chemicals, these three images can be colored separately so as to reproduce by superposition the original multicolored pattern.

22.4   GOLD

Gold is a very rare element, being about one-tenth as abundant as silver. It occurs naturally as *native gold* (where it is usually alloyed with silver) and less frequently as compounds of tellurium, such as $AuTe_2$ (gold telluride, or calaverite). The recovery is generally a mechanical process which makes use of the very high density (19.3 g. per cc.) of the metal. Chemical extraction is usually by a cyanide process like that used for silver:

$$4Au(s) + 8CN^- + O_2(g) + 2H_2O \rightarrow 4Au(CN)_2^- + 4OH^-$$

Although it is the most malleable and ductile of all metals and is a very good conductor of heat and electricity, the principal use of gold is for currency and jewelry. As a reducing agent, it is rather inert.

The compounds of gold correspond to the $+1$ and $+3$ oxidation states; these are called aurous and auric, respectively, after the Latin word for gold, *aurum*. The aurous ion, Au^+, cannot exist in aqueous solution, because it is such a good oxidizing agent. The oxidation potential for $Au(s) \rightleftharpoons Au^+ + e^-$ is -1.7 volts, thus making Au^+ about as strong an oxidizing agent as permanganate ion. It will, in fact, oxidize itself to Au^{+3}. However, the $+1$ state of gold can be stabilized by complexing with cyanide ion to form $Au(CN)_2^-$. The oxidation potential for $Au(s) + 2CN^- \rightleftharpoons Au(CN)_2^- + e^-$ is $+0.60$ volt.

In the $+3$ state, gold exists as complex ions. The most common of these is the chloraurate ion, $AuCl_4^-$, which is obtained when gold is dissolved in aqua regia. Aqua regia, which consists of one part of concentrated nitric acid and about three parts of concentrated hydrochloric acid, can dissolve gold, whereas concentrated HNO_3 or concentrated HCl alone cannot. The reason for this is that HNO_3 cannot oxidize gold unless the chloride ion is present to complex the product. In other words, the half-reaction $Au(s) + 4Cl^- \rightleftharpoons AuCl_4^- + 3e^-$ with -1.0 volt is easier to carry out than the half-reaction $Au(s) \rightleftharpoons Au^{+3} + 3e^-$ with -1.42 volts.

The net equation for dissolving gold in aqua regia is usually written

$$Au(s) + 3NO_3^- + 4Cl^- + 6H^+ \rightarrow AuCl_4^- + 3NO_2(g) + 3H_2O$$

22.5   ZINC SUBGROUP

The elements of the zinc subgroup are zinc, cadmium, and mercury. They are more active than the elements of the copper subgroup, but their chemistry is somewhat more simple. The zinc-subgroup elements have a characteristic oxidation state of $+2$, except for mercury, which also forms $+1$ compounds. Some of the more important properties are listed in Table 22.2.

As seen from the electronic configurations, each of these elements has two electrons in the outermost energy level. The situation is reminiscent of that found for the alkaline-earth elements (Sec. 19.1). The low melting points may at first sight be surprising, but they are not entirely unexpected. In progressing from left to right through the transition sequence, the low point in the atomic volume has been passed (see Table 3.10), and the atoms get bigger from here on. As the atoms get bigger, they are farther apart, and forces of attraction are smaller. Thus, it becomes easier to melt the elements. Probably of greater importance is the fact that the d shells of the second-outermost shells are filled; therefore there is little chance for the covalent binding between ions found in other transition elements. In mercury, the interatomic forces are so weak that its melting point is below room temperature.

There is a striking difference between these elements and the analogous group II elements. In Table 22.3 the element zinc is compared with calcium, a typical element of group II. Although both of these elements have but two electrons in the outermost shell, and have no partially filled shells, their properties are quite different. For example, as shown by the oxidation potentials, calcium is a very powerful reducing agent, whereas zinc is only moderately strong. The fundamental reason for the change in properties is the decreased size of the zinc atom. Since the nuclear charge has increased

Table 22.2   Elements of Zinc Subgroup

Symbol	Z	Electronic configuration	Melting point, °C.	Boiling point, °C.	Ionization potential, e.v.	Oxidation potential (to M^{++}), volts
Zn	30	2, 8, 18, 2	419	907	9.39	$+0.76$
Cd	48	2, 8, 18, 18, 2	321	767	8.99	$+0.40$
Hg	80	2, 8, 18, 32, 18, 2	-38.9	357	10.43	-0.85

Table 22.3 Comparison of Calcium and Zinc

Property	Calcium	Zinc
Atomic number	20	30
Electronic configuration	2, 8, 8, 2	2, 8, 18, 2
Atomic volume, cc.	26	9
Size of M^{++} (radius), A.	0.94	0.70
First ionization potential, e.v.	6.11	9.39
Second ionization potential, e.v.	11.87	17.89
Third ionization potential, e.v.	51.21	40.0
Density, g./cc.	1.55	7.14
Melting point, °C.	810	419
Boiling point, °C.	1300(?)	907
Oxidation potential, volts	+2.87	+0.76

by 10 units in going from $Z = 20$ to $Z = 30$, there is a greater attraction for the electrons in zinc, and the shells are pulled in. The atom is thus smaller. The valence electrons are fourth-shell electrons in both cases and are held more tightly in the zinc atom.

22.6 ZINC

About a hundred times as abundant as copper, zinc occurs principally as the mineral sphalerite (ZnS), also called zinc blende. The metal is prepared by roasting the sulfide in air to convert it to oxide and then reducing the oxide with finely divided carbon. The reactions are

$$2ZnS(s) + 3O_2(g) \rightarrow 2ZnO(s) + 2SO_2(g)$$

$$ZnO(s) + C(s) \rightarrow Zn(g) + CO(g)$$

Since the second reaction is carried out at about 1200°C., above the boiling point of Zn, the metal forms as a vapor and must be condensed. Very rapid condensation produces the fine powder known as zinc dust.

Massive zinc has fairly good metallic properties except that it is rather brittle, especially at 200°C., where it can be ground up into a powder. It is a moderately active metal and can even reduce water to hydrogen, but only when heated. With acids, ordinary Zn gives the well-known evolution of H_2. Strangely enough, this is very rapid when the Zn is impure, but almost too slow to be observed when the Zn is very pure. Apparently the impurities (especially arsenic and antimony) speed dissolving by serving as centers from which hydrogen gas can evolve.

In air, zinc tarnishes but slightly, probably because it forms a self-protective coat of oxide or carbonate. Because it itself withstands corrosion so well and because it can give cathodic protection (Sec. 21.4) to iron, zinc is often used as a coating on iron to keep it from rusting. Iron protected in this way is called galvanized iron and can be made by dipping the iron into molten zinc or by plating zinc on it from an electrolytic bath. The other important use of zinc is in alloys such as the brasses, which are essentially copper-zinc alloys.

In all its compounds, zinc shows only a $+2$ oxidation state. The zinc ion, Zn^{++}, is colorless and not paramagnetic. In aqueous solutions it hydrolyzes to give slightly acid solutions. The hydrolysis, usually written

$$Zn^{++} + H_2O \rightleftharpoons Zn(OH)^+ + H^+ \qquad K_h = 2.5 \times 10^{-10}$$

does not proceed so far toward the right as that of Cu^{++} ion. Thus, for equal concentrations, solutions of zinc salts are less acid than those of cupric salts. When base is added to solutions of zinc salts, white zinc hydroxide, $Zn(OH)_2$, is precipitated. This hydroxide is amphoteric, and therefore further addition of base dissolves it to give zincate ion, variously formulated as $Zn(OH)_3^-$, $Zn(OH)_4^{--}$, $HZnO_2^-$, or ZnO_2^{--}. Whatever the formula of zincate ion, the concentration of Zn^{++} in equilibrium with it in basic solution is very small. This means (by the principle of Le Chatelier) that the half-reaction

$$Zn(s) \rightarrow Zn^{++} + 2e^-$$

has greater tendency to go to the right in basic solution (small concentration of Zn^{++}) than in acid solution. Consequently, zinc metal is a stronger reducing agent (has higher oxidation potential) for basic solutions than for acid solutions. For basic solutions, the half-reaction can be written

$$Zn(s) + 4OH^- \rightarrow Zn(OH)_4^{--} + 2e^-$$

and the oxidation potential is $+1.22$ volts. As indicated in Table 22.2, the oxidation potential for acid solutions is $+0.76$ volt.

Like other transition elements, zinc has great tendency to form stable complex ions. For example, zinc hydroxide is easily dissolved in aqueous ammonia because of the formation of a zinc-ammonia complex, $Zn(NH_3)_4^{++}$. The hydroxide can also be dissolved in cyanide solutions because of the formation of a zinc-cyanide complex, $Zn(CN)_4^{--}$. As shown by the following equilibrium constants:

$$Zn(NH_3)_4^{++} \rightleftharpoons Zn^{++} + 4NH_3 \qquad K = 3.4 \times 10^{-10}$$

$$Zn(CN)_4^{--} \rightleftharpoons Zn^{++} + 4CN^- \qquad K = 1.2 \times 10^{-18}$$

the cyanide complex is less dissociated than the ammonia complex. The greater stability of the cyanide complex is reflected in the fact that zinc metal is a stronger reducing agent in cyanide solutions than in ammonia solutions. The oxidation potentials are

$$Zn(s) + 4CN^- \rightarrow Zn(CN)_4^{--} + 2e^- \qquad +1.26 \text{ volts}$$

$$Zn(s) + 4NH_3 \rightarrow Zn(NH_3)_4^{++} + 2e^- \qquad +1.04 \text{ volts}$$

When hydrogen sulfide is passed through solutions of zinc salts which are not too acid, white zinc sulfide precipitates. Although the solubility product of ZnS (1×10^{-22}) is rather small, so that ZnS is essentially insoluble in neutral solutions, addition of acid lowers the sulfide-ion concentration (as described in Sec. 17.10) sufficiently that ZnS becomes soluble. The enhanced solubility of ZnS in acid solution gives a method for separating it from other sulfides such as CuS, Ag_2S, and CdS.

Zinc sulfide is used extensively in the white pigment, lithopone, an approximately equimolar mixture of ZnS and $BaSO_4$. ZnS is also used in making fluorescent screens, because impure ZnS acts as a phosphor, i.e., it can convert energy such as that of an electron beam into visible light. The action of these phosphors is very complex and is closely related to the properties of defects in solid-state structures (Sec. 8.5). The simplest view is that an electron beam impinging on impure ZnS uses its energy to kick electrons out of an impurity center. This electron wanders through the crystal until it finds some other center to which it can return by giving off a flash of light. Many television screens are coated with zinc sulfide phosphor.

22.7 CADMIUM

The properties of cadmium are so similar to those of zinc that the two elements invariably occur together. There are no important minerals of cadmium, which is only about one-thousandth as abundant as zinc. The principal source of cadmium is the flue dust from the purification of zinc by distillation. Since Cd is more volatile than Zn, it evaporates first and concentrates in the first distillates. The principal use of Cd is as a protective plate on other metals, such as steel. It is particularly good for alkaline conditions because, unlike Zn, it is not amphoteric and does not dissolve in base. The other principal use of cadmium is in making low-melting alloys, such as Wood's metal (m.p., 70°C.).

In its compounds, the usual oxidation state of cadmium is $+2$. It exists in aqueous solutions as colorless Cd^{++} ion. With H_2S, it forms insoluble, yellow CdS ($K_{s.p.} = 1.0 \times 10^{-28}$), which is used as the pigment "cadmium yellow." Like zinc, cadmium forms a variety of complex ions, including $Cd(NH_3)_4^{++}$, $Cd(CN)_4^{--}$, $CdCl_4^{--}$, and CdI_4^{--}. Some of the salts of cadmium are peculiar, in the sense that they do not dissociate completely into ions in aqueous solution as practically all other salts do. Cadmium sulfate, for example, has a dissociation constant of 5×10^{-3} and so can be called a weak salt.

22.8   MERCURY

The only common mineral of mercury is cinnabar (HgS), from which the element is produced by roasting in air.

$$HgS(s) + O_2(g) \rightarrow Hg + SO_2(g)$$

Unlike any other metal,* mercury is a liquid at room temperature, and its symbol emphasizes this, since it comes from the Latin *hydrargyrum*, meaning liquid silver. The liquid is not very volatile (vapor pressure is 0.0018 mm. Hg at 25°C.), but the vapor is very poisonous, and *prolonged exposure even to the liquid should be avoided.*

Liquid mercury has a high metallic luster, but it is not a very good metal, as it has a higher electric resistance than any of the other transition metals. However, for some uses, as in making electrical contacts, the mobility of liquid mercury is such a great advantage that its mediocre conductivity can be tolerated. Furthermore, its inertness to air oxidation, its relatively high density, and its uniform expansion with temperature lead to special uses as in barometers and thermometers.

Liquid mercury dissolves many metals, especially the softer ones like copper, silver, gold, and the alkali elements. The resulting alloys, which may be solid as well as liquid, are called *amalgams.* Probably their most distinctive property is that the reactivity of the metal dissolved in the mercury is thereby lowered. For example, in sodium amalgam the reactivity of sodium is so low that sodium amalgam can be kept in water with only slow evolution of hydrogen.

In its compounds, mercury shows both +1 (mercurous) and +2 (mercuric) oxidation states. In this respect, it is unlike the other members of the zinc subgroup. The mercurous compounds are unusual because they all contain two mercury atoms bound together. In aqueous solutions, the ion is a double ion corresponding to Hg_2^{++}, in which there is a covalent bond between the two mercury atoms. Experimental evidence for this is the lack of paramagnetism of mercurous compounds. The ion Hg^+ would have one unpaired electron in its $6s$ orbital and would be paramagnetic, whereas the

---

*Cesium metal has a melting point of 28.5°C., or 83.3°F., and gallium metal has a melting point of 29.8°C., or 85.6°F. Thus, the uniqueness of mercury as a liquid metal disappears on hot days.

ion Hg_2^{++} would have the two electrons paired as a covalent bond and would not be paramagnetic. Further experimental evidence for Hg_2^{++} comes from a study of the equilibrium between liquid mercury, mercuric ion, and mercurous ion. There are two possible ways of writing this equilibrium, depending on whether mercurous mercury exists as Hg_2^{++} or Hg^+:

$$Hg(l) + Hg^{++} \rightleftharpoons Hg_2^{++} \qquad K = [Hg_2^{++}]/[Hg^{++}]$$

$$Hg(l) + Hg^{++} \rightleftharpoons 2Hg^+ \qquad K' = [Hg^+]^2/[Hg^{++}]$$

If the amounts of mercurous mercury and mercuric mercury in solution are determined for various equilibrium solutions, it is found that the ratio of mercurous to mercuric is constant, but the ratio of mercurous squared to mercuric is not. In other words, K is found to be a true constant (1.7×10^2) for all experiments, but K' is not. Apparently, there is little, if any, Hg^+ in solution.

Except for the doubling, mercurous ion behaves much like Ag^+; e.g., it reacts with chloride ion to precipitate white mercurous chloride, Hg_2Cl_2, also known as calomel. When exposed to light, calomel darkens by partial disproportionation into Hg and $HgCl_2$. Just as the silver halides decrease in solubility in going from AgF to AgI, so do the mercurous halides. Mercurous fluoride, Hg_2F_2, is quite soluble in water, but the solution immediately decomposes to form HF and insoluble, black Hg_2O. For the other halides the solubility products are as follows:

$$Hg_2Cl_2(s) \rightleftharpoons Hg_2^{++} + 2Cl^- \qquad K_{s.p.} = 1.1 \times 10^{-18}$$

$$Hg_2Br_2(s) \rightleftharpoons Hg_2^{++} + 2Br^- \qquad K_{s.p.} = 1.3 \times 10^{-22}$$

$$Hg_2I_2(s) \rightleftharpoons Hg_2^{++} + 2I^- \qquad K_{s.p.} = 4.5 \times 10^{-29}$$

Unlike Ag^+, mercurous ion does not form an ammonia complex. When aqueous ammonia is added to Hg_2Cl_2, the solid turns black because of formation of finely divided mercury.

$$Hg_2Cl_2(s) + 2NH_3 \rightarrow HgNH_2Cl(s) + Hg + NH_4^+ + Cl^-$$

The compound $HgNH_2Cl$, mercuric ammonobasic chloride, is white, but its color is obscured by the intense black. This difference in behavior toward NH_3 provides a simple test for distinguishing AgCl from Hg_2Cl_2.

In the +2 state, mercury is frequently represented as the simple ion Hg^{++}, although it is usually found in the form of complex ions, insoluble solids, or weak salts. For example, in a solution of mercuric chloride, the concentration of Hg^{++} is much smaller than the concentration of undissociated $HgCl_2$ molecules. With excess chloride ion, the complexes $HgCl_3^-$ and $HgCl_4^{--}$ are also formed. In ammonia solutions, complex ions containing one, two, three, and four NH_3 molecules are known. For complete dissociation of $Hg(NH_3)_4^{++}$, the constant is 5.2×10^{-20}. The complex $Hg(CN)_4^{--}$ is even more stable ($K = 4 \times 10^{-42}$).

Although mercuric sulfide as found in nature is red, when H_2S is passed through a mercuric solution, a black precipitate of HgS is obtained. The color difference may be due to differences in crystal structure. The solubility product of black HgS is very low (1.6×10^{-54}), but not so low as that of platinum sulfide, PtS ($K_{s.p.} = 8 \times 10^{-73}$). In order to dissolve these very insoluble sulfides, drastic measures are required. HgS, for example, will not dissolve even in boiling nitric acid. Aqua regia, however, which supplies both nitrate for oxidizing the sulfide and chloride for complexing the mercuric, does take it into solution.

The oxidation potentials

$$2Hg(l) \rightleftharpoons Hg_2^{++} + 2e^- \qquad -0.79 \text{ volt}$$

$$Hg_2^{++} \rightleftharpoons 2Hg^{++} + 2e^- \qquad -0.92 \text{ volt}$$

are so close that practically any oxidizing agent which is able to oxidize mercury to mercurous ion is also able to oxidize mercurous ion to mercuric ion. Conversely, any reducing agent that can reduce mercuric to mercurous can also reduce mercurous to mercury. If a limited amount of reducing agent such as Sn^{++} (stannous ion) is added to a mercuric solution, only Hg_2^{++} is formed; if Sn^{++} is added in excess, the reduction goes all the way to Hg.

22.9   QUALITATIVE ANALYSIS

Mercurous ion and silver ion can be separated from the other cations by adding HCl to precipitate white, insoluble Hg_2Cl_2 and AgCl. If NH_3 is added to a mixture of these chlorides, a black color appears, owing to formation of Hg and $HgNH_2Cl$. Since NH_3 converts AgCl into soluble $Ag(NH_3)_2^+$ and Cl^-, the filtrate contains the silver, and AgCl can be reprecipitated by addition of HNO_3.

If H_2S is added to an acidic solution containing Cd^{++}, Hg^{++}, Cu^{++}, and Zn^{++}, the first three precipitate as insoluble sulfides (yellow CdS, black HgS, and black CuS). If the solution is then made basic with NH_3, white ZnS is formed. A confirmatory test for ZnS would be to dissolve it in HCl plus HNO_3, evaporate to dryness, and reprecipitate by addition of H_2S in a $SO_4^{--} - HSO_4^-$ buffer.

The separation of CdS, HgS, and CuS makes use of the fact that CdS and CuS are soluble in boiling HNO_3 whereas HgS is not. HgS can be confirmed by dissolving in aqua regia and reducing with $SnCl_2$ to Hg_2Cl_2 and Hg. Addition of NH_3 to a solution containing Cu^{++} and Cd^{++} gives the blue color characteristic of $Cu(NH_3)_4^{++}$. Cadmium can be detected by first precipitating out the Cu^{++} with H_2S in acid solution in the presence of high-concentration chloride ion (which keeps Cd^{++} in solution as $CdCl_4^{--}$) and then adding $NaC_2H_3O_2$ and H_2S. The added acetate ion serves to reduce the H^+ concentration, thereby raising the S^{--} concentration sufficiently to precipitate yellow CdS.

QUESTIONS

22.1   *Electron configuration.* Indicate the electronic configuration of each of the following: Ag^+, Cu^{++}, Au^{+3}, Hg_2^{++}.

22.2   *Comparison of Rb and Ag.* Compare qualitatively rubidium and silver with respect to the properties listed in Table 22.3.

22.3   *Electrorefining.* In the electrolytic refining of copper, tell what would happen to the typical impurities iron and gold.

22.4   *Equilibrium constant.* Calculate (Sec. 17.14) the equilibrium constant for the disproportionation of cuprous ion.

22.5   *Photography.* Trace the history of the silver ions in a photographic process.

22.6   *Aqua regia.* Platinum, like gold, is dissolved by aqua regia but not by HNO_3 or HCl alone. Explain.

22.7   *Equations.* Write equations for each of the following: (*a*) roasting of cinnabar to form SO_2; (*b*) dissolving of $Cu(OH)_2$ by ammonia solution, followed by reprecipitation with acid; (*c*) cyanide process for gold; (*d*) dissolving of zinc hydroxide in basic solution; (*e*) dissolving of zinc metal in basic solution to liberate H_2; (*f*) dissolving of cadmium iodide in iodide solution.

22.8   *Hydrolysis.*   Calculate the pH of a solution made by dissolving 3.0 g. of $Zn(NO_3)_2 \cdot 6H_2O$ in enough water to make 0.10 liter of solution.   *Ans.* 5.3

22.9   *Electrode potentials.* How would the oxidation potential of zinc in sulfide solution compare with that in cyanide solution? Justify your answer.

22.10   *Solubility.* Calculate the chloride-ion concentration in saturated solutions of AgCl and Hg_2Cl_2.

22.11   *Proof of Hg_2^{++}.* (*a*) Using K from Sec. 22.8, calculate the concentration of Hg_2^{++} in equilibrium with liquid mercury and 1.0×10^{-5} M Hg^{++}. Repeat the calculation for 1.0×10^{-3} M Hg^{++}. (*b*) By converting the values calculated in (*a*) to the equivalent concentration of Hg^+, show that the K' in Sec. 22.8 is not a constant.

22.12   *Solubility.* A solution is made by mixing 100 ml. of 0.10 M NaI, 100 ml. of 0.20 M NaBr, 100 ml. of 0.30 M NaCl, and 100 ml. of 0.50 M $AgNO_3$. Assuming the total volume to be 400 ml., calculate the concentration of bromide ion in the final solution.   *Ans.* 7.4×10^{-5} M

22.13 *Complex equilibria.* When a solution containing $CuCl_2^-$ and Cl^- is diluted, it is observed that solid CuCl precipitates. By considering the equilibria

$$CuCl_2^- \rightleftharpoons CuCl(s) + Cl^-$$

$$CuCl_3^{--} \rightleftharpoons CuCl(s) + 2Cl^-$$

show that the observation supports the view that there also must be other complex species such as $CuCl_3^{--}$ in the solution.

22.14 *Stoichiometry.* Given a sample containing only Ag_2SO_4 and $AgNO_3$ and weighing 3.258 g. Let the entire sample be dissolved in enough water to make exactly 100 ml. of solution. When 25.00 ml. of the resulting solution is titrated, it apparently takes just 40.00 ml. of 0.1250 *M* NaCl to precipitate all the Ag^+. (*a*) Calculate the mole fraction of Ag_2SO_4 in the original sample. (*b*) Suppose that the burette used had been incorrectly calibrated, so that the true volume of NaCl solution used was 40.12 ml. What is the true mole fraction of Ag_2SO_4 in the original sample? *Ans.* 0.333; 0.365

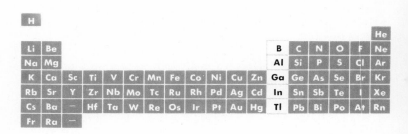

23 *Group* III *Elements*

THE PECULIAR ELECTRONIC EXPANSION responsible for the transition elements is completed with the zinc subgroup. The next elements, of group III, like those of groups I and II, are again main-group elements. Although the insertion of transition elements between groups II and III can modify the properties of later elements of group III, the early members, boron and aluminum, follow the alkaline-earth elements directly. Therefore, it is not surprising that the group III elements have the same relationship to the alkaline-earth elements as the alkaline-earth elements have to the alkali metals, i.e., the group properties are modified by a third valence electron.

23.1 GROUP PROPERTIES

The elements of group III are boron, aluminum, gallium, indium, and thallium. Their properties are listed in Table 23.1. Except for boron, which may be classed as a *semimetal*, these elements show typically metallic properties. The special character of boron stems principally from the small size of the boron atom. Like lithium of group I and beryllium of group II, boron has only the *K* shell underlying the valence electrons, whereas other

Table 23.1   Elements of Group III

Sym-bol	Z	Electronic configuration	Melting point, °C.	Boiling point, °C.	Ioni-zation poten-tial, e.v.	Oxidation potential, volts
B	5	2, 3	2300	2550(?)	8.30	$+0.87$(to H_3BO_3)
Al	13	2, 8, 3	659.7	2300	5.98	$+1.66$(to Al^{+3})
Ga	31	2, 8, 18, 3	29.8	2000	6.00	$+0.53$(to Ga^{+3})
In	49	2, 8, 18, 18, 3	155	1450	5.79	$+0.34$(to In^{+3})
Tl	81	2, 8, 18, 32, 18, 3	304	1460	6.11	$+0.34$(to Tl^+)

members of the group have additional shells populated. Consequently, the B atom is smaller and, as shown by the ionization potentials in Table 23.1, gives up electrons less readily than do other atoms of the group. Since, as discussed in Sec. 18.1, low ionization potential favors metallic properties, it is not surprising that boron is the least metallic of the group III elements. However, ionization potential is not the only factor which determines whether an element is metallic. For example, gold has a higher ionization potential than boron and yet is a typical metal. The detailed structure of the solid and the specific interactions are also important. Gold has a simple structure with 12 atoms as nearest neighbors; boron has a very complex structure, with some of the B atoms having 6 nearest neighbors, and others but 4.

From the electronic configurations given in Table 23.1, it might be expected that all the group III elements would form $+3$ ions. However, as just mentioned, boron has such firm hold on its three valence electrons that it does not exist as B^{+3} cations in its compounds but takes part in chemical combination only through covalent binding. Even so, in its compounds it is assigned oxidation state $+3$, because usually the compounds are formed with more electronegative elements. The other members of the group give up their electrons more readily; hence formation of a $+3$ ion becomes progressively easier down the group. In the case of thallium, it is also possible to remove only one electron from the neutral atom, thus forming a $+1$ ion.

As discussed in Sec. 17.12, a highly charged cation in water can pull electrons to itself sufficiently to facilitate the rupture of O—H bonds in water. The larger the cation, the smaller is the effect, because a large cation exerts a smaller pull on the electrons. In going down group III, the effect of this change is illustrated. Boron is so small that, if a B^{+3} ion were placed in water, it would pull electrons to itself from H_2O strongly enough to rupture the O—H bond and release H^+. In other words, $B(OH)_3$ and the corresponding oxide B_2O_3 are acidic. Al^{+3} and Ga^{+3} are larger than B^{+3}, and they hydrolyze less; $Al(OH)_3$, Al_2O_3, and the corresponding compounds of gallium are amphoteric. In^{+3} and Tl^{+3} are still larger. Their interactions with water are so small that the O—H bond of water is essentially unperturbed; i.e., the ions are but slightly hydrolyzed. Their hydroxides are basic. Thus, in going down group III there is a trend from acidic behavior to basic behavior of the oxides and hydroxides. Similar trends favoring the basic behavior for the larger atoms of a group are also found in later groups of the periodic table.

23.2   BORON

Both as an element and in its compounds, boron differs markedly in properties from the other members of group III. In nature, it is moderately rare (0.0003 per cent abundance) and occurs principally as the borates (oxyboron anions) of calcium and sodium, e.g., colemanite, $Ca_2B_6O_{11} \cdot 5H_2O$, and borax, $Na_2B_4O_7 \cdot 10H_2O$. The element may be produced by reducing the oxide, B_2O_3, with a metal such as Mg, electrolyzing fused borates, or reducing boron trichloride, BCl_3, with hydrogen at high temperature. Only the last method gives a reasonably pure product.

Massive boron is very hard but brittle. It has a dull metallic luster but is a poor conductor of electricity and is not classified as a metal. When its temperature is raised, its conductivity increases. This is unlike metallic behavior; therefore boron and substances like it (silicon and germanium) are called *semiconductors*. The explanation of semiconductivity is that, at room temperature, electrons are bound rather tightly to local centers, but as the temperature is raised, they are freed and are able to wander through the crystal. The higher the temperature, the greater the number of electrons freed; hence the conductivity increases, even though lattice vibrations offer more resistance at the higher temperature (Sec. 14.1).

At room temperature, boron is inert to all except the most powerful oxidizing agents, such as fluorine and concentrated nitric acid. However, when fused with alkaline oxidizing mixtures, such as NaOH and $NaNO_3$, it reacts to form borates. Boron also dissolves in molten aluminum, from which there separates on cooling an aluminum boride, AlB_{12}. This same boride is formed when boron oxide is reduced with aluminum and for a long time was considered to be pure boron. In fact AlB_{12} is still referred to as "crystalline boron." Other borides such as Mg_3B_2 are known and can be prepared by direct union of the elements.

When magnesium boride reacts with acids, several boron-hydrogen compounds are formed which have puzzled chemists since their discovery.

The simplest of these boron hydrides would be BH_3, formed by sharing the three valence electrons of boron with three H atoms. However, this compound is not known. Instead, boron forms a series of hydrides ranging from B_2H_6 (diborane) to $B_{10}H_{14}$ (decaborane). All of these compounds are surprising, since there seem to be too few electrons to hold them together. Diborane, for example, has only 12 valence electrons (3 from each B and 1 from each H) for what appears to be seven bonds (three bonds in each BH_3 unit and one bond between them). Figure 23.1 shows several of the many interesting structures that have been proposed. Structure (*a*) contains two one-electron bonds; structure (*b*), a no-electron bond; structure (*c*), two hydrogen bridges; and structure (*d*), a protonated double bond, i.e., a double bond between the two boron atoms with two protons embedded in it. Not one of these structures satisfactorily accounts for all the observed properties of diborane. For one thing, the compound behaves as if it were not paramagnetic, which is inconsistent with structures (*a*) and (*c*). Furthermore, structure (*b*) not only suffers from having a "no-electron bond" but also disagrees with the observation that two of the six hydrogen atoms behave differently from the others. Finally, the experimentally determined boron-boron distance is longer than that predicted from structure (*d*). The existence of molecules such as diborane emphasizes the statement made in Chap. 4 that all the electrons in a molecule participate in bonding. The assumption that a pair of electrons is localized in a bond between two atoms is a simplification which is not valid in all cases. In fact, it is becoming increasingly acceptable to describe diborane and other boron hydrides as containing "three-center bonds," which consist of an electron pair spread out over three atoms. In diborane there are two three-center bonds, each consisting of an electron pair spread over the two boron atoms and one of the middle hydrogen atoms.

All the boron hydrides, ranging from gaseous B_2H_6 to solid $B_{10}H_{14}$, inflame in air to give dark-colored products of unknown composition. In the absence of air, they decompose on heating to boron and hydrogen. With water, they react to form hydrogen and boric acid.

The only important oxide of boron is B_2O_3, boric oxide. As already mentioned, it is acidic, dissolving in water to form H_3BO_3, boric acid. Boric

Fig. 23.1   *Structures suggested for diborane.*

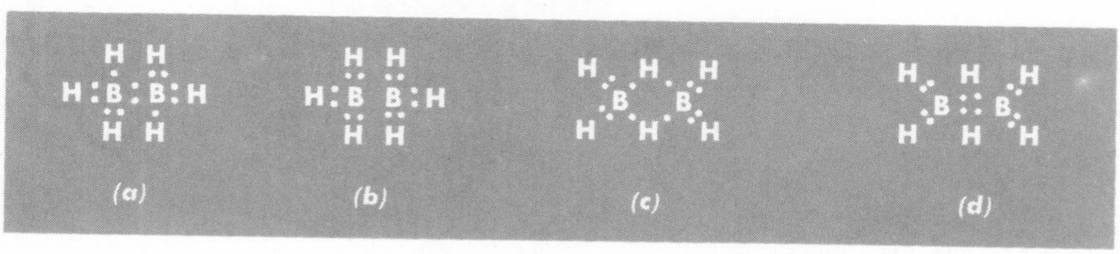

acid is an extremely weak acid for which K_I is 6.0×10^{-10}. Because its acidity is so slight, it can safely be used as an eyewash to take advantage of its antiseptic properties.

The borates, formed either by neutralization of boric acid or reaction of B_2O_3 with basic oxides, are extremely complicated compounds. Although a few, such as $LaBO_3$, contain discrete BO_3^{-3} ions, most contain more complex anions in which boron atoms are joined together by oxygen bridges. As shown in Fig. 23.2, the simple BO_3^{-3}, or orthoborate ion, is a planar ion with the three oxygen atoms at the corners of an equilateral triangle. In more complex anions such as the one shown, there are still three oxygen atoms about each boron atom, but some of these are joined to other boron atoms. An extended structure similar to this, containing $B_2O_4^{--}$ as a repeating unit, is found in CaB_2O_4. Other borates are even more complex and may have, in addition to triangular BO_3 units, tetrahedral BO_4 units. This seems to be true for borax, which is the most common of the borates. It is extensively used in water softening, partly because it reacts with Ca^{++} to form insoluble calcium borate and partly because it hydrolyzes to give an alkaline solution (Sec. 19.7). Because borax dissolves many metal oxides to form easily fusible borates, it is used widely as a flux in soldering operations. By removing oxides such as Cu_2O from the surface of hot brass, the flux allows fresh metal surfaces to fuse together.

The boron halides (BF_3, BCl_3, BBr_3, and BI_3) are also unusual in several respects. For one thing, unlike the halides formed by typical metals, these are molecular substances and do not contain ions in the solid state. For another thing, the boron atom in these molecules has only a sextet of electrons; hence it can accommodate another pair of electrons. This occurs, for example, in the reaction

Fig. 23.2 **Borate ions.**

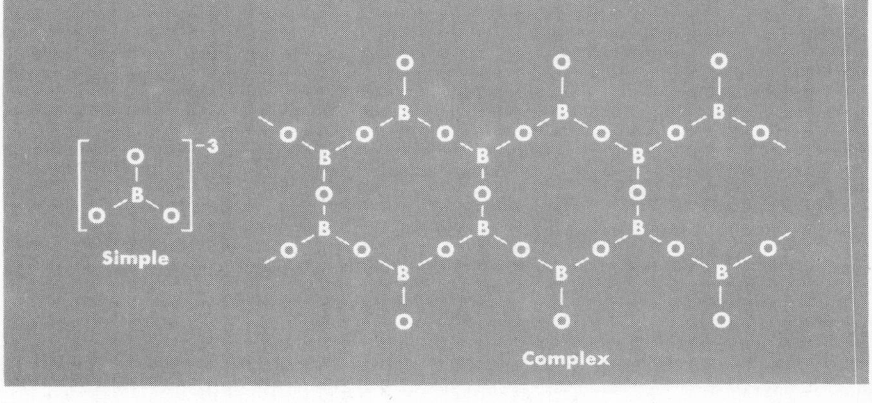

$$\begin{array}{ccc} :\!\ddot{F}\!: & H & :\!\ddot{F}\!:H \\[-2pt] :\!\ddot{F}\!:\!B & +\ :\!\ddot{N}\!:H \rightarrow :\!\ddot{F}\!:\!B\!:\!\ddot{N}\!:H \\[-2pt] :\!\ddot{F}\!: & H & :\!\ddot{F}\!:H \end{array}$$

where the product is sometimes called an *addition compound*. The action of BF_3 as a Lewis acid, i.e., its ability to draw a pair of electrons to itself, makes it useful as a catalyst for many reactions that are also catalyzed by H^+.

23.3   ALUMINUM

Although aluminum is the most abundant metal and, in fact, is the third most abundant element (8 per cent of the earth's crust), it is of secondary importance to iron, partly because of the difficulties in its preparation. It occurs primarily as complex aluminum silicates, such as felspar ($KAlSi_3O_8$), from which it is economically unfeasible to separate pure aluminum. Further, unless the product Al is completely free of iron and silicon, its properties are practically useless. Fortunately, there are natural deposits of oxide in the form of bauxite ($Al_2O_3 \cdot xH_2O$) from which pure Al can be obtained by electrolytic reduction. However, before electrolysis is carried out, it is necessary to remove iron and silicon impurities from the ore.

Purification of bauxite is accomplished by the Bayer process, which makes use of the amphoterism of aluminum. The crude oxide is treated with hot NaOH solution, in which the aluminum oxide dissolves because of the formation of aluminate ion $[Al(OH)_4{}^-]$. Silicon oxide also dissolves (to form silicate ions), but ferric oxide stays undissolved, since Fe_2O_3, unlike Al_2O_3, is not amphoteric. The solution is filtered to remove Fe_2O_3 and cooled. On agitation with air and addition of crystalline aluminum hydroxide as a seed, aluminum hydroxide precipitates, leaving the silicate in solution.

The production of metallic aluminum from purified bauxite is usually carried out by the Hall-Héroult process. Bauxite, dissolved in a molten mixture of fluorides, such as cryolite* (Na_3AlF_6), calcium fluoride, and sodium fluoride, is electrolyzed at about $1000°C$. in cells like that represented schematically in Fig. 23.3. The anode consists of graphite (carbon) rods dipping into the molten mixture; the cathode, of a graphite lining supported by an iron box. The electrode reactions are very complicated and

---

* The mineral cryolite occurs in nature almost exclusively as an enormous geologic dike in Greenland. In appearance, the mineral looks like glacial ice. Since it can be melted readily even in a candle flame, it was thought by the Eskimos to be a special kind of ice. The name cryolite comes from the Greek, *krios* (frost) and *lithos* (stone).

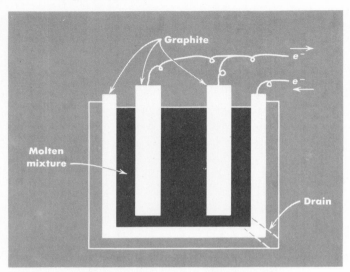

Fig. 23.3   *Electrolytic preparation of aluminum.*

only imperfectly understood. At the cathode, oxyfluoaluminum complex ions (perhaps of the type $AlOF_5^{-4}$) are reduced to liquid aluminum (m.p., $659.7°C.$). At the anode, a series of products is formed including oxygen, fluorine, and various carbon compounds of these elements. The carbon anodes gradually corrode away and must be replaced periodically. Continual addition of bauxite and recurrent draining off of the liquid aluminum allow uninterrupted operation. Because the equivalent weight of aluminum is so low, only 9 g., electric power consumption is high. Consequently, the process is economically feasible only near cheap sources of electric current.

Pure aluminum is quite soft and weak but, when alloyed with other metals, becomes quite strong. Because it is so light (density, 2.7 g. per cc.), aluminum finds extensive use as a structural material. Although chemically active, it resists corrosion because of a self-protecting oxide coat. It is also a good conductor of heat and electricity and so is used in cooking utensils and electrical equipment.

Although not so active as group I and II metals, aluminum is an excellent reducing agent, as shown by the oxidation potential

$$Al(s) \rightarrow Al^{+3} + 3e^- \qquad +1.66 \text{ volts}$$

In view of the high ionization potentials of aluminum (first, 5.98 e.v.; second, 18.82 e.v.; third, 28.44 e.v.), its high oxidation potential is somewhat surprising. Just as in the case of the alkaline-earth elements (Sec. 19.1), it is the hydration of the ion which enables the reaction to proceed. It has been estimated that over 1000 kcal. of heat are evolved when 1 mole of Al^{+3} ions is hydrated. The main reasons for this great hydration energy are the high charge of Al^{+3} and its small size (0.52 A. radius).

The high oxidation potential indicates that aluminum should reduce water, but the reaction is too slow to detect, probably because of the oxide coat. However, the oxide (being amphoteric) is soluble in acid and in base, and consequently Al liberates hydrogen from both acid and basic solutions. The net reactions may be written

$$2Al(s) + 6H^+ \rightarrow 2Al^{+3} + 3H_2(g)$$

$$2Al(s) + 2OH^- + 6H_2O \rightarrow 2Al(OH)_4^- + 3H_2(g)$$

The first of these equations seems to imply that aluminum dissolves in any acid. However, this is not the case. It is true that Al dissolves readily in hydrochloric acid, but in nitric acid no visible reaction occurs. The situation is somewhat reminiscent of the passivity of iron (Sec. 21.2) and is attributed here also to an oxide coat. A coating of Al_2O_3 should be quite stable because of the great strength of the Al—O bond.

Further indication of the great affinity of aluminum for oxygen comes from the high heat of formation of Al_2O_3. When aluminum burns in air to form solid Al_2O_3,

$$2Al(s) + \tfrac{3}{2}O_2(g) \rightarrow Al_2O_3(s) + 399 \text{ kcal.}$$

a large amount of heat is evolved, which can be used effectively in the reduction of less stable oxides. For example, since it requires 197 kcal. to decompose 1 mole of Fe_2O_3 into the elements, Al can reduce Fe_2O_3 with energy left over. The over-all reaction can be considered to be the sum of two separate reactions:

$$2Al(s) + \tfrac{3}{2}O_2(g) \rightarrow Al_2O_3(s) + 399 \text{ kcal.}$$

$$197 \text{ kcal.} + Fe_2O_3(s) \rightarrow 2Fe(s) + \tfrac{3}{2}O_2(g)$$

$$\overline{2Al(s) + Fe_2O_3(s) \rightarrow 2Fe(s) + Al_2O_3(s) + 202 \text{ kcal.}}$$

Actually, when the reaction is carried out, the heat evolved is sufficient to produce Fe and Al_2O_3 in the molten state. The production of molten iron by this reaction, frequently called the *thermite reaction,* has been used for welding operations. Because of the high temperature that results (estimated at 3000°C.), it has also been used in incendiary bombs.

Often, in the preparation of pure metals from their oxides, the common reducing agents hydrogen and carbon are unsuitable because of the formation of hydrides and carbides. In such cases, aluminum is sometimes used for the reduction, as, for example, in the preparation of manganese and chromium from their oxides. The reduction of oxides with Al is called the Goldschmidt reaction and owes its success to the great stability of Al_2O_3.

Aqueous solutions of most aluminum salts are acid because of hydrolysis of Al^{+3} (Sec. 17.11). The ion is certainly hydrated, and its formula is probably $Al(H_2O)_6^{+3}$. When base is progressively added to aqueous aluminum solutions, a white, gelatinous precipitate is formed. This precipitate, variously formulated as $Al(OH)_3$ or $Al_2O_3 \cdot xH_2O$, is readily soluble in acid or excess base, but only if freshly precipitated. On standing, aluminum hydroxide progressively becomes more difficult to dissolve. The explanation suggested for this "aging" is that oxygen bridges are formed between neighboring aluminum atoms. In basic solutions, aluminum forms aluminate ion, $Al(OH)_4^-$, or AlO_2^-. The actual ionic species in solution are almost certainly more complex than these formulas indicate.

Because of its small size and high charge, Al^{+3} forms a series of quite stable complex ions with fluoride ion. Progressive addition of fluoride to an aluminum solution produces AlF^{++}, AlF_2^+, AlF_3, AlF_4^-, AlF_5^{--} and AlF_6^{-3} (except for the last of these, all probably contain enough H_2O to provide six neighbors for each Al). The anion AlF_6^{-3} is found in the solid, cryolite. With the larger chloride ion, the tendency of Al^{+3} to form complexes is much less. Compared to the transition elements, aluminum forms many fewer complex ions, presumably because it has less tendency to form covalent bonds.

Like other $+3$ ions, aluminum ion may be crystallized (usually by slow evaporation of water) from aqueous solutions containing sulfate and singly charged cations to give *alums*. These alums are double salts having the general formula $MM'(SO_4)_2 \cdot 12H_2O$, where M is a singly charged cation, such as K^+, Na^+, or NH_4^+, and M' is a triply charged cation, such as Al^{+3}, Fe^{+3}, or Cr^{+3}. Ordinary alum is $KAl(SO_4)_2 \cdot 12H_2O$. Of the 12 hydrate waters, 6 are bound directly to the aluminum to give a distinct $Al(H_2O)_6^{+3}$ ion. The other 6 waters are symmetrically placed about the K^+ ion, but there is no distinct $K(H_2O)_6^+$ ion. The crystals of alum are usually large octahedra and have great chemical purity. Because of this purity, $KAl(SO_4)_2 \cdot 12H_2O$ is useful in the dyeing industry, where the alum serves as a source of Al^{+3} uncontaminated by Fe^{+3}. The Al^{+3} is precipitated on cloth as aluminum hydroxide, which acts as a binding agent (mordant) for dyes. The absence of Fe^{+3} is imperative for producing clear colors.

When aluminum hydroxide is heated to high temperature, it loses water and eventually forms Al_2O_3, sometimes called *alumina*. This is a very inert material of high melting point (about $2000°C.$), which finds use as a refractory in making containers for high-temperature reactions. Ordinarily, alumina is white, but it can be colored by the addition of such oxides as

Cr_2O_3 or Fe_3O_4. Synthetic rubies, for example, can be made by mixing Al_2O_3 and Cr_2O_3 powders and dropping them through the flame of an oxyhydrogen torch. Because of the great hardness of Al_2O_3, such synthetic jewels are used as bearing points in watches and other precision instruments.

23.4   GALLIUM

There are no simple minerals of gallium, but since it resembles aluminum so closely, it occurs in trace amounts in all aluminum ores. It is also found in zinc blende, which is the best source of the element. Separation from Zn is accomplished by precipitation of slightly soluble gallium hydroxy-sulfate, which can be electrolytically reduced. The metal is soft and has a low melting point (29.8°C.). With a boiling point of about 2000°C., its liquid range is longer than that of any other substance which is liquid near room temperature.

The chemistry of gallium is much like that of aluminum. Usually, only the $+3$ oxidation state is observed. The hydroxide, $Ga(OH)_3$, dissolves in excess base to give gallate ion, which may be written as $Ga(OH)_4^-$.

23.5   INDIUM

Indium is quite rare (1×10^{-5} per cent abundance), and its best source is the impurities separated from zinc and lead minerals. Indium metal takes a very high polish, and for this reason it has been used in plating special mirrors. It also is a very soft metal, which, however, has a higher melting point than gallium. The metal is not very reactive, is not corroded by moist air, but dissolves in acids to liberate hydrogen. The compounds are essentially those of the $+3$ ion, although InCl and $InCl_2$ have been prepared. These disproportionate in water to form In^{+3} and In. Although $In(OH)_3$ is slightly soluble in very alkaline solution, it is usually classed as basic.

23.6   THALLIUM

Approximately as abundant as indium, thallium is also obtained as a by-product of the purification of other metals, such as cadmium and lead. The metal is very soft and can easily be cut with a knife. It is oxidized by air and must be kept under oil. The compounds are of two types, thallous ($+1$) and thallic ($+3$). Thallous compounds are similar to those of silver, in that TlF is soluble and the other halides are insoluble. However, TlOH resembles alkali-metal hydroxides in being a soluble, strong base. Thallic compounds are like those of other group III metals, except that $Tl(OH)_3$ is not even slightly soluble in basic solution and Tl^{+3} is a good oxidizing agent.

$$Tl^+ \rightarrow Tl^{+3} + 2e^- \qquad -1.25 \text{ volt}$$

Like most heavy metals, thallium and its compounds are poisonous. In fact, thallium compounds have been used to kill off rodents.

23.7 QUALITATIVE ANALYSIS

The only element of this group commonly encountered in qualitative analysis is aluminum. Like the alkali and alkaline-earth elements, aluminum cannot be precipitated as the sulfide from aqueous solution. In the usual schemes of analysis, aluminum precipitates as the hydroxide when NH_3 is added to the solution from which H_2S has removed acid-insoluble sulfides. Aluminum can be separated from other cations which precipitate as sulfides and hydroxides at this point by taking advantage of the fact that of these cations only Al^{+3}, Cr^{+3}, and Zn^{++} are amphoteric. Zinc can be differentiated from aluminum, either by using the fact that ZnS but not $Al(OH)_3$ precipitates when $(NH_4)_2S$ is added in the presence of a SO_4^{--}–HSO_4^- buffer or by using the fact that $Zn(OH)_2$ but not $Al(OH)_3$ is soluble in excess ammonia. Chromium can be differentiated from aluminum by oxidizing the chromium in basic solution with H_2O_2 to CrO_4^{--}, which can be precipitated as yellow, insoluble $PbCrO_4$, or $BaCrO_4$. A possible confirmatory test for aluminum is the formation of a red precipitate from $Al(OH)_3$ and the dye ammonium aurintricarboxylate (aluminon).

QUESTIONS

23.1 *Basicity.* Account for the change in basic character of the hydroxides in going down group III.

23.2 *Bayer process.* Recalling that Fe_2O_3 is not amphoteric, write equations for the method by which bauxite can be purified of Fe_2O_3 before electrolysis.

23.3 *Group properties.* Contrast the chemical behavior of each of the following pairs of elements: (*a*) B and Al; (*b*) Mg and Al; (*c*) Cr and Al; (*d*) Ga and Tl.

23.4 *Oxidation states of Al.* Suggest reasons why aluminum forms $+3$ ions in aqueous solution but not $+1$ or $+2$ ions.

23.5 *Concentrations.* (*a*) Ignoring hydrolysis, calculate the concentrations of K^+, Al^{+3}, and SO_4^{--} in a solution made by dissolving 95 g. of $KAl(SO_4)_2 \cdot 12H_2O$ and 33 g. of $Al_2(SO_4)_3 \cdot 18H_2O$ in enough water to make 1.0 liter of solution. (*b*) For the hydrolysis reaction $Al^{+3} + H_2O \rightleftharpoons AlOH^{++} + H^+$, the constant is 1.4×10^{-5}. Calculate the pH of the solution in (*a*).

Ans. (*a*) 0.20 M K^+; 0.30 M Al^{+3}; 0.55 M SO_4^{--}. (*b*) 2.69

23.6 *Equations.* Write equations for each of the following changes: (*a*) reaction of boron with fluorine gas, F_2; (*b*) reduction of B_2O_3 with Mg; (*c*) formation of $LaBO_3$ from B_2O_3; (*d*) oxidation of diborane by air to B_2O_3 and water; (*e*) dissolving of $Al(OH)_3$ in acid and base; (*f*) reduction of Cr_2O_3 by Al; (*g*) dissolving of gallium in acid and base; (*h*) disproportionation of In^+; (*i*) oxidation of vanadium to $V(OH)_4^+$ by thallic ion in acid solution.

23.7 *Oxidation potential.* How would you expect the oxidation potential of Al in fluoride solution to compare with that in chloride solution?

23.8 *Thallium.* Using the oxidation potential of Tl from Table 23.1 and that of Tl^+ from Sec. 23.6, show that Tl^+ does not disproportionate.

23.9 *Borate structure.* Boron forms some compounds called metaborates, for which the *simplest* formula of the anion is BO_2^-. Show that an extended chain in which each B is bound to three oxygens and in which two of the oxygens are bound to other B atoms will correspond to this simplest formula.

23.10 *Heat of reaction.* Given 1.00 g. of a powdered mixture that consists only of Al and Fe. When this sample is completely oxidized to Al_2O_3 and Fe_2O_3 in a calorimeter, it is found that 6.0 kcal. of heat is liberated. Calculate the per cent composition by weight of the original sample. *Ans.* 25% Fe, 75% Al

23.11 *Stoichiometry.* You are instructed to synthesize 0.10 mole of $K_3Al(C_2O_4)_3 \cdot 3H_2O$ by digesting on a steam bath a mixture of $K_2C_2O_4 \cdot H_2O$, $Al_2(SO_4)_3 \cdot 18H_2O$, BaC_2O_4, and water. Assuming the yield to be 100%, calculate the weight of starting materials required. Note that all the sulfate is to be precipitated as $BaSO_4$.

23.12 *Solid-state calculation.* Metallic aluminum crystallizes in the face-centered cubic arrangement. The unit-cell-edge length is 4.04 A. Calculate: (*a*) the apparent atomic radius; (*b*) the density of metallic aluminum.

Ans. 1.43 A.; 2.72 g./cc.

23.13 *Equilibria.* A solution is made by dissolving 0.10 mole of H_3BO_3 and 0.010 mole of $Al_2(SO_4)_3 \cdot 18H_2O$ in sufficient water to make 0.50 liter of solution. What will be the pH of the solution? *Ans.* 3.12

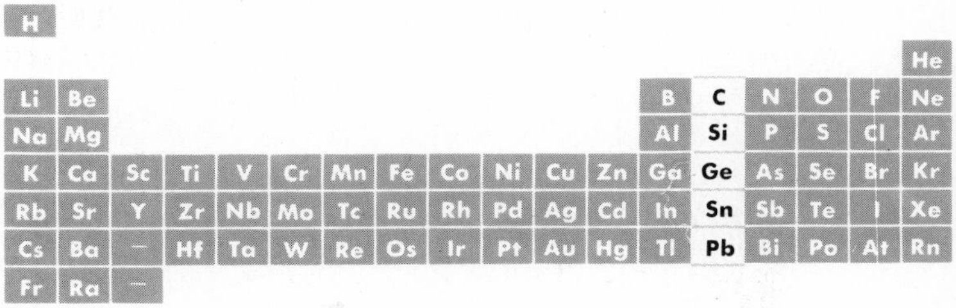

H

He

Li Be | B C N O F Ne
Na Mg | Al Si P S Cl Ar
K Ca Sc Ti V Cr Mn Fe Co Ni Cu Zn Ga Ge As Se Br Kr
Rb Sr Y Zr Nb Mo Tc Ru Rh Pd Ag Cd In Sn Sb Te I Xe
Cs Ba – Hf Ta W Re Os Ir Pt Au Hg Tl Pb Bi Po At Rn
Fr Ra –

24   *Group* IV *Elements*

THE ELEMENTS OF GROUP IV are carbon, silicon, germanium, tin, and lead. Like the members of group III, they show a pronounced change from acidic behavior for the light elements to more basic behavior for the heavy elements. Also, like group III, the lightest member of the group, carbon, forms a solid of complex structure which does not exhibit metallic properties. The factors which produce nonmetallic behavior apparently extend to the second and third members of the group, silicon and germanium, for they also cannot be classed as metals, but only as semimetals.

The first two elements, carbon and silicon, are important, since between them their compounds account for all living material and practically all the earth's minerals.

24.1   GROUP PROPERTIES

As indicated in Table 24.1, each of the group IV elements has four electrons in its outermost energy level. Since the outermost shell can usually accommodate but eight electrons, it becomes questionable whether the atom would find it energetically favorable to lose electrons or gain electrons. For

Table 24.1   Elements of Group IV

Sym-bol	z	Electronic configuration	Melting point, °C.	Boiling point, °C.	Ioni-zation poten-tial, e.v.	Oxidation potential, volts
C	6	2, 4	3500	4200	11.26	−0.20(to CO_2)
Si	14	2, 8, 4	1420	2400(?)	8.15	+0.86(to SiO_2)
Ge	32	2, 8, 18, 4	959	2700(?)	8.13	+0.1(to GeO_2)
Sn	50	2, 8, 18, 18, 4	232	2260(?)	7.33	+0.14(to Sn^{++})
Pb	82	2, 8, 18, 32, 18, 4	327	1600(?)	7.42	+0.13(to Pb^{++})

carbon and silicon, and to some extent for germanium, the compromise is to share electrons in all compounds; for tin and lead, the formation of cations is favored. This difference in bonding is reflected in the melting points of the elements. C, Si, and Ge form an interlocked, covalent structure, whereas Sn and Pb are typically metallic; the melting points of the first three·are correspondingly high, and those of the last two are correspondingly low.

24.2   CARBON

Although not very plentiful in the earth's crust ($<$0.1 per cent), carbon is the second most abundant element (oxygen is first) in the human body (17.5 per cent). It occurs in all plant and animal tissues, combined with hydrogen and oxygen, and in their geological derivatives, petroleum and coal, where it is combined mostly with hydrogen in the form of hydrocarbons. Combined with oxygen, carbon also occurs in the atmosphere as CO_2 and in rocks as carbonate minerals such as limestone. In the free state, carbon occurs to a slight extent as diamond and graphite, the two allotropic forms of the element.

As shown in Fig. 24.1, the principal difference between diamond and graphite is that, in the former, each carbon atom has four nearest neighbors while, in the latter, each carbon has three. In the diamond lattice the distance between centers of adjacent carbon atoms is 1.54 A., with each atom bonded to four other atoms at the corners of a tetrahedron. Since each of these carbon atoms in turn is tetrahedrally bonded to four carbon atoms, the result is an interlocked structure extending in three dimensions. The molecule formed is very hard (the hardest naturally occurring substance

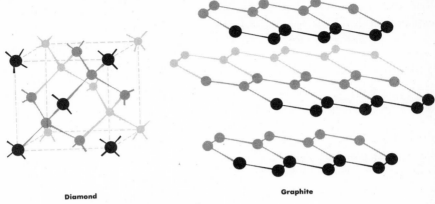

Diamond

Graphite

Fig. 24.1   Allotropic forms of carbon.

known) and has a high melting point (3500°C.). These properties presumably arise because the bonds are directed in space and because the positions of atoms are rigidly defined. Furthermore, diamond is a nonconductor of electricity. Since the sharing of four additional electrons fills all the orbitals, it is impossible for another electron to move in on a given carbon atom. In other words, all the pairs of electrons in the diamond structure are localized between specific pairs of C atoms and are not free to migrate through the crystal, because no other C atom can accommodate them. For this reason, diamond is an insulator for electric current.

Diamond is also characterized by a high refractive index; i.e., light rays entering diamond from air are bent strongly away from their original straight-line path. The effect is thought to be primarily due to a slowing down of the light wave by the tightly bound electrons. Because of high refractive index, much of the light falling on a diamond is internally reflected off interior surfaces, as shown in Fig. 24.2. The traditional sparkle of gem stones is primarily due to their shapes, which take maximum advantage of this internal reflection. Also, the refraction of different colors of light is not equal; therefore, when held at the proper angle, the diamond reflects only a portion of the spectrum of white light to the eye. This

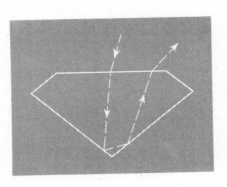

Fig. 24.2   Internal reflections in diamond.

high dispersion effect, which always accompanies high refractive index, explains the brilliant "fire" observed from well-cut diamonds.

In graphite, the structure consists of giant sheetlike molecules which are held to each other, 3.40 A. apart, probably by van der Waals forces. Within the sheets each carbon atom is covalently bound to three neighbors 1.42 A. away, which in turn are also bound to three carbon atoms. Since each carbon has four valence electrons and only three carbons to bond to, there are more than enough electrons to establish single bonds. However, since there can be no preference as to where the last electron should be located (all the three neighbors being equivalent), it must be considered as belonging to all three bonds. The electronic configuration of graphite may be represented as a resonance hybrid (Sec. 4.8) of the three formulas shown in Fig. 24.3.

Massive graphite is a soft, gray, high-melting solid with a dull metallic luster and fairly good electric conductivity. The softness is attributed to the weak sheet-to-sheet bonding, which permits adjacent layers to slide over each other. The high melting point is traceable to the strong covalent binding within the sheets, which makes difficult the disordering necessary for melting. The conductivity and metallic luster presumably stem from the freedom of electrons (one per carbon) to move from atom to atom. Because of its high melting point and its electric conductivity, graphite finds extensive use as electrode material, as, for example, in the electrolytic preparation of aluminum.

Besides massive graphite, there are several porous forms of carbon which apparently are graphitic in character. These include coke (made by heating coal in the absence of air), charcoal (made from wood in the same way), and carbon black (soot). They all have tremendous surface areas; for example, a 1-cm. cube of charcoal can have a surface of 500 sq. ft., which is equivalent to at least 2 billion holes drilled through the cube. Since each exposed carbon atom at the surface can use its extra valence electron to bind other atoms, these forms of carbon have strong adsorption properties (Sec. 11.6).

Fig. 24.3   Resonance formulas of graphite.

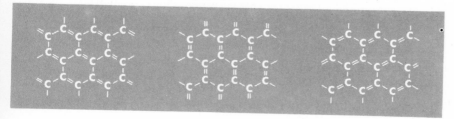

Under normal conditions graphite is the stable form of carbon, but the rate of conversion from diamond to graphite is too slow to observe. At high pressure, the principle of Le Chatelier predicts that diamond should become stable, since its density (3.51 g. per cc.) exceeds that of graphite (2.25 g. per cc.). By raising the pressure and working at high temperature (to increase the rate), diamonds have been prepared synthetically. Although not of gem quality, the synthetic material finds industrial application as an abrasive.

24.3 COMPOUNDS OF CARBON

Although at room temperature carbon is rather inert, at higher temperature it reacts with a variety of other elements. With metals and semimetals, carbon forms solid carbides of complex structure, such as silicon carbide (SiC), iron carbide (Fe_3C), and calcium carbide (CaC_2). Silicon carbide, formed by heating sand (SiO_2) with graphite, is the industrial abrasive carborundum. There are at least six different polymorphic forms of solid SiC, one of which has Si and C atoms occupying alternate positions in a diamond lattice. Iron carbide, mentioned in Sec. 21.2 as the essential constituent of white cast iron, has an extremely complex structure. Calcium carbide, obtained by heating CaO with coke, reacts with water to liberate acetylene

$$CaC_2(s) + 2H_2O \rightarrow Ca^{++} + 2OH^- + C_2H_2(g)$$

and so is used in the commercial preparation of C_2H_2. The formation of acetylene from CaC_2 reflects the fact that the CaC_2 lattice contains Ca^{++} and $C_2{}^{--}$ ions. The arrangement of these ions is the same as that of Na^+ and Cl^- ions in NaCl (see Fig. 8.7).

With nonmetals, carbon forms molecular compounds, which vary from simple carbon monoxide to extremely complex hydrocarbons. With the nonmetal sulfur, carbon reacts at high temperature to form carbon disulfide (CS_2). At room temperature, CS_2 is unstable with respect to decomposition to the elements. However, the rate of decomposition is unobservably slow, and liquid CS_2 is a familiar solvent, particularly for such substances as rubber and sulfur. Use of CS_2 as a solvent is hazardous, because it is toxic and highly flammable. When carbon disulfide vapor is heated with chlorine gas, the following reaction occurs:

$$CS_2(g) + 3Cl_2(g) \rightarrow CCl_4(g) + S_2Cl_2(g)$$

The carbon tetrachloride (CCl_4) thus formed resembles carbon disulfide in being a molecular liquid at room temperature, and therefore it is a good solvent for molecular solutes. As a cleaning fluid, CCl_4 should be used with caution, because, although it is not flammable, the liquid can penetrate the skin, and because the vapor is quite toxic.

With oxygen, carbon forms oxides, the most important of which are carbon monoxide (CO) and carbon dioxide (CO_2). Their electronic formulas are usually represented as follows:

$$:C:::O: \qquad \ddot{:}O::C::\ddot{O}:$$

These oxides are most conveniently prepared by combustion of carbon or hydrocarbons, with CO predominating when the supply of oxygen is limited. As previously indicated (Secs. 15.2 and 21.2), carbon monoxide is an important industrial fuel and reducing agent. It is a colorless, odorless gas that is quite poisonous, because it interferes with the normal oxygen-carrying function of the hemoglobin in the red blood cells. Instead of forming a complex compound with oxygen molecules, hemoglobin forms a more stable complex compound with CO (carboxyhemoglobin). The tissue cells are thus starved for lack of oxygen, and death may result. Concentrations of 0.2 per cent in air cause unconsciousness in about half an hour and death in about three hours. Because CO is present in the exhaust gases of motorcars, near-toxic concentrations frequently are approached in congested areas during peak traffic hours.

Unlike CO, CO_2 is not poisonous and, in fact, is necessary for various physiological processes, e.g., the maintenance of the proper pH of blood. Since it is *produced* by respiration and is *used up* in photosynthesis, the concentration in the atmosphere remains fairly constant at about 0.04 per cent. The principal sources of commercial CO_2 are the distilling industry, where the fermentation of sugar to alcohol

$$C_6H_{12}O_6 \xrightarrow[\text{yeast}]{} 2C_2H_5OH + 2CO_2(g)$$

cheaply produces large amounts of by-product CO_2, and the thermal decomposition of limestone to form CO_2 and CaO. The gas is formed conveniently in the laboratory by thermal decomposition of bicarbonates such as $NaHCO_3$ or by the reaction of bicarbonates or carbonates with acid. The gas is rather dense (approximately one and a half times the density of air) and settles in pockets to displace the lighter air. Since it is not combustible itself, it acts as an effective blanket to shut out air in fire fighting. The phase relations of carbon dioxide and the use of CO_2 as a refrigerant have been indicated in Sec. 9.5.

Compared to most gases, CO_2 is quite soluble in water; at 1 atm. pressure and room temperature, the solubility is 0.03 M. (It is twice as soluble in alcohol, where it has the peculiar physiological effect of increasing the rate of passage of alcohol from the stomach to the intestines, where it is taken up by the blood.) The aqueous solutions are acid, with a pH of about

4. Although it has been suggested that this acidity arises primarily from the weak carbonic acid, H_2CO_3, formed by the reaction of CO_2 with H_2O, this acid has never been isolated. Recent experiments indicate that, in aqueous CO_2 solutions, more than 99 per cent of the solute remains in the form of linear $:\overset{..}{O}::C::\overset{..}{O}:$ molecules. However, a small amount of CO_2 does react to form H_2CO_3, which can dissociate to H^+ and bicarbonate ion. Thus there are the two simultaneous equilibria

$$CO_2 + H_2O \rightleftharpoons H_2CO_3 \rightleftharpoons H^+ + HCO_3^-$$

which can be written more simply as

$$CO_2 + H_2O \rightleftharpoons H^+ + HCO_3^-$$

since species in equilibrium with the same species are in equilibrium with each other. The constant for this last equilibrium, loosely called the first dissociation of carbonic acid, is 4.2×10^{-7}.* The dissociation of bicarbonate ion into H^+ and carbonate ion, CO_3^{--}, has a constant of 4.8×10^{-11}.

The carbonate and bicarbonate ions are planar ions, containing carbon bonded to three oxygen atoms at the corners of an equilateral triangle. The situation is reminiscent of graphite, with more than enough electrons to form single bonds to all three oxygens; as a result, the electronic distribution is represented as a resonance hybrid. For carbonate ion, the contributing resonance forms are usually written as in Fig. 24.4.

Derived from carbonic acid are the two series of salts: bicarbonates, such as $NaHCO_3$, and carbonates, such as Na_2CO_3. The former can be made by neutralizing 1 mole of CO_2 (or H_2CO_3) with 1 mole of NaOH; the latter, by neutralizing 1 mole of CO_2 with 2 moles of NaOH. The net reactions are

$$CO_2 + OH^- \rightarrow HCO_3^-$$

$$CO_2 + 2OH^- \rightarrow CO_3^{--} + H_2O$$

Actually, the compounds are industrially so important that cheaper methods are used. The most famous is the Solvay process, which uses ammonia to neutralize the acidity of CO_2 and relies on the limited solubility of $NaHCO_3$ for separation. The process is essentially one in which CO_2 (from the thermal decomposition of limestone) and NH_3 (recycled in the process) are dissolved in NaCl solution. Since NH_3 has affinity for H^+ ($NH_3 + H^+ \rightarrow NH_4^+$), it neutralizes CO_2 by the reaction

---

* By taking advantage of the fact that $CO_2 + H_2O \rightleftharpoons H_2CO_3$ is a slow reaction whereas $H_2CO_3 \rightleftharpoons H^+ + HCO_3^-$ is rapid, it has been possible to determine the equilibrium constant for the latter equilibrium in times too short to allow readjustment of the former equilibrium. The value thus obtained for K_{diss} of H_2CO_3 is 1.3×10^{-4}.

*Fig. 24.4   Resonance for-
mulas of carbonate ion.*

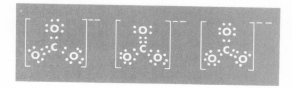

$$NH_3 + CO_2 + H_2O \rightarrow NH_4^+ + HCO_3^-$$

to form HCO_3^-, which precipitates as $NaHCO_3$ if the temperature of the brine is 15°C. or lower. On thermal decomposition, $NaHCO_3$ is decomposed to give Na_2CO_3.

$$2NaHCO_3(s) \rightarrow Na_2CO_3(s) + CO_2(g) + H_2O(g)$$

Sodium carbonate and sodium bicarbonate are industrial chemicals of primary importance. Na_2CO_3, or soda ash, is used, for example, in making glass where it is used directly, and in making soap where it is first converted to NaOH, or lye, by addition of $Ca(OH)_2$ and then boiled with animal or vegetable fats. When recrystallized from water, the hydrate $Na_2CO_3 \cdot 10H_2O$, or washing soda, is formed. The mild basic reaction resulting from hydrolysis of carbonate ion

$$CO_3^{--} + H_2O \rightleftharpoons HCO_3^- + OH^-$$

is used to supplement soap in laundering. $NaHCO_3$, or baking soda, is a principal component of baking powders, used to replace yeast in baking. Yeast ferments sugars, releasing CO_2 gas, which raises the dough; with baking powder, the CO_2 for leavening is obtained by the action of $NaHCO_3$ with acid substances such as alum.

In addition to the compounds that carbon forms with oxygen, there are numerous compounds in which carbon is bonded to the nonmetal nitrogen. The simplest of these carbon-nitrogen compounds is cyanogen, C_2N_2, made by thermal decomposition of cyanides such as AgCN. At room temperature, cyanogen is a colorless gas with the odor of bitter almonds; it is very poisonous. In many chemical reactions C_2N_2 behaves like the heavier halogens (Chap. 27). For example, in basic solution it disproportionates according to the equation

$$C_2N_2(g) + 2OH^- \rightarrow CN^- + OCN^- + H_2O$$

which is like the reaction of chlorine

$$Cl_2(g) + 2OH^- \rightarrow Cl^- + OCl^- + H_2O$$

The cyanide ion, CN^-, resembles chloride ion in that both give insoluble silver salts, AgCN ($K_{s.p.} = 1.6 \times 10^{-14}$) and AgCl ($K_{s.p.} = 1.7 \times 10^{-10}$).

Cyanide salts can also be made by the following high-temperature reaction:

$$Na_2CO_3(s) + 4C(s) + N_2(g) \rightarrow 2NaCN(s) + 3CO(g)$$

Cyanide ion forms many complex ions with transition-metal ions, e.g., $Fe(CN)_6^{-3}$. Unlike chloride ion, CN^- combines with H^+ to form a weak acid, HCN, which in solution is called hydrocyanic acid (prussic acid). At room temperature, pure HCN is a liquid, which might be surprising, because HCN is isoelectronic with N_2, i.e., both have the same number of electrons. Since the number of electrons is the same, N_2 and HCN should have about equal van der Waals attractions (Sec. 6.14) and, consequently, about equal boiling points. Yet the boiling point of N_2 is $-196°C$.; that of HCN is $26°C$. Apparently, in HCN there is considerable hydrogen bonding, which leads to molecular association like that in H_2O (Sec. 16.5). Like cyanogen, HCN is poisonous.

The anion OCN^-, formed by the disproportionation of cyanogen, is called the cyanate ion. It exists in many salts, e.g., ammonium cyanate, NH_4OCN. This last compound is of special interest because on heating it is converted to urea, $CO(NH_2)_2$, the principal end product of protein metabolism. The discovery of this reaction by Wöhler in 1828 was a milestone in chemistry. It represented the first time that man was able to synthesize in the laboratory a compound previously thought to be produced only in living organisms.

Related to the cyanate ion, OCN^-, is the thiocyanate ion, SCN^-. Salts containing thiocyanate ion can be prepared by fusing cyanides with sulfur. For example, heating NaCN with sulfur produces NaSCN, sodium thiocyanate. Like CN^-, SCN^- precipitates Ag^+ and also forms complex ions, e.g., $FeSCN^{++}$. With mercuric ion, SCN^- forms slightly soluble mercuric thiocyanate, $Hg(SCN)_2$. When $Hg(SCN)_2$ is heated, it forms a voluminous, snakelike ash known as Pharaoh's serpent.

24.4 HYDROCARBONS AND DERIVATIVES

There is a fantastic number of compounds containing carbon and hydrogen. Some of these are composed solely of carbon and hydrogen and are called hydrocarbons; others contain additional elements and are called hydrocarbon derivatives. Together, hydrocarbons and their derivatives are called *organic compounds,* because at one time it was thought that they could be made only by living organisms. The field of organic chemistry, the study of organic compounds, is so extensive that we can discuss here only some of the general principles. In Chap. 28 there is more detailed discussion of the subject.

It has been estimated that the hydrocarbons and their derivatives number more than half a million. Why are there so many? In the first place, carbon atoms can bond to each other to form chains of varying length. Second, adjacent carbon atoms can share one, two, or three pairs of electrons; therefore a carbon chain of given length can have different numbers of attached H atoms. Third, the more atoms a molecule contains, the more ways they may be arranged to give compounds having the same composition but differing in structure. Finally, different atoms or groups of atoms can be substituted for H atoms to yield a large number of derivatives. In the following paragraphs, these four factors are briefly discussed and illustrated.

The carbon atom has four valence electrons, and, as discussed in Sec. 4.9, it is expected to form four covalent bonds directed to the corners of a tetrahedron. It matters little whether the bonds are formed to other carbon atoms or to hydrogen atoms, because C and H are of about the same electronegativity. This means that, instead of being restricted to the simplest hydrocarbon, CH_4 (methane), a whole series of compounds is possible, such as C_2H_6 (ethane), C_3H_8 (propane), and C_4H_{10} (butane). The structural formulas of these are usually written as in Fig. 24.5, although it should be remembered that the molecules are three-dimensional, as shown in the lower part of the figure. Excellent sources of hydrocarbons are natural gas and petroleum, the former consisting of the light hydrocarbons (mostly methane and ethane), and the latter of heavier hydrocarbons all the way up to molecules containing at least 40 carbon atoms. Since the hydrocarbons differ in boiling points, they can be separated from each other by distillation. At room temperature they all are chemically inert, but at higher temperature they can be burned in air to form CO, CO_2, and H_2O and thus are used as fuels. The mixture of hydrocarbons ranging from C_7H_{16} (heptane) to $C_{10}H_{22}$ (decane)

Fig. 24.5   *Some hydrocarbons.*

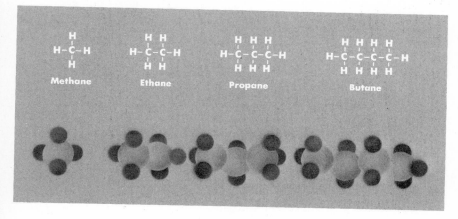

is gasoline. In order to improve the yield of gasoline from petroleum, large molecules (with more than 10 carbon atoms) can be broken down by the process of *catalytic cracking*, or small molecules (with fewer than seven carbon atoms) can be combined by *catalytic re-forming*.

As discussed in Sec. 4.7, unsaturated hydrocarbons contain double or triple bonds. Examples are ethylene, C_2H_4, acetylene, C_2H_2, and butadiene, C_4H_6, for which the structural formulas are shown in Fig. 24.6. In general, they are more reactive than the saturated hydrocarbons. For example, they undergo addition reactions, in which hydrogen or other atoms add to the multiple bonds. Such an addition reaction is responsible for the conversion of vegetable oils to synthetic fats by catalytic hydrogenation. Unsaturated hydrocarbons also undergo *polymerization* reactions, in which small molecules couple together to form extended chains. For example, ethylene polymerizes to form the plastic, polyethylene, in a manner which can be visualized as follows:

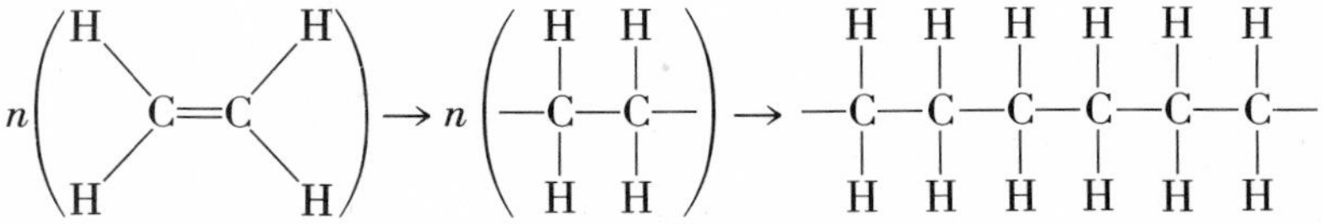

$$n\left(\begin{array}{c} H \\ \diagdown \\ C=C \\ \diagup \\ H \end{array}\begin{array}{c} H \\ \diagup \\ \\ \diagdown \\ H \end{array}\right) \rightarrow n\left(\begin{array}{cc} H & H \\ | & | \\ -C-C- \\ | & | \\ H & H \end{array}\right) \rightarrow \begin{array}{cccccc} H & H & H & H & H & H \\ | & | & | & | & | & | \\ -C-C-C-C-C-C- \\ | & | & | & | & | & | \\ H & H & H & H & H & H \end{array}$$

The double bond seems to open up to form an unstable intermediate, which joins with other molecules to produce a high polymer. The term *high polymer* is applied to any large molecule which contains recognizable repeating units.

The third factor mentioned as contributing to the large number of organic compounds is *isomerism*, i.e., the existence of more than one compound with the same molecular formula. As an illustration, C_2H_6O can signify either

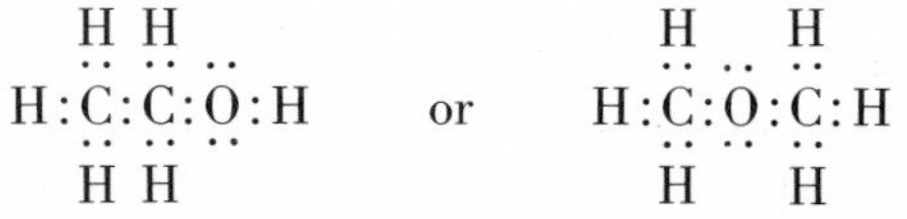

$$\begin{array}{ccc} H & H & \\ H:\overset{..}{\underset{..}{C}}:\overset{..}{\underset{..}{C}}:\overset{..}{\underset{..}{O}}:H & \quad\text{or}\quad & H:\overset{..}{\underset{..}{C}}:\overset{..}{\underset{..}{O}}:\overset{..}{\underset{..}{C}}:H \\ H & H & H \qquad H \end{array}$$

The first is ethyl alcohol (b.p., 78.5°C.), and the second is dimethyl ether (b.p., −23.7°C.); they have different properties, owing to the changed position of the oxygen. Compounds which, like ethyl alcohol and dimethyl ether, have the same composition but different structures are referred to as *isomers*. There are many examples of isomerism in the saturated hydrocarbon

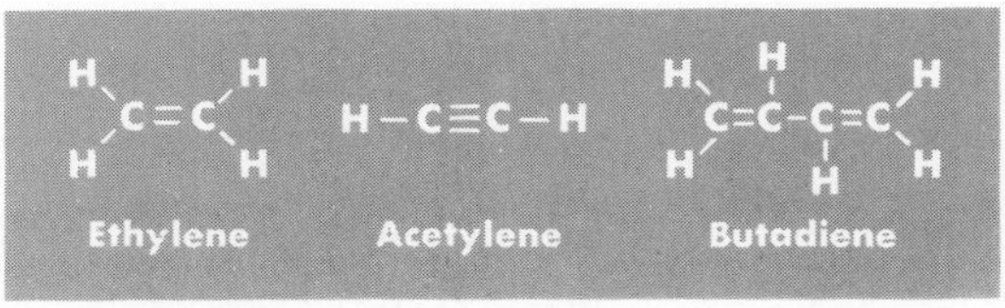

Fig. 24.6 Some unsaturated hydrocarbons.

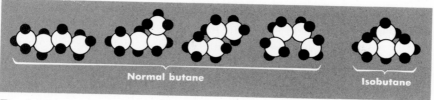

Normal butane   Isobutane

Fig. 24.7   Various configurations of butane molecules. (Open circles represent carbon atoms; black circles, hydrogen atoms.)

series. All the members from butane on have two or more isomers. ($C_{40}H_{82}$ has been calculated to have more than 61 trillion isomers.) For butane, there are only two: normal butane and isobutane. Their conventional (two-dimensional) structural formulas are

Normal butane   *Isobutane*

Though it might seem possible that there are other isomers of C_4H_{10}, these are the only ones. Other two-dimensional formulas can be written, but they can be shown to be equivalent to one or the other of the above. The problem arises because the two-dimensional formulas do not take into account the three-dimensional nature of these molecules. In a saturated hydrocarbon, each carbon is tetrahedrally surrounded by four groups, and the molecule can assume various configurations by rotation about individual bonds. The spatial relations can best be seen by the use of molecular models like those diagramed in Fig. 24.7. Of the five configurations shown, the first four correspond to the same molecule (normal butane) twisted into different shapes; the fifth corresponds to a different molecule (isobutane), and no amount of twisting can convert it to the normal isomer. Isomers always differ in properties, but sometimes the differences are so slight as to make separation difficult.

A complicating feature which increases the number of isomers is the possibility of having atoms arranged in rings. The most common of these cyclic compounds is benzene, C_6H_6, which consists of six carbon atoms at the corners of a hexagon with a hydrogen atom attached to each carbon atom with all 12 atoms in one plane. The carbon-carbon bonds are all equivalent, and therefore the molecule can be considered as a resonance hybrid. The contributing forms are usually written as shown in Fig. 24.8. Other groups may be substituted for one or more of the H atoms to give derivatives.

The fourth reason for the large number of organic compounds is the formation of derivatives. These derivatives differ in properties from the parent hydrocarbons, and, in fact, their properties are mainly determined by the nature of the substituent. Because the hydrocarbon residue usually remains intact throughout chemical reactions, it is convenient to consider such hydrocarbon derivatives as combinations of hydrocarbon residues and substituents. The substituents are called *functional groups*, and each imparts characteristic properties to the molecule. A simple example of a functional group is the alcohol, or OH, group. In methyl alcohol (CH_3OH) and ethyl alcohol (C_2H_5OH), derived respectively from methane (CH_4) and ethane (C_2H_6), the OH has the effect of bestowing waterlike properties on what was originally a volatile but inert hydrocarbon. In the higher alcohols (containing many C atoms) the influence of OH in changing properties is less pronounced. The general formula for any alcohol can be written ROH, where R stands for a hydrocarbon residue. In methyl alcohol, R is the methyl group, CH_3; in ethyl alcohol, R is the ethyl group, C_2H_5.

The functional group consisting of a carbon with a doubly bonded

$$\overset{\textstyle O}{\overset{\textstyle \|}{}}$$

oxygen and a singly bonded OH, usually written COOH or $-\overset{O}{\overset{\|}{C}}-OH$, imparts acid properties to organic molecules. Compounds containing the COOH group are called organic acids and have the general formula $RCOOH$. If R stands for CH_3, the acid is CH_3COOH, acetic acid, which we have earlier written as $HC_2H_3O_2$. Like acetic acid ($K_{diss} = 1.8 \times 10^{-5}$), other organic acids are generally weak electrolytes. As acids, they undergo the usual neutralization reactions with bases. They also react with alcohols in an entirely different reaction called *esterification*. Esterification reactions can be described by the general equation

$$R-\overset{O}{\overset{\|}{C}}-O-H + R'-O-H \rightarrow R-\overset{O}{\overset{\|}{C}}-O-R' + H_2O$$

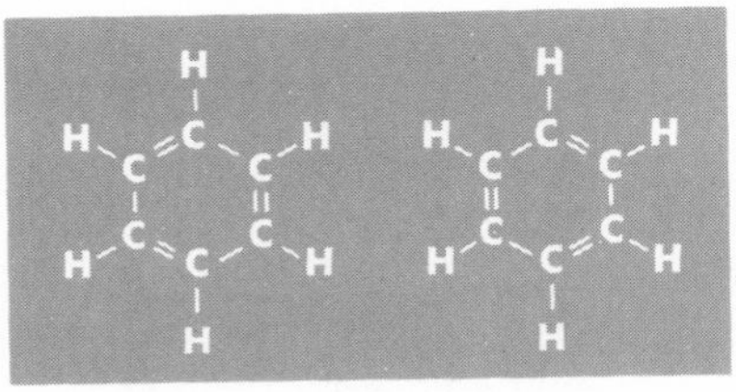

Fig. 24.8   Resonance formulas of benzene.

Fig. 24.9   Stearin.

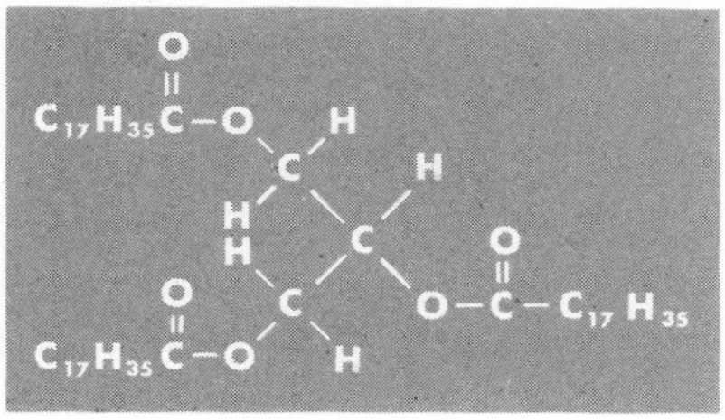

$$
\begin{array}{c}
\text{O} \\
\parallel \\
C_{17}H_{35}C-O \\
\end{array}
$$

which shows the splitting out of H_2O and the formation of an ester, *RCOOR'*. Although these reactions superficially look like a neutralization, they differ in three ways. In the first place, the reactions are slow and may require hours at elevated temperatures; second, the reactions are not between the ions H^+ and OH^-; finally, as shown by isotope-tracer experiments, the acid contributes the OH and the alcohol the H to the product water. In that they are slow and in that they involve only parts of molecules, esterification reactions are typical of most organic reactions.

Esters are quite common in nature. For example, animal fats and vegetable oils are composed of mixtures of esters such as stearin, the main component of beef fat. As shown in Fig. 24.9, stearin is a polyfunctional ester containing three ester groups. When boiled with sodium hydroxide, it undergoes a *saponification* reaction, which breaks it down to a polyalcohol and a sodium salt of stearic acid (sodium stearate, $NaOOCC_{17}H_{35}$, or soap). The general equation for saponification is

$$
\underset{\textit{Ester}}{RCOOR'} + OH^- \rightarrow \underset{\textit{Ion of acid}}{RCOO^-} + \underset{\textit{Alcohol}}{R'OH}
$$

Soap (which we shall consider as sodium stearate, even though it can be the salt of any long-chain acid) is remarkable because it gives ions which are essentially hydrocarbons, modified by a charged group at one end. When placed in water, these ions do not really dissolve, because hydrocarbons are insoluble in polar solvents. Instead, *micelles* are formed in which the hydro-

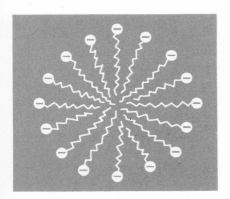

carbon parts of the stearate ions cluster together, as shown in Fig. 24.10. The negative charges at the surface of the micelle are dissolved in the water; the hydrocarbon chains in the interior are dissolved in each other. X-ray investigations of soap suspensions show that at

Fig. 24.10   Soap micelle.

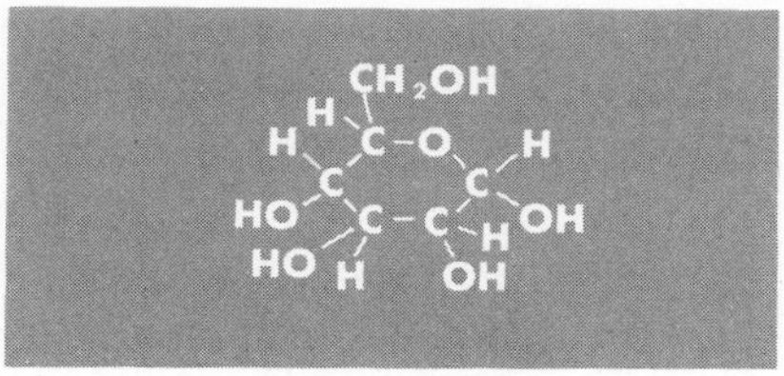

Fig. 24.11   Glucose.

low concentrations the micelles are approximately spherical with a diameter of about 50 A. The cleansing action of soap is thought to stem from the dissolving of grease (essentially hydrocarbon in nature) in these hydrocarbon clusters.

In addition to the fats, the two other major groups of substances of which living material is composed are the *carbohydrates* and *proteins*. The carbohydrates were so named because the common ones can be represented by formulas $C_x(H_2O)_y$; they contain H and O in a 2:1 ratio just as in water. However, they are not hydrates in any sense of the word but consist of rather complex ring structures, in which the C atoms have H atoms and OH groups attached to them. One of the simpler carbohydrates is glucose, $C_6H_{12}O_6$, which occurs in many fruits and the blood of many animals. As shown in Fig. 24.11, the molecule contains a six-membered ring consisting of five C atoms and one O atom. Sucrose, $C_{12}H_{22}O_{11}$, which is the most important commercial sugar, contains two rings in the molecule. Starch and cellulose are natural high-polymer carbohydrates consisting of long chains of glucose rings hooked together by oxygen bridges.

The proteins are extremely complex molecules, which are also natural high polymers. When boiled in acid or base, they undergo hydrolysis to form relatively simple *amino acids* (organic acids containing the amino or NH_2 group). About 20 such amino acids have been identified, and all proteins, as in hair, fingernails, skin, muscles, tendons, and blood, are considered to be condensation products of two or more of these acids. The characteristic

feature of all proteins is the group —N—C—, called the *peptide link*. Figure 24.12 shows how the peptide link might be established between two amino-acid molecules by splitting out H_2O. Further polymerization is possible, since there is a free NH_2 group (on the far left) and a free acid group (on the far right). Silk and wool are high-molecular-weight proteins containing long polypeptide chains.

Fig. 24.12   Formation of a peptide link.

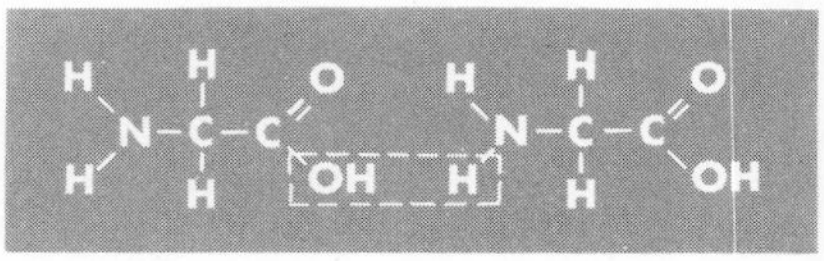

24.5 SILICON

The chemistry of silicon, the second member of group IV, resembles that of carbon in several respects. For example, silicon forms a tetrahedral SiH_4 and a few higher hydrosilicons which contain chains of silicon atoms. However, since Si—O bonds are formed preferentially to Si—H or Si—Si bonds, the chemistry of silicon is primarily concerned with oxygen compounds rather than with hydrosilicons. Furthermore, unlike the smaller carbon atom, which forms multiple bonds, silicon invariably forms single bonds. As a result, the oxygen-silicon compounds contain Si—O—Si bridges in which oxygen is bonded by single bonds to two silicon atoms instead of being bonded by a double bond to one silicon atom. This is unlike the case of carbon, where oxygen is frequently found bonded to a single carbon atom as the $>C{=}O$ group.

Silicon is the second most abundant element in the earth's crust (26 per cent) and is about as important in the mineral world as carbon is in the organic. As SiO_2, it accounts for sand, flint, quartz, and opal; as complex silicates of aluminum, iron, magnesium, and other metals, it accounts for practically all rocks, clays, and soils.

The preparation of pure silicon is quite difficult. It can be accomplished by the reduction of SiO_2 with Mg or by the reduction of the chloride with Na. Since it is mainly used for addition to steel, it is more usually prepared as ferrosilicon by reduction of mixtures of SiO_2 and iron oxides with coke. The element is a semimetal with a crystal structure like that of diamond. At room temperature it is inert to most reagents but will dissolve in basic solutions to liberate H_2. At elevated temperatures it reacts with many metals such as magnesium to form silicides (such as Mg_2Si).

The compounds of silicon are almost all oxy compounds. However, other compounds can be prepared which are unstable with respect to conversion to the oxy compounds. Thus, the hydrosilicons, prepared by reaction of silicides with acid and analogous to the hydrocarbons, are unstable in oxygen with respect to rapid conversion to SiO_2. Silane (SiH_4), for example, is oxidized as follows:

$$SiH_4(g) + 2O_2(g) \rightarrow SiO_2(s) + 2H_2O$$

Fig. 24.13 *Tetrahedral SiO₄ unit.*

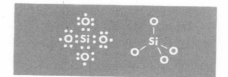

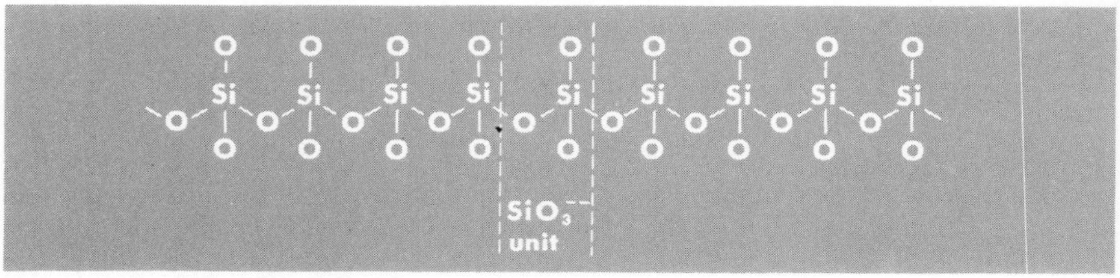

Fig. 24.14   Silicate chain.

Disilane (Si_2H_6), trisilane (Si_3H_8), and tetrasilane (Si_4H_{10}) have been prepared, but they are progressively less stable as the silicon-silicon chain length increases. Derivatives of the silanes such as silicon tetrachloride ($SiCl_4$) are also known but are unstable with respect to SiO_2.

The silicates (oxy compounds of silicon) have been extensively investigated, and in every* case the silicon atom is found to be tetrahedrally bonded to four oxygen atoms. As shown in Fig. 24.13, four valence electrons from Si and six valence electrons from each O are insufficient to complete the octets of all the atoms. Consequently, to produce a stable compound, the oxygen atoms may obtain electrons from some other atoms and become negative in the process. This produces the discrete anion, SiO_4^{-4}, found, for example, in the mineral zircon ($ZrSiO_4$). Alternatively, the oxygen atoms may complete their octets by sharing electrons with other silicon atoms. Since one, two, three, or four of the oxygen atoms can thus bridge to other silicon atoms, many complex silicates are possible. One bridge oxygen per silicon atom gives $Si_2O_7^{-6}$ analogous to $Cr_2O_7^{--}$. Two bridge oxygens per silicon lead to formation of extended chains (Fig. 24.14) as found in the mineral spodumene, $LiAl(SiO_3)_2$. The chains are negatively charged anions, because each of the oxygen atoms which is not a bridge atom has picked up an electron to complete its octet. In the compounds, cations such as Li^+ or Al^{+3} hold the solid together by ionic attractions. With three bridge oxygen atoms per silicon, extended two-dimensional sheets are built up, which can be thought of as sheets of SiO_4 tetrahedra, each sharing three corner atoms with other tetrahedra. A portion of such a sheet is shown in Fig. 24.15, where the open circles represent oxygen atoms above the plane of the paper, and the filled circles, silicon atoms in the plane of the paper with oxygen atoms below the plane. The oxygen atoms sticking below the plane are negatively charged and are attracted to positive ions, which in turn are attracted to other similar sheet silicate ions. Stacks of sheetlike silicate ions such as these are found in mica and clay minerals. Their compositions are usually further complicated because of partial replacement of silicon atoms by aluminum. A charac-

---

* It has been reported that in the compound SiP_2O_7 the silicon has six near oxygen neighbors. However, there is a question whether this compound is properly classified as a silicate.

teristic property of these sheetlike minerals is easy cleavage parallel to the sheets.

In the limit there can be four bridge oxygen atoms per silicon. This leads to the three-dimensional structure found in felspars (e.g., orthoclase, $KAlSi_3O_8$), zeolites (e.g., analcite, $NaAlSi_2O_6 \cdot H_2O$), and silica (e.g., quartz, SiO_2). In the felspars and zeolites, some of the Si (oxidation state $+4$) is replaced by Al (oxidation state $+3$). Consequently, the framework has a net negative charge which must be balanced by cations held in lattice holes. In zeolites, the latticework is more open than in felspars, and thus the cations can be replaced by ion exchange (Sec. 19.8). In silica, the framework contains only Si and O atoms and is electrically neutral. If the framework is an ordered one, the silica is crystalline, as in quartz; if it has been disordered, as by supercooling molten SiO_2, the silica is noncrystalline. Crystalline silica has a very high melting point, but noncrystalline (or vitreous) silica can be softened at a considerably lower temperature. Thus softened, it can be blown into various forms such as laboratory ware which take advantage of its desirable properties. SiO_2 transmits both visible and ultraviolet light, has a low thermal coefficient of expansion (only about one-twentieth that of glass or steel), and is inert to most chemical reagents. However, it is dissolved by solutions of HF to form complex fluosilicate ions, SiF_6^{--}, and to a limited extent by basic solutions, to form various silicate ions.

Derived from SiO_2 are other silicate systems of practical importance, e.g., glass and cement. Glass is made by fusing SiO_2 (as sand) with basic substances like CaO and Na_2CO_3. Special glasses such as pyrex contain other acidic oxides (B_2O_3) substituted for some of the SiO_2. Like silica, glass will dissolve in solutions of HF and also is slowly etched by basic solutions. As a consequence of the latter reaction, it is frequently observed that glass stoppers stick fast in reagent bottles containing basic solutions such as NaOH and Na_2CO_3. Cement, a complex aluminum silicate, is made by sintering limestone and clay at high temperature and grinding the prod-

Fig. 24.15 *Silicate sheet.*

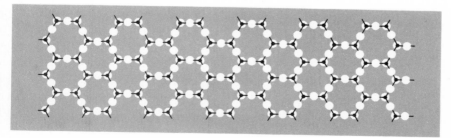

uct to a fine powder. When mixed with water and allowed to stand, it sets to a hard, rigid solid by a series of complex reactions. Although these reactions are still only imperfectly understood, they seem to involve slow hydration of silicates to form some sort of interlocking structure. The hydration is accompanied by the evolution of considerable heat, which may cause cracking unless provision is made for its removal.

The high thermal stability of Si—O—Si chains has been exploited in the *silicones,* compounds in which organic residues are bonded to Si atoms in place of negatively charged silicate oxygens. A typical example of a silicone is the chainlike methyl silicone shown in Fig. 24.16. Thanks to the methyl groups, this silicone has lubricating properties characteristic of hydrocarbon oils, but unlike hydrocarbons it is unreactive, even at high temperatures. More complicated silicone polymers are made possible by having oxygen or hydrocarbon bridges between chains. These rubbery materials are used as electric insulators at elevated temperatures.

24.6   GERMANIUM

The least abundant (0.0007 per cent) of the group IV elements is germanium, the principal source of which is zinc ores. The element may be prepared by the reduction of GeO_2 with carbon or hydrogen. In many respects, compounds of germanium resemble those of silicon. For example, magnesium germanide (Mg_2Ge) reacts with acid to produce hydrogen compounds, but only GeH_4, Ge_2H_6, and Ge_3H_8 are known. These compounds, like the hydrosilicons, are unstable with respect to oxidation to GeO_2. Germanates, derived from GeO_2 and analogous to silicates, have been but slightly investigated. Like Si, germanium forms a volatile tetrachloride which fumes in air because of hydrolysis to GeO_2.

The element has recently taken on industrial importance because of the special properties of slightly impure germanium. Like silicon, Ge has the diamond structure and is a semiconductor; by incorporating traces of a group III or group V element in the lattice, the conductivity can be greatly increased. This increase in conductivity comes about because the substituted element creates a deficiency or excess of valence electrons compared to the four demanded by the diamond structure. As a result, there is mobility of electrons in the lattice either because the excess electron from a substituted group V atom has no preferred location and hence may move through the entire structure, or because a deficiency due to a substituted group III atom is filled by an electron from a neighboring bond, which in turn allows

Fig. 24.16   Methyl silicone chain.

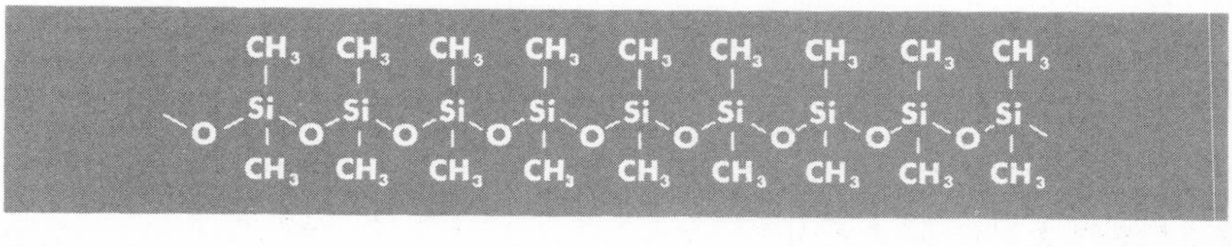

further electron motion of the germanium valence electrons. By joining two crystals of germanium, one containing group III impurity and the other containing group V impurity, a junction is formed which passes electricity more easily in one direction than in the other. This junction can be used to convert alternating current to direct current. Combination of two junctions produces a transistor, which can act like a radio tube in amplifying electric signals.

24.7   TIN

The principal source of tin is cassiterite (SnO_2), from which the element is prepared by carbon reduction. Although usually considered a metal, the element also exists in a nonmetallic form (gray tin), which is stable below 13°C.* Ordinary tin (white tin) is a rather inert metal which resists corrosion because of an oxide coat. Because of its inertness, it is widely used as a protective plating for steel, especially in making "tin cans." The steel is coated, either by being dipped in molten tin or by being made the cathode in an electrolytic bath which contains dissolved tin salts. For reasons mentioned in Sec. 21.4, tin-plated steel does not corrode until the tin coat is punctured, whereupon corrosion of the steel is accelerated by the presence of the tin.

Two series of tin compounds, stannous ($+2$) and stannic ($+4$), are known. The $+2$ state is formed when metallic tin is dissolved in acid solution; however, the rate of reaction is rather slow. In solution, the Sn^{++} ion is colorless and hydrolyzes according to the reaction

$$Sn^{++} + H_2O \rightleftharpoons SnOH^+ + H^+$$

for which the equilibrium constant is about 0.01. Thus, Sn^{++} is about as strong an acid as HSO_4^-. Gradual addition of base to solutions of stannous salts precipitates a white solid usually described as stannous hydroxide, $Sn(OH)_2$. Further addition of base dissolves the precipitate to form stannite ion, which is written both as $Sn(OH)_3^-$ and $HSnO_2^-$. Stannite ion is a powerful reducing agent. Furthermore, on standing, solutions of stannite disproportionate to give the 0 and $+4$ oxidation states:

$$2Sn(OH)_3^- \rightarrow Sn(s) + Sn(OH)_6^{--}$$

In acid solution, stannous ion is frequently complexed with anions. For example, in chloride solutions the whole series $SnCl^+$, $SnCl_2$, $SnCl_3^-$, and $SnCl_4^{--}$ has been identified. Solutions of stannous chloride are frequently

---

* The conversion of metallic tin to gray tin was first observed on the tin organ pipes in early European cathedrals. At the low temperatures prevalent in these unheated churches, the metallic pipes slowly developed grotesque, cancerous "growths." The phenomenon, called "tin disease," was first blamed on the devil, then on microorganisms, and finally on the more prosaic allotropy of tin.

used as convenient, mild reducing agents. The reducing species in these solutions is usually represented as Sn^{++} and assigned an oxidation potential

$$Sn^{++} \rightarrow Sn^{+4} + 2e^- \qquad -0.15 \text{ volt}$$

Chloride complexing of Sn^{++} would make the potential slightly more negative, but the effect is somewhat canceled, since chloride ion also forms complexes with Sn^{+4}.

In the stannic state, tin is often represented as the simple Sn^{+4} ion. However, because of its high charge, Sn^{+4} probably does not exist as such in aqueous solution but is extensively hydrolyzed, even in quite acid solutions. When base is added to stannic solutions, a white precipitate forms, which may be $Sn(OH)_4$ or, more probably, a hydrated oxide, $SnO_2 \cdot xH_2O$. The precipitate is soluble in excess base to give stannate ion, usually written $Sn(OH)_6^{--}$ or SnO_3^{--}.

Both stannous and stannic sulfides are insoluble in water and can be precipitated by H_2S in acid solution. Stannic sulfide, SnS_2, is a yellow solid which is soluble in high concentrations of sulfide ion. The reaction can be written

$$SnS_2(s) + S^{--} \rightarrow SnS_3^{--}$$

where the complex ion, SnS_3^{--}, is called the thiostannate ion and is analogous to stannate ion, SnO_3^{--}. The dissolving of SnS_2 in excess S^{--} can be used to distinguish it from another yellow sulfide, CdS. Owing to the stability of the thiostannate ion, brown-black insoluble stannous sulfide, SnS, can be oxidized by the relatively poor oxidizing agent S_2^{--}, polysulfide ion.

$$SnS(s) + S_2^{--} \rightarrow SnS_3^{--}$$

When solutions of thiostannate are acidified, SnS_2 is precipitated.

24.8   LEAD

Conforming to the general trend of increasing metallic character down a group, lead is the most metallic of the group IV elements. Like tin, it shows oxidation states of $+2$ and $+4$, but the $+4$ state is difficult to attain. It might be pointed out here that, on the right side of the periodic table, the heavier elements show a maximum oxidation state corresponding to the group number and a second state two units lower, e.g., in group III, Tl^{+3} and Tl^+. This presumably stems from leaving the pair of s electrons in the outer shell.

Lead occurs principally as the mineral galena, PbS, from which the element is produced in several different ways. In one of these, the sulfide ore is roasted in air until it is completely converted to the oxide, which is then reduced with carbon in a small blast furnace.

$$2PbS(s) + 3O_2(g) \rightarrow 2PbO(s) + 2SO_2(g)$$

$$2PbO(s) + C(s) \rightarrow 2Pb(l) + CO_2(g)$$

In an alternate process, the sulfide ore is only partially oxidized by air, the product containing a mixture of PbO, PbS, and $PbSO_4$. This mixture is then smelted in the absence of air, with the result that the PbS reduces PbO and $PbSO_4$ to lead.

$$PbS(s) + 2PbO(s) \rightarrow 3Pb(l) + SO_2(g)$$

$$PbS(s) + PbSO_4(s) \rightarrow 2Pb(l) + 2SO_2(g)$$

The crude lead may contain impurities such as antimony, copper, and silver. If lead of high purity is required, it can be refined by an electrolytic process analogous to that used for copper (Sec. 22.2). Pure lead is a soft, low-melting metal which, when freshly cut, has a silvery luster that rapidly dulls on exposure to air. The tarnishing is due to the formation of a surface coat of oxides and carbonates. Primary uses of lead are in the manufacture of lead storage batteries (Sec. 14.7), alloys such as type metal and solder, and white lead paint (hydrated lead hydroxycarbonate).

Practically all the common lead compounds correspond to lead in the $+2$ state. This state is called plumbous, from the Latin name for the element, *plumbum*. In aqueous solutions of plumbous salts, e.g., $Pb(NO_3)_2$, the lead is usually formulated as Pb^{++} ion. However, like stannous ion, Pb^{++} forms many complex ions. The series of equilibria

$$PbCl^+ \rightleftharpoons Pb^{++} + Cl^- \qquad K = 0.8$$

$$PbBr^+ \rightleftharpoons Pb^{++} + Br^- \qquad K = 0.07$$

$$PbI^+ \rightleftharpoons Pb^{++} + I^- \qquad K = 0.03$$

shows that, although the complexes are not especially stable, there is increasing stability in going from chloride to iodide. This trend of stability is the same as that found for other heavy-metal ions on the right side of the periodic table, e.g., Hg^{++}, Cd^{++}, and Sn^{++}. When the halide concentration of plumbous solutions is increased, insoluble plumbous halides form. In excess halide ion, the precipitates redissolve, presumably because of the formation of complex ions of the type $PbCl_3^-$ and $PbBr_4^{--}$. Unlike the two other common insoluble chlorides, AgCl and Hg_2Cl_2, $PbCl_2$ can also be dissolved by raising the temperature of its saturated solution.

Plumbous ion hydrolyzes somewhat less than stannous ion. When base is added, white $Pb(OH)_2$ is precipitated. Being amphoteric, it dissolves in excess base to form plumbite ion [$Pb(OH)_3^-$ or $HPbO_2^-$]. Unlike stannite ion, plumbite is stable in solution. The potential

$$Pb(s) + 3OH^- \rightarrow Pb(OH)_3^- + 2e^- \qquad +0.54 \text{ volt}$$

indicates that lead in basic solution is a stronger reducing agent than it is in acid solution:

$$Pb(s) \rightarrow Pb^{++} + 2e^- \qquad +0.13 \text{ volt}$$

With most -2 anions, Pb^{++} forms insoluble salts, e.g., $PbSO_4$, $PbCO_3$, PbS, $PbCrO_4$, $PbHPO_4$. Lead sulfide is the least soluble of these, and the others convert to it in the presence of sulfide ion.

The principal compound of lead in the $+4$, or plumbic, state is PbO_2, lead dioxide. This compound, used in large amounts for the cathode of lead storage batteries (Sec. 14.7), can be made by oxidation of plumbite with hypochlorite ion in basic solution. The reaction can be written

$$Pb(OH)_3^- + ClO^- \rightarrow Cl^- + PbO_2(s) + OH^- + H_2O$$

With acid solutions, PbO_2 is a potent oxidizing agent

$$2H_2O + Pb^{++} \rightleftharpoons PbO_2(s) + 4H^+ + 2e^- \qquad -1.46 \text{ volts}$$

which is made even more potent in the presence of concentrated acid and anions which precipitate Pb^{++}. In very concentrated solutions of base, PbO_2 dissolves to form plumbates, such as PbO_4^{-4}, PbO_3^{--}, $Pb(OH)_6^{--}$. Red lead, Pb_3O_4, much used as an undercoat for painting structural steel, can be considered to be plumbous plumbate, Pb_2PbO_4. Its use in preventing corrosion depends on the fact that, as a strong oxidizing agent, it renders iron passive (Secs. 21.2 and 21.4).

Like most heavy metals, lead and its compounds are poisonous. Fairly large doses are required for toxicity, but the danger is amplified because the lead tends to accumulate in the body (central nervous system). The toxicity may be due to the fact that lead and other heavy metals are powerful inhibitors of enzyme reactions.

24.9 QUALITATIVE ANALYSIS

Lead and tin precipitate as sulfides in 0.3 N acid solution, although much of the lead may precipitate as white $PbCl_2$ along with $AgCl$ and Hg_2Cl_2 when HCl is added to the original unknown. $PbCl_2$ can be separated from the other two by leaching with hot water. Addition of K_2CrO_4 and acetic acid to the leach solution gives the confirmatory, yellow precipitate, $PbCrO_4$.

Lead sulfide (black) can be separated from tin sulfide, either SnS (brown-black) or SnS$_2$ (yellow), by treatment with ammonium polysulfide, which converts SnS and SnS$_2$ to SnS$_3^{--}$ but leaves the PbS undissolved. PbS can be dissolved with hot HNO$_3$ (unlike black HgS) and reprecipitated as a white sulfate with H$_2$SO$_4$ (unlike Cd^{++}, Bi^{+3}, and Cu^{++}). To confirm, the PbSO$_4$ is dissolved in ammonium acetate and precipitated as PbCrO$_4$.

If, to a solution containing SnS$_3^{--}$, HCl is added in excess, the tin (unlike As$_2$S$_3$) stays in solution, probably as a chloride complex. Evaporation (to drive off H$_2$S) in the presence of an iron wire followed by HgCl$_2$ addition confirms tin if a precipitate of white Hg$_2$Cl$_2$ or black Hg is observed.

The carbonate and bicarbonate anions can easily be detected by adding acid to the unknown and allowing any escaping gas to come in contact with Ba(OH)$_2$ solution. A white milkiness develops, owing to formation of BaCO$_3$.

QUESTIONS

24.1 *Group properties.* How do the following properties change in going down group IV: metallic character, formation of long-chain hydrogen compounds, formation of $+2$ ions, acidity of oxides in the $+4$ state?

24.2 *Carbon structure.* Show how the structures of diamond and graphite account for their properties.

24.3 *Carbonate equilibria.* Explain why solutions of CO$_2$ are acidic, solutions of Na$_2$CO$_3$ are basic, and solutions of NaHCO$_3$ are in between.

24.4 *Organic compounds.* Why are there so many compounds of carbon? Illustrate with specific examples.

24.5 *Terms.* Tell what is meant by each of the following terms: functional group, polyester, residue, silicone, germanides, micelle, protein.

24.6 *Isomers.* Write structural formulas for the seven possible isomers of C$_4$H$_{10}$O.

24.7 *Organic chemistry.* Why are oxidation numbers not especially useful in discussing organic chemistry?

24.8 *Silicon.* Contrast the structure and properties of SiO$_2$ and CO$_2$. Show how the silicates and silicones are related to SiO$_2$.

24.9 *Germanium.* Describe the structure of solid germanium. Show why its conductivity can be increased by presence of: (*a*) traces of Ga; (*b*) traces of As.

24.10 *Electrochemistry.* A given lead storage battery is marked 150 amp.-hr. This means that, in principle, such a battery could deliver 150 amp. for 1 hr. or 1 amp. for 150 hr. What weight of PbO$_2$ would be required to produce this much electricity by the usual half-reaction? *Ans.* 670 g.

24.11   *Carbonate equilibria.* Which concentration, HCO_3^- or CO_3^{--}, is greater in each of the following solutions? Justify your answer. (a) 1 M $NaHCO_3$; (b) 1 M Na_2CO_3; (c) saturated solution of CO_2.

24.12   *Equations.* Write equations for each of the following changes: (a) conversion of CO_2 to Na_2CO_3; (b) conversion of Na_2CO_3 to CO_2 (*Note:* Heating is not a practical method); (c) oxidation of Sn to Sn^{++} by acid; (d) precipitation and redissolving of stannous hydroxide with base; (e) reduction of ferric ion to ferrous ion by Sn^{++}; (f) dissolving of tin in basic solution; (g) disproportionation in basic solution of stannite ion; (h) oxidation of Pb by PbO_2 in sulfuric acid.

24.13   *Tin and lead.* Why does Pb^{++} hydrolyze less than Sn^{++}?

24.14   *Isomerism.* Write structural formulas for two noncyclic isomers of benzene.

24.15   *Lead.* By writing equations, trace the path of lead atoms through the following consecutive conversions: (a) extraction of metal from ore; (b) metal dissolved in dilute nitric acid; (c) gradual addition of base; (d) addition of H_2S.

24.16   *Lead.* By reference to the oxidation potential half-reaction and Le Chatelier's principle, show that PbO_2 is a stronger oxidizing agent in H_2SO_4 than in either HNO_3 or Na_2SO_4.

24.17   *pH of CO_2 solutions.* Freshly distilled water is neutral, but distilled water that has stood in contact with the atmosphere usually has enough dissolved CO_2 in it to make it slightly acid. How much CO_2 would need to be dissolved to account for a pH of 5.3?   *Ans.* 6.0×10^{-5} M

24.18   *pH of CO_2 solutions.* The average pH of beer, cider, and soda pop are 4.5, 3.1, and 3.0, respectively. What would the concentration of CO_2 have to be in order to account for the pH of these beverages?

24.19   *Hydrolysis of carbonate.* Which solution has a higher concentration of OH^-, 1.0 M Na_2CO_3 or 0.010 M NaOH? Justify your answer.

24.20   *Hydrolysis of Sn^{++}.* Which solution has a higher concentration of H^+, 1.0 M $SnSO_4$ or 0.010 M H_2SO_4? Justify your answer.

24.21   *Stoichiometry.* How many liters of hydrogen at 25°C. and 72.0 cm. pressure can be produced by dissolving completely 35.6 g. of tin in 0.400 liter of 12.0 M NaOH? Assume the tin goes to $Sn(OH)_6^{--}$. What will be the final concentration of hydroxide ion?

24.22   *Carbonate solution.* A solution is made by dissolving 0.025 mole of $NaHCO_3$, 0.015 mole of Na_2CO_3, and 0.015 mole of NaOH in 0.050 liter of water. Calculate the final concentrations of Na^+, CO_3^{--}, HCO_3^-, and OH^- in the final solution.

Ans. 1.4 M Na^+; 0.60 M CO_3^{--}; 0.20 M HCO_3^-; 6.3×10^{-4} M OH^-

24.23   *Fermentation stoichiometry.* One of the principal commercial sources of CO_2 is the fermentation industry. How many gallons of beer would you have to make in order to get a ton of dry ice? Assume that beer has a density of 1.0 lb per pint, that it is essentially a dilute solution of alcohol in water, that the alcoholic content is 4.0% C_2H_5OH by weight, and that the C_2H_5OH comes from the fermentation reaction.

24.24   *Hydrolysis.* Solutions of washing soda have a slippery feel, owing to the rather appreciable hydrolysis of carbonate ion. If the dissociation constant of HCO_3^- is 4.8×10^{-11}, what would be the pH of 0.5 M Na_2CO_3? What per cent of the carbonate ion has hydrolyzed?   *Ans.* 12.0; 2%

24.25   *Carbonate solution.* A solution is made by dissolving 0.84 g. of $NaHCO_3$, 1.06 g. of Na_2CO_3, and 0.80 g. of $NaOH$ in enough water to give 50.0 ml. of solution. What will be the concentration of Na^+, HCO_3^-, CO_3^{--}, and OH^- in the final solution?

24.26   *Molecular weight of polyethylene.* A given batch of polyethylene contains the following distribution of polymers: 20.0% of the polymer molecules have 70 carbon atoms per molecule; 40.0%, 90 carbons; 20.0%, 110 carbons; 10.0%, 130 carbons; and 10.0%, 150 carbons. Calculate the average molecular weight of the molecules in the sample.

24.27   *Silicate.* The mineral beryl, $Be_3Al_2Si_6O_{18}$, contains the discrete anion $Si_6O_{18}^{-12}$. Suggest a possible structure for these anions consistent with tetrahedral coordination of four oxygen atoms to each silicon atom.

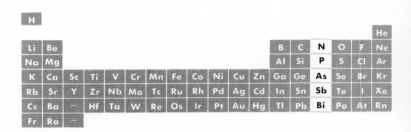

25   *Group V Elements*

IN GROUP V there is a complete change of properties from nonmetallic to metallic in going down the group. The lighter members of the group, nitrogen and phosphorus, are typical nonmetals and form only acidic oxides; the middle members, arsenic and antimony, are semimetals and form amphoteric oxides; the heaviest member, bismuth, is a metal and forms essentially only basic oxides.

25.1   GROUP PROPERTIES

Table 25.1 summarizes some of the specific properties of the group V elements. As shown, each of the atoms has five valence electrons in its outermost energy level. Since this corresponds to an outer octet which is only slightly more than half filled, complete loss of five electrons or gain of three electrons is unlikely. Sharing electrons with more electronegative atoms would correspond to a maximum oxidation state of $+5$; sharing with less electronegative atoms, to a minimum oxidation state of -3. Both of these states are observed for all the group V elements, though the stability of the -3 state decreases down the group. In addition, a $+3$ state correspond-

Table 25.1   *Elements of Group* **V**

Sym-bol	z	Electronic configuration	Melting point, °C.	Boiling point, °C.	Ioni-zation poten-tial, e.v.	Oxidation potential, volts
N	7	2, 5	-210.0	-195.8	14.5	-1.25(to NO_3^-)
P	15	2, 8, 5	44.1	280	11.0	$+0.50$(to H_3PO_3)
As	33	2, 8, 18, 5	Sublimes	Sublimes	10	-0.23(to As_4O_6)
Sb	51	2, 8, 18, 18, 5	631	1380	8.6	-0.21(to $Sb(OH)_2^+$)
Bi	83	2, 8, 18, 32, 18, 5	271	1500	8	-0.32(to $Bi(OH)_2^+$)

ing to leaving an unshared pair of electrons on the group V atom is common for all. Nitrogen, and apparently phosphorus, are unusual in that they show all the oxidation states from -3 to $+5$, inclusive.

The pronounced change from nonmetallic to metallic behavior down the group is due principally to the increasing size of the atoms. As the ionization potentials of Table 25.1 indicate, it is much more difficult to pull electrons off the small nitrogen atoms than off the larger bismuth atoms. Furthermore, the nitrogen atom, being a small atom and holding its electrons tightly, can, like the preceding element carbon, form multiple bonds to other atoms. One of the results is that nitrogen forms simple diatomic molecules, whereas under ordinary conditions other members of the group do not. However, phosphorus, arsenic, and possibly antimony do form discrete tetratomic molecules [P_4, As_4, Sb_4(?)] in at least some of their allotropic forms, indicating that the tendency to form covalent bonds persists down the group. Bismuth, which holds its electrons least tightly and hence is most metallic, still retains some of this covalent character. It shows up, for example, in the fact that bismuth is not a very good metal—rather brittle, it has even greater electric resistance than mercury. Also, elementary bismuth has an extraordinarily high diamagnetism (repulsion out of magnetic fields) compared to other metals. This behavior is taken to indicate that the electron cloud in bismuth metal is unlike that in typical metals and that the electrons are restricted in their motion.

The increasing basicity of oxides going down the group is also primarily due to increasing size. As pointed out in Sec. 17.13, the action of an oxide or hydroxide as an acid or base depends on the extent of hydrolysis, which in turn depends on the charge and on the size of the atom. Since N^{+3} would be much smaller than Bi^{+3}, it would interact with water more strongly and be more likely to result in acid properties. Thus, it is not surprising that N_2O_3 is strictly an acidic oxide, dissolving in water to give H^+ and neutralizing bases, whereas Bi_2O_3 is strictly a basic oxide, dissolving to give OH^- and neutralizing acids. Of the intermediate elements, phosphorus forms the acidic oxide, P_2O_3, while arsenic and antimony form the amphoteric oxides, As_2O_3 and Sb_2O_3.

In the elementary state, none of the group V elements is particularly reactive. This is partly due to slowness of the reactions and partly due to the low oxidation potentials. In the $+5$ state all the elements except phosphorus form compounds which are powerful oxidizing agents.

25.2   NITROGEN

Nitrogen is about one-third as abundant as carbon and occurs principally *free* as diatomic N_2 in the atmosphere and *combined* as Chile saltpeter ($NaNO_3$). In plants and animals, nitrogen is found combined in the form of proteins, which average in composition 51 per cent C, 25 per cent O, 16 per cent N, 7 per cent H, 0.4 per cent P, and 0.4 per cent S.

Elementary nitrogen is usually obtained by fractional distillation of liquid air. Since N_2 has a lower boiling point ($-195.8°C.$) than O_2 ($-183.0°C.$), it is more volatile and evaporates preferentially in the first fractions (Sec. 16.2). Very pure N_2 can be made by thermal decomposition of some nitrogen compounds, such as ammonium nitrite, NH_4NO_2.

$$NH_4NO_2(s) \rightarrow N_2(g) + 2H_2O(g)$$

It is interesting to note that pure nitrogen obtained from decomposition of compounds such as NH_4NO_2 was the key that led to the discovery of the inert gases. Lord Rayleigh, in 1894, was the first to note that nitrogen from the decomposition of compounds was of lower density (1.2505 g. per liter at STP) than the residual gas obtained from the atmosphere by removal of O_2, CO_2, and H_2O (1.2572 g. per liter at STP). In conjunction with Sir William Ramsay, Rayleigh removed the nitrogen from the air residue by various reactions, such as the combination of nitrogen with hot magnesium to form solid magnesium nitride, Mg_3N_2. After removal of the nitrogen, there was still some gas remaining which, unlike any gas known at that time, was completely unreactive. It was christened argon from the Greek word meaning lazy. Later spectroscopic investigations (Sec. 3.8) showed that crude argon, and hence the atmosphere, contains the other inert elements helium, neon, krypton, and xenon. Including the inert gases, the average composition of the earth's atmosphere is as shown in Table 25.2. In addition to the inert gases listed, there are traces of radon, Rn, in the atmosphere. The concentration is very low and variable, because radon is produced by radioactive decay of other elements and is itself unstable to nuclear

Table 25.2   Composition of Dry Air

Component	% by volume	Boiling point, °K.
Nitrogen (N_2)	78.03	77.3
Oxygen (O_2)	20.99	90.2
Argon (Ar)	0.94	87.4
Carbon dioxide (CO_2)	0.023–0.050	Sublimes
Hydrogen (H_2)	0.01	20.4
Neon (Ne)	0.0015	27.2
Helium (He)	0.0005	4.2
Krypton (Kr)	0.00011	121.3
Xenon (Xe)	0.000009	163.9

disintegration. As can be seen from the table, nitrogen is by far the predominant constituent of the atmosphere.

The N_2 molecule contains a triple bond and may be written

:N:::N:

Although very stable with respect to dissociation into single atoms, it is unstable with respect to oxidation by O_2 in the presence of water to nitrate ion, NO_3^-. It is fortunate that this reaction is very slow; otherwise, atmospheric N_2 and O_2 would combine with the oceans to form solutions of nitric acid. In practice, nitrogen is frequently used when an inert atmosphere is required, as, for example, in incandescent lamp bulbs to retard filament evaporation.

The compounds of nitrogen, though not so numerous as those of carbon, are just as varied. In many respects, their chemical reactions are more complicated, because there are usually no residues which retain identity throughout a reaction. Only a few of the compounds and their reactions can be considered here.

The principal compound of nitrogen is probably ammonia, NH_3. It occurs to a slight extent in the atmosphere, primarily as a product of the putrefaction of nitrogen-containing animal or vegetable matter. Commercially it is important as the most economical pathway for nitrogen "fixation," i.e., the conversion of atmospheric N_2 into useful compounds. In the Haber process, synthetic ammonia is made by passing a nitrogen-hydrogen mixture through a bed of catalyst consisting essentially of iron oxides. By using a temperature of about 500°C. (a compromise between the requirements of kinetics and equilibrium) and a pressure of about 1,000 atm., there is about 50 per cent conversion of N_2 to NH_3.

$$N_2(g) + 3H_2(g) \rightleftharpoons 2NH_3(g) + 22 \text{ kcal.}$$

NH$_3$ is a polar molecule, pyramidal in shape, with the three hydrogen atoms occupying the base of the pyramid and an unshared pair of electrons, the apex. The structure, shown in Fig. 25.1, leads to a compound which is easily condensed (condensation temperature of $-33°$C.) to a liquid of great solvent power. In many respects, liquid ammonia is as versatile a solvent as water, and, like water, it can dissolve a great variety of salts. In addition, it has the rather unique property of dissolving alkali and alkaline-earth metals to give solutions which contain solvated electrons (Sec. 18.5).

Ammonia gas is very soluble in water, which is easily explained by the fact that both NH$_3$ and H$_2$O are polar molecules. Not so easy to explain is the basic character of the aqueous solutions formed. At one time it was thought that the NH$_3$ molecules react with H$_2$O to form molecules of the weak base, ammonium hydroxide

$$\text{H}:\overset{..}{\underset{..}{\text{N}}}:\text{H}:\overset{..}{\underset{..}{\text{O}}}:$$

(with H above and H, H below)

which could then dissociate into ammonium ions (NH$_4^+$) and hydroxide ions. However, nuclear magnetic experiments indicate that, in aqueous ammonia solutions, protons jump back and forth so rapidly between nitrogen and oxygen atoms that the distinction between NH$_3$ plus H$_2$O and NH$_4$OH is arbitrary. Thus, the basic nature of aqueous ammonia can be represented by either of the equilibria

$$NH_3 + H_2O \rightleftharpoons NH_4^+ + OH^-$$

$$NH_4OH \rightleftharpoons NH_4^+ + OH^-$$

and K for either is 1.8×10^{-5}. By neutralizing ammonia with acids, ammonium salts can be formed; these contain the tetrahedral NH$_4^+$ ion. They resemble potassium salts, except that they give slightly acid solutions. This can be interpreted either as a hydrolysis

$$NH_4^+ + H_2O \rightleftharpoons NH_4OH + H^+$$

or as a dissociation

$$NH_4^+ \rightleftharpoons NH_3 + H^+$$

and K for either is 5.5×10^{-10}. Some ammonium salts, such as ammonium nitrate, NH$_4$NO$_3$, and ammonium dichromate, (NH$_4$)$_2$Cr$_2$O$_7$, are thermally

Fig. 25.1 Ammonia molecule.

unstable because they undergo auto-oxidation. As illustration, NH_4NO_3 sometimes explodes when heated to produce nitrous oxide, N_2O, by the reaction

$$NH_4NO_3(s) \rightarrow N_2O(g) + 2H_2O(g)$$

Whereas ammonia and ammonium salts represent nitrogen in its lowest oxidation state (-3), the highest oxidation state of nitrogen $(+5)$ appears in the familiar compounds nitric acid (HNO_3) and nitrate salts. Nitric acid is one of the most important industrial acids, and large quantities of it are produced, principally by the catalytic oxidation of ammonia. In this process, called the Ostwald process, the following steps are important:

$$4NH_3(g) + 5O_2(g) \xrightarrow{Pt} 4NO(g) + 6H_2O(g)$$
$$2NO(g) + O_2(g) \rightarrow 2NO_2(g)$$
$$3NO_2(g) + H_2O \rightarrow 2H^+ + 2NO_3^- + NO(g)$$

In the first step, a mixture of NH_3 and air is passed through a platinum gauze heated at about $800°C$. On cooling, the product nitric oxide (NO) is then oxidized to nitrogen dioxide (NO_2), which disproportionates in solution to form nitric acid and NO. By keeping a high concentration of O_2, the remaining NO is converted to NO_2, and the last reaction is driven to the right. To get 100 per cent acid, it is necessary, to distill off volatile HNO_3.

Pure nitric acid is a colorless liquid which, on exposure to light, turns brown because of slight decomposition to brown NO_2.

$$4HNO_3 \rightarrow 4NO_2(g) + O_2(g) + 2H_2O$$

It is a strong acid in that it is 100 per cent dissociated in dilute solutions to H^+ and nitrate ion, NO_3^-. Like carbonate ion (Fig. 24.4), nitrate ion is planar and can be represented as a resonance hybrid of three contributing formulas. The ion is colorless and forms a great variety of nitrate salts, most of which are quite soluble in aqueous solutions.* Owing to the poor complexing ability of nitrate ion, practically all these salts are completely dissociated in aqueous solution.

In acid solution, nitrate ion is a good oxidizing agent. By proper choice of concentrations and reducing agents it can be reduced to compounds of nitrogen in all the other oxidation states. The possible half-reactions and their oxidation potentials are

$$NO_2(g) + H_2O \rightleftharpoons NO_3^- + 2H^+ + e^- \qquad\qquad -0.79 \text{ volt}$$

---

* Because of the solubility of the nitrates, it is not usual to find solid nitrates occurring naturally as minerals. The extensive deposits of $NaNO_3$ in Chile occur in a desert region where there is insufficient rainfall to wash them away. These deposits probably originated from the decomposition of nitrogenous deposits of marine organisms which were cut off from the sea.

$$HNO_2 + H_2O \rightleftharpoons NO_3^- + 3H^+ + 2e^- \qquad -0.94 \text{ volt}$$

$$NO(g) + 2H_2O \rightleftharpoons NO_3^- + 4H^+ + 3e^- \qquad -0.96 \text{ volt}$$

$$N_2O(g) + 5H_2O \rightleftharpoons 2NO_3^- + 10H^+ + 8e^- \qquad -1.12 \text{ volts}$$

$$N_2(g) + 6H_2O \rightleftharpoons 2NO_3^- + 12H^+ + 10e^- \qquad -1.25 \text{ volts}$$

$$NH_3OH^+ + 2H_2O \rightleftharpoons NO_3^- + 8H^+ + 6e^- \qquad -0.73 \text{ volt}$$

$$N_2H_5^+ + 6H_2O \rightleftharpoons 2NO_3^- + 17H^+ + 14e^- \qquad -0.83 \text{ volt}$$

$$NH_4^+ + 3H_2O \rightleftharpoons NO_3^- + 10H^+ + 8e^- \qquad -0.88 \text{ volt}$$

Since all the oxidation potentials are quite negative, nitrate ion is a much better oxidizing agent than H^+ by itself. This presumably is responsible for the observation that some metals such as copper and silver, which are too poor as reducing agents to dissolve in HCl, for example, will dissolve in HNO_3. Both of these acids contain the oxidizing agent H^+, but only the nitric has the additional oxidizing agent NO_3^-. Some metals such as gold, which are insoluble in HCl and also in HNO_3, are soluble in a mixture of the two acids. This mixture is called aqua regia and usually consists of 1 part of concentrated HNO_3 to 3 parts of concentrated HCl. As mentioned in Sec. 22.4, the dissolving power of aqua regia is due to the oxidizing ability of nitrate ion in strong acid plus the complexing ability of chloride ion.

Reduction of NO_3^- usually produces a mixed product. Since the various oxidation potentials of nitrate shown above are very roughly the same, the reduction may yield any of several species. The actual composition of the product depends on the rates of the different reactions. These rates in turn are influenced by the concentration of NO_3^-, the concentration of H^+, the temperature, and the reducing agent used. Thus, for example, in *concentrated* nitric acid, copper reacts to give brown NO_2 gas, but in *dilute* nitric acid, copper reacts to form colorless NO gas. However, since NO is easily oxidized by air to NO_2, some brown fumes may also appear when dilute nitric acid is used.

As can be seen from the above list of reduction products of NO_3^-, compounds of nitrogen are possible in the $+4$, $+3$, $+2$, $+1$, -1, and -2 states, as well as $+5$ and -3. Some of the more common representative species of these states are discussed below.

1   The $+5$ state. In addition to nitric acid and the nitrates, nitrogen corresponding to the $+5$ state is found in nitrogen pentoxide, N_2O_5. This material, which is the acid anhydride of HNO_3, can be produced by treating concentrated nitric acid with a very strong dehydrating agent such as phosphoric oxide, P_4O_{10}. At room temperature, N_2O_5 is a white solid which decomposes slowly into NO_2 and oxygen. With water, it reacts quite vigorously to form HNO_3.

2 The +4 state. When concentrated nitric acid is reduced with metals, brown fumes are evolved. The brown gas is NO_2, nitrogen dioxide. Since the molecule contains an odd number of valence electrons (five from the nitrogen and six from each of the oxygens), it should be and is paramagnetic. When brown NO_2 gas is cooled, the color fades, and the paramagnetism diminishes. These observations are interpreted as indicating that two NO_2 molecules pair up (dimerize) to form a single molecule of N_2O_4, nitrogen tetroxide. The equilibrium

$$2NO_2(g) \rightleftharpoons N_2O_4(g) + 14.6 \text{ kcal.}$$

is such that at 60°C. and 1 atm. pressure half the nitrogen is present as NO_2 and half as N_2O_4. As the temperature is raised, decomposition of N_2O_4 is favored. The mixture NO_2—N_2O_4 is poisonous and is a strong oxidizing agent. As already mentioned in connection with the Ostwald process, NO_2, or more correctly a mixture of NO_2 and N_2O_4, dissolves in water to form HNO_3 and NO.

3 The +3 state. The most common representatives of the +3 oxidation state of nitrogen are the salts called nitrites. Nitrites such as $NaNO_2$ can be made by heating sodium nitrate above its melting point.

$$2NaNO_3(l) \rightarrow 2NaNO_2(l) + O_2(g)$$

They can also be made by chemical reduction of nitrates with substances like C or Pb. Nitrites are important industrially as sources of the $-NO_2$ group for making many synthetic dyes. When acid is added to a solution of nitrite, the weak acid HNO_2, nitrous acid ($K_{diss} = 4.5 \times 10^{-4}$), is formed. It is unstable and slowly decomposes by several complex reactions, including

$$3HNO_2 \rightarrow H^+ + NO_3^- + 2NO(g) + H_2O$$

$$2HNO_2 \rightarrow NO(g) + NO_2(g) + H_2O$$

4 The +2 state. The oxide NO, nitric oxide, is, like NO_2, an odd molecule in that it contains an uneven number of electrons. However, unlike NO_2, NO is colorless and does not dimerize appreciably in the gas phase. In the liquid phase, as shown by a decrease of paramagnetism, some dimerization occurs to form N_2O_2. The existence of simple NO molecules in the gas phase poses a problem in writing an electronic formula. There is magnetic evidence that the odd electron spends half its time with the N and half with the O. This situation is sometimes represented by a three-electron bond instead of the conventional electron pair. Such a formula is written $:\overset{..}{N}::\overset{..}{O}:$ which clearly violates the octet rule. This is one of the cases where the molecular-orbital description (Sec. 4.1) is called for.

Nitric oxide can be made in several ways:

$$4NH_3(g) + 5O_2(g) \rightarrow 4NO(g) + 6H_2O$$

$$3Cu(s) + 8H^+ + 2NO_3^- \rightarrow 3Cu^{++} + 2NO(g) + 4H_2O$$

$$N_2(g) + O_2(g) \rightarrow 2NO(g)$$

The first of these reactions is the catalytic oxidation that is the first step of the Ostwald process for making HNO_3. The second is observed with dilute nitric acid but not with concentrated. The third is extremely endothermic (by 43 kcal.) and can occur only when large amounts of energy are added. Apparently, this last reaction occurs when lightning bolts pass through the atmosphere and is one of the paths by which atmospheric nitrogen is made available to plants. In air, NO is rapidly oxidized to brown NO_2.

$$2NO(g) + O_2(g) \rightarrow 2NO_2(g)$$

Nitric oxide also combines with many transition-metal cations to form complex ions. The most familiar of these complexes is $FeNO^{++}$, the ferrous nitroso ion, which forms in the brown-ring test for nitrates. When concentrated sulfuric acid is carefully poured into a solution containing ferrous ion and nitrate, a brown layer appears at the juncture of the H_2SO_4 and the nitrate-containing solution. The NO for the complex is formed by reduction of NO_3^- by Fe^{++}.

5 *The* $+1$ *state.* When solid ammonium nitrate is gently heated, it melts and undergoes auto-oxidation according to the following equation:

$$NH_4NO_3(l) \rightarrow N_2O(g) + 2H_2O(g)$$

The compound formed, N_2O, called nitrous oxide, or laughing gas, has a linear molecule with the oxygen atom at one end. Although rather inert at low temperatures, N_2O decomposes to N_2 and O_2 at higher temperatures. Perhaps because of this decomposition, substances which burn briskly in air actually burn more vigorously in N_2O. Compared to the other oxides of nitrogen, nitrous oxide is considerably less poisonous. However, small doses are mildly intoxicating; large doses produce general anesthesia and in dentistry are frequently used for this purpose. Nitrous oxide has an appreciable solubility in fats, a property which has been exploited in making self-whipping cream. Cream is packaged with N_2O under pressure to increase its solubility. When the pressure is released, the N_2O escapes to form tiny bubbles which produce whipped cream.

6 *The* -1 *state.* Hydroxylamine, NH_2OH, is representative of nitrogen with oxidation number -1. It can be considered to be derived from

NH_3 by substituting a hydroxyl group for one of the hydrogen atoms. However, the preparation of NH_2OH does not involve ammonia but rather the reduction of nitrates or nitrites by appropriate reducing agents such as sulfur dioxide (SO_2) or tin. Pure hydroxylamine is a solid at room temperature and is unstable, especially at higher temperatures. The decomposition, which is sometimes explosive, produces a mixture of products including NH_3, H_2O, N_2, and N_2O. In dilute aqueous solution, the decomposition is slow. Like NH_3, NH_2OH has an unshared pair of electrons and so can pick up a proton to form NH_3OH^+.

$$\begin{matrix} H \\ \ddots \ddots \\ H:N:O:H \\ \ddots \ddots \end{matrix} + H_2O \rightleftharpoons \left[\begin{matrix} H \\ \ddots \ddots \\ H:N:O:H \\ \ddots \ddots \\ H \end{matrix} \right]^+ + OH^-$$

Thus, hydroxylamine solutions are slightly basic, but less so than ammonia solutions. Analogous to ammonium salts, such as $[NH_4]Cl$, there are hydroxylammonium salts, such as $[NH_3OH]Cl$. Since hydroxylamine and its salts correspond to nitrogen in an intermediate oxidation state, they can act both as oxidizing agents and as reducing agents.

7   *The −2 state.* In many ways similar to ammonia is the compound hydrazine, N_2H_4. This compound can be made by bubbling chlorine through a solution of ammonia.

$$Cl_2(g) + 4NH_3 \rightarrow N_2H_4 + 2NH_4^+ + 2Cl^-$$

When pure, N_2H_4 is a colorless liquid at room temperature. Like liquid ammonia, it is a good solvent for many salts and even for the alkali metals. Hydrazine is unstable with respect to disproportionation

$$2N_2H_4(l) \rightarrow N_2(g) + 2NH_3(g) + H_2(g)$$

and is violently explosive in the presence of air or other oxidizing agents. It is quite poisonous. In aqueous solution, it acts as a base, since it can add one or two protons to the unshared pairs of electrons.

$$\begin{matrix} H \; H \\ \ddots \; \ddots \\ H:N:N:H \\ \ddots \; \ddots \end{matrix} + H^+ \rightarrow \left[\begin{matrix} H \; H \\ \ddots \; \ddots \\ H:N:N:H \\ \ddots \; \ddots \\ H \end{matrix} \right]^+$$

Salts of the type $[N_2H_5]Cl$ and $[N_2H_6]Cl_2$ are known. In aqueous solution, hydrazine and its salts are good oxidizing and reducing agents, though sometimes reaction is slow.

Recently, hydrazine has become important as a rocket propellant. For example, the reaction

$$N_2H_4(l) + 2H_2O_2(l) \rightarrow N_2(g) + 4H_2O(g)$$

which takes place in the presence of Cu^{++} ion as catalyst, is strongly exothermic and is accompanied by a large increase in volume. The heat liberated expands the gases still further and adds to the thrust.

8 *The* -3 *state.* In addition to ammonia and the ammonium salts, nitrogen forms other compounds in which it is assigned an oxidation state of -3. These include the nitrides, such as Na_3N, Mg_3N_2, and TiN, many of which can be formed by direct combination of the elements. Some of these, e.g., Na_3N and Mg_3N_2, are quite reactive and combine with water to liberate ammonia. Others, e.g., TiN, are very inert and can be used to make containers for high-temperature reactions. The compound nitrogen tri-iodide (NI_3) might also be included with the -3 oxidation state of nitrogen, since nitrogen is more electronegative than iodine. At room temperature, NI_3 is a solid which is violently explosive and is well known for the fact that even a fly's landing on it can set it off.

The above list of nitrogen compounds is by no means exhaustive, but it does serve to indicate the great complexity of nitrogen chemistry. Even more complexity is found in the proteins, the nitrogen compounds which are essential constituents of all living matter. As described in Sec. 24.4, the proteins are natural high polymers containing the peptide link, or

$$\underset{|}{\overset{H}{\underset{-N-}{}}}\ \underset{\|}{\overset{O}{\underset{-C-}{}}}$$

group. There are a great variety of protein molecules, most of which are of extraordinarily high molecular weight, sometimes as high as a million. The structure of none of these many different kinds of protein molecules has been completely worked out. Furthermore, the synthesis of proteins by organisms remains incompletely understood, but it seems to involve amino acids as intermediates (Sec. 24.4). In nature there is constant interconversion between animal and plant proteins. However, the interconversion is not without loss, because the decay of protein material produces some elementary nitrogen which escapes to the atmosphere. Living organisms, with the exception of some bacteria, are unable to utilize elementary nitrogen for the production of proteins. Thus, in order to maintain life, nitrogen must somehow be restored to a biologically useful form.

The *nitrogen cycle,* which traces the path of nitrogen atoms in nature, is shown in simplified form in Fig. 25.2. When plant and animal proteins are broken down, as in digestion and decay, the principal end products are NH_3 and N_2, which are released to the atmosphere, and various nitrogen-containing ions, which are added to the soil. Ammonia in the atmosphere can be returned to the soil by being dissolved in rain. Elemental nitrogen can be returned by two paths: (1) nitrogen-fixing bacteria which live on the roots of leguminous plants convert N_2 to proteins and other nitrogen compounds; (2) lightning discharges initiate the otherwise slow combination of N_2 and

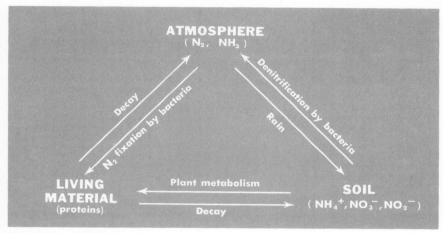

Fig. 25.2   Nitrogen cycle.

O_2 to form NO, which in turn is oxidized to NO_2. The NO_2 dissolves in rain water to form nitrates and nitrites, which are washed into the soil. As a final step of the cycle, plants absorb nitrogen compounds from the soil and convert these to plant proteins. Ingested as food, the plant proteins are broken down by animals and reassembled as animal proteins or excreted as waste to the soil. In addition, there are some forms of denitrifying bacteria which convert some of the nitrogen compounds in the soil directly to atmospheric nitrogen.

The nitrogen cycle as outlined above is in precarious balance. Frequently, the balance is locally upset, as, for example, by intensive cultivation and removal of crops. In such cases, it is necessary to replenish the nitrogen by addition of synthetic fertilizers, such as NH_3, NH_4NO_3, or KNO_3.

25.3   PHOSPHORUS

The second element of group V, phosphorus, is considerably more abundant than nitrogen. Its principal natural form is $Ca_3(PO_4)_2$, as is found in phosphate rock. Like nitrogen, phosphorus compounds are essential constituents of all animal and vegetable matter. Bones, for example, contain about 60 per cent $Ca_3(PO_4)_2$. Elementary phosphorus can be made by reduction of calcium phosphate with coke in the presence of sand. The reaction can be represented by the equation

$$Ca_3(PO_4)_2(s) + 3SiO_2(s) + 5C(s) \rightarrow 3CaSiO_3 + 5CO(g) + P_2(g)$$

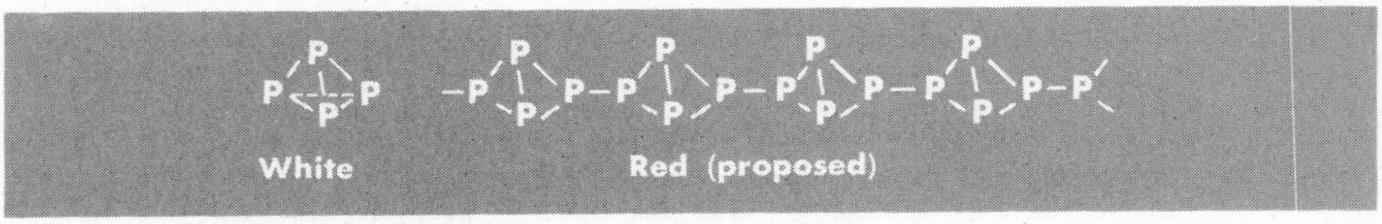

Fig. 25.3   White and red phosphorus.

Since the reaction is carried out at high temperature, the phosphorus is formed as a gas, which is condensed to a solid by running the product gases through water. This condensation serves not only to separate the phosphorus from the carbon monoxide but also to protect it from reoxidation by air.

There are several forms of solid phosphorus, but only the white and red forms are important. White phosphorus consists of discrete tetrahedral P_4 molecules, as shown on the left of Fig. 25.3. The structure of red phosphorus has not yet been completely determined, but there is evidence that it is polymeric and consists of chains of P_4 tetrahedra linked together, possibly in the manner shown in Fig. 25.3. At room temperature, the stable modification of elemental phosphorus is the red form. Because of its highly polymerized structure, it is less volatile, less soluble (especially in nonpolar solvents), and less reactive than white phosphorus. The white form must be handled with care, because it ignites spontaneously in air and is extremely poisonous.

At relatively low temperatures (below 800°C.), phosphorus vapor consists primarily of P_4 molecules. At higher temperatures there is considerable dissociation to give P_2 molecules. Thus, only at very high temperature does elemental phosphorus resemble elemental nitrogen in being diatomic. The favoring of phosphorus molecules that are more complex than those of nitrogen may be attributed to the larger size of the phosphorus atom. In general, large atoms have more difficulty than small atoms do in forming multiple bonds, which would be required in

$$:P:::P:$$

At room temperature, ordinary red phosphorus is not especially reactive, but at higher temperatures it reacts with many other elements to form a variety of compounds. For example, when heated with calcium, it forms solid calcium phosphide, Ca_3P_2. With chlorine, it can form either liquid phosphorus trichloride, PCl_3, or solid phosphorus pentachloride, PCl_5, depending on the relative amount of chlorine present. The three compounds just mentioned illustrate the three most important oxidation states of phosphorus, -3, $+3$, and $+5$.

When Ca_3P_2 is placed in water, it reacts vigorously to form phosphine, PH_3, gas.

$$Ca_3P_2(s) + 6H_2O \rightarrow 2PH_3(g) + 3Ca^{++} + 6OH^-$$

In structure, PH_3 resembles NH_3 in being a pyramidal molecule. Like NH_3, PH_3 can add a proton to form a phosphonium ion, PH_4^+, which however is found only in solid salts, such as $[PH_4]I$. Compared to ammonia, phosphine is practically insoluble in water and is much less basic. In air, PH_3 usually bursts into flame, apparently because it is ignited by a spontaneous oxidation of the impurity P_2H_4.*

When phosphorus is burned in a limited supply of oxygen, it forms the oxide P_4O_6 (phosphor*ous* oxide). Below room temperature this compound is a white solid which melts at 23.8°C. Its structure, shown in Fig. 25.4, can be visualized as derived from a P_4 tetrahedron by insertion of an oxygen atom between each pair of phosphorus atoms. P_4O_6 is the anhydride of phosphorous acid, and when cold water is added to it, H_3PO_3 is formed. Phosphorous acid is peculiar because, although it contains three hydrogen atoms per molecule, only two can dissociate.

$$H_3PO_3 \rightleftharpoons H^+ + H_2PO_3^- \qquad K_I = 1.6 \times 10^{-2}$$

$$H_2PO_3^- \rightleftharpoons H^+ + HPO_3^{--} \qquad K_{II} = 7 \times 10^{-7}$$

It has been suggested that the reason for the lack of dissociation of the third H is that it is attached directly to the P instead of to an O. The structure of H_3PO_3 would then be

```
        H                              H
        ..                             ..
       :O:                            :O:
  .... .. ....                   .... .. ....
  H:O:P:O:      instead of       H:O:P:O:H
  .... .. ....                   .... .. ....
        H
```

Phosphorous acid can also be made by the hydrolysis of phosphorus trichloride. The reaction

$$PCl_3 + 3H_2O \rightarrow H_3PO_3 + 3H^+ + 3Cl^-$$

is quite vigorous and liberates considerable heat, partly because of the high heat of hydration of the hydrogen ion liberated to the solution. Neutralization of H_3PO_3 by bases can produce two series of salts, the dihydrogen phosphites, e.g., NaH_2PO_3 and the monohydrogen phosphites, e.g., Na_2HPO_3. The phosphites, especially in basic solutions, are very strong

---

*The will-o'-the-wisp, or faint flickering light, sometimes observed in marshes may be due to spontaneous ignition of impure PH_3. The PH_3 might be formed by reduction of naturally occurring phosphorus compounds.

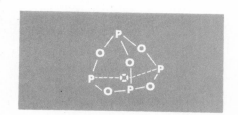

Fig. 25.4 P_4O_6.

reducing agents. Even in acid solution (where they immediately are converted to H_3PO_3) they are moderately good reducing agents

$$H_3PO_3 + H_2O \rightarrow H_3PO_4 + 2H^+ + 2e^- \qquad +0.28 \text{ volt}$$

being slightly better than nickel metal.

In the $+5$ state, phosphorus exists as several oxy compounds of varying complexity. In contrast with the oxy compounds of nitrogen in the $+5$ state, none of these compounds of phosphorus is an especially good oxidizing agent. The least complicated of the phosphorus oxy compounds corresponding to oxidation number $+5$ is the oxide, P_4O_{10}, called phosphoric oxide, phosphorus pentoxide, or phosphoric anhydride. This is the white solid which is usually formed when red phosphorus is burned in an unlimited supply of oxygen or when white phosphorus spontaneously catches fire in air. Though called a pentoxide (because of its simplest formula, P_2O_5), this material both in the vapor and in the most stable solid modification is known to consist of discrete P_4O_{10} molecules. The structure can be visualized as being derived from Fig. 25.4 by the addition of an oxygen atom sticking out from each P. Consistent with the molecular nature of the solid, P_4O_{10} is quite volatile and can be readily sublimed. At $360°C.$, the vapor pressure of the solid is about 1 atm. It is remarkable that further heating of P_4O_{10} to about $500°C.$ converts it not to a liquid but to a highly polymerized solid. Apparently some of the P—O—P bonds in the P_4O_{10} unit are broken and reestablished to adjacent P_4O_{10} units.

When exposed to moisture, P_4O_{10} turns gummy as it picks up water. The affinity for water is so great that P_4O_{10} is frequently used as an efficient dehydrating agent. With a large amount of water, the acid H_3PO_4, or orthophosphoric acid, is formed. This is a triprotic acid for which the stepwise dissociation is as follows:

$$H_3PO_4 \rightleftharpoons H^+ + H_2PO_4^- \qquad K_I = 7.5 \times 10^{-3}$$

$$H_2PO_4^- \rightleftharpoons H^+ + HPO_4^{--} \qquad K_{II} = 6.2 \times 10^{-8}$$

$$HPO_4^{--} \rightleftharpoons H^+ + PO_4^{-3} \qquad K_{III} = 10^{-12}$$

(Like SO_4^{--} and CrO_4^{--}, PO_4^{-3} is tetrahedral in structure.) From H_3PO_4, three series of salts are possible, the dihydrogen phosphates, the monohydrogen phosphates, and the normal phosphates. When dissolved in water, salts such as NaH_2PO_4 (monosodium dihydrogen phosphate) give slightly acid solutions. The slight acidity results from the fact that the dissociation of $H_2PO_4^-$ to produce H^+ and HPO_4^{--} ($K_{II} = 6.2 \times 10^{-8}$) slightly exceeds the hydrolysis of $H_2PO_4^-$ to produce OH^- and H_3PO_4 ($K_h = K_w/K_I = 1.3 \times 10^{-12}$). Solutions of Na_2HPO_4 are slightly basic, because the hydrolysis of HPO_4^{--} to produce OH^- and $H_2PO_4^-$ ($K_h = K_w/K_{II} =$

1.6×10^{-7}) slightly exceeds the dissociation of HPO_4^{--} to produce H^+ and PO_4^{-3} ($K_{III} = 10^{-12}$). Solutions of Na_3PO_4 are quite basic, because there is no acid dissociation to counterbalance the strong hydrolysis of PO_4^{-3} to produce OH^- and HPO_4^{--} ($K_h = K_w/K_{III} = 10^{-2}$). Since $H_2PO_4^-$ in water gives an acid reaction, $Ca(H_2PO_4)_2$ is used with $NaHCO_3$ in some baking powders to produce CO_2. The reaction may be written

$$H_2PO_4^- + HCO_3^- \rightarrow CO_2(g) + H_2O + HPO_4^{--}$$

but it does not occur until water is added to the baking powder. Since PO_4^{-3} in water gives a basic reaction, and also since $Ca_3(PO_4)_2$ is rather insoluble, trisodium phosphate is used in water softening (Sec. 19.7).

H_3PO_4 is only one of a series of phosphoric acids that may be formed by the hydration of P_4O_{10}. To distinguish it from other phosphoric acids, H_3PO_4 is called orthophosphoric acid, and its salts orthophosphates. Among the other phosphoric acids are pyrophosphoric acid, $H_4P_2O_7$, and metaphosphoric acid, HPO_3, both of which can be made by heating H_3PO_4. Unlike H_3PO_4 and $H_4P_2O_7$, which are discrete molecules, HPO_3 is polymeric; i.e., several HPO_3 groups are bound together. On standing in water, all the phosphoric acids convert to orthophosphoric acid. Perhaps more important than pyro- and metaphosphoric acids are their salts, of which a great variety are known. The pyrophosphates are relatively simple; two series of salts are known, the normal pyrophosphates (e.g., $Na_4P_2O_7$) and the dihydrogen pyrophosphates (e.g., $Na_2H_2P_2O_7$). The structure of the normal pyrophosphate ion is shown in Fig. 25.5 and consists of two PO_4 tetrahedra sharing a corner. In the dihydrogen pyrophosphate ion, a proton is bound to one of the oxygen atoms on each of the tetrahedra. Pyrophosphates are used for water softening and as complexing agents in electroplating baths.

The metaphosphates, with simplest formula MPO_3, exist in a bewildering variety of more or less complex salts. They are all polymeric in structure and can be thought of as being built up of PO_3^- units in such a way that each phosphorus atom remains tetrahedrally associated with four oxy-

Fig. 25.5   *Pyrophosphate ion.*

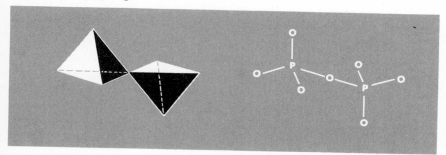

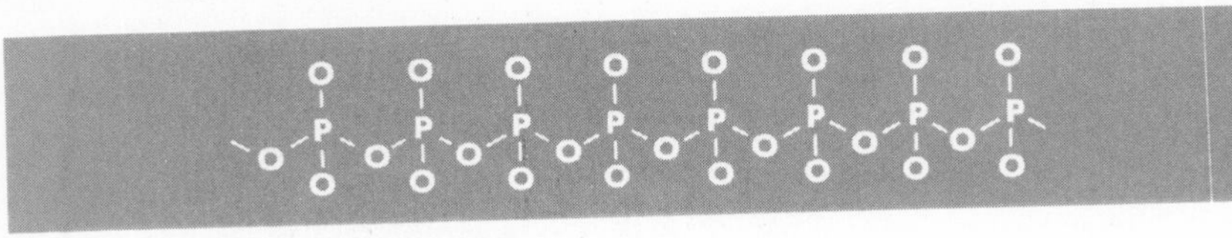

Fig. 25.6   Metaphosphate chain.

gen atoms. In other words, there must be oxygen bridges between phosphorus atoms, and, furthermore, two of the four oxygen atoms about a given phosphorus atom must be bridge oxygens. Thus, the situation in the metaphosphates (illustrated in Fig. 25.6) is in some respects comparable to that of the silicate chains (shown in Fig. 24.14). Of the many metaphosphates reported, some of which are certainly not pure substances but are mixtures instead, we might mention the trimetaphosphate, $Na_3P_3O_9$. This material is a white, crystalline solid which is produced by heating NaH_2PO_4 for several hours at about 550°C. The reaction can be written

$$3NaH_2PO_4 \rightarrow Na_3P_3O_9(s) + 3H_2O(g)$$

The product is quite readily soluble in water but, unlike many of the other metaphosphates, does not precipitate Pb^{++} or Ag^+ out of solutions of their salts. It is generally believed that the trimetaphosphate ion is a cyclic polymer with a structure like that shown in Fig. 25.7. When heated above 620°C., $Na_3P_3O_9$, and indeed all other forms of metaphosphate, melt to a clear, colorless liquid. If this liquid is cooled suddenly (quenched), it does not crystallize but instead forms a glass (sometimes called Graham's salt). The glass is quite soluble in water and in solution can precipitate Ag^+ and Pb^{++} but not Ca^{++}. In fact, it seems to form a complex with Ca^{++} which makes it impossible to precipitate Ca^{++} with the usual reagents such as carbonate. Because of the sequestering action on Ca^{++}, the material has been used extensively in water softening under the trade name Calgon. At one time it was believed that Graham's salt was a hexametaphosphate, $Na_6P_6O_{18}$, but recent investigations indicate that it is a much higher polymer of the type $(NaPO_3)_n$, where n can be as high as 1,000. It no doubt consists of a mixture of chains of varying length made up of PO_3 units. The two ends of the chains might be terminated by —OH groups.

Like nitrogen, phosphorus is an essential constituent of living cells. It occurs as phosphate groups in complex organic molecules. One of the principal functions of these phosphate groups is to provide a means for storing energy in the cells. For example, when water splits a phosphate group off adenosine triphosphate (ATP) to form adenosine diphosphate (ADP), approximately 11 kcal. of heat is liberated per mole. This energy can be used for the mechanical work of muscle contraction. Further discussions of this interesting subject are found in textbooks of biochemistry.

25.4   ARSENIC

Conforming to the increasing metallic character going down group V, elementary arsenic exists as a metallic modification (gray arsenic) as well as a nonmetallic one (yellow arsenic). The metallic form is the stable modification at room temperature and can be made by carbon reduction of arsenious oxide, As_4O_6, or by the thermal decomposition to As and FeS of naturally occurring arsenical pyrites (FeAsS). Yellow arsenic, the analogue of white phosphorus, can be made by sudden cooling of arsenic vapor. Like white phosphorus, it consists of tetratomic molecules, As_4, and is volatile and soluble in nonpolar solvents.

The principal oxidation states of arsenic are $+3$ and $+5$. The -3 state, represented by the poisonous compound AsH_3 (arsine), is even less stable to air oxidation than the corresponding state for phosphorus. In the $+3$ state, arsenic forms arsenious oxide (As_4O_6), commonly called "white arsenic." When treated with water, As_4O_6 gives a slightly acid solution which is thought to contain the hydroxide $As(OH)_3$ or H_3AsO_3 (also written $HAsO_2$). This hydroxide is amphoteric; it can neutralize acids to give solutions containing $As(OH)_2{}^+$, and it can neutralize bases to give solutions containing arsenite ions [variously written as $H_2AsO_3{}^-$, $AsO_2{}^-$, or $As(OH)_4{}^-$].

$$As(OH)_3(s) + H^+ \rightarrow As(OH)_2{}^+ + H_2O$$

$$As(OH)_3(s) + OH^- \rightarrow H_2AsO_3{}^- + H_2O$$

When H_2S is bubbled into an arsenious solution, a yellow precipitate is formed, which is usually described as As_2S_3 but probably has the molecular formula As_4S_6. As discussed in Sec. 11.5, arsenious sulfide has great tendency to form colloids stabilized by adsorption of negative ions. These colloids can be coagulated by addition of H^+ or other positive ions. Like stannous sulfide, arsenious sulfide can be oxidized by polysulfide, $S_2{}^{--}$.

In the $+5$ state, the principal compounds of arsenic are arsenic acid and its derivatives, the arsenates. Arsenic acid is primarily orthoarsenic acid, H_3AsO_4, a triprotic acid with successive dissociation constants of 2.5×10^{-4}, 5.6×10^{-8}, and 3×10^{-13}. Salts of arsenic acid, especially lead arsenate and calcium arsenate, are much used as insecticides. Arsenate ion is considerably better as an oxidizing agent than is phosphate. For example, the oxidation potential for the half-reaction

$$As(OH)_3(s) + H_2O \rightleftharpoons H_3AsO_4 + 2H^+ + 2e^- \qquad -0.56 \text{ volt}$$

indicates that H_3AsO_4 will oxidize I^- to I_2 ($2I^- \rightleftharpoons I_2 + 2e^-$, -0.54 volt), though the reaction can be reversed at low H^+ concentration. When H_2S is bubbled through a solution containing arsenic acid, a yellow precipitate, As_2S_5 (or perhaps As_4S_{10}), is formed. This sulfide is dissolved by excess sulfide ion to produce thioarsenate ions, $AsS_4{}^{-3}$. Addition of acid lowers the sulfide-ion concentration and reprecipitates As_2S_5.

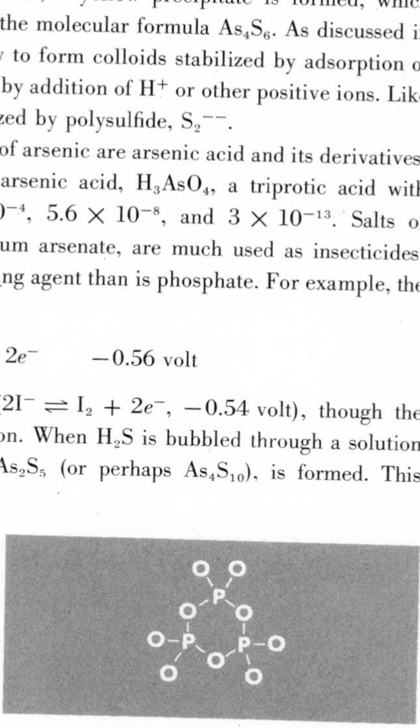

Fig. 25.7   *Trimetaphosphate.*

The compounds of arsenic are among the most important of the systemic poisons. Because they are practically tasteless, they were great favorites in the Middle Ages for homicidal purposes. At the present time, they are no longer popular because of sensitive chemical tests for traces of arsenic compounds. Useful antidotes for arsenic poisoning are lime-water $[Ca(OH)_2]$ and epsom salts $(MgSO_4 \cdot 7H_2O)$, because they precipitate oxyanions of arsenic.

25.5   ANTIMONY

The element antimony is not very abundant (0.0001 per cent, about one-fifth as abundant as arsenic), but it occurs in concentrated form as stibnite, Sb_2S_3. Its symbol Sb comes from *stibium*, the Latin name for the element. In order to prepare the element, stibnite can be heated with scrap iron.

$$Sb_2S_3(s) + 3Fe(s) \rightarrow 3FeS(s) + 2Sb$$

The element exists in several allotropic forms, the stable one at room temperature being gray antimony. Yellow antimony, which is presumably the analogue of yellow arsenic, is stable below $-90°C$. Explosive antimony, prepared by electrolysis of antimony trichloride, is a black material which, on being scratched, converts to the gray form with considerable violence. Ordinary gray antimony has a metallic appearance but is a rather poor metal. It is used principally in alloys with lead, as in making battery plates and shrapnel.

In the -3 state, antimony forms the very unstable compound, SbH_3 (stibine). This, like arsine, is quite poisonous and easily oxidized to the metal. In the $+3$ state, antimony forms the oxide Sb_2O_3 (antimony trioxide, or antimony sesquioxide), which, at least in one crystal modification, exists as Sb_4O_6 molecules. It is an amphoteric oxide, dissolving in acid to give $Sb(OH)_2^+$ (or SbO^+) ion and dissolving in base to give antimonite anions, usually written SbO_2^- or $Sb(OH)_4^-$. When solutions of antimonites (such as $NaSbO_2$) are gradually acidified, a white precipitate is first formed which has the composition $Sb_2O_3 \cdot xH_2O$. Apparently, no simple $Sb(OH)_3$ is formed. The sulfide, Sb_2S_3, is orange when freshly precipitated. In many respects, its chemical reactions are like those of arsenious sulfide.

In the $+5$ state antimony forms the pentoxide Sb_2O_5, which is a slightly stronger oxidizing agent than H_3AsO_4. It is practically insoluble in acid but does dissolve in base to give antimonate ion, usually written $Sb(OH)_6^-$. The fact that this ion has six oxygens about the central atom, rather than four as in arsenate, is ascribed to the larger size of Sb. Unlike As_2S_5, Sb_2S_5 is soluble in acid, but solution is accompanied by reduction of antimony to the $+3$ state.

25.6   BISMUTH

Since the bismuth minerals, bismuth glance (Bi_2S_3) and bismuth ochre (Bi_2O_3), are rather rare, most commercial bismuth is produced as a by-product of lead production and electrolytic refining of copper. It is a rather poor metal which is used principally to make easily fusible alloys such as Wood's metal (50 per cent Bi, 25 per cent Pb, 13 per cent Sn, and 12 per cent Cd) and is added in small amounts to harden lead plates for storage batteries.

Like antimony, bismuth forms an unstable hydrogen compound, BiH_3 (bismuthine), and a sesquioxide, Bi_2O_3. However, Bi_2O_3 is basic and not amphoteric like Sb_2O_3. Although insoluble in water, it dissolves in acid solution to give hydrolyzed bismuth ion, which may be BiO^+, $BiOH^{++}$, or $Bi(OH)_2{}^+$. Two series of salts are known: simple bismuth salts, e.g., $Bi(NO_3)_3 \cdot 5H_2O$, and oxysalts, e.g., bismuthyl nitrate, $BiONO_3$.

When fused with strong oxidizing agents such as Na_2O_2 in the presence of NaOH, Bi_2O_3 is converted to a compound with remarkable oxidizing power. For example, it oxidizes Mn^{++} to $MnO_4{}^-$. Though called sodium bismuthate and given the formula $NaBiO_3$, it is insoluble and probably is not a definite compound but a mixture of oxides, which may include Bi_2O_5.

The only known sulfide of bismuth is Bi_2S_3. It is formed as a black precipitate when H_2S is passed through bismuth-containing solutions. Bi_2S_3 is insoluble in dilute acids but dissolves in hot concentrated nitric acid as a result of oxidation of sulfide to elemental sulfur. Unlike the corresponding sulfides of arsenic and antimony, bismuth sulfide is not dissolved by either sulfide ion or polysulfide ion.

25.7   QUALITATIVE ANALYSIS

The ammonium ion is easily detected by adding NaOH to the unknown and heating to expel NH_3, which can be detected by its characteristic odor or by allowing the vapor to turn moist litmus blue. Nitrate ion may be detected by the brown ring test described in part (4) of Sec. 25.2.

The anions phosphate and arsenate can be recognized by their formation of white, insoluble magnesium ammonium salts ($MgNH_4PO_4$ and $MgNH_4AsO_4$). Arsenate in the presence of phosphate can be distinguished by addition of $AgNO_3$ and acetic acid, which converts $MgNH_4AsO_4$ to red Ag_3AsO_4. Phosphate in the presence of arsenate is more difficult and requires preliminary removal of arsenic as insoluble As_2S_3. This is accomplished by reducing the arsenic from the $+5$ oxidation state to the $+3$ with I^- in acid solution and then adding H_2S. From the filtrate, yellow insoluble ammonium phosphomolybdate, $(NH_4)_3[PMo_{12}O_{40}]$, can be precipitated by treatment with hot ammonium molybdate solution, $(NH_4)_2MoO_4$.

The cations of arsenic, antimony, and bismuth precipitate as As_2S_3 (red-yellow), Sb_2S_3 (black-red), and Bi_2S_3 (brown-black) when H_2S is added in 0.3 N acid. Bi_2S_3 differs from Sb_2S_3 and As_2S_3 in being insoluble in $(NH_4)_2S$ solution. The presence of bismuth can be confirmed by reducing $Bi(OH)_3$ to black bismuth metal with stannite ion in basic solution. From the solution containing $AsS_3{}^{-3}$ and $SbS_3{}^{-3}$, obtained by the $(NH_4)_2S$ treatment, As_2S_3 precipitates on addition of 6 M HCl. (The arsenic can be confirmed by reducing to AsH_3 with aluminum metal in strong base and allowing the AsH_3 vapor to blacken paper wet with silver nitrate solution. The black color results from the formation of finely divided silver metal.) The presence of dissolved antimony can be shown by the formation of a characteristic orange-red color (possibly an oxysulfide) on addition of $Na_2S_2O_3$.

QUESTIONS

25.1 *Group properties.* Compare the group V elements with respect to each of the following properties: allotropy, metallic character, oxidation states, amphoterism.

25.2 *Nitric acid.* Outline the conversion of atmospheric nitrogen to nitric acid. Include equations and indicate necessary conditions.

25.3 *HNO_3 reduction.* When H_2S is bubbled into fairly concentrated nitric acid, the products are sulfur, NO_2, NO, N_2, and $NH_4{}^+$. Write four balanced equations that account for these products.

25.4 *Phosphorus.* Account for each of the following observations: (*a*) white phosphorus has a higher vapor pressure than red phosphorus; (*b*) 1 mole of phosphorous acid can neutralize only 2 moles of sodium hydroxide; (*c*) there are several different phosphoric acids; (*d*) solutions of Na_3PO_4 are basic, solutions of NaH_2PO_4 are acidic.

25.5 *H_3AsO_4 reduction.* Write a balanced equation for the oxidation of I^- by H_3AsO_4. Calculate the equilibrium constant (Sec. 17.14), and explain why the reaction can be reversed by the addition of Na_2HPO_4.

25.6 *Sb_2O_3 amphoterism.* Show with equations how Sb_2O_3 can neutralize acids and bases.

25.7 *Bismuth and antimony.* Given a white solid which is either $BiCl_3$ or $SbCl_3$. How could you prove which it is?

25.8 *pH of NH_3 solutions.* Calculate the pH of each of the following solutions: (*a*) 0.425 g. of NH_3 in 0.100 liter of H_2O; (*b*) 0.050 mole of NH_3 plus 0.050 mole of HCl in 50.0 ml. of H_2O; (*c*) a solution made by mixing 20.0 ml. of 0.30 M NH_3 with 30.0 ml. of 0.20 M HCl.   *Ans.* 2.68; 4.63; 5.09

25.9 *Equations.* Write net equations for each of the following changes: (*a*) neutralization of aqueous ammonia by a solution of acetic acid; (*b*) disproportionation of NO_2 in dilute solution to form nitrate ion and nitrous acid; (*c*) hydrolysis of sodium nitrite; (*d*) dissolving of copper in concentrated nitric acid; (*e*) dissolving of platinum in aqua regia to form $PtCl_6{}^{--}$; (*f*) preparation of nitrous oxide; (*g*) air oxidation of phosphine: (*h*) decomposition of pyrophosphoric acid in water; (*i*) precipitation of $CaCO_3$ from temporarily hard water by addition of Na_3PO_4.

25.10 *Nitrogen cycle.* Trace two different paths whereby nitrogen atoms may be converted from atmospheric N_2 to proteins in the human body.

25.11 *Fertilizers.* The following compounds, for which typical prices per ton are shown in parentheses, have been used in fertilizers: $NaNO_3$ ($45), NH_3 ($87), $(NH_4)_2SO_4$ ($44), and NH_4NO_3 ($67). Rank these in terms of increasing cost per pound of nitrogen.

25.12 *Phosphates and phosphites.* From each of the following pairs, select the solution of higher pH. Justify your answers. (*a*) 0.1 *M* H_3PO_3 and 0.1 *M* H_3PO_4; (*b*) 0.1 *M* NaH_2PO_3 and 0.1 *M* NaH_2PO_4; (*c*) a solution made by mixing 100 ml. of 0.1 *M* H_3PO_3 with 100 ml. of 0.3 *M* NaOH, and a solution made by mixing 100 ml. of 0.1 *M* H_3PO_4 with 100 ml. of 0.3 *M* NaOH.

25.13 *Amino acids.* Amino acids, such as H_2NCH_2COOH (see Sec. 24.4), can act both as acids and as bases. (*a*) Write equations for the neutralization of both a base and an acid with an amino acid, using structural formulas. (*b*) Considering the amino acid as a derivative of NH_3 and of acetic acid and by comparing the dissociation constants of NH_4^+ and CH_3COOH, show that the amino acid H_2NCH_2COOH should exist in water as H_3NCH_2COO.

25.14 *Rocket fuel.* As noted in Sec. 25.2, mixtures of hydrazine and hydrogen peroxide can be used as rocket propellants. For the reaction as written, 154 kcal. of heat is liberated. Assume that for the product gases 8 cal. per mole are required to raise the temperature by 1°C. (*a*) Estimate the final temperature produced by exploding a mixture of 32 g. of N_2H_4 and 68 g. of H_2O_2 in a volume of 100 cc. (*b*) Using the perfect-gas law, estimate the final pressure in the container.

25.15 *Phosphoric acid.* Calculate the pH of a solution that is made by dissolving 0.49 g. of H_3PO_4 in enough water to make 150 ml. of solution. What would be the concentration of HPO_4^{--} in this solution?   *Ans.* 1.80; 6.2×10^{-8}

25.16 *Hydrolysis.* Calculate the pH of a solution that is made by dissolving 0.49 g. of Na_3PO_4 in enough water to make 150 ml. of solution. (Consider only the first hydrolysis step.) What would be the concentration of HPO_4^{--} in this solution?

26   *Group* **VI** *Elements*

THE MOST IMPORTANT ELEMENT OF GROUP VI, oxygen, has already been discussed in Chap. 16. The other members of the group, sulfur, selenium, tellurium, and polonium, differ markedly from oxygen, especially in the formation of positive oxidation states. Although oxygen can also show a positive oxidation state, its highest state is $+2$ and this is extremely rare. On the other hand, all the other elements of the group form compounds in which oxidation numbers $+4$ and $+6$ are assigned. The -2 state is common to all. In the earth's crust, selenium, tellurium, and polonium are extremely rare, and sulfur is much less plentiful than the very abundant oxygen.

26.1   GROUP PROPERTIES

On the far right of the periodic table, the elements have characteristically high ionization potentials, and metallic properties are hard to find. However, in going down the group, electrons are held less tightly; hence there is some suggestion of metallic behavior in the heavier elements of groupVI. Ionization potentials and other properties are given in Table 26.1.

Oxygen stands alone from the group in being a diatomic gas at room

Table 26.1   Elements of Group VI

Symbol	Z	Electronic configuration	Melting point, °C.	Boiling point, °C.	Ionization potential, e.v.	Oxidation potential, volts (H_2X to X)
O	8	2, 6	−219	−183.0	13.61	−1.23
S	16	2, 8, 6	119	444.6	10.36	−0.14
Se	34	2, 8, 18, 6	220	685	9.75	+0.40
Te	52	2, 8, 18, 18, 6	450	1390	9.01	+0.72
Po	84	2, 8, 18, 32, 18, 6	—	—	—	>1.0

temperature. The other elements are solids with structural units more complex than diatomic molecules. All the elements of the group show allotropy. Just as oxygen can exist both as diatomic O_2 and triatomic O_3, the other elements can be obtained in more than one form, the forms differing either in the number of atoms per molecule or in the arrangement of molecules in the solid. There is, in going down the group, increasing tendency toward formation of long strings of atoms held together by covalent bonds. However, the structure of the radioactive element polonium is in doubt, and it may even be that one of its allotropic modifications is metallic. The increasing complexity of structure from simple diatomic O_2 to near-metallic Po is principally due to increasing atomic size down the group. In general, the larger the atom, the less the tendency to form multiple bonds, and the greater the tendency of each atom to be bound to more than one other atom.

Because of the increasing number of electronic shells populated, we would expect an increase of the atomic size from O to Po. This increase in atomic size is reflected in the values assigned to the radii of the −2 ions. From X-ray studies of crystal structures the following radii have been assigned: O^{--}, 1.40 A.; S^{--}, 1.84 A.; Se^{--}, 1.98 A.; and Te^{--}, 2.21 A. These values are quite high compared to those of positive ions having the same electronic configuration. For example, Na^+, which is isoelectronic with O^{--}, has an ionic radius of 0.98 A. The comparison can be extended by noting the ionic radii of the other alkali-metal ions given in Table 18.1. The fact that the nuclear charges of the alkali-metal ions are greater than those of isoelectronic group VI ions is apparently the main reason for the difference of size.

Perhaps the most striking variation in these elements is the decreasing oxidizing strength from oxygen to polonium. As the oxidation potentials in the last column of Table 26.1 indicate, there is much greater tendency for oxygen to form H_2O than for polonium to form H_2Po. In fact, unlike H_2O and H_2S, the compounds H_2Se, H_2Te, and H_2Po are better reducing agents than hydrogen.

When bound to more electronegative atoms, the elements of group VI show positive oxidation states. With oxygen, positive oxidation states are found only in compounds with fluorine, since fluorine is the only element more electronegative than oxygen. All the other elements of group VI form oxy compounds in which the elements, being less electronegative than oxygen, are assigned positive oxidation numbers. An examination of the composition of these compounds shows that the $+4$ and $+6$ states are the most common. There is thus a difference of two units between the values of the most common positive oxidation states in group VI; this is also true in group V (most common positive states, $+3$ and $+5$) and in group VII, at least for chlorine and iodine (most common positive states, $+5$ and $+7$). This difference of two units is consistent with the notion that electrons in molecules generally exist as pairs.

26.2   SULFUR

Although not very abundant (0.05 per cent), sulfur is readily available because of its occurrence in large beds of the free element. These beds, usually located several hundred feet underground, are thought to be due to bacterial decomposition of calcium sulfate. They are exploited by pumping superheated water (at about 170°C.) down to the beds to melt the sulfur and blowing it to the surface with compressed air. Since the product is about 99.5 per cent pure, it can be used without purification for most commercial purposes. Besides being found as the free element, sulfur occurs naturally in many sulfide and sulfate minerals, such as $CuFeS_2$, Cu_2S, and $CaSO_4 \cdot 2H_2O$.

There are several allotropic modifications of sulfur, the most important being rhombic and monoclinic sulfur, which differ from each other in the symmetry of their crystals. In the rhombic form, which is the stable one

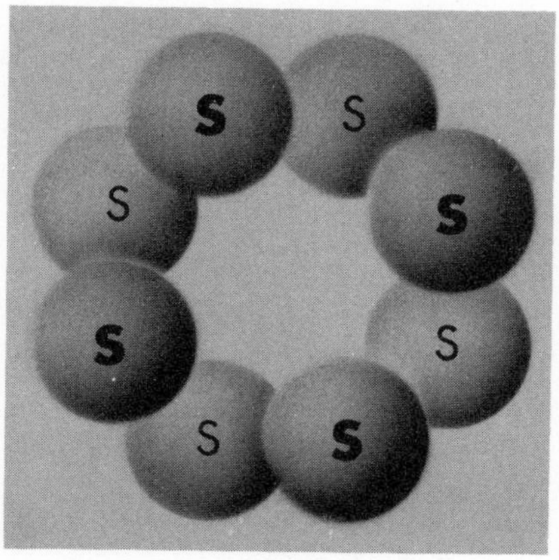

Fig. 26.1 S_8 molecule.

at room temperature, sulfur atoms are linked to each other as puckered, eight-membered rings having the configuration shown in Fig. 26.1. Above 96°C., monoclinic sulfur is stable; the arrangement of S atoms in it is not known. When heated above the melting point, sulfur goes through a variety of changes. Starting as a mobile, pale yellow liquid, it gradually thickens above 160°C. and then becomes less viscous as the boiling point is approached. If the thick liquid, which may be dark red if impurities are present, is poured into water, amorphous, or plastic, sulfur is produced. X-ray analysis of amorphous sulfur shows that it contains long strings of sulfur atoms. In accordance with this, the change in viscosity with temperature has been attributed to opening of S_8 rings, which then couple up to form less mobile long chains. These in turn are broken into fragments as their kinetic energy is increased.

The phase relationships of sulfur are shown in the phase diagram (Fig. 26.2). Because sulfur can exist in two solid modifications, the diagram contains four regions, corresponding to two solid states, one liquid, and one gas. At any temperature and pressure lying within the triangle, monoclinic sulfur is the stable form. Thus, if rhombic sulfur is heated at 1 atm. pressure to about 100°C. and held there, it slowly converts by atomic rearrangement in the solid to monoclinic sulfur. This is a very slow process, and under usual conditions of heating the transformation is not observed. For the usual, rapid melting of sulfur, the effective phase diagram is that delineated by the dotted lines instead of the solid ones. In other words, if heating is so rapid that equilibrium is not attained, solid rhombic sulfur superheats without changing to monoclinic and melts at a temperature below the melting point of monoclinic sulfur.

Although much of the sulfur produced is used directly in insecticides, fertilizers, paper and pulp fillers, and rubber, most of it is converted to industrially important compounds, especially sulfuric acid. As we have already noted in Sec. 13.7, sulfuric acid is produced from sulfur dioxide, SO_2, usually made by burning sulfur in air

$$S(s) + O_2(g) \rightarrow SO_2(g)$$

Sulfur dioxide is also a by-product of the preparation of various metals from their sulfide ores. For example, SO_2 is formed in the roasting of the copper ore chalcocite, or Cu_2S.

$$Cu_2S(s) + O_2(g) \rightarrow 2Cu(s) + SO_2(g)$$

In the contact process, which accounts for nearly all the H_2SO_4 production, the SO_2 is oxidized by air in the presence of catalysts such as vanadium pentoxide (V_2O_5) or platinum.

$$2SO_2(g) + O_2(g) \rightarrow 2SO_3(g)$$

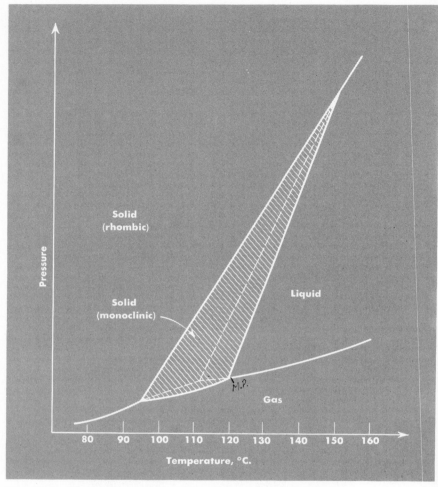

Fig. 26.2   Phase diagram for sulfur. (Pressure axis distorted.)

The kinetics of this reaction are discussed in Sec. 13.7. The product, SO_3, or sulfur trioxide, is the anhydride of H_2SO_4, and we would expect the final step in preparing sulfuric acid to be the dissolving of SO_3 in H_2O. However, SO_3 reacts with water to form a fog of H_2SO_4, and the uptake of SO_3 by H_2O is extremely slow. The usual method for circumventing this difficulty is to dissolve the SO_3 in pure H_2SO_4 in a reaction which goes smoothly to produce $H_2S_2O_7$, pyrosulfuric acid. On dilution with water, 100 per cent H_2SO_4 results.

$$SO_3(g) + H_2SO_4 \rightarrow H_2S_2O_7$$

$$H_2S_2O_7 + H_2O \rightarrow 2H_2SO_4$$

Pure H_2SO_4 is a liquid at room temperature which freezes at $10°C$. In many respects, liquid H_2SO_4 resembles water. For example, it slightly conducts electricity, presumably because, like water, it is dissociated into ions

$$2H_2SO_4 \rightleftharpoons H_3SO_4^+ + HSO_4^-$$

Furthermore, like water it dissolves many substances, even ionic solids. However, H_2SO_4 differs from water in that its extent of dissociation is considerably greater and in that H_2SO_4 may force a proton on any dissolved species. For instance, when acetic acid is placed in pure H_2SO_4, the following reaction occurs:

$$CH_3COOH + H_2SO_4 \rightarrow HSO_4^- + CH_3COOH_2^+$$

Pure H_2SO_4 has great affinity for water and forms several compounds, or hydrates, with water such as $H_2SO_4 \cdot H_2O$ and $H_2SO_4 \cdot 2H_2O$. Ordinary commercially available concentrated sulfuric acid is approximately 93 per cent H_2SO_4 by weight and can be thought of as a solution of H_2SO_4 and $H_2SO_4 \cdot H_2O$. The monohydrate may be H_3O^+ and HSO_4^-, and the large heat observed to be liberated when concentrated sulfuric acid is added to water may be due to formation of H_3O^+ and subsequent hydration of it and of HSO_4^-. Frequently, concentrated H_2SO_4 is used as a dehydrating agent, as for example, in desiccators to keep substances dry. It is also used in reactions to favor splitting off of water. As an example of the latter, H_2SO_4 is used in the manufacture of ethers from alcohols.

$$2C_2H_5OH \xrightarrow[H_2SO_4]{} C_2H_5OC_2H_5 + H_2O$$

In aqueous solutions, H_2SO_4 is a strong acid, but only for dissociation of one proton. The dissociation constant for the second proton is 1.3×10^{-2}. Because of the dissociation

$$HSO_4^- \rightarrow H^+ + SO_4^{--}$$

solutions of HSO_4^-, such as solutions of sodium hydrogen sulfate ($NaHSO_4$), are acid. Because of the reverse reaction, solutions of SO_4^{--}, such as solutions of sodium sulfate (Na_2SO_4), are slightly basic. However, the extent of hydrolysis is extremely small ($K_h = 7.7 \times 10^{-13}$), and these solutions of sulfate salts are essentially neutral.

For the half-reaction

$$H_2SO_3 + H_2O \rightleftharpoons HSO_4^- + 3H^+ + 2e^-$$

the oxidation potential is -0.11 volt. This means that HSO_4^- at $1\ m$ concentration is a mild oxidizing agent. However, its action as an oxidizing agent in dilute solution at room temperature is not observed because reaction is so slow. With hot, concentrated solutions of sulfuric acid, oxidation is observed. For example, sodium bromide plus hot H_2SO_4 produces some bromine by oxidation of Br^- to Br_2. Furthermore, some of the less active metals such as copper are soluble in hot, concentrated sulfuric acid, presumably because of oxidation by sulfate.

Although sulfate is not an especially good oxidizing agent, there is a closely related derivative which is an extremely powerful oxidizing agent. This derivative is produced by electrolytic oxidation of cold, concentrated sulfuric acid and has been assigned the formula $H_2S_2O_8$. The acid, called peroxydisulfuric acid, and its salts are peroxy compounds, since they contain an oxygen-oxygen bond. The structural relation between H_2SO_4 and $H_2S_2O_8$ is shown in the following half-reaction:

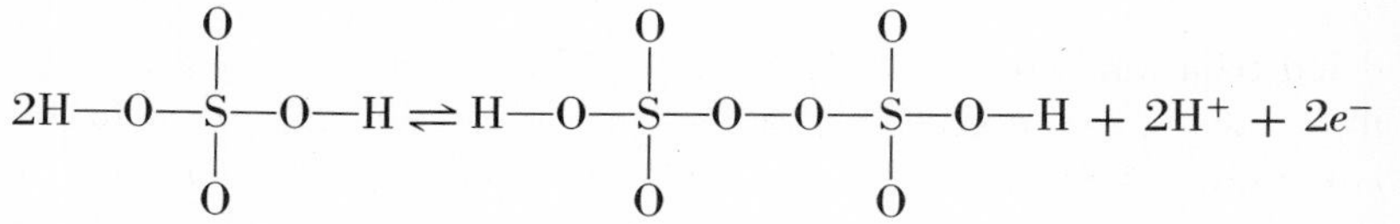

$$2H-O-\overset{\overset{\displaystyle O}{|}}{\underset{\underset{\displaystyle O}{|}}{S}}-O-H \rightleftharpoons H-O-\overset{\overset{\displaystyle O}{|}}{\underset{\underset{\displaystyle O}{|}}{S}}-O-O-\overset{\overset{\displaystyle O}{|}}{\underset{\underset{\displaystyle O}{|}}{S}}-O-H + 2H^+ + 2e^-$$

The forward reaction applies to the electrolytic preparation; the reverse reaction, to the action of $H_2S_2O_8$ as an oxidizing agent. Both the acid and its salts, such as ammonium peroxydisulfate, $(NH_4)_2S_2O_8$, are very strong oxidizing agents and can, for example, oxidize manganous salts to permanganate. On a relative scale, the peroxydisulfates are about as good oxidizing agents as ozone. In addition to their use as oxidizing agents, the peroxydisulfates are important as intermediates in the preparation of hydrogen peroxide.

$$K_2S_2O_8(s) + 2H^+ + 2H_2O \rightarrow 2H_2SO_4 + H_2O_2 + 2K^+$$

An interesting derivative of sulfuric acid is found in some of the synthetic detergents used in place of soap. In the preparation of these derivatives, H_2SO_4 reacts with a hydrocarbon as illustrated in the following equation:

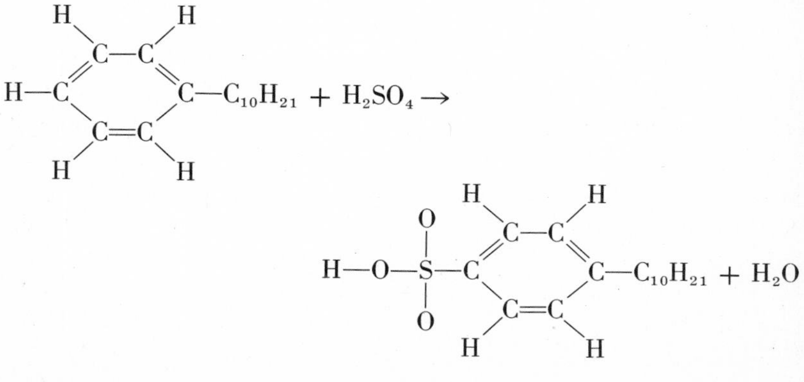

The product is called a sulfonic acid, and its salts, made by neutralizing the H of the OH group, are called sulfonates. In water, sulfonates behave like soap in forming micelles (see Fig. 24.10) but have an advantage over soap in not forming precipitates with calcium ion.

In addition to the oxy compounds that sulfur forms in the $+6$ oxidation state, there are important oxy compounds corresponding to the $+4$ state of sulfur. The simplest of these is the dioxide, SO_2, which is formed either by burning sulfur in air or by reducing sulfates. At room temperature, SO_2 is a gas, but it is quite easily liquefied (b.p., $-10°C$.). The easy liquefaction reflects the fact that the molecule is polar because it has a nonlinear arrangement of atoms (shown in Sec. 4.8). Sulfur dioxide has a disagreeable, choking odor and is somewhat poisonous. It is especially toxic to lower organisms such as fungi and for this reason is used for sterilizing dried fruit and wine barrels. With water, SO_2 dissolves to give acid solutions, which are believed to contain sulfurous acid, H_2SO_3. However, the compound H_2SO_3 has never been isolated pure, and any attempt to concentrate the solution, as by heating, simply expels SO_2. Apparently, H_2SO_3 is a weak diprotic acid

$$H_2SO_3 \rightleftharpoons H^+ + HSO_3^- \qquad K_I = 1.3 \times 10^{-2}$$

$$HSO_3^- \rightleftharpoons H^+ + SO_3^{--} \qquad K_{II} = 5.6 \times 10^{-8}$$

and forms two series of salts. The sulfites, e.g., Na_2SO_3, give slightly basic solutions owing to hydrolysis of SO_3^{--}; the hydrogen sulfites, e.g., $NaHSO_3$, give slightly acid solutions, because the dissociation of HSO_3^- outweighs its hydrolysis. Addition of concentrated acids to either solid sulfites or solid hydrogen sulfites liberates SO_2 and is a convenient way of making sulfur dioxide in the laboratory. Sulfites, hydrogen sulfites, and sulfurous acid are mild reducing agents and are relatively easily oxidized to sulfates, though sometimes the reaction is quite slow.

When solutions containing sulfite ion are boiled with elemental sulfur, the solid sulfur dissolves in a reaction

$$S(s) + SO_3^{--} \rightleftharpoons S_2O_3^{--}$$

which is easily reversed by addition of acid. The ion formed, $S_2O_3^{--}$, is called thiosulfate ion, where the prefix *thio-* indicates substitution of a sulfur atom for an oxygen atom. Apparently, $S_2O_3^{--}$ contains two different kinds of sulfur atoms, as found by the following experiment: Solid sulfur containing a radioactive isotope of sulfur was boiled with a solution containing nonradioactive sulfite ions. The thiosulfate ions formed were found to be radioactive, but after acid was added so as to reverse the above reaction, all the radioactivity was recovered as precipitated solid sulfur. The implication is that the same S atom which adds on to SO_3^{--} to form

$S_2O_3^{--}$ is dropped off when acid is added. This can be true only if the added S atom is bound in $S_2O_3^{--}$ in a way that is unlike the binding of the S atom already in SO_3^{--}. Otherwise, the two S atoms in $S_2O_3^{--}$ would be identical, and the addition of acid would not preferentially drop off the added radioactive S atom but would have a 50-50 chance of retaining it and its activity in the complex SO_3^{--}. The structure proposed for $S_2O_3^{--}$, which accounts for these observations, is shown in the following equation:

$$\ddot{:}\ddot{S}: + \begin{bmatrix} :\ddot{O}: \\ :\ddot{S}:\ddot{O}: \\ :\ddot{O}: \end{bmatrix}^{--} \rightleftharpoons \begin{bmatrix} :\ddot{O}: \\ :\ddot{S}:\ddot{S}:\ddot{O}: \\ :\ddot{O}: \end{bmatrix}^{--}$$

In three dimensions, the thiosulfate ion is tetrahedral; it has one sulfur atom at the center of a tetrahedron with the other sulfur atom and the three oxygen atoms at the four corners of the tetrahedron. (Although in the above equation the adding sulfur atom is shown as a single atom, it should more properly be shown as part of an S_8 molecule.) The reverse reaction is brought about by acid, because H^+ unites with SO_3^{--}, and thus, by the principle of Le Chatelier, acid should favor the back reaction. This reaction is quite slow, at least so far as formation of visible solid sulfur is concerned. Indeed, when acid is added to thiosulfate solutions, nothing is observed at first. Then a white milkiness develops as colloidal sulfur (Sec. 11.3) is produced by gradual agglomeration of S atoms. In another reaction besides the above, thiosulfate ion acts as a mild reducing agent

$$2S_2O_3^{--} \rightarrow S_4O_6^{--} + 2e^- \qquad -0.08 \text{ volt}$$

and has, for example, the ability of reducing iodine, I_2, to iodide ion, I^-. The reaction, which produces tetrathionate ion, $S_4O_6^{--}$, is frequently used to determine the amount of iodine in a solution. It also makes possible the quantitative analysis of many oxidizing agents. The unknown oxidizing agent is reduced with an excess of I^-, and the liberated I_2 is titrated with a thiosulfate solution. Thiosulfate ion also has the ability to form complex ions with the ions of some metals, especially Ag^+. The silver-thiosulfate complex ion is so stable

$$Ag^+ + 2S_2O_3^{--} \rightarrow Ag(S_2O_3)_2^{-3} \qquad K = 1.6 \times 10^{13}$$

that thiosulfate solutions can dissolve the insoluble silver halides (see Sec. 22.3 for the use of thiosulfate in the photographic fixing process).

Besides occurring in the positive oxidation states, sulfur forms compounds corresponding to negative oxidation states, especially -2. The most familiar of these compounds is probably hydrogen sulfide, H_2S, notorious for its rotten-egg odor. Not so well known is the fact that hydrogen sulfide is as poisonous as hydrogen cyanide and four times as poisonous as carbon monoxide. The presence of H_2S in sewer gas is due to putrefaction of sulfur-containing organic material. The pure compound can be made by bubbling hydrogen gas through molten sulfur. In the laboratory, it is conveniently prepared by interaction of some sulfide such as FeS with acid

$$FeS(s) + 2H^+ \rightarrow Fe^{++} + H_2S(g)$$

or by the warming of a solution of thioacetamide

Thioacetamide   *Acetamide*

This latter reaction is becoming increasingly popular as an easily controlled laboratory source of hydrogen sulfide. Like H_2O, H_2S has a bent molecule and is polar; however, it is considerably harder to liquefy (b.p., $-61°C.$), presumably because of the lack of hydrogen bonding (Sec. 15.5) in the liquid. Gaseous H_2S burns to produce H_2O and either sulfur or sulfur dioxide, depending on the temperature and the oxygen supply. It is a mild reducing agent and can, for example, reduce ferric ion to ferrous ion

$$2Fe^{+3} + H_2S(g) \rightarrow 2Fe^{++} + S(s) + 2H^+$$

During the course of the reaction, the solution becomes milky from the production of colloidal sulfur. In aqueous solution, H_2S is a weak diprotic acid for which the dissociation constants are $K_I = 1.1 \times 10^{-7}$ and $K_{II} = 1 \times 10^{-14}$. A detailed consideration of the equilibria in aqueous H_2S solutions is given in Sec. 17.10.

Derived from H_2S are the sulfides, such as Na_2S and HgS. In regard to their solubility in water the sulfides vary widely, from those which, like Na_2S, are quite soluble in water to those which, like HgS, require drastic treatment to be brought into solution.* In Table 26.2 are listed various representative sulfides and methods required to dissolve them. The alkali-metal and alkaline-earth-metal sulfides dissolve readily in water to give basic solutions, with extensive hydrolysis of sulfide ion.

$$Na_2S(s) + H_2O \rightarrow 2Na^+ + HS^- + OH^-$$

This equation represents the principal net reaction; about 10 per cent of the sulfide ion remains unhydrolyzed. Because the sulfides of the group I

---

* HgS can be "dissolved" by heating it with aqua regia, but it is questionable that this is a good description of the process. Although the mercury dissolves as $HgCl_4^{--}$, the sulfur does not dissolve but is oxidized to insoluble elemental sulfur.

Table 26.2 Solubilities of Sulfides

Soluble in water	Na_2S, K_2S, $(NH_4)_2S$
Soluble in 0.3 M H^+	ZnS, FeS
Soluble in hot HNO_3	CuS, Ag_2S, PbS, SnS
Soluble in aqua regia	HgS

and group II metals are so soluble, they cannot be precipitated by bubbling H_2S through solutions of their salts. As already discussed in Sec. 17.10, some sulfides that are insoluble in water can be dissolved simply by raising the H^+ concentration. ZnS, for example, is soluble in 0.3 M H^+, because the H^+ serves to lower the concentration of sulfide ion (in equilibrium with solid ZnS) by combining with it to form H_2S. The net equation can be represented as

$$ZnS(s) + 2H^+ \rightarrow Zn^{++} + H_2S$$

The sulfides in the third row of Table 26.2 are so insoluble that they cannot be dissolved by H^+ alone. However, hot nitric acid oxidizes sulfide to sulfur and hence lowers the sulfide-ion concentration sufficiently to permit solubility. For CuS, the net reaction can be written

$$3CuS(s) + 8H^+ + 2NO_3^- \rightarrow 3Cu^{++} + 3S(s) + 2NO(g) + 4H_2O$$

The least soluble of the sulfides shown in Table 26.2, mercuric sulfide, is not appreciably soluble in hot HNO_3. In order to "dissolve" it, aqua regia must be used in order that oxidation of the sulfide ion may be accompanied by complexing of the mercuric ion. The net reaction might be written

$$HgS(s) + 2NO_3^- + 4Cl^- + 4H^+ \rightarrow$$

$$HgCl_4^{--} + 2NO_2(g) + S(s) + 2H_2O$$

although the reduction product of nitrate is probably a mixture rather than just NO_2. The differences in solubility behavior of metal sulfides can be used to great advantage in the separation and identification of various elements, as in qualitative analysis.

In addition to sulfides, sulfur forms polysulfides, in which two or more sulfur atoms are bound together in a chain. These polysulfides can be made, for example, by boiling a solution of a soluble sulfide with elemental sulfur. With Na_2S and sulfur, the product is usually described as Na_2S_x and is thought to consist of Na^+ ions and $[S_x]^{--}$ ions. The polysulfide chains are of varying length and can be considered as being formed by progressive addition of sulfur atoms to sulfide ion.

$$[:\ddot{S}:]^{--} + \ddot{S}: \rightarrow [:\ddot{S}:\ddot{S}:]^{--}$$

$$[:\ddot{S}:\ddot{S}:]^{--} + \ddot{S}: \rightarrow [:\ddot{S}:\ddot{S}:\ddot{S}:]^{--} \text{ etc.}$$

The simplest of the polysulfide chains is the disulfide, S_2^{--}; it is found in the mineral FeS_2, iron pyrites, or fool's gold. Solid FeS_2 has a NaCl-like structure (Fig. 8.5) consisting of an array of alternating Fe^{++} and S_2^{--} ions. In acid solution, disulfides (and other polysulfides) break down to form solid sulfur and H_2S. In some respects, disulfides resemble peroxides. They are, for example, oxidizing agents, especially for metal sulfides. Thus, a solution of Na_2S_2 can oxidize stannous sulfide, SnS ($+2$ state of tin), to SnS_3^{--} ($+4$ state of tin).

$$SnS(s) + S_2^{--} \rightarrow SnS_3^{--}$$

Tin is assigned oxidation number $+4$ in the thiostannate ion, SnS_3^{--}, because acidification produces stannic sulfide, SnS_2. The SnS_2 is identical with that precipitated from stannic solutions by H_2S.

26.3   SELENIUM

Selenium is about as rare as gold. It occurs principally along with sulfur, both as elementary selenium in native sulfur and as selenides in various sulfide minerals. Most commercial selenium is obtained as a by-product of the electrolytic refining of copper. The element exists in several allotropic forms, the most stable of which at room temperature is hexagonal, or "metallic," selenium. In this form, selenium atoms are joined in infinitely long spiral chains arranged parallel to each other. When dissolved in molten sulfur, these chains form Se_8 molecules, as is indicated by the freezing-point depression of the sulfur (Sec. 10.3).

"Metallic" selenium is a poor conductor of electricity in the dark, but its conductivity increases proportionally to its illumination, i.e., it is a photoconductor. This property is utilized in the selenium photocell, used in exposure meters for measuring light intensity. The basic feature of the cell is a sandwich consiting of a copper plate, a selenium coating, and a thin, translucent gold film. Electric leads go to the copper and to the gold film, but the circuit is not complete until light falls on the selenium. In the selenium rectifier, for converting alternating to direct current, a similar cell is used, differing in that the gold film of the photocell is replaced by alloys such as Wood's metal. The selenium-to-alloy junction acts as a barrier to current, but in only one direction. In spite of these interesting properties, most selenium goes to the glass industry, where it is added in small amounts to molten glass to counteract the objectionable green color due to iron impurities. In large amounts, it gives red glass.

The chemistry of selenium is similar to that of sulfur. It reacts with metals to form selenides, e.g., Al_2Se_3, which decompose in acid to give gaseous hydrogen selenide, H_2Se. This, like H_2S, is toxic and burns to give Se or SeO_2, but it is a stronger reducing agent than

H_2S. Selenium dioxide, SeO_2, is a colorless solid which dissolves in water to give the weak selenious acid, H_2SeO_3 ($K_I = 2.7 \times 10^{-3}$ and $K_{II} = 2.5 \times 10^{-7}$). Selenic acid, H_2SeO_4, the analogue of sulfuric acid, can be formed by oxidation of selenious acid with hydrogen peroxide or chlorine. It is a colorless solid which is not so strong an acid as H_2SO_4 but is a stronger oxidizing agent.

26.4 TELLURIUM

Nearly as abundant as selenium, tellurium is the only element with which gold occurs chemically combined in nature. It is also present as tellurides in copper and lead minerals and, in fact, is obtained principally as a by-product of their refining. The most stable modification of the element is hexagonal, or "metallic," tellurium. Its structure is much like that of selenium, but its photoconductivity is only slight. Because it is a semiconductor, its principal but limited use is in making rectifiers.

Hydrogen telluride, H_2Te, is a vile-smelling gas, unstable with respect to decomposition to the elements. In water, it acts as a moderately weak acid ($K_I = 2.3 \times 10^{-3}$), slightly stronger than H_2Se ($K_I = 1.9 \times 10^{-4}$), which in turn is stronger than H_2S. Tellurium dioxide (TeO_2) and tellurous acid (H_2TeO_3) resemble the corresponding selenium compounds. Unlike selenic acid, telluric acid (H_6TeO_6) contains six oxygen atoms bound to the central tellurium atom, presumably because of the larger size of the tellurium atom. It is a very weak acid but a strong oxidizing agent.

Investigation of the chemical behavior of tellurium compounds, and to some extent of selenium compounds, has been retarded because of the foul-smelling nature of the compounds. These are taken up by the body and given off in the perspiration and breath. Elimination is slow, and the stench of "tellurium breath" may linger for months.

26.5 POLONIUM

Work on polonium has been retarded because of its high radioactivity. The nucleus is unstable and, like radium, decomposes with the emission of alpha particles (Sec. 3.5). Since alpha radiation is damaging to the human body, the element is extremely dangerous. Amounts greater than 0.000000000004 g. cannot be tolerated in the body.

Polonium occurs naturally in uranium minerals such as pitchblende, but only to the extent of 5×10^{-9} per cent of the mineral. It is constantly being produced by the radioactive decay of other elements, but since it itself decays, the concentration stays constant.

X-ray studies of trace amounts indicate that the element exists in two forms which may be metallic, one of which seems to resemble lead. Little is known of its compounds, but it appears to form PoH_2, Po^{++}, PoO_2, and PoO_3.

26.6 QUALITATIVE ANALYSIS

An unknown solution might contain sulfur as sulfide, sulfate, or sulfite. The sulfide, on addition of acid, generates H_2S gas which can be detected either by its odor or by its blackening (due to PbS formation) of filter paper wet with a solution of lead acetate. Sulfate, on addition of barium nitrate and acid, produces white insoluble $BaSO_4$. If sulfite is present, it will not precipitate with Ba^{++} in acid solution; however, if Br_2 is added, the sulfite will be oxidized to sulfate and $BaSO_4$ forms.

QUESTIONS

26.1 *Group properties.* In what ways does the behavior of oxygen differ from that of the other group VI elements?

26.2 *Sulfur compounds.* Suggest a method for each of the following conversions: solid sulfur to 100% H_2SO_4; solid Na_2SO_3 to solid Na_2SO_4; H_2S gas to solid $NaHSO_3$.

26.3 *Oxyacids.* Compare H_2SO_3 and H_2SO_4 with each other and with the oxyacids of Se and Te.

26.4 *Equations.* Write equations to account for each of the following: (*a*) zinc sulfide dissolves in acid solution; (*b*) when H_2S flame is directed at a cold surface, a yellow deposit is formed; (*c*) bubbling SO_2 through aqueous H_2S solution produces the same precipitate as acidification of a thiosulfate solution; (*d*) formation of bromine by oxidation of NaBr with hot, concentrated H_2SO_4; (*e*) dissolving of copper in hot, concentrated H_2SO_4; (*f*) formation of a purple color from reaction between Mn^{++} and $S_2O_8^{--}$ in acid solution; (*g*) formation of I^- from I_2 by thiosulfate; (*h*) dissolving of silver bromide in sodium thiosulfate solution; (*i*) dissolving of silver sulfide in hot nitric acid.

26.5 *Freezing-point depression.* List the data which must be obtained to show that selenium exists as Se_8 in molten sulfur.

26.6 *Selenium and tellurium.* In what ways does the chemistry of selenium resemble that of sulfur? In what ways does it differ from that of tellurium?

26.7 *Polonium.* How much pitchblende is required to produce the maximum tolerable dose of polonium? How many polonium atoms is this?

26.8 *Oxygen and sulfur.* Why is elementary oxygen a better oxidizing agent than elementary sulfur?

26.9 *Sulfite and sulfate.* Given two white solids, one of which is Na_2SO_3 and the other is Na_2SO_4. Devise a method to distinguish which is which.

26.10 *Analysis.* Given a solution which contains K^+, Zn^{++}, and Pb^{++}. Devise a method based on H_2S precipitation to separate these ions.

26.11 *Hydrolysis.* Calculate the pH of 0.10 *M* Na_2SO_3. *Ans.* 10.13

26.12 *H_2S precipitation.* (*a*) How many liters of H_2S gas measured at 27°C. and 72.0 cm. Hg pressure must be used to precipitate all the metal cations from a solution made by mixing 10 ml. of 0.20 *M* Cu^{++}, 20 ml. of 0.30 *M* Ag^+, and 30 ml. of 0.060 *M* Pb^{++}? (*b*) What will be the concentration of H^+ in the final solution? *Ans.* 0.18 liter; 0.23 *M*

26.13 *CuS solubility.* Using the equilibrium constants given in Sec. 17.10, calculate the maximum concentration of Cu^{++} in a solution saturated with H_2S and containing H^+ at a concentration of 0.3 M.

26.14 *Oxidation-reduction titration.* Given 40.0 ml. of a $KMnO_4$ solution of unknown concentration. Excess KI is added with acid until all the permanganate is reduced to Mn^{++}. If it takes 45.0 ml. of 0.0500 M $Na_2S_2O_3$ to just titrate the liberated I_2, what was the concentration of the original $KMnO_4$ solution?

Ans. 0.0113 M

26.15 *Stoichiometry.* (*a*) Write the two half-reactions and the net equation for the following change in basic solution:

$$ClO^- + S_2O_3^{--} \rightarrow SO_4^{--} + Cl^-$$

(*b*) Calculate the final concentration of Na^+, Cl^-, SO_4^{--}, and OH^- in a solution made by mixing 10.0 ml. of 0.10 M $Na_2S_2O_3$, 20.0 ml. of 0.20 M NaOH, and 30.0 ml. of 0.30 M NaClO.

H

Li Be   B C N O F He
Na Mg   Al Si P S Cl Ne / Ar
K Ca Sc Ti V Cr Mn Fe Co Ni Cu Zn Ga Ge As Se Br Kr
Rb Sr Y Zr Nb Mo Tc Ru Rh Pd Ag Cd In Sn Sb Te I Xe
Cs Ba — Hf Ta W Re Os Ir Pt Au Hg Tl Pb Bi Po At Rn
Fr Ra —

27   *The Halogens*

ALTHOUGH THE CHEMISTRY OF THE GROUP VII ELEMENTS is somewhat complex, similarities within the group are more pronounced than in any of the other groups except I and II. The elements, fluorine, chlorine, bromine, iodine, and astatine, are collectively called halogens (from the Greek *halos*, salt, and *genes*, born), or salt producers, because, with seven valence electrons, they all have high electronegativity and form negative halide ions such as are found in ionic salts. Except for fluorine, they also show positive oxidation states.

27.1   GROUP PROPERTIES

Because of their high electronegativity, the halogens show practically no metallic properties, though solid iodine has a somewhat metallic appearance. Astatine, the heaviest member of the group, may also have some metal properties, but it is a short-lived radioactive element and not enough of it has been prepared to see whether the solid is metallic. Other properties of the group are shown in Table 27.1. All the elements have seven electrons in the outermost energy level. The octet can be completed either by gaining one

Table 27.1   Elements of Group VII

Symbol	Z	Electronic configuration	Melting point, °C.	Boiling point, °C.	Ionization potential, e.v.	Oxidation potential, volts (X^- to X_2)
F	9	2, 7	−223	−187	17.42	−2.87
Cl	17	2, 8, 7	−102	−34.6	13.01	−1.36
Br	35	2, 8, 18, 7	−7.3	58.78	11.84	−1.09
I	53	2, 8, 18, 18, 7	114	183	10.44	−0.54
At	85	2, 8, 18, 32, 18, 7	—	—	—	−0.2

electron completely to form a −1 ion or by gaining a share of one electron to form a single covalent bond. The former occurs when a halogen atom combines with an atom of low electronegativity to form an ionic bond, as in NaF or KCl; the latter occurs when the halogen atom combines with another atom of similar high electronegativity to form a covalent bond, as in Cl_2. The existence of the halogens as diatomic molecules can be represented as arising from the following equation:

$$2(:\overset{..}{\underset{..}{X}} \cdot) \rightarrow :\overset{..}{\underset{..}{X}}:\overset{..}{\underset{..}{X}}:$$

Although the bond between the halogen atoms is fairly strong (see Table 4.2), the attraction between X_2 molecules is quite weak and due only to van der Waals forces. In going down the group, there is an increasing number of electrons per X_2 molecule, and we would expect van der Waals attraction to increase. Thus, it is not surprising that the boiling points increase in going from F_2 to I_2. At room temperature, fluorine and chlorine are gases; bromine is a liquid; and iodine is a solid.

As indicated by the relatively high values of the ionization potentials, it is fairly difficult to remove an electron from a halogen atom. In fact, it requires more energy to remove an electron from a halogen atom than from any other atom in the same period except for the inert gases (compare values in Table 3.13). Within the group itself, there is, of course, a decrease in the ionization potential; the larger the halogen atom, the less firmly bound are the outermost electrons and the less the energy required to remove an electron from the neutral atom. Of greater significance chemically are the oxidation potentials, given in the last column of Table 27.1. As given, the oxidation potentials describe the relative tendency of the half-reaction

$$2X^- \rightarrow X_2 + 2e^-$$

to go from left to right in aqueous solution. Since the value for F^- to go to $F_2(g)$ is more negative than any of the others, F^- has the smallest tendency to lose an electron. This means that fluoride ion is an extremely poor reducing agent and that astatide ion, At^-, is the best reducing agent of the halide ions. Conversely, if the sign of the oxidation potential is changed, then it indicates the relative tendency of the half-reaction to go from right to left, i.e., from X_2 to X^-. In other words, the potentials with changed sign refer to the half-reaction

$$X_2 + 2e^- \rightarrow 2X^-$$

and indicate that the relative tendency of $F_2(g)$ to pick up electrons ($+2.87$ volts) is greater than that of the other halogens. Thus, fluorine gas is the best oxidizing agent of the halogens, and astatine is the poorest. In fact, fluorine gas is such a good oxidizing agent that it can oxidize any of the other halide ions. Chlorine gas, the second best oxidizing agent of the group, can oxidize Br^-, I^-, and At^- but not F^-. Comparison of the oxidation potentials listed in Appendix 7 shows that, compared to other oxidizing agents, chlorine is relatively strong but fluorine is the strongest of the lot.

Why is fluorine gas such a good oxidizing agent or, more particularly, why is it a better oxidizing agent than chlorine gas? Perhaps the problem is best explored by considering that the half-reaction

$$X_2(g) + 2e^- \rightarrow 2X^-$$

can be broken down into the following steps:

$$X_2(g) \rightarrow 2X(g) \tag{1}$$

$$2X(g) + 2e^- \rightarrow 2X^-(g) \tag{2}$$

$$2X^-(g) \rightarrow 2X^-(aq.) \tag{3}$$

Step (1) corresponds to the dissociation of X_2 and requires an amount of energy equal to the bond energy (Table 4.2); step (2) liberates energy equal to twice the electron affinity (Sec. 3.15); step (3) liberates energy equal to twice the hydration energy of the ion. Comparison of the three steps for fluorine and chlorine shows the following: step (1) for F_2 requires less energy (19 kcal.) than for Cl_2; step (2) for F liberates slightly less energy (3 kcal.) than for Cl; step (3) for F^- liberates considerable more energy (34 kcal.) than for Cl^-. Hence, for comparison of fluorine and chlorine, steps (1) and (2) are less important than step (3). In other words, it is the greater hydration energy of F^- that is principally responsible for the fact that F_2 is a stronger oxidizing agent than Cl_2 in aqueous solution. That the hydration energy of F^- is greater than that of Cl^- is reasonable, since fluoride ion is considerably smaller (ionic radius 1.36 A.) than chloride ion (1.81 A.). The smaller the halide ion, the more strongly it can interact with water molecules.*

Since fluorine is the most electronegative of all the elements, it can show only a negative oxidation state. However, the other halogens also show positive oxidation states in compounds with more electronegative elements. Most of these compounds contain oxygen, which has electronegativity between that of fluorine and chlorine. In their oxy compounds, chlorine and iodine show a maximum oxidation number of $+7$, but the corresponding $+7$ bromine compounds have not been prepared. In addition, Cl, Br, and I form compounds in which the halogen atom is assigned oxidation numbers $+1$ and $+5$.

27.2   FLUORINE

Fluorine is about half as abundant as chlorine and is widely distributed in nature. It occurs principally as the minerals fluorspar, CaF_2; cryolite, Na_3AlF_6; and fluorapatite, $Ca_5F(PO_4)_3$. Because none of the ordinary chemical oxidizing agents is capable of extracting electrons from fluoride ions, elemental fluorine is prepared only by electrolytic oxidation of molten fluorides, such as KF-HF mixtures. Fluorine is a pale yellow gas at room temperature which is extremely corrosive and reactive. With hydrogen, it forms violently explosive mixtures because of the reaction

$$H_2(g) + F_2(g) \rightarrow 2HF(g) + 128 \text{ kcal.}$$

On the skin, it causes severe burns which are quite slow to heal.

Hydrogen fluoride is usually made by the action of sulfuric acid on fluorspar. Because of hydrogen bonding (Sec. 15.5), liquid HF has a higher boiling point (19.5°C.) than any of the other hydrogen halides. Hydrogen bonding is also present in the gas phase and accounts for polymeric species, $(HF)_x$, where x is some small number such as 6 or less. In aqueous solutions, HF is called hydrofluoric acid and is unique among the hydrogen halides in being a weak, rather than a strong, acid ($K_{diss} = 6.7 \times 10^{-4}$) and in being able to dissolve glass. The latter reaction is attributed to the formation of fluosilicate ions as in the equation

$$SiO_2(s) + 6HF \rightarrow SiF_6^{--} + 2H_2O + 2H^+$$

where glass is represented for simplicity as SiO_2. Other complex ions of fluorine are known, e.g., AlF_6^{-3}, ZrF_7^{-3}, TaF_8^{-3}, in which the small size

---

* Although this discussion has been confined to aqueous solutions, the uniquely great oxidizing strength of fluorine shows up even when water solutions are not involved. Thus, for example, dry F_2 can oxidize solid NaCl to Cl_2 and NaF. In these cases oxidation results because the smaller size of the fluoride ion leads to more stable products (e.g., NaF).

of fluoride ion permits relatively large numbers of them to be attached to another atom.

In general, most simple fluoride salts formed with $+1$ cations are soluble (e.g., KF and AgF) and give slightly basic solutions because of the hydrolysis of F^- to HF. With $+2$ cations, however, the fluorides are usually insoluble (e.g., CaF_2 and PbF_2), but their solubility is somewhat increased in acid solution. The formation of insoluble, inert fluorides as surface coatings is apparently the reason that fluorine and its compounds can be stored in metal containers such as copper.

With oxygen, fluorine forms two compounds, oxygen difluoride (OF_2) and dioxygen difluoride (O_2F_2). The first can be prepared by passing fluorine very rapidly through dilute NaOH solution.

$$2F_2(g) + 2OH^- \rightarrow 2F^- + OF_2(g) + H_2O$$

It is somewhat less reactive than F_2 and slowly reacts with water to form HF and O_2. O_2F_2 results as a red liquid when an electric discharge is passed through a mixture of fluorine and oxygen below $-100°C$. It is unstable with respect to decomposition to the elements.

Most amazing of the fluorine compounds are the fluorocarbons. These are materials which can be considered to be derived from the hydrocarbons (Sec. 24.4) by substitution of fluorine atoms for hydrogen atoms. Thus, the fluorocarbon corresponding to methane, CH_4, is tetrafluoromethane, CF_4. This compound is typical of the saturated (i.e., containing no double bonds) fluorocarbons in being extremely inert. For example, unlike methane, it can be heated in air without burning. Furthermore, it can be treated with boiling nitric acid, concentrated sulfuric acid, and strong oxidizing agents such as potassium permanganate with no change. Reducing agents such as hydrogen or carbon do not affect it even at temperatures as high as $1000°C$. Because of their inertness, the fluorocarbons find application for special uses. For example, $C_{12}F_{26}$ is an ideal insulating liquid for heavy-duty transformers that operate at high temperature. Just as ethylene, C_2H_4, can polymerize to form polyethylene (Sec. 24.4), tetrafluoroethylene, C_2F_4, can polymerize to form polytetrafluoroethylene. The polymerization can be imagined to proceed by the opening up of the double bond to form an unstable intermediate which joins with other molecules to produce a high polymer.

The high polymer is a plastic known commercially as Teflon, and like the other saturated fluorocarbons, it is inert to chemical attack. It is unaffected even by boiling aqua regia or ozone. Though still rather expensive, fluorocarbon polymers show considerable promise as structural materials where corrosive conditions are extreme, as in chemical plants.

27.3   CHLORINE

Chlorine is the most abundant (0.2 per cent) of the halogens and occurs as chloride ion in sea water, salt wells, and salt beds, where it is combined with Na^+, K^+, Mg^{++}, and Ca^{++}. On a small scale, the element can be made by chemical oxidation, as with MnO_2:

$$MnO_2(s) + 2Cl^- + 4H^+ \rightarrow Mn^{++} + Cl_2(g) + 2H_2O$$

On a commercial scale, chlorine is more economically prepared by electrolytic oxidation of either aqueous or molten NaCl (see Secs. 14.3 and 14.4). The element is a greenish-yellow gas (in fact, it gets its name from the Greek *chloros*, green) and has a choking odor. Although not so reactive as fluorine, it is a good oxidizing agent and explodes with hydrogen when mixtures of H_2 and Cl_2 are exposed to ultraviolet light. In fact, chlorine has such great affinity for hydrogen that it reacts with hydrogen-containing compounds such as turpentine ($C_{10}H_{18}$) to form HCl and carbon. Most of the commercial chlorine is used as a bleach for paper and wood pulp and for large-scale disinfecting of public water supplies. Both of these uses depend on its oxidizing action.

The most important compounds of chlorine are those which correspond to the oxidation states -1, $+1$, $+5$, and $+7$, although there are compounds of chlorine in the other positive states, $+2$, $+3$, $+4$, and $+6$. The -1 state is familiar as the one assigned to chlorine in HCl and chloride salts. Although HCl can be produced by direct combination of the elements, a more convenient method of preparation is the heating of NaCl with concentrated H_2SO_4.

$$NaCl(s) + H_2SO_4 \rightarrow NaHSO_4(s) + HCl(g)$$

Hydrogen chloride gas is very soluble in water, and its solutions are referred to as hydrochloric acid. Commercially available concentrated hydrochloric acid is 37 per cent HCl by weight, or 12 *M*. Unlike HF, HCl is a strong acid and is essentially completely dissociated into ions in 1 *M* solution. Why is HCl so much stronger as an acid than HF? The higher hydration energy of the fluoride ion would tend to favor the dissociation of HF. The fact that HCl is more highly dissociated apparently arises because the bond in HCl is weaker than that in HF. Inasmuch as HCl is a strong acid, there is no appreciable tendency for chloride ion to hydrolyze in aqueous solution. Thus, solutions of NaCl and KCl, for example, are neutral. Of the common chlorides, silver chloride (AgCl), mercurous chloride (Hg_2Cl_2), and lead chloride ($PbCl_2$) are rather insoluble.

The +1 oxidation state of chlorine is represented by hypochlorous acid, HOCl, and its salts, the hypochlorites. Hypochlorous acid is produced to a slight extent when chlorine gas is dissolved in water. Disproportionation of the dissolved chlorine occurs according to the equation

$$Cl_2 + H_2O \rightleftharpoons Cl^- + H^+ + HOCl \qquad K = 4.7 \times 10^{-4}$$

The yield of products can be greatly increased by tying up the Cl^- and H^+, as by adding silver oxide (Ag^+ to precipitate AgCl and oxide to neutralize H^+). The formula of hypochlorous acid is usually written HOCl instead of HClO, to emphasize the fact that the proton is bonded to the oxygen and not directly to the chlorine. In agreement with this, the electronic formula

$H:\overset{\cdot\cdot}{\underset{\cdot\cdot}{O}}:\overset{\cdot\cdot}{\underset{\cdot\cdot}{Cl}}:$ is preferred. The acid is weak, with a dissociation constant of

3.2×10^{-8}, and exists only in aqueous solution. Even in solution it slowly decomposes with evolution of oxygen.

$$2HOCl \rightarrow 2H^+ + 2Cl^- + O_2(g)$$

HOCl is a powerful oxidizing agent, as shown by the oxidation potential for the half-reaction

$$Cl_2(g) + 2H_2O \rightleftharpoons 2HOCl + 2H^+ + 2e^- \qquad -1.63 \text{ volts}$$

The value is more negative than that for permanganate ion in acid solution (-1.51 volts), indicating that HOCl is a stronger oxidizing agent than MnO_4^-. Hypochlorites, such as NaClO, can be made by neutralization of HOCl solutions, but they are produced more economically by the disproportionation of chlorine in basic solution:

$$Cl_2 + 2OH^- \rightarrow Cl^- + ClO^- + H_2O$$

Commercially, the process is efficiently carried out by electrolyzing cold aqueous NaCl solutions and stirring vigorously. The stirring serves to mix chlorine produced at the anode

$$2Cl^- \rightarrow Cl_2 + 2e^-$$

with hydroxide ion produced at the cathode

$$2e^- + 2H_2O \rightarrow H_2(g) + 2OH^-$$

so that reaction can occur. Solutions of hypochlorite ion so produced are sold as laundry bleaches, e.g., Clorox. Another common household bleach which owes its action to the oxidizing power of hypochlorite ion is bleaching powder, or chlorinated lime. Its formula can be written $Ca(OCl)Cl$, and it is prepared by treating calcium hydroxide with chlorine.

In aqueous solution, hypochlorite ion is unstable with respect to self-oxidation and, when warmed, disproportionates by the equation

$$3ClO^- \rightarrow 2Cl^- + ClO_3^-$$

to produce chloride ion and chlorate ion (ClO_3^-). Chlorate ion contains chlorine in oxidation state $+5$. Its structure is pyramidal with the three oxygen atoms forming the base of the pyramid with the chlorine atom at the apex. The structure and the electronic configuration are shown in Fig. 27.1. Probably the most important chlorate salt is $KClO_3$, used as an oxidizing agent in matches, fireworks, and some explosives. Since $KClO_3$ is only moderately soluble in water, it can be precipitated by addition of KCl to chlorate-containing solutions. The chlorate solutions can be produced by electrolyzing hot chloride solutions that are vigorously stirred. Steps in the production can be summarized as follows:

$$2Cl^- + 2H_2O \xrightarrow{\text{electrolyze}} Cl_2 + 2OH^- + H_2(g)$$

$$3Cl_2 + 6OH^- \xrightarrow{\text{stir, heat}} 5Cl^- + ClO_3^- + 3H_2O$$

$$K^+ + ClO_3^- \rightarrow KClO_3(s)$$

As seen from the equation for the second step, only one-sixth of the chlorine is converted to ClO_3^-, which makes the process seem rather inefficient. However, on continued electrolysis the chloride produced in the second step is reoxidized in the first step.

Unlike hypochlorite ion, chlorate ion is the anion of a strong acid. The parent acid, $HClO_3$, chloric acid, has not been prepared in the pure state, since it is unstable. When attempts are made to concentrate chloric acid solutions, as by evaporation, violent explosions occur. The principal reaction is

$$4HClO_3 \rightarrow 4ClO_2(g) + O_2(g) + 2H_2O(g)$$

but the chlorine dioxide, ClO_2, produced may decompose further. In acid

Fig. 27.1   *Chlorate ion.*

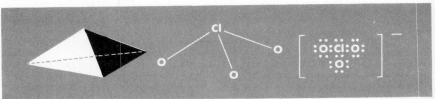

Fig. 27.2   Perchlorate ion.

aqueous solutions, chlorate ion, like hypochlorite ion, is a good oxidizing agent. The oxidation potential for the half-reaction

$$Cl_2(g) + 6H_2O \rightleftharpoons 2ClO_3^- + 12H^+ + 10e^- \qquad -1.47 \text{ volts}$$

indicates that ClO_3^- is almost the equal of MnO_4^-.

When $KClO_3$ is heated, it can decompose by two reactions

$$2KClO_3(s) \rightarrow 2KCl(s) + 3O_2(g)$$

$$4KClO_3(s) \rightarrow 3KClO_4(s) + KCl(s)$$

the first of which is catalyzed by surfaces, such as powdered glass or MnO_2, from which oxygen can readily escape. In the absence of such catalysts, especially at lower temperatures, the formation of potassium perchlorate ($KClO_4$) is favored. A more efficient method of preparing perchlorates is to use electrolytic oxidation of chlorate solutions. Since $KClO_4$ is only sparingly soluble in water (less than $KClO_3$), it can be made by addition of K^+ to perchlorate solutions. The perchlorate ion has a tetrahedral configuration, as shown in Fig. 27.2. The chlorine atom is at the center of the tetrahedron, and the four oxygen atoms are at the corners. In aqueous solutions, perchlorate ion is potentially a good oxidizing agent

$$Cl_2(g) + 8H_2O \rightleftharpoons 2ClO_4^- + 16H^+ + 14e^- \qquad -1.39 \text{ volts}$$

especially in acid solution, but its reactions are so very slow that they are usually not observed. For example, a solution containing ClO_4^- and the very strong reducing agent Cr^{++} (chromous ion) can be kept for weeks without any appreciable oxidation to Cr^{+3} (chromic ion).

Like chlorate ion, perchlorate ion is an anion of a strong acid. Consequently, in aqueous solution there is practically no association of ClO_4^- with H^+. However, when perchlorate salts are treated with sulfuric acid, pure hydrogen perchlorate ($HClO_4$) may be distilled off under reduced pressure. The anhydrous compound is a liquid at room temperature and is extremely dangerous, because it may explode spontaneously. With water, $HClO_4$ forms a series of hydrates. The monohydrate, $HClO_4 \cdot H_2O$, is a crystalline solid which actually contains H_3O^+ and ClO_4^- at the lattice points. Like the anhydrous material, the hydrate should be treated with respect because of the possibility of explosions. The danger is especially great in the presence of reducing agents such as organic material (e.g., wood, cloth, etc.). Dilute aqueous solutions of $HClO_4$ are safe and are useful reagents for the chemist. For one thing, perchlorate ion has less tendency to form complex ions with metal cations than any other anion. For another thing, perchloric acid is probably the strongest of all common acids and in aqueous solution is more completely dissociated than the usual strong acids hydrochloric, sulfuric, and nitric. Why is perchloric a stronger acid than the other oxyacids of chlorine? The dissociation of an oxyacid involves breaking a hydrogen-oxygen bond to form a hydrated hydronium ion and a hydrated anion. The bigger the anion, the less its hydration energy. Consequently, since ClO_4^- is obviously bigger than ClO^-, for example, we might expect $HClO_4$ to be less dissociated than $HOCl$. Since the reverse is true, the bond holding the proton to OCl^- must be stronger than the bond holding H^+ to ClO_4^-. That this is reasonable can be seen by noting that oxygen is more electronegative than chlorine; therefore addition of oxygen atoms to the $HOCl$ molecule pulls electrons away from the H—O bond and tends to weaken it. This picture is supported by observing that the intermediate oxyacid $HOClO$ (chlorous acid) has a dissociation constant, $K_{diss} = 1.1 \times 10^{-2}$, larger than that of $HOCl$, $K_{diss} = 3.2 \times 10^{-8}$. In general, for any series of oxyacids the acid corresponding to highest oxidation number is the most highly dissociated.

The above discussion of the oxy compounds of chlorine primarily concerned the oxidation states $+1$, $+5$, and $+7$. Brief mention was made of two compounds which represent two other states, ClO_2 ($+4$ state) and $HClO_2$ ($+3$ state). The first of these compounds, chlorine dioxide, is produced when $HClO_3$ explodes, but a safer method of preparing it involves reduction of acid chlorate solutions with sulfur dioxide, SO_2, or oxalic acid, $H_2C_2O_4$. Pertinent equations are

$$2ClO_3^- + SO_2(g) + H^+ \rightarrow 2ClO_2(g) + HSO_4^-$$

$$2ClO_3^- + H_2C_2O_4 + 2H^+ \rightarrow 2ClO_2(g) + 2CO_2(g) + 2H_2O$$

Chlorine dioxide is a yellow gas at room temperature but is easily condensed to a red liquid (b.p., $11°C.$). The gas is paramagnetic, indicating that the molecule contains an unpaired electron. Despite the fact that ClO_2 is explosive, it is produced in large quantities for bleaching flour, paper, etc. Its use depends on the fact that it is both a strong and a rapid oxidizing agent. When placed in basic solution, chlorine dioxide disproportionates thus:

$$2ClO_2(g) + 2OH^- \rightarrow ClO_2^- + ClO_3^- + H_2O$$

One product is chlorate ion, previously discussed; the other is chlorite ion, ClO_2^-, which is frequently prepared commercially by this reaction. Chlorite ion is the anion of the moderately weak acid, $HClO_2$, or chlorous acid. Like $HOCl$, it exists only in solution, and even in solution it decomposes. The principal reaction seems to be

$$5HClO_2 \rightarrow 4ClO_2(g) + H^+ + Cl^- + 2H_2O$$

Chlorites are important industrial bleaching agents because they can bleach without appreciably affecting other properties of the substance bleached. Like other oxy compounds of chlorine, they must be used with caution, because the dry salts may explode when in contact with organic material.

27.4 BROMINE

Bromine, from the Greek word *bromos* for stink, occurs as bromide ion in sea water, brine wells, and salt beds and is less than a hundredth as abundant as chlorine. The element is usually prepared by chlorine oxidation of bromide solutions, as by sweeping chlorine gas through sea water. Since chlorine is a stronger oxidizing agent than bromine, the reaction

$$Cl_2(g) + 2Br^- \rightarrow Br_2 + 2Cl^-$$

occurs as indicated. Removal of the bromine from the resulting solution can be accomplished by sweeping the solution with air, because bromine is quite volatile. At room temperature pure bromine is a mobile, but dense, red liquid of pungent odor. It is a dangerous substance, since it attacks the skin to form slow-healing sores.

Although less powerful an oxidizing agent than chlorine, bromine readily reacts with other elements to form bromides. Hydrogen bromide, like HCl, is a strong acid but is more easily oxidized than is HCl. Whereas HCl can be made by heating the sodium salt with H_2SO_4, HBr cannot. The hot H_2SO_4 oxidizes HBr to Br_2, and a nonoxidizing acid such as H_3PO_4 must be used instead.

In basic solution, bromine disproportionates to give bromide ion and hypobromite ion (BrO^-). The reaction is quickly followed by further disproportionation

$$3BrO^- \rightarrow 2Br^- + BrO_3^-$$

to give bromate ion, BrO_3^-. Bromic acid, $HBrO_3$, has never been prepared pure. In aqueous solution, it is a strong acid and a good oxidizing agent. The oxidation potential

$$Br_2 + 6H_2O \rightleftharpoons 2BrO_3^- + 12H^+ + 10e^- \qquad -1.50 \text{ volts}$$

indicates that bromate is a slightly stronger oxidizing agent than chlorate. It has the added virtue of being faster in its action. No compounds are known at present corresponding to bromine in the $+7$ state, although many attempts have been made to prepare them. This is somewhat surprising, considering that both chlorine and iodine form such compounds. There is no satisfactory explanation for the apparently anomalous behavior of bromine.

One of the important uses of bromine is in making silver bromide for photographic emulsions (Sec. 22.3). However, the principal use of bromine is in making dibromoethane ($C_2H_4Br_2$) for addition to gasolines which contain tetraethyllead. Tetraethyllead, $(C_2H_5)_4Pb$, added to gasoline as an anti-knock agent, decomposes on burning to form lead deposits. The dibromo-ethane prevents accumulation of lead deposits in the engine.

27.5   IODINE

Of the halogens, iodine is the only one which occurs naturally in a positive oxidation state. In addition to its occurrence as I^- in sea water and salt wells, it is also found as sodium iodate ($NaIO_3$), small amounts of which are mixed with $NaNO_3$ in Chile saltpeter. The Chilean ore is processed by the reduction of $NaIO_3$ with controlled amounts of $NaHSO_3$. The principal reaction is

$$5HSO_3^- + 2IO_3^- \rightarrow I_2 + 5SO_4^{--} + 3H^+ + H_2O$$

Excess hydrogen sulfite must be avoided, for it would reduce I_2 to I^-. In the United States, most of the iodine is produced by chlorine oxidation of I^- from salt wells.

At room temperature, iodine crystallizes as black leaflets with metallic luster. Although, as shown by X-ray analysis, the solid consists of discrete I_2 molecules, its properties are different from those of usual molecular solids. For example, its electric conductivity, though small, increases with increasing temperature like that of a semiconductor (Sec. 23.2). Furthermore, liquid iodine also has perceptible conductivity, which decreases with increasing temperature like that of a metal. Thus, feeble as they are, metallic properties do appear even in the halogen family.

When heated, solid iodine readily sublimes to give a violet vapor, which consists of I_2 molecules. The violet color is the same as that observed for many iodine solutions, such as those in CCl_4 and in hydrocarbons.

However, in water and in alcohol the solutions are brown, presumably because of unusual interactions between I_2 and the solvent. When iodine is brought in contact with starch, a characteristic deep blue color results, which has been attributed to a starch-I_2 complex. The formation of the blue color is the basis for using starch-potassium iodide mixtures as a qualitative test for the presence of oxidizing agents. Oxidizing agents convert I^- to I_2, which with starch forms the colored complex. With very strong oxidizing agents, the color may fade with oxidation of I_2 to a higher oxidation state.

Iodine is only slightly soluble in water ($0.001\ M$), but the solubility is vastly increased by the presence of iodide ion. The color changes from brown to deep red because of the formation of the tri-iodide ion, I_3^-. The tri-iodide ion is also known in solids such as NH_4I_3, where X-ray investigations indicate that the I_3^- ion is linear. No electronic formula conforming to the octet rule can be written for this ion. Apparently an iodine atom, perhaps because of its large size, can accommodate more than eight electrons in its valence shell. In basic solutions, I_2 disproportionates to form iodide ion and hypoiodite ion (IO^-).

$$I_2 + 2OH^- \rightarrow I^- + IO^- + H_2O$$

Further disproportionation to give iodate ion (IO_3^-) is hastened by heating or by addition of acid. Iodate ion in acid solution is a weaker oxdizing agent than either bromate ion or chlorate ion. This is shown by the oxidation potential

$$I_2 + 6H_2O \rightleftharpoons 2IO_3^- + 12H^+ + 10e^- \qquad -1.20 \text{ volts}$$

Since IO_3^- is a weaker oxidizing agent than ClO_3^-, iodates can be made by oxidizing I_2 with ClO_3^-. Furthermore, iodate salts are not quite so explosive as chlorates or bromates. The greater stability of iodates also is evident in the fact that HIO_3, unlike $HClO_3$ and $HBrO_3$, can be isolated pure (as a white solid); the latter acids detonate when attempts are made to concentrate them.

Whereas bromate cannot be oxidized to the $+7$ state, iodate can; however it takes a very strong oxidizing agent to accomplish this. In the $+7$ state, the oxysalts of iodine are called periodates, but there are several kinds of periodates. There are those derived from HIO_4 (metaperiodic acid), those derived from H_5IO_6 (paraperiodic acid), and possibly others. In the metaperiodates, the iodine is bonded tetrahedrally to four oxygen atoms (this ion is analogous to ClO_4^-); in the paraperiodates, there are six oxygen atoms bound octahedrally to the iodine atom. The fact that there are paraperiodates but no paraperchlorates is apparently due to the larger size of the iodine atom. As in I_3^-, it is necessary to assume that in the paraperiodates the valence shell of iodine is expanded to contain more than eight electrons. Paraperiodic acid, H_5IO_6, is moderately weak ($K_I = 5.1 \times 10^{-4}$), but metaperiodic acid, HIO_4, seems to be strong.

In going down the halogen group, the atoms of the elements get progressively larger, and it becomes easier to oxidize the halide ion to the free halogen. This shows up in the instability of iodide solutions to air oxidation. The oxidation is slow for basic and neutral solutions but becomes appreciably faster for acid solutions.

So far as uses are concerned, iodine is less widely used than other halogens. It finds limited use for its antiseptic properties, both as tincture of iodine (solution of I_2 in alcohol) and as iodoform (CHI_3). Since small amounts of iodine are required in the human diet, traces of sodium iodide (1 part per 10^5) are frequently added to table salt.

27.6   ASTATINE

Since astatine does not occur to an appreciable extent in nature, all that is known about it is based on experiments done with trace amounts of artifically produced element. It can be made by bombarding bismuth nuclei with alpha particles, and its chemistry is studied by observing whether radioactive astatine is carried along with iodine through the course of chemical reactions. On the basis of such tracer studies, it is concluded that astatine forms an astatide ion (At^-) and compounds in two positive oxidation states, probably $+1$ and $+5$.

27.7   INTERHALOGEN COMPOUNDS

In view of the fact that halogen atoms combine with each other to form diatomic molecules, it is not surprising that an atom of one halogen can combine with an atom of another halogen. Thus, we have compounds such as ICl, iodine monochloride, which can be prepared by direct union of the elements. ICl can also be made by reaction of iodate with iodide in concentrated HCl.

$$6H^+ + IO_3^- + 2I^- + 3Cl^- \rightarrow 3ICl + 3H_2O$$

Pure ICl exists as a low-melting red solid (m.p., $27°C$.), which, when melted, can be electrolyzed to produce I_2 at the cathode and Cl_2 at the anode. Since molten ICl conducts electric current and since iodine is discharged at the cathode, it has been assumed that the liquid contains I^+ ions. In dilute acid solution, ICl hydrolyzes to give chloride ion and probably hypoiodous acid (HOI), but the latter disproportionates, giving the net reaction

$$5ICl + 3H_2O \rightarrow 5Cl^- + IO_3^- + 2I_2 + 6H^+$$

ICl is sometimes used for adding iodine to organic molecules.

In addition to ICl there are other interhalogen compounds of the type XY. In fact, all combinations except IF are known. More surprising than these compounds of type XY is the existence of more complex interhalogens of types XY_3, XY_5, and XY_7. Although there are three examples of XY_3 (ClF_3, BrF_3, and ICl_3) and two of XY_5 (BrF_5 and IF_5), there is only one XY_7 (IF_7). All of these compounds are of interest as examples of failure of the octet rule.

27.8   QUALITATIVE ANALYSIS

Fluoride differs from Cl^-, Br^-, and I^- in forming an insoluble magnesium salt but a soluble silver salt.

Iodide can be distinguished from Br^- and Cl^- in that its silver salt is insoluble in excess NH_3. Its presence can be confirmed by oxidizing I^- to I_2, which imparts a violet color to CCl_4.

Br^- and Cl^- both form insoluble silver salts, but AgBr is more yellowish than the pure white of AgCl. Furthermore, AgBr dissolves with greater difficulty in excess NH_3 than does AgCl. Finally, when Br^- is oxidized to Br_2 in the presence of CCl_4, the CCl_4 solution is brown whereas Cl_2 in CCl_4 is yellow.

The oxyanions ClO_3^-, BrO_3^-, and IO_3^- can be detected by reducing them in acid (by adding sulfite or nitrite) and then analyzing for the corresponding halide ions as above.

Perchlorate ion, once encountered only rarely but now becoming increasingly common, can be recognized easily because it is one of the few anions that forms a white, sparingly soluble potassium salt.

QUESTIONS

27.1   Group properties. Compare the halogens to the alkali metals with respect to electronic configurations, ionization potentials, electronegativity, metallic character, characteristic oxidation states, and acidity of hydroxy compounds.

27.2   Fluorine. Why is electrolytic oxidation of fluoride ion used instead of chemical oxidation in producing fluorine?

27.3   Equilibrium calculations. (a) Calculate the concentration of H^+ and of OH^- in 0.70 M HOCl. (b) Calculate the concentration of H^+ and of OH^- in 0.70 M NaOCl. (c) What is the pH of the above solutions?   *Ans.* (c) 3.82 and 10.68

27.4   Water fluoridation. A given sample of water with temporary hardness has a calcium-ion concentration of about 1.0×10^{-3} M. If the solubility product of CaF_2 is 1.7×10^{-10}, what is the maximum concentration of fluoride ion that can be attained in temporarily hard water before CaF_2 should precipitate? Compare this number with the recommended concentration of 1 part per million (1 g. of fluorine per million g. of water) in fluoridated public water supplies.

27.5   Chlorine. How could you convert: (a) chlorine to $KClO_3$; (b) bleaching powder to Cl_2; (c) HCl to NaClO?

27.6 *Equations.* Write equations for the following: (*a*) bubbling chlorine through bromide solution; (*b*) heating solid NaBr with H_3PO_4; (*c*) heating solid NaBr with H_2SO_4; (*d*) disproportionation of I_2 in hot basic solution; (*e*) reduction of IO_3^- to I_2 with H_2SO_3 in acid solution; (*f*) oxidation of I_2 to IO_4^- by Cl_2 in basic solution; (*g*) turning brown of an acidified iodide solution on oxidation by air.

27.7 *Starch-KI test.* How could you account for the fact that starch-potassium iodide paper placed in a hypochlorite solution first turns blue and then decolorizes? Write equations.

27.8 *Strong acids.* (*a*) Which is a stronger acid, H_2SO_4 or $HClO_4$? (*b*) Which has higher H^+ concentration, 0.10 *M* H_2SO_4 or 0.10 *M* $HClO_4$? Explain.

27.9 *Oxidizing agents.* Arrange the following in order of increasing oxidizing strength under conditions where oxidation potentials apply: F_2, Cl_2, Br_2, I_2, F^-, Cl^-, Br^-, I^-, ClO_3^-, BrO_3^-, IO_3^-.

27.10 *Halogen comparison.* From each of the following sets, select the substance which best fits the requirement specified.

(*a*) Strongest acid	$HOCl$, $HClO_2$, $HClO_3$
(*b*) Biggest atom	Cl, I, Br, F
(*c*) Smallest ionization potential	Cl, I, Br, F
(*d*) Largest electron affinity	Cl, I, Br, F
(*e*) Best reducing agent	Cl^-, I^-, Br^-, F^-
(*f*) Weakest acid	HCl, HBr, HI, HF
(*g*) Planar ion	ClO_2^-, ClO_3^-, ClO_4^-
(*h*) Most volatile	HF, HCl, HBr, HI
(*i*) Highest pH in 0.10 *M* solution	$HClO_4$, $NaClO_4$, $NaClO$, NaF

27.11 *Concentrations.* Suppose that 0.100 liter of each of the following solutions is mixed: 0.10 *M* NaCl, 0.10 *M* NaBr, 0.10 *M* NaI, and 0.25 *M* $AgNO_3$. If the final volume is 0.400 liter, calculate the concentration of each ion in the final solution. The solubility products of AgCl, AgBr, and AgI are 1.7×10^{-10}, 5.0×10^{-13}, and 8.5×10^{-17}, respectively.

27.12 *Br_2 disproportionation.* (*a*) Given in acid solution:

$$2Br^- \rightleftharpoons Br_2 + 2e^- \qquad\qquad -1.09 \text{ volts}$$
$$Br_2 + 6H_2O \rightleftharpoons 2BrO_3^- + 12H^+ + 10e^- \qquad -1.50 \text{ volts}$$

Calculate (see Sec. 17.14) the equilibrium constant for the reaction

$$3H_2O + 3Br_2 \rightleftharpoons BrO_3^- + 5Br^- + 6H^+$$

(*b*) In basic solution, the disproportionation of Br_2 is essentially complete. Show that this is consistent with the value of the analagous equilibrium constant for the net reaction in basic solution.

Ans. (*a*) $K = 2.2 \times 10^{-35}$. (*b*) $K = 2.2 \times 10^{49}$

27.13 *Stoichiometry.* Given a white solid sample that consists only of KI and NaI. When 3.309 g. of this material is oxidized by KIO_3 in acid, then 3.198 g. of I_2 is formed. Caculate the weight per cent KI in the original sample.

Ans. 50.2%

27.14 *Mixing problem.* Compute the concentrations of Cl^- and of SO_4^{--} in the final solution, volume 0.100 liter, made by mixing 10.0 ml. of 0.100 M NaOH, 30.0 ml. of 0.200 M Na_2SO_3, 30.0 ml. of 0.0300 M NaClO, and 30.0 ml. of 0.0400 M $NaClO_3$.

28 *Organic Chemistry*

THE FIELD OF ORGANIC CHEMISTRY, which concerns itself with hydrocarbons and their derivatives, is an extensive one, because such a great variety of compounds is possible. The importance of organic chemistry becomes evident when we consider that all biological systems are composed of organic compounds. Furthermore, a large share of chemical industry is devoted to the production of organic compounds which have become essential to our standard of living. In this chapter we can make but a brief survey of the principles and facts of organic chemistry. We shall first consider the classification of organic compounds by functional groups and then, following a short discussion of organic reactions, explore the methods used in synthesizing organic compounds. Finally, we shall turn to the problem of identifying natural products and of defining the role of organic compounds in some biochemical processes.

28.1 FUNCTIONAL GROUPS

Organic compounds are usually viewed as being composed of one or more hydrocarbon residues attached to functional groups. Simply stated, a functional group is any particular arrangement of a few atoms which bestows characteristic properties on an organic molecule. As a specific example, the grouping —O—H is a functional group which, when joined to a hydrocarbon residue, gives rise to properties characteristic of alcohols. Table 28.1 lists some of the common functional groups, the general formulas (R stands for any hydrocarbon residue) for the compounds in which they are found, and the name of that class of compound.

Before discussing the various classes of compounds, we should note that the identity of the hydrocarbon residue R fixes the specific name of the compound and also may modify the class properties. Thus, if the hydrocarbon residue in ROH is the methyl group, CH_3—, related to the hydrocarbon methane (CH_4), then the alcohol CH_3OH is called methanol, if the hydrocarbon residue is the hexyl group, C_6H_{13}—, related to the hydrocarbon hexane (C_6H_{14}), then the alcohol $C_6H_{13}OH$ is called hexanol. Both CH_3OH and $C_6H_{13}OH$ behave like alcohols, in the sense that they show the characteristic behavior outlined below, but in hexanol the hydrocarbon part is such a large fraction of the molecule that some of the —O—H properties are obscured. For example, whereas CH_3OH is completely miscible with water, $C_6H_{13}OH$ has only limited solubility in H_2O.

1   Alcohols. The simplest of the alcohols is CH_3OH, methanol, or methyl alcohol, sometimes also called wood alcohol, since it results when wood is heated in the absence of air. On a large scale, CH_3OH is produced

Table 28.1   Classes of Compounds

Functional group	General formula	Name
—O—H	ROH	Alcohols
$\overset{\displaystyle O}{\overset{\|}{-C-H}}$	$RCHO$	Aldehydes
$\overset{\displaystyle O}{\overset{\|}{-C-}}$	$RCOR'$	Ketones
$\overset{\displaystyle O}{\overset{\|}{-C-O-H}}$	$RCOOH$	Acids
$\overset{\displaystyle O}{\overset{\|}{-C-O-}}$	$RCOOR'$	Esters
—O—	ROR'	Ethers
$\overset{\displaystyle H}{\overset{\|}{-N-H}}$	RNH_2	Amines

by combining carbon monoxide and hydrogen at high pressures (200 to 300 atm.) and high temperatures (300 to 400°C.) in the presence of catalysts such as $ZnO\text{-}Cr_2O_3$ mixtures.

$$CO(g) + 2H_2(g) \rightarrow CH_3OH(g)$$

Ethanol, C_2H_5OH, also called ethyl alcohol, or grain alcohol, results from the fermentation of sugars. In the fermentation process, enzymes, e.g., zymase, which are secreted by yeast cells, act as catalysts for the breakdown of sugar molecules. A typical reaction is

$$C_6H_{12}O_6 \xrightarrow[\text{zymase}]{} 2CO_2(g) + 2C_2H_5OH$$
glucose

Although alcohols contain the —O—H group, their reactions are considerably different from those of inorganic hydroxides. Instead of dissociating to give OH^-, the oxygen atom is bound so tightly to carbon that the O—H bond is broken more easily, and the alcohols behave as extremely weak acids (K_{diss} for C_2H_5OH is 7.3×10^{-20}). The slight acid nature of alcohols shows up in their reactions with active metals. For example, sodium reacts gently with ethyl alcohol to liberate hydrogen

$$2Na(s) + 2C_2H_5OH \rightarrow H_2(g) + 2Na^+ + 2C_2H_5O^-$$

Evaporation of the excess alcohol produces a white solid, sodium ethoxide ($NaOC_2H_5$), which in water is completely hydrolyzed to C_2H_5OH.

$$NaOC_2H_5(s) + H_2O \rightarrow Na^+ + OH^- + C_2H_5OH$$

Because alcohols are so slightly dissociated, the pure substances can be viewed as aggregates of neutral molecules. The lower alcohols, i.e., those containing few carbon atoms per molecule, are liquids at room temperature and are held together primarily by attractions between the polar molecules. The oxygen end of alcohol molecules, like that of H_2O, is more negative than the other end, i.e., in alcohols, the hydrocarbon end. Perhaps the primary reason for association of alcohol molecules is hydrogen bonding established between the H of one OH group and the O of another. The situation is less complex than that in water (Sec. 16.5), as is shown in Fig. 28.1, because the hydrogen atoms of the methyl groups do not form hydrogen bonds to any appreciable extent.

Fig. 28.1 Hydrogen bonding in alcohol. (Locations of shared hydrogens are the average of the two possible positions.)

Because of their polar nature, liquid alcohols can dissolve ionic solutes. However, more important is their ability to dissolve molecular solutes. In carrying out organic reactions, alcohol solutions are almost as common as aqueous solutions are for inorganic reactions. In addition, alcohols are extremely important as starting materials for the preparation of other compounds. This use of alcohols is illustrated below in the description of methods used to prepare the other classes of organic compounds.

2   *Aldehydes.* When an alcohol which contains a hydroxyl group on a terminal carbon atom is oxidized, the product contains the functional group —CHO and is called an aldehyde. Thus, for example, when a solution of sodium dichromate and sulfuric acid is heated with ethyl alcohol, the following conversion occurs:

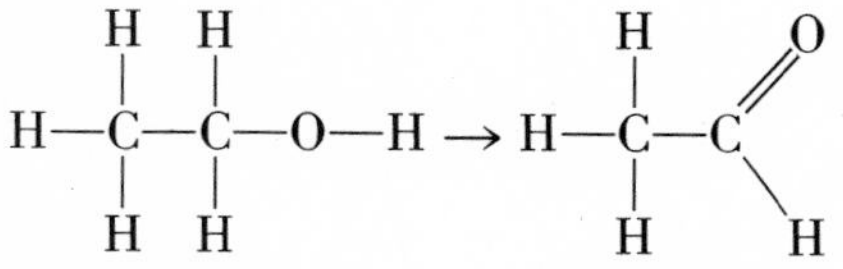

Ethyl alcohol   *Acetaldehyde*

for which the balanced equation is

$$3CH_3CH_2OH + Cr_2O_7^{--} + 8H^+ \rightarrow 3CH_3CHO(g) + 2Cr^{+3} + 7H_2O$$

The heating serves two purposes: it hastens the otherwise slow reaction, and it volatilizes the aldehyde so as to remove it from the reaction mixture before it can be oxidized further. Like ethyl alcohol, acetaldehyde is miscible with water, but it differs from ethyl alcohol in being more volatile. The principal importance of acetaldehyde lies in its being an intermediate in the preparation of other compounds such as acetic acid.

The lower aldehydes are characterized by a sharp irritating odor, but the higher ones like $C_8H_{17}CHO$ have flowery odors when dilute and so are used in perfumery. In general, aldehydes are mild reducing agents and can be used to reduce solutions containing $Ag(NH_3)_2^+$ to make silver mirrors. Many sugars behave as if they contain aldehyde groups and therefore can act as reducing agents. These reducing sugars can be tested for by their reaction with Fehling solution, which is an alkaline solution containing a complex ion of cupric copper. On reaction, the copper is reduced to cuprous oxide, an easily identified red precipitate. When an aldehyde is oxidized, it is converted to an organic acid; when it is reduced, as by hydrogen in the presence of nickel catalyst, an alcohol results.

A unique aldehyde is formaldehyde, HCHO, produced by oxidation of methanol, as by air in the presence of hot copper. It is a gas at room temperature but has a great tendency to polymerize, sometimes with explosive violence, to form a solid.

$$n \underset{\text{H}}{\overset{\text{H}}{\diagup}}\text{C}=\text{O} \rightarrow \cdots \underset{\text{H}}{\overset{\text{H}}{\text{C}}}-\text{O}-\underset{\text{H}}{\overset{\text{H}}{\text{C}}}-\text{O}-\underset{\text{H}}{\overset{\text{H}}{\text{C}}}-\text{O}-\underset{\text{H}}{\overset{\text{H}}{\text{C}}}-\text{O}\cdots$$

Formaldehyde is probably best known as its aqueous solution, called formalin. Because it is toxic to lower forms of life, it finds wide application as a disinfectant and for the preservation of biological specimens.

3   Ketones. When an alcohol which contains a hydrogen atom and a hydroxyl group on a nonterminal carbon atom is oxidized, the product contains the functional group —CO— and is called a ketone. The functional group of a ketone differs from that of an aldehyde in that the —CO— group is attached to two carbon atoms instead of one carbon atom and one hydrogen atom. The most important ketone is dimethyl ketone, or acetone, CH_3COCH_3. It can be made by the oxidation of isopropyl alcohol or, what amounts to the same thing, by dehydrogenation (removal of hydrogen) in the presence of copper catalyst. The change can be written

$$\underset{\underset{\text{H}}{\overset{|}{\text{H}-\text{O}-\text{H}}}}{\overset{\text{H H H}}{\text{H}-\text{C}-\text{C}-\text{C}-\text{H}}} \xrightarrow[\text{200–300°C.}]{\overset{\text{Cu}}{\text{catalyst}}} \underset{\text{H O H}}{\overset{\text{H}\qquad\text{H}}{\text{H}-\text{C}-\text{C}-\text{C}-\text{H}}} + \text{H}_2$$

Isopropyl alcohol   *Acetone*

At room temperature, acetone is a liquid, but it is quite volatile (b.p., 56°C.). Like alcohols and aldehydes, it catches fire rather easily. Because it is a good solvent for organic compounds, it is extensively used to dissolve varnishes, plastics, etc. It is characteristic of ketones that they are less easily oxidized than aldehydes, and they do not give a positive test with Fehling solution.

4   Acids. We have already encountered an example of an organic acid in our old friend acetic acid, CH_3COOH. This acid, which is the essential constituent of vinegar, can be made by air oxidation of acetaldehyde in the presence of suitable catalysts. In the presence of certain microorganisms, the fermentation of sugar in fruit juices such as cider does not stop at alcohol but in the presence of air continues on to produce acetic acid. Pure acetic acid, called glacial acetic acid, is usually made from acetylene by reaction with water and air. The reaction occurs in steps, both of which require catalysts.

$$H-C\equiv C-H + H_2O \rightarrow H-\underset{\underset{H}{|}}{\overset{\overset{H}{|}}{C}}-C\overset{O}{\underset{H}{\diagdown}}$$

Acetylene   *Acetaldehyde*

$$H-\underset{\underset{H}{|}}{\overset{\overset{H}{|}}{C}}-C\overset{O}{\underset{H}{\diagdown}} + \tfrac{1}{2}O_2 \rightarrow H-\underset{\underset{H}{|}}{\overset{\overset{H}{|}}{C}}-C\overset{O}{\underset{O-H}{\diagdown}}$$

Acetaldehyde   *Acetic acid*

Pure acetic acid is a liquid at room temperature but freezes at 16.6°C. It is extensively used in the preparation of materials such as plastics, dyes, pharmaceuticals, etc.

Other organic acids are like acetic acid in being weak acids. However, the higher acids differ from acetic acid in being less soluble in water, because the hydrocarbon residue becomes the more significant fraction of the molecule. Long-chain acids, such as stearic acid, $C_{17}H_{35}COOH$, are called fatty acids, since they can be made from natural fats. Salts of the fatty acids are used as soap (Sec. 24.4).

5 *Esters.* As discussed in Sec. 24.4, an alcohol and an organic acid can react to produce an ester. The functional group of an ester is the same as that of an acid except that the hydrogen has been replaced by a hydrocarbon residue. In general, esters have pleasant tastes and odors and are the principal flavor constituents of many fruits. For example, methyl butyrate (the methyl ester of butyric acid, C_3H_7COOH) has the structure

$$H-\underset{\underset{H}{|}}{\overset{\overset{H}{|}}{C}}-\underset{\underset{H}{|}}{\overset{\overset{H}{|}}{C}}-\underset{\underset{H}{|}}{\overset{\overset{H}{|}}{C}}-\overset{\overset{O}{\|}}{C}-O-\underset{\underset{H}{|}}{\overset{\overset{H}{|}}{C}}-H \quad \text{or} \quad C_3H_7COOCH_3$$

and is found in pineapple. Synthetic esters are frequently used to make artificial flavors and perfumes, but their most extensive use is as solvents, especially for lacquers.

Most esters, particularly those containing many carbon atoms per molecule, are sparingly soluble in water. They all react with water to some extent in a hydrolysis reaction which is just the reverse of the ester formation.

$$RCOOR + H_2O \rightleftharpoons RCOOH + ROH$$

Both the forward and the reverse reactions are very slow but are catalyzed somewhat by acids. Study of the kinetics of the forward and reverse changes has helped considerably in determining the factors that influence reaction velocity.

In nature, some of the most important esters are the complex esters which make up animal fats and vegetable oils. These complex esters, which are typified by the stearin molecule shown in Fig. 24.9, contain three ester functional groups per molecule. The stearin molecule can be visualized as being formed by an esterification reaction in which three stearic acid molecules combine with one glycerin (also called glycerol) molecule as follows:

$$3C_{17}H_{35}COOH + \begin{array}{c} H \\ | \\ H-O-C-H \\ | \\ H-O-C-H \\ | \\ H-O-C-H \\ | \\ H \end{array} \rightarrow \begin{array}{c} H \\ | \\ C_{17}H_{35}COO-C-H \\ | \\ C_{17}H_{35}COO-C-H \\ | \\ C_{17}H_{35}COO-C-H \\ | \\ H \end{array} + 3H_2O$$

Stearic acid   *Glycerin*   *Stearin*

In the stearin molecule, the hydrocarbon chains ($C_{17}H_{35}$—) are probably coiled up and intertwined in such a way that the molecule is rather spherical in shape. When stearin is boiled with NaOH solution, glycerin and sodium stearate are formed. There is no fat that is pure stearin. All the natural fats and oils are mixtures of stearin and related esters. Depending on the relative percentages of the various components, we have beef tallow, lard, olive oil, cottonseed oil, etc. The oils are of interest because they contain a high percentage of molecules in which the hydrocarbon chains are unsaturated. For example, in olive oil about 75 per cent of the molecules have $C_{17}H_{33}$— side chains in which there is a double bond between two carbons. By adding hydrogen to a controlled fraction of such double bonds, as in the nickel-catalyzed hydrogenation of cottonseed oil, the vegetable oil can be converted to a solid synthetic fat of practically any desired softening temperature. Synthetic shortenings such as margarine are basically mixtures of vegetable oils, animal fats, and partially hydrogenated vegetable oils.

6   Ethers. When two alcohol molecules are brought together so that an H atom from one and an OH group from the other can be split out as water, the two fragments may link together to form an ether. The splitting out of water is favored in the presence of concentrated sulfuric acid; hence ethers can be made by heating alcohols in the presence of concentrated H_2SO_4. Diethyl ether, which is the ordinary ether usually encountered, is made from ethanol as follows:

$$C_2H_5OH + HOC_2H_5 \xrightarrow[\text{H}_2\text{SO}_4]{\text{conc.}} C_2H_5-O-C_2H_5 + H_2O$$

Ethers in general are relatively inert to many chemical reagents, but they do catch fire quite readily. Their principal use is as solvents, for they readily dissolve a large variety of nonpolar substances which are only sparingly soluble in water. In using ethers, one curious hazard that should be noted is that occasionally, on long exposure to air, ethers pick up oxygen to form explosive peroxides. Consequently, before an ether is distilled, it should be tested for the presence of peroxides (as by use of acidified KI) and the peroxides destroyed by some reducing agent (such as $FeSO_4$). To prevent peroxide formation, ether is often stored in contact with a piece of iron wire.

7   *Amines.* The organic amines can be considered to be derived from ammonia by substitution of one or more of the H atoms of NH_3 by hydro-carbon residues. Since one, two, or three of the hydrogen atoms can be replaced, it is possible to have primary, secondary, or tertiary amines, respectively. All three are usually formed as a mixture when ammonia is treated with a halogen derivative of a hydrocarbon. For example, when NH_3 is treated with CH_3I, the product includes CH_3NH_2, $(CH_3)_2NH$, and $(CH_3)_3N$. Like NH_3, the amines have an unshared pair of electrons on the nitrogen atom and hence can function as bases. This action as a base is easily observed by noting that a solution of an amine in water (in which, by the way, amines are quite soluble, but not so soluble as NH_3) can neutralize acids. A typical reaction is

$$\begin{array}{c} \text{H H} \\ \overset{..}{\text{H}}\text{:}\overset{..}{\text{C}}\text{:}\overset{..}{\text{N}}\text{:H} \\ \overset{..}{\text{H}} \end{array} + \text{H}^+ \rightarrow \left[\begin{array}{c} \text{H H} \\ \overset{..}{\text{H}}\text{:}\overset{..}{\text{C}}\text{:}\overset{..}{\text{N}}\text{:H} \\ \text{H H} \end{array}\right]^+$$

Methylamine   *Methylammonium ion*

which is quite analogous to neutralization of acids by ammonia

$$\begin{array}{c} \text{H} \\ \overset{..}{\text{H}}\text{:}\overset{..}{\text{N}}\text{:H} \\ \overset{..}{} \end{array} + \text{H}^+ \rightarrow \left[\begin{array}{c} \text{H} \\ \overset{..}{\text{H}}\text{:}\overset{..}{\text{N}}\text{:H} \\ \text{H} \end{array}\right]^+$$

When an aqueous solution containing methylammonium ion is evaporated, a methylammonium salt can be produced. Such salts are usually crystalline solids, which on being heated with NaOH regenerate the amine.

Closely related to the amines are the important compounds known as amino acids. Structurally, they are bifunctional, in the sense that they contain the two functional groups, an amine group and the organic-acid group. The simplest amino acid is glycine, NH_2CH_2COOH, also called aminoacetic acid. It differs from acetic acid (CH_3COOH) in that an NH_2 group has been substituted for one of the methyl's hydrogen atoms. Because glycine, like other amino acids, contains a basic NH_2 group and an acidic COOH group, it has the ability to act both as a base and as an acid. This is illustrated by the following reactions:

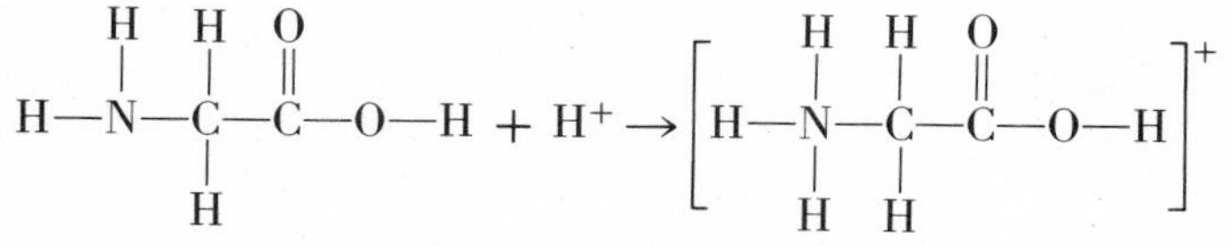

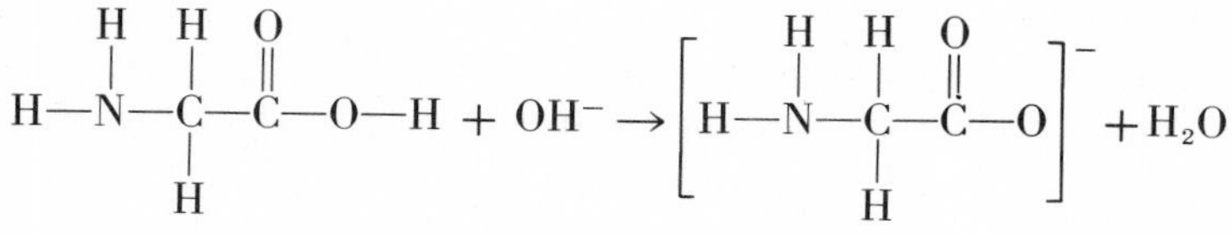

$$\begin{array}{ccc} H & H & O \\ | & | & \| \\ H-N-C-C-O-H \end{array} + H^+ \rightarrow \left[\begin{array}{ccc} H & H & O \\ | & | & \| \\ H-N-C-C-O-H \\ | & | \\ H & H \end{array}\right]^+$$

$$\begin{array}{ccc} H & H & O \\ | & | & \| \\ H-N-C-C-O-H \\ | \\ H \end{array} + OH^- \rightarrow \left[\begin{array}{ccc} H & H & O \\ | & | & \| \\ H-N-C-C-O \\ | \\ H \end{array}\right]^- + H_2O$$

In the first of these reactions the H^+ is neutralized by being joined to the amino acid through the unshared pair of electrons on the nitrogen atom. In the second reaction, the OH^- is neutralized by interaction with a proton from the COOH group. Since the first reaction constitutes *addition of* H^+ to an amino acid and the second reaction to *removal of* H^+ from an amino acid, the two processes can occur without external addition of acid or base. In fact, in aqueous solutions of glycine, the most abundant species is one in which the proton has been transferred from the COOH group to the NH_2 group. The process can be represented as follows:

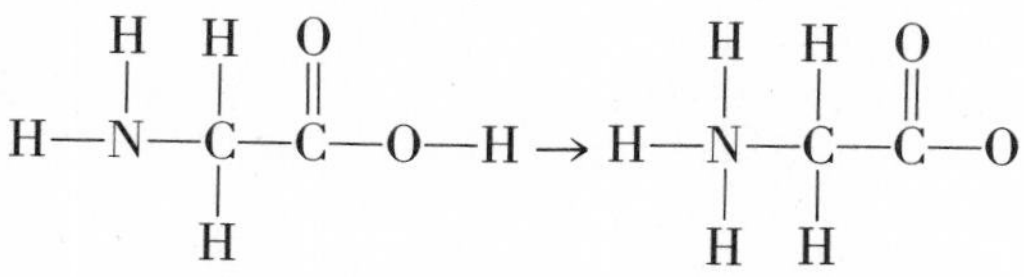

$$\begin{array}{ccc} H & H & O \\ | & | & \| \\ H-N-C-C-O-H \\ | \\ H \end{array} \rightarrow \begin{array}{ccc} H & H & O \\ | & | & \| \\ H-N-C-C-O \\ | & | \\ H & H \end{array}$$

It is essentially a self-neutralization reaction. The species produced is highly polar because of the shift of the proton from one end of the molecule to the other. To emphasize this shift, the formula is usually written $^+NH_3CH_2COO^-$, and the molecule is called a *zwitter ion*. The net charge on the zwitter ion is still zero.

The most common source of amino acids is from the breakdown of protein molecules. Such breakdown can be achieved by boiling the protein with water in the presence of acids or bases. At the present time, more than 20 different amino acids are recognized as being produced when proteins are fragmented in this way. Although the structure of most proteins is not yet known in detail, it seems that all proteins are composed of these amino acids polymerized together. Since even a relatively simple protein such as oval-bumen (from egg white) has a molecular weight of about 42,000, it is no easy task to discover how the different amino acids are strung together in the polymer.

28.2   ORGANIC REACTIONS

There are two important features which, in general, characterize the reactions between organic compounds. One of these features is the relative slowness of most organic reactions compared to many familiar inorganic reactions. For example, whereas the reaction between hydrochloric acid and sodium hydroxide is practically instantaneous, the esterification between acetic acid and ethyl alcohol takes hours, and occurs even then only if the reaction mixture is heated and a catalyst such as H_2SO_4 is added. The other characteristic feature of organic reactions is that, in general, the greater part of the reacting molecule remains relatively unchanged during the course of the reaction. In other words, many of the atoms are undisturbed by the reaction and maintain their arrangement relative to their neighbors, even though somewhere else in the molecule fairly extensive changes are going on.

Both the slowness of the reactions and the retention of the major part of a molecule's identity can be exceedingly exasperating at times, but in general they prove very useful. For one thing, they allow the organic chemist to focus his attention on a small portion of the molecule with the confident belief that the rest of the molecule will not change much while he carries out his reaction. For another thing, the slowness of the reactions allows the changes to be stopped well before equilibrium is established. As a result, it is frequently possible to isolate compounds which, if allowed to remain in the reaction mixture, would react further to give different products. Even so, it is not practicable to eliminate completely side reactions which lead to other than the desired products. Consequently, the organic chemist must often be content with considerably less than 100 per cent of the theoretically possible yield of the compound desired.

Of the many types of organic reactions, some of the most commonly encountered are addition, substitution, and polymerization. A simple example of an addition reaction is the adding of HBr to C_2H_4, ethylene. The over-all change is

$$\underset{\text{Ethylene}}{\overset{\displaystyle \overset{\text{H}}{\diagdown}\;\;\overset{\text{H}}{\diagup}}{\underset{\text{H}}{\diagup}\text{C}=\text{C}\underset{\text{H}}{\diagdown}} + \text{H—Br} \rightarrow \underset{\text{Ethyl bromide}}{\text{H—}\overset{\displaystyle \text{H}}{\underset{\displaystyle \text{H}}{\text{C}}}\text{—}\overset{\displaystyle \text{H}}{\underset{\displaystyle \text{H}}{\text{C}}}\text{—Br}}$$

The mechanism of the reaction is believed to involve dissociation of HBr to form a proton and a bromide ion, each of which adds to the ethylene molecule. A possible sequence is

$$C_2H_4 + H^+ \rightarrow C_2H_5^+$$

$$C_2H_5^+ + Br^- \rightarrow C_2H_5Br$$

Substitution reactions are somewhat more complicated than addition reactions, because they involve removal of an attached atom or group of atoms and the addition of a different atom or group. An important class of substitution reactions are those involving benzene and its derivatives. We take as an example the chlorination of benzene:

$$C_6H_6 + Cl_2 \rightarrow C_6H_5Cl + HCl$$

In writing the structural formulas of benzene and its derivatives, a problem arises because of resonance (Fig. 24.8). Usually, only one of the resonance formulas is written, and for simplicity it is represented by a hexagon with nonreacting C and H atoms omitted. Thus, the chlorination of benzene can be represented as follows:

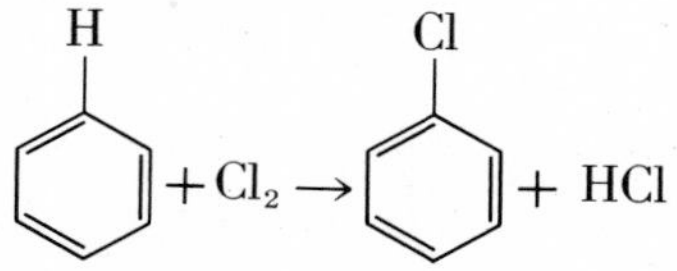

H

Cl

$+ Cl_2 \rightarrow$

$+ HCl$

Benzene   *Chlorobenzene*

The reaction is hastened by the presence of $FeCl_3$ and is believed to take place by a mechanism somewhat like the following:

$$Cl_2 + FeCl_3 \xrightarrow{\text{fast}} Cl^+ + FeCl_4^-$$

$$Cl^+ + C_6H_6 \xrightarrow{\text{slow}} C_6H_5Cl + H^+$$

The positive ion Cl^+ is not a species normally encountered and may not be the actual intermediate in this reaction.

It should be noted that all the hydrogen atoms in the benzene molecule are equivalent; therefore it makes no difference which H atom is replaced by Cl. In other words, only one kind of chlorobenzene molecule is possible. However, in chlorobenzene all the H atoms are not equivalent (since some are closer than others to the Cl atom), and when a second chlorine atom is substituted, three different products are possible. As shown below, these are

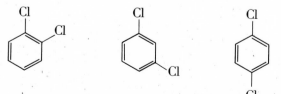

Orthodichlorobenzene   *Metadichlorobenzene*   *Paradichlorobenzene*

They differ from each other in that orthodichlorobenzene has the two chlorine atoms attached to adjacent carbon atoms; metadichlorobenzene has the two chlorine atoms attached to carbon atoms separated by a single CH group; paradichlorobenzene has the two chlorine atoms attached to carbon atoms separated by two CH groups. All three dichlorobenzenes have the molecular formula $C_6H_4Cl_2$ and hence are isomers. When monochlorobenzene is converted to dichlorobenzene, all three isomers are formed, but the ortho and para isomers predominate.

The third type of reaction mentioned, polymerization, can be of two very different kinds. In one of these, called *addition polymerization,* molecules add together to form giant molecules; in the other, called *condensation polymerization,* small molecules are split out as the giant molecule is built up. The formation of polyethylene is a typical addition polymerization. Polymerization can be initiated by heating ethylene at high pressure or by use of initiators such as organic peroxides. Peroxide-initiated polymerization is rather common for the production of polymers other than polyethylene and is thought to proceed in the following manner:

$$R\!-\!O\!-\!O\!-\!R \rightarrow R\!-\!O\cdot \ + \ \cdot O\!-\!R$$

In the first step, the peroxide is assumed to have broken a covalent bond so as to leave an unpaired electron (shown by the dot) on each R—O • residue. This residue, called a *free radical,* is very reactive and, as shown in the second step, can combine with an ethylene molecule to form a new free radical which is one —CH_2CH_2— unit greater than the original. Chain propagation thus continues, and a giant molecule is progressively built up until the free radical is destroyed, either by combining with another free radical or by reacting with some chemical added as an inhibitor. Such a mechanism accounts satisfactorily for the observation that the final polymer product contains giant molecules of different molecular weights. It also explains the fact that a small amount of initiator can produce a great deal of polymerization. It should be noted that, in the final giant molecules, the *RO* end groups are an insignificant fraction of the molecules and so the polymers are essentially aggregations of C_2H_4 units added together.

In condensation polymerization, the build-up of the polymer occurs not by the addition of a whole molecule to a lengthening chain but by reaction of a lengthening chain with a small molecule, accompanied by elimination of a simpler species such as H_2O. In order that polymerization may occur, two conditions must be met: One end of molecule *A* must be able to interact with the other end of molecule *B* so as to split out a small group such as H_2O. Second, both molecules *A* and *B* must contain two functional groups so that, after *A* and *B* combine, the free ends can continue to react to extend the polymer. An example of condensation polymerization is the formation of nylon. Here the reaction is between diaminohexane, $H_2N(CH_2)_6NH_2$, and adipic acid, $HOOC(CH_2)_4COOH$, and involves elimination of water. The reaction can be pictured as follows:

This first step is then followed by reactions at both ends of the molecule to give giant polymers.

28.3 SYNTHESIS OF ORGANIC COMPOUNDS

One of the important aspects of organic chemistry is the synthesis of rather complicated molecules from simpler substances. Synthesis of even a comparatively small molecule such as aspirin (acetylsalicylic acid)

requires a large number of consecutive reactions. To illustrate the general problems involved in organic synthesis, we consider the steps necessary to make aspirin from simple, familiar chemicals.

As can be seen from its formula, the aspirin molecule contains a benzene ring with two side chains attached. Let us first synthesize benzene. We can do this by heating carbon as coke with lime (CaO) to form calcium carbide (CaC$_2$), treating the calcium carbide with water to form acetylene (C$_2$H$_2$), and then heating acetylene at high pressure. Equations for the steps are

$$CaO(s) + 3C(s) \rightarrow CaC_2(s) + CO(g)$$

$$CaC_2(s) + 2H_2O \rightarrow C_2H_2(g) + Ca^{++} + 2OH^-$$

$$3C_2H_2(g) \rightarrow C_6H_6(g)$$

Once the benzene is obtained, the problem is to introduce the side chains. Since benzene is a rather inert hydrocarbon, somewhat drastic measures are needed to introduce substituents. If it is heated with concentrated sulfuric acid, the following reaction occurs:

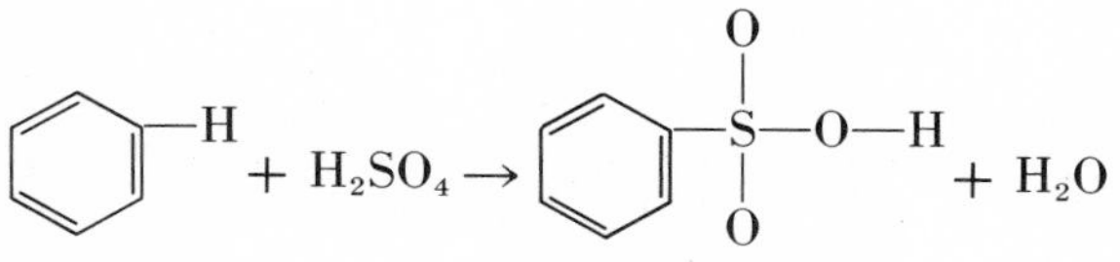

Benzene   *Benzenesulfonic acid*

When the product is heated with sodium hydroxide at 350°C., the SO$_3$H group is replaced by a negatively charged oxygen atom.

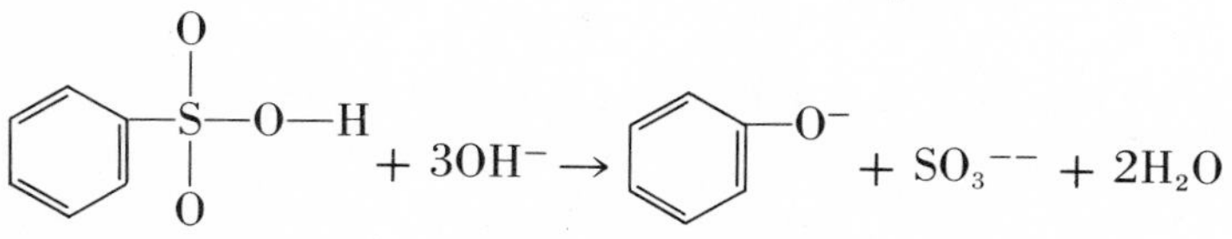

Benzenesulfonic acid   *Phenolate ion*

At 150°C. the phenolate ion picks up carbon dioxide (under pressure) as follows:

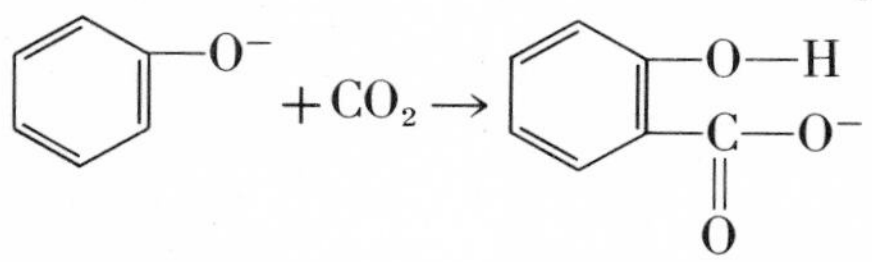

Phenolate ion   *Salicylate ion*

Subsequent acidification produces salicylic acid.

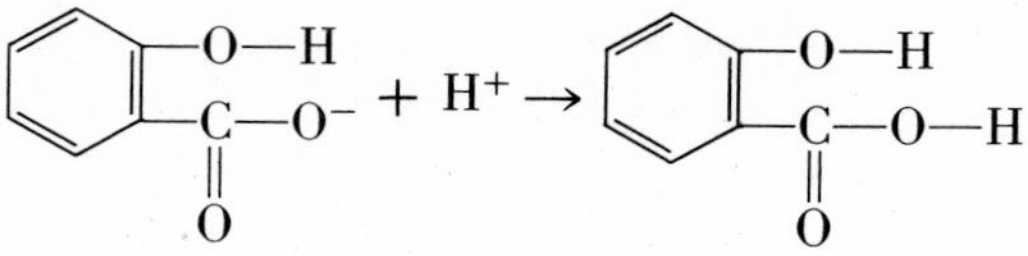

Salicylate ion   *Salicylic acid*

At this stage, the product contains one of the desired side chains (COOH) and is ready for the addition of the other. The reagent necessary for this addition is acetic anhydride, which can be prepared by the reaction of acetic acid with sulfur chloride, S_2Cl_2. Sulfur chloride is formed when chlorine gas is bubbled through molten sulfur

$$2S + Cl_2(g) \rightarrow S_2Cl_2(g)$$

Acetic acid results from the air oxidation of acetaldehyde, which in turn comes form the reaction of acetylene with water in the presence of catalysts. Pertinent equations leading to acetic anhydride are

$$C_2H_2(g) + H_2O \xrightarrow{\text{catalyst}} CH_3-\overset{\overset{\displaystyle O}{\|}}{C}-H$$

Acetylene   *Acetaldehyde*

$$CH_3-\overset{\overset{\displaystyle O}{\|}}{C}-H + \tfrac{1}{2}O_2 \rightarrow CH_3-\overset{\overset{\displaystyle O}{\|}}{C}-O-H$$

Acetaldehyde   *Acetic acid*

$$8CH_3-\overset{\overset{\displaystyle O}{\|}}{C}-O-H + 3S_2Cl_2 \rightarrow$$

Acetic acid

$$4CH_3-\overset{\overset{\displaystyle O}{\|}}{C}-O-\overset{\overset{\displaystyle O}{\|}}{C}-CH_3 + H_2SO_4 + 6HCl + 5S$$

Acetic anhydride

Now, at long last, we are ready for the final step. Acetic anhydride and salicylic acid are heated together, and aspirin results by the following reaction:

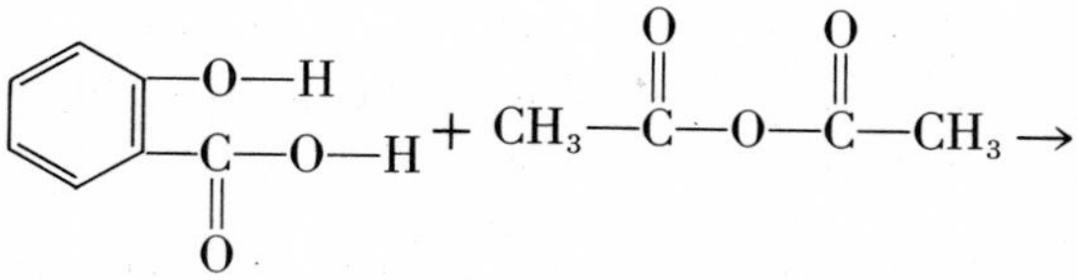

Salicylic acid   *Acetic anhydride*

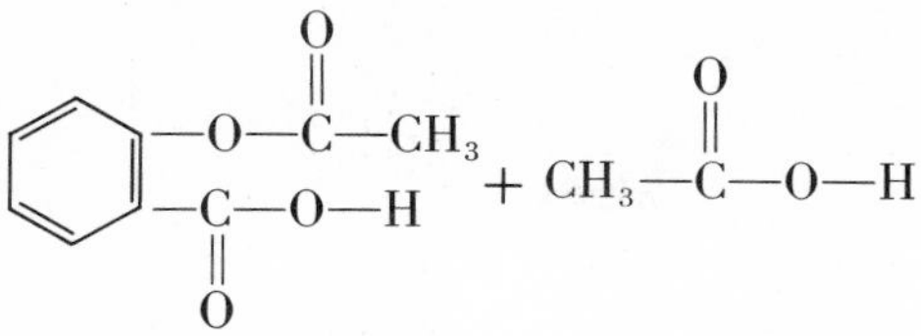

Aspirin   *Acetic acid*

28.4 NATURAL PRODUCTS

The term natural products is used in organic chemistry to refer to those organic compounds which are synthesized in nature either by plants or animals. The principal aim of natural-products research is to determine the structure of these naturally occurring molecules. The first problem is to isolate the compound of interest so as to obtain it in a pure state. Various techniques are used for the separation, including distillation, absorption on surfaces, and extraction by various solvents. Proof of purity is difficult, but it can be inferred from the reproducibility of chemical analysis of samples purified in different ways. Also, a sharp melting point as contrasted to melting over a wide temperature range is taken to indicate isolation of a pure compound.

Once the compound is isolated, it can be chemically analyzed for the constituent elements and its simplest formula thus determined. Freezing-point lowering of an appropriate solvent (Sec. 10.3) gives information leading to the molecular formula. At this point the problem really begins. How are the atoms arranged in the molecule? Because organic reactions frequently leave large groups of atoms intact, it is useful to subject the unknown molecule to a series of reactions in the hope that some of these reactions will lead to products of known structure. From the arrangement of atoms in the known products, inferences can be drawn about the structure of the parent molecule. As an example of how this is done, we consider the following reactions of the natural product nicotine, a nitrogen-containing organic compound found in tobacco:

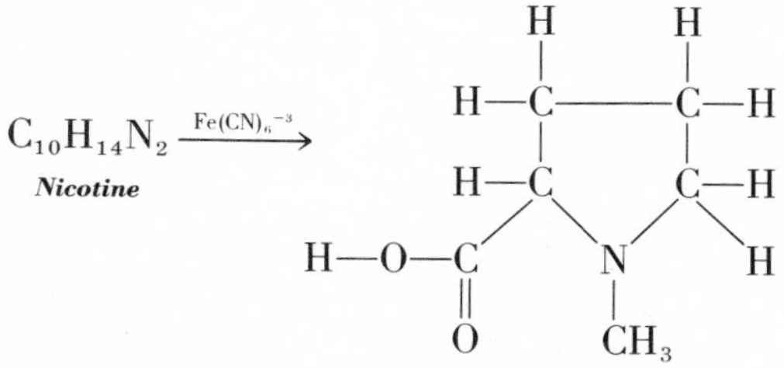

N-Methylpyrrolidine-
2-carboxylic acid

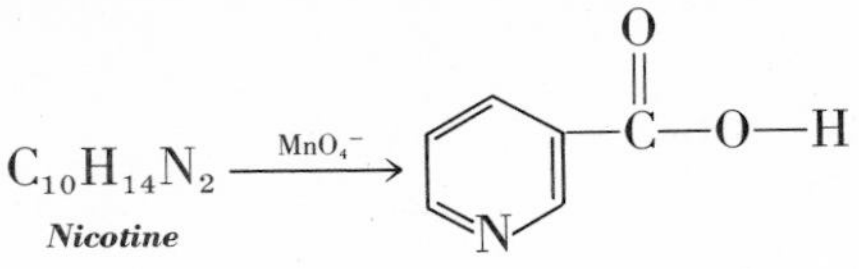

$$C_{10}H_{14}N_2 \xrightarrow{MnO_4^-}$$

Nicotine

Nicotinic acid

As shown, two different oxidizing agents [$Fe(CN)_6^{-3}$ and MnO_4^-] form two different products, each of which is a compound of known structure. The products contain different rings of atoms to which COOH groups are attached. Since the COOH group is frequently formed when a group attached to a ring is oxidized, it is reasonable to suppose that nicotine consists of the two rings hooked together and has the structure

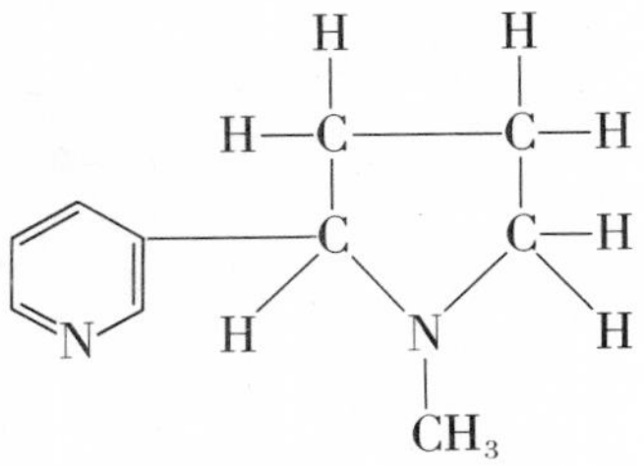

Nicotine

Apparently ferricyanide oxidizes away the left-hand ring, and permanganate the right-hand ring. Ultimate proof of structure of nicotine and other natural products comes from successful laboratory synthesis starting with compounds of known structure.

28.5   BIOCHEMICAL PROCESSES

Chemical reactions which occur in biological systems are generally extremely complicated and are far from being well understood. Part of the difficulty stems from the complexity of the molecules involved and part from the problem of tracing the path of atoms through many successive steps in a living system. In the case of large molecules such as proteins, the structure of the molecules has not been completely determined, much less their chemical reactions in biochemical processes. Even in the case of relatively small molecules, such as the simpler carbohydrates (Sec. 24.4), only recently have investigations been able to shed light on the way these molecules are formed in nature.

It is a well-known fact that in green plants carbon dioxide and water are converted in the presence of sunlight to carbohydrates and oxygen. The over-all reaction can be written

$$CO_2(g) + H_2O(g) \xrightarrow[\text{sunlight}]{} \text{carbohydrates} + O_2(g)$$

and is called *photosynthesis*. The importance of photosynthesis cannot be overestimated, since it represents the principal way by which solar energy is made available to living organisms. For example, carbohydrates such as sugars and starches are oxidized in the body to provide needed energy.* Since the oxidation of carbohydrates is the reverse of the photosynthesis reaction, the energy liberated in respiration must ultimately have come from the sun. In order to gain an idea of the magnitude of the energy involved, we might consider the photosynthesis process that produces glucose, a simple carbohydrate sugar. The energy for the reaction

$$674 \text{ kcal.} + 6CO_2(g) + 6H_2O(g) \rightarrow C_6H_{12}O_6(s) + 6O_2(g)$$

indicates that 674 kcal. must be supplied for every mole of glucose formed. Although glucose is found in plants, it is not the end product of photosynthesis. More complex carbohydrates, for example, sucrose, starch, and cellulose, are formed by plants from glucose.

The net equation for the formation of glucose shows the disappearance of 6 molecules of carbon dioxide and 6 molecules of water. It is highly improbable that these 12 molecules react in a single step. There must be a series of steps, but there has been a great deal of controversy as to what they are. At one time it was believed that the first step was the combination of CO_2 with H_2O to form formaldehyde (HCHO), but this hypothesis has been convincingly disproved. Recently, with the aid of radioactive carbon atoms introduced into the photosynthesis process as CO_2, it has been possible to trace the path of carbon atoms from carbon dioxide to glucose.

The process is a complex cyclic one in which various components of the final sugar molecule enter the cycle at different points. A fundamental problem has been to identify the step in which CO_2 is taken into the cycle. Apparently, the key step is a reaction in which a phosphate derivative of a five-carbon carbohydrate (I) reacts with a CO_2 molecule and H_2O as follows:

---

* The liberation of energy by the oxidation of carbohydrates also occurs when cellulose, a highly polymerized carbohydrate, is burned as the common fuel wood. Furthermore, carbohydrates are believed to be the materials from which the natural hydrocarbons in petroleum and coal are formed. Thus, much of the energy liberated when gasoline, for example, is burned is also traceable to the sun.

$$
\begin{array}{c}
\text{H} \\
| \\
\text{H}-\text{C}-\text{O}-\text{PO}_3\text{H}_2 \\
| \\
\text{C}=\text{O} \\
| \\
\text{H}-\text{C}-\text{OH} \\
| \\
\text{H}-\text{C}-\text{OH} \\
| \\
\text{H}-\text{C}-\text{O}-\text{PO}_3\text{H}_2 \\
| \\
\text{H}
\end{array}
\quad + \text{CO}_2 + \text{H}_2\text{O} \rightarrow 2
\begin{bmatrix}
\text{H} \\
| \\
\text{H}-\text{C}-\text{O}-\text{PO}_3\text{H}_2 \\
| \\
\text{H}-\text{O}-\text{C}-\text{H} \\
| \\
\text{C}-\text{O}-\text{H} \\
\| \\
\text{O}
\end{bmatrix}
$$

(I)   *(II)*

The acid functional group COOH in (II) is then reduced in an enzyme-catalyzed reaction to form an aldehyde functional group CHO. The reduction product (III) then rearranges to (IV):

$$
\begin{array}{c}
\text{H} \\
| \\
\text{H}-\text{C}-\text{O}-\text{PO}_3\text{H}_2 \\
| \\
\text{H}-\text{O}-\text{C}-\text{H} \\
| \\
\text{C}-\text{H} \\
\| \\
\text{O}
\end{array}
\quad \rightarrow \quad
\begin{array}{c}
\text{H} \\
| \\
\text{H}-\text{C}-\text{O}-\text{PO}_3\text{H}_2 \\
| \\
\text{C}=\text{O} \\
| \\
\text{H}-\text{C}-\text{O}-\text{H} \\
| \\
\text{H}
\end{array}
$$

(III)   *(IV)*

The rearranged product (IV) reacts with an unrearranged molecule (III) to form a six-membered carbohydrate derivative (V):

$$
\begin{array}{c}
\text{H} \\
| \\
\text{H}-\text{C}-\text{O}-\text{PO}_3\text{H}_2 \\
| \\
\text{H}-\text{O}-\text{C}-\text{H} \\
| \\
\text{C}-\text{H} \\
\| \\
\text{O}
\end{array}
\; + \;
\begin{array}{c}
\text{H} \\
| \\
\text{H}-\text{C}-\text{O}-\text{PO}_3\text{H}_2 \\
| \\
\text{C}=\text{O} \\
| \\
\text{H}-\text{C}-\text{O}-\text{H} \\
| \\
\text{H}
\end{array}
\; \rightarrow \;
\begin{array}{c}
\text{H} \\
| \\
\text{H}-\text{C}-\text{O}-\text{PO}_3\text{H}_2 \\
| \\
\text{C}=\text{O} \\
| \\
\text{H}-\text{O}-\text{C}-\text{H} \\
| \\
\text{H}-\text{C}-\text{O}-\text{H} \\
| \\
\text{H}-\text{C}-\text{O}-\text{H} \\
| \\
\text{H}-\text{C}-\text{O}-\text{PO}_3\text{H}_2 \\
| \\
\text{H}
\end{array}
$$

(III)   *(IV)*   *(V)*

Reaction of the final product with water leads to glucose. Other reactions between the final product and intermediates in its formation regenerate the five-carbon molecule needed in the first step.

The result of the changes shown above is to introduce CO_2 into the cycle and to lengthen the carbon chain from five carbons to six carbons. It must be emphasized that this is but a portion of the over-all process and, in fact, the regeneration of (I) constitutes a major portion of the known cycle.

Still unknown are the steps which account for the evolution of oxygen that accompanies photosynthesis. Furthermore, the role of sunlight and the green pigment chlorophyll, so necessary to the process, has not been worked out. Much intensive research is currently being devoted to these vital problems.

QUESTIONS

28.1   *Functional groups.* Classify each of the following compounds according to its functional group: C_2H_5CHO, $(C_3H_7)_3N$, $(CH_3)_2O$, C_3H_7COOH, $CH_3COOC_2H_5$, $CH_3COC_2H_5$.

28.2   *Structural formulas.* Write out the structural formula for each compound shown in Question 28.1.

28.3   *Alcohols.* Show that alcohols are more similar to inorganic acids than they are to inorganic bases.

28.4   *Fermentation.* It is estimated that the soft-drink industry uses 33,000 tons of carbon dioxide per year. How much glucose would the breweries have to ferment to produce this much carbon dioxide?

28.5   *Aldehydes.* Write a balanced equation for the formation of a silver mirror from the reaction of $Ag(NH_3)_2{}^+$ with acetaldehyde in basic solution.

28.6   *Ketones.* Ketones are quite difficult to oxidize but under appropriate conditions can be oxidized to give a mixture of acids. Account for the fact that oxidation of the ketone $C_2H_5COC_4H_9$ can lead to formation of the following: CH_3COOH, C_2H_5COOH, C_3H_7COOH, C_4H_9COOH.

28.7   *Acids.* Oxalic acid, $H_2C_2O_4$, is a diprotic acid which is sometimes classed as an organic acid. Write a structural formula to account for this.

28.8   *Ester synthesis.* How would you go about synthesizing methyl acetate, starting with coke as the only source of carbon.

28.9   *Ethers.* The concentrated sulfuric acid process is not satisfactory for the preparation of pure $CH_3-O-C_2H_5$. Explain.

28.10   *Amines.* (*a*) How could you convert $C_2H_5NH_2$ to $C_2H_5NH_3Cl$? (*b*) How could you accomplish the reverse conversion?

28.11   *Addition reactions.* Show that two isomers can be formed by the addition of HBr to $CH_3CH{=}CH_2$.

28.12   *Substitution reactions.* How many isomers can be obtained when one chlorine atom is substituted for a hydrogen atom in each of the three dichloro-benzenes?

28.13   *Polymerization.* Account for the fact that addition of a reducing agent to polymerizing polyethylene leads to a shorter average chain length.

28.14   *Quantitative synthesis.* Suppose you want to make one aspirin tablet containing 0.32 g. of aspirin. How much benzene would you need? Assume 75% yield for all steps except 100% for the final acidification.

28.15   *Molecular formula.* Caffeine has the weight percentage composition 49.5% C, 5.2% H, 28.8% N, and 16.5% O. If 0.97 g. of it, dissolved in 25 g. of benzene, lowers its freezing point by 0.98°C., what is the molecular formula of caffeine? (The molal freezing-point lowering constant is 4.90°C.)

29 Nuclear Structure and Radioactivity

IN THE PRECEDING CHAPTERS, the emphasis has been on interpretation of chemical behavior in terms of the electronic aspects of atoms. Little has been said of the nucleus because, except for its charge, which controls the electronic arrangement, it has essentially no influence on chemical behavior. In this final chapter some of the other aspects of nuclear behavior are considered.

29.1 NUCLEAR STABILITY

As discussed in Sec. 3.6, the nucleus is thought to contain Z protons, where Z is the atomic number, and $(A - Z)$ neutrons, where A is the mass number, in a region which is about 10^{-13} cm. in radius. The difficult thing to understand is how positive charges can be packed together into such a small space without flying apart as a result of electric repulsion. Neutrons must be at least partly responsible for the binding, because, first, there is no nucleus consisting solely of protons (plural!) and, second, the more protons there are in a nucleus, the more neutrons required per proton for stability. This latter point is demonstrated by the "belt of stability" shown in Fig.

29.1, where a plot is made of the stable (nonradioactive) nuclei. Each point corresponds to a known nucleus containing a given number of protons and a given number of neutrons. The straight line represents the line along which nuclei would lie if they all contained an equal number of neutrons and protons. It is evident that, whereas for the light elements, nonradioactive

Fig. 29.1   Stable nuclei.

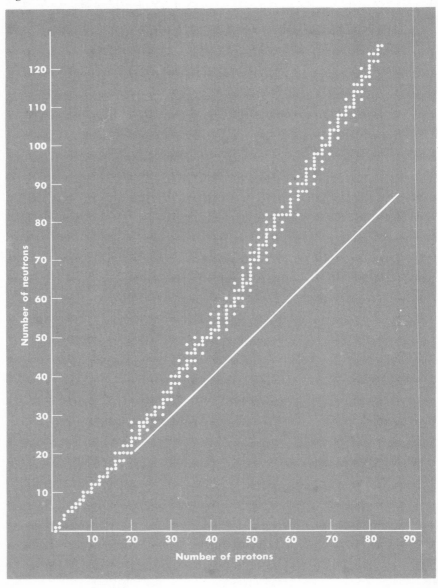

nuclei contain approximately equal numbers of neutrons and protons, for the heavier elements, nonradioactive nuclei contain considerably more neutrons than protons. Furthermore, it is observed that nuclei which do not fall within this belt of stability are radioactive; i.e., their neutron-to-proton ratios are either too high or too low for stability, and some kind of radioactive process (such as those discussed in the following section) must occur in order to bring the nucleus back to stability. The bigger question as to how neutrons act to bind the protons is still essentially unanswered.

At the present time there are two models used for the nucleus: the liquid-drop model and the shell model. The two are not mutually exclusive but emphasize different aspects of the nucleus. The liquid-drop model, first proposed by Bohr (1936), imagines the nucleus as consisting of neutrons and protons aggregated in a random, disordered fashion reminiscent of molecules in a drop of liquid. The strongest support for the model comes from the fact that the nuclear density is approximately constant at about 10^{14} g. per cc. for all atoms of the periodic table. The nuclear shell model, due mainly to Mayer (1950), considers nuclear particles to be arranged in energy levels in the nucleus just as are electrons outside the nucleus. There are special complications arising from the fact that two kinds of particles (neutrons and protons) must be accommodated, but the model gains considerable support from the special stability of certain nuclei.* These specially stable nuclei occur whenever the number of neutrons or the number of protons equals one of the so-called "magic numbers," 2, 8, 20, 50, 82, or 126, a situation reminiscent of closed shells of electrons. Nuclei which contain simultaneously a magic number of protons and a magic number of neutrons are the most stable, e.g., $_2He^4$, $_8O^{16}$, $_{20}Ca^{40}$, and $_{82}Pb^{208}$.

29.2   TYPES OF RADIOACTIVITY

If a nucleus lies outside the belt of stability, it tends to reach a stable configuration by a radioactive process which changes the number of neutrons and/or protons to a more favorable value. How does a nucleus get outside the belt of stability? There are two general cases which might be distinguished: *induced radioactivity* and *natural radioactivity*. Induced radioactivity results when stable nuclei are subjected to bombardment by other

---

* One of the ways of indicating the relative stability of nonradioactive nuclei is to specify the amount of energy required to break the nuclei into isolated protons and neutrons. This amount of energy can be calculated by comparing the experimentally determined mass of a given nucleus with the total mass expected for the corresponding number of neutrons and protons. In the case of helium, as described more fully in Sec. 29.5, it requires 650 million kcal. to break up a mole of helium into protons and neutrons.

particles. If the energy of the incoming particles is of the proper magnitude, bombarded nuclei combine with incident particles to form new nuclei which, if unstable, undergo radioactive decay. An example of such a process occurs when $_6C^{12}$ nuclei are bombarded with protons which have been accelerated to high energies in a cyclotron. The process can be described by the nuclear equation

$$_6C^{12} + {}_1H^1 \rightarrow {}_7N^{13} + \text{energy}$$

The equation is balanced in that it shows conservation of charge, denoted by the subscripts, and of mass, denoted by the superscripts. The nucleus produced, $_7N^{13}$, is unstable and lies below the belt of stability, with too few neutrons (6) for the number of protons (7). Nuclear rearrangement occurs so as to give emission of a *positron*, a positive electron. This has the effect of decreasing the number of protons to 6, making the new nucleus a carbon nucleus, and increasing the number of neutrons to 7. The decay process can be written

$$_7N^{13} \rightarrow {}_1e^0 + {}_6C^{13}$$

where $_1e^0$ represents the positron, a particle of $+1$ charge and essentially zero mass (like the electron), and $_6C^{13}$ is the resulting stable nucleus.

The rate at which radioactive disintegration occurs gives a measure of the stability of a nucleus and is usually expressed in terms of the *half-life* of the nucleus, the time required for half of a given number of atoms to disintegrate. For the above decay of $_7N^{13}$, the half-life, usually designated as $t_{1/2}$, is 10.1 min. This means that, of any aggregation of $_7N^{13}$ nuclei, half of them will have disintegrated in 10.1 min.; in another 10.1 min., half of the remainder will have disintegrated, etc. Since radioactive decay is a statistical process essentially unaffected by changes in temperature or chemical binding, no one can predict which specific $_7N^{13}$ nucleus of a collection will disintegrate next; only the probability of decay can be stated, and this is done by specifying the half-life. The shorter the half-life, the more probable the decay.

Natural radioactivity, as the name implies, refers to the decay of naturally occurring unstable isotopes. These unstable natural species are of long half-life, or else they are the result of other radioactive disintegrations and can be traced back to some long-lived isotope. For example, although there are no stable nuclei with atomic numbers higher than 83, still there are appreciable amounts of $_{90}Th^{234}$ in nature even though it has a half-life of only 24.1 days. With such a half-life, it would be expected that after a couple of years the $_{90}Th^{234}$ in nature would have disintegrated. The fact is, however, that $_{90}Th^{234}$ is constantly being regenerated by the decay of $_{92}U^{238}$. This disintegration

$$_{92}U^{238} \rightarrow {}_{90}Th^{234} + {}_2He^4$$

has a half-life of 4.5×10^9 years. If we take the age of the earth as roughly 5 billion years, then approximately half the $_{92}U^{238}$ originally present at the creation is still with us and continues to replenish the $_{90}Th^{234}$ supply.

Although consideration of radioactivity as artificially induced or natural is convenient, it is sometimes more useful to classify radioactive reactions according to the types of particles which unstable nuclei eject. In terms of the belt of stability shown in Fig. 29.1, three cases can be considered: (1) the unstable nucleus is above the belt of stability; (2) the unstable nucleus is below the belt of stability; or (3) the unstable nucleus lies beyond ($Z > 83$) the belt of stability.

In case 1, the nucleus has too high a neutron-proton ratio and can remedy matters either by ejecting a neutron or by forming and ejecting a beta particle (electron). Simple neutron ejection is rarely observed, because it usually occurs so rapidly. For example, the decay

$$_2He^5 \rightarrow {}_2He^4 + {}_0n^1$$

to produce an alpha particle and a neutron ($_0n^1$) has been calculated to have a half-life of 2×10^{-21} sec., much too short to be observed.*

Beta emission is much more common. It corrects a neutron-proton ratio that is too high by removing one unit of negative charge and thereby increasing the positive charge of the nucleus. Since a β particle (or electron, designated $_{-1}e^0$) has very little mass, its emission does not change the weight of a nucleus appreciably. A few examples of β decay are:

$$_6C^{14} \rightarrow {}_7N^{14} + {}_{-1}e^0 \qquad t_{1/2} = 5{,}580 \text{ years}$$

$$_{11}Na^{24} \rightarrow {}_{12}Mg^{24} + {}_{-1}e^0 \qquad t_{1/2} = 15.0 \text{ hr.}$$

$$_{53}I^{136} \rightarrow {}_{54}Xe^{136} + {}_{-1}e^0 \qquad t_{1/2} = 86 \text{ sec.}$$

If, as in case 2, an unstable nucleus lies below the belt of stability, it has too low a neutron-proton ratio and must increase the number of neutrons, decrease the number of protons, or do both simultaneously. For such nuclei, one of the common devices leading to a gain in stability is to absorb into the nucleus one of the orbital electrons, usually one of the electrons from the K shell. Such K capture reduces the nuclear charge by one unit, leaving the nuclear mass essentially unchanged, as in the following example:

---

* However, there are some neutron emissions which are delayed long enough so that they are observable. These occur, for instance, in some of the products resulting from the fission of $_{92}U^{235}$ nuclei. A specific case of this is found in the decay of high-energy $_{36}Kr^{87}$ by the reaction

$$_{36}Kr^{87} \rightarrow {}_{36}Kr^{86} + {}_0n^1$$

for which the half-life appears to be about 1 min.

$$_{18}\text{Ar}^{37} \xrightarrow[K \text{ capture}]{} {}_{17}\text{Cl}^{37} \qquad t_{1/2} = 35 \text{ days}$$

Invariably, when a K electron is captured, an outer-shell electron of the atom drops into the K shell to fill the vacancy, thus liberating energy, usually as an X ray.

Another device to raise a neutron-proton ratio that is too low is for the nucleus to emit a positron ($_1e^0$, a positive electron). This process, typified by

$$_{15}\text{P}^{30} \rightarrow {}_{14}\text{Si}^{30} + {}_1e^0 \qquad t_{1/2} = 2.5 \text{ min.}$$

decreases the nuclear charge by one unit and leaves the mass essentially unchanged.

In case 3, the nuclei lie beyond the belt of stability; they have too many protons crammed into one nucleus for stability, no matter how many neutrons are present. For nuclei with 84 or more protons, no one of the above steps by itself can lead to a stable nucleus. Instead, it is necessary to split off larger pieces, and even then a series of steps may be required. Most commonly, the piece split off is an alpha particle, symbol $_2\text{He}^4$ (two protons plus two neutrons), and, in fact, most of the heavy nuclei are alpha emitters. With $_{84}\text{Po}^{212}$, a single step is sufficient to reach stability.

$$_{84}\text{Po}^{212} \rightarrow {}_{82}\text{Pb}^{208} + {}_2\text{He}^4 \qquad t_{1/2} = 0.3 \times 10^{-6} \text{ sec.}$$

With $_{92}\text{U}^{234}$, many steps are required, involving a combination of α and β decays, as in the following:

$$_{92}\text{U}^{234} \xrightarrow{\alpha} {}_{90}\text{Th}^{230} \xrightarrow{\alpha} {}_{88}\text{Ra}^{226} \xrightarrow{\alpha} {}_{86}\text{Rn}^{222} \xrightarrow{\alpha} {}_{84}\text{Po}^{218} \xrightarrow{\alpha} {}_{82}\text{Pb}^{214} \xrightarrow{\beta}$$

$$_{83}\text{Bi}^{214} \xrightarrow{\alpha} {}_{81}\text{Tl}^{210} \xrightarrow{\beta} {}_{82}\text{Pb}^{210} \xrightarrow{\beta} {}_{83}\text{Bi}^{210} \xrightarrow{\beta} {}_{84}\text{Po}^{210} \xrightarrow{\alpha} {}_{82}\text{Pb}^{206}$$

Other steps leading to the same stable nucleus, $_{82}\text{Pb}^{206}$, are also possible.

Finally, to complete the discussion of the types of radioactive decay, mention must be made of γ rays (gamma rays). These are essentially bundles of energy, much like very high energy X rays, which frequently accompany beta emission and positron emission. They represent the principal way in which excited nuclei can get rid of excess energy.

29.3   TRANSURANIUM ELEMENTS

Until recently, it was thought that there were only 92 elements in the periodic table. However, as radioactive processes were studied in greater detail, it was observed that atoms of atomic number higher than 92 could be produced. These transuranium elements have now been extended up to $Z = 102$ and will probably go even higher (but not much).

The first transuranium element to be prepared (1940) was neptunium, made by irradiation of $_{92}U^{238}$ with neutrons. The nucleus formed, $_{92}U^{239}$, decays by beta emission

$$_{92}U^{239} \rightarrow \ _{93}Np^{239} + _{-1}e^0 \qquad t_{1/2} = 23.5 \text{ min.}$$

to produce $_{93}Np^{239}$, which is also beta active. It decays

$$_{93}Np^{239} \rightarrow \ _{94}Pu^{239} + _{-1}e^0 \qquad t_{1/2} = 2.3 \text{ days}$$

to produce plutonium, the second transuranium element, which is alpha-active. Higher elements have been produced by similar irradiation of transuranium elements with neutrons or even with nuclei of the lighter elements such as helium or carbon. The transuranium elements have different chemical properties and can be separated from each other by chemical means. The isolation of plutonium is important, because the element is used as a source of nuclear energy.

29.4   RADIOCHEMISTRY

In chemistry, radioactive nuclei are useful because they are easy to follow. Their presence can be detected even in trace amounts by the darkening of photographic plates or by the use of various devices such as the Geiger counter, which can count individual particles because of ionization of gases by the particles. These counters operate because an alpha particle, for example, in passing through a gas-filled chamber, produces ions which can conduct an electric pulse between charged plates.

One of the most useful applications of radioactive tracers to chemistry has been in the elucidation of the mechanism of complex organic reactions. For example, by feeding radioactive carbon dioxide (labeled with $_6C^{14}$) to plants, it has been shown that, in the photosynthetic conversion of CO_2 to carbohydrates, the CO_2 is first converted to an organic phosphate and then stepwise to sugar. As mentioned in Sec. 28.5, each of the steps has been determined and the entire path of the $_6C^{14}$ traced.

The fact that $_6C^{14}$ is radioactive has led to the development of a rather novel method for dating archaeological discoveries. The basic ideas of the method are as follows: Carbon dioxide in the atmosphere contains mostly $_6C^{12}$ and a little $_6C^{13}$, both of which are nonradioactive. In addition, there is a small amount of $_6C^{14}$, which, even though it is constantly decaying, remains rather uniform in abundance, apparently because cosmic rays act on $_7N^{14}$ of the atmosphere to form $_6C^{14}$. Because the rate of decay balances the rate of production, the ratio of $C^{14}O_2$ to $C^{12}O_2$ in the atmosphere does not change with time. Now, it is well known that plants absorb CO_2 from the atmosphere in the process of photosynthesis. So long as the plant is alive and growing, the ratio of $_6C^{14}$ to $_6C^{12}$ atoms in the plant carbohydrates will be the same as that in the atmosphere. However, once the plant has been removed from the life cycle, as, for instance, when a tree is chopped down, the ratio of $_6C^{14}$ to $_6C^{12}$ begins to diminish as the $_6C^{14}$ atoms undergo radioactive decay. The half-life of $_6C^{14}$ is 5,580 years; therefore at the end of 5,580 years the ratio of $_6C^{14}$ to $_6C^{12}$ becomes half as great as it is in the atmosphere. To determine the age of a wooden relic or, for that matter, of any once-living material, a sample is burned to CO_2, and the ratio of $_6C^{14}$ to $_6C^{12}$ is measured.*

Another application of radioactivity has been made in determining the rate at which an electron can be transferred between two similar species in aqueous solution. Such a transfer between MnO_4^{--} and MnO_4^{-} has been found to be very rapid; that between $Co(NH_3)_6^{++}$ and $Co(NH_3)_6^{+3}$, very slow. For the latter case, one of the complexes is made with radioactive cobalt and mixed with the other, which is originally nonradioactive. From time to time, the solution is sampled and the cobalt species separated to see how fast radioactive cobalt appears in the originally nonradioactive species. Since the loss of an electron by radioactive $Co(NH_3)_6^{++}$ produces radioactive $Co(NH_3)_6^{+3}$, the rate of appearance of radioactivity in $Co(NH_3)_6^{+3}$ measures the rate of electron transfer.

Perhaps the most spectacular application of tracer techniques has been the elucidation of chemical properties of artificially produced elements. In the case of mendelevium, element 101, with a sample of only 17 atoms it was possible to decide that its properties are somewhat similar to those of thulium ($Z = 69$).

29.5   NUCLEAR ENERGY

In the preceding sections of this chapter, we have considered stability of nuclei with respect to radioactive decay. In this section, we consider stability of nuclei with respect to conversion of mass to energy. That such a conversion can exist is seen by considering the helium nucleus. A helium nucleus is believed to contain two neutrons and two protons. Since the mass of a neutron is 1.00866 a.m.u. and since the mass of a proton is 1.00732 a.m.u., we might expect that the mass of a helium nucleus would be

$$2(1.00866) + 2(1.00732) = 4.03196 \text{ a.m.u.}$$

---

* Confidence in the reliability of radiocarbon dating is being undermined by the production of C^{14} caused by nuclear-bomb testing and subsequent fall-out.

However, the experimentally observed (Sec. 3.3) mass of the helium nucleus is 4.002 a.m.u. What has happened to the missing mass of 0.030 a.m.u.? At present it is believed that, in forming a helium nucleus from protons and neutrons, mass is converted to energy. The amount of energy equivalent to the lost mass can be calculated from the Einstein relation

$$E = mc^2$$

where E is the energy equivalent in ergs (1 erg is 2.39×10^{-8} cal.) of the mass m in grams and c is the velocity of light, 3.00×10^{10} cm. per sec. For the helium nucleus, the loss of 0.030 a.m.u. of mass corresponds to the liberation of 650 million kcal. per mole of helium. Conversely, the same amount of energy is required to break up 1 mole of helium nuclei into protons and neutrons and so gives a measure of the binding energy of the nucleus.

Similar calculations for other nuclei show that different nuclei have different binding energies. The binding energy per nuclear particle—i.e., the total binding energy of one nucleus divided by the number of protons plus neutrons in the nucleus—is plotted in Fig. 29.2 for each of the different elements. As can be seen, intermediate elements of mass number about 60 have the highest binding energies per particle and are the most stable.

Fig. 29.2 *Binding energies of the elements (energy per nuclear particle).*

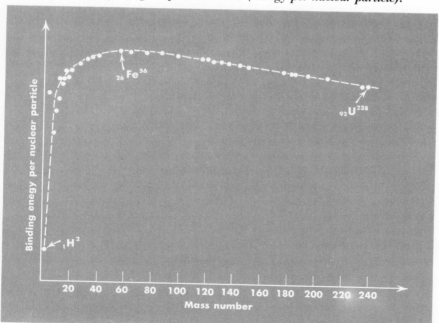

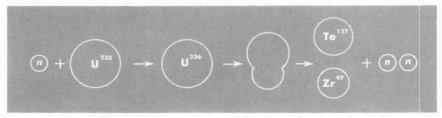

Fig. 29.3   A typical fission.

The other elements are unstable with respect to conversion to them. This means, for example, that, if a heavy element such as uranium is converted to iron, energy should be liberated. Similarly, if a light element such as hydrogen is converted to iron, energy should also be liberated. Such conversions are the bases for utilization of nuclear energy.

One method by which nuclear binding energy is made available is *nuclear fission*, the process in which a heavy nucleus breaks down to two approximately equal nuclei of intermediate mass. A typical fission process is shown in Fig. 29.3, where a neutron impinging on a U^{235} nucleus produces an unstable U^{236} nucleus that cleaves into a Te^{137} nucleus, a Zr^{97} nucleus, and two neutrons. Both the product nuclei have very high neutron-to-proton ratios and subsequently decay with the emission of beta particles. Actually, the fission shown is just one of the many ways in which a U^{236} nucleus can split. Some of the ways of splitting result in nuclei which undergo decay by neutron emission. Since in any fission more neutrons are produced than are needed to initiate the fission, once started, fission can become self-sustaining as a chain reaction.

For the very heaviest transuranium elements, fission is spontaneous, but for others, e.g., $_{92}U^{235}$ and $_{94}Pu^{239}$, fission can be initiated by exposure to neutrons. No matter how fission occurs, there is a change from a less stable nucleus (lower binding energy per nuclear particle) to more stable nuclei (higher binding energies per nuclear particle). In going from the less stable state to the more stable state, energy is liberated in large amounts. This release of energy by nuclear fission is the basis of nuclear reactors and atomic bombs. In nuclear reactors, fissionable material* such as U^{235} or Pu^{239} is stacked together with some "moderator" material (heavy water or graphite) which can remove energy from the neutrons produced in fission

---

* Natural uranium is 99.3 per cent U^{238} and 0.7 per cent U^{235}. The more abundant isotope requires high-energy neutrons to initiate fission; the less abundant one undergoes fission with readily available low-energy neutrons. Therefore, in practice it is desirable to have uranium enriched in U^{235}. Separation can be achieved by the diffusion process described in Sec. 6.10.

so that they can be captured to initiate new fission. The rate of the chain reaction is controlled by the insertion of cadmium rods, which have the ability to absorb neutrons. The energy released by the controlled chain reaction appears principally as heat and can be removed from the reactor by a circulating coolant to provide power for steam turbines. In atomic bombs, fissionable material is concentrated in a small region, so that the chain reaction builds up rapidly, and tremendous explosions result. It has been estimated that the fission of 1 lb. of U^{235} liberates the heat equivalent of more than 1,000 tons of coal.

Another method by which nuclear binding energy can be made available is *nuclear fusion,* the process in which two or more light nuclei combine to produce a single nucleus of heavier mass. Because of the steepness of the binding-energy curve (Fig. 29.2) at the low end, greater energy can be liberated per nuclear particle by nuclear fusion than by nuclear fission. However, the process has a much higher activation energy and so requires enormous temperatures (of the order of a million degrees) in order to occur. In the sun, temperatures are high enough so that nuclear fusion can take place to produce the energy that the sun pours out into space. It has been proposed that the chief source of this energy is the conversion of hydrogen to helium. The following steps have been suggested:

$$2 \times (_1H^1 + {}_1H^1 \rightarrow {}_1H^2 + {}_1e^0)$$

$$2 \times (_1H^2 + {}_1H^1 \rightarrow {}_2He^3)$$

$$_2He^3 + {}_2He^3 \rightarrow {}_2He^4 + {}_1H^1 + {}_1H^1$$

Net change: $_1H^1 + {}_1H^1 + {}_1H^1 + {}_1H^1 \rightarrow {}_2He^4 + {}_1e^0 + {}_1e^0$

For the consumption of 1 lb. of hydrogen by the over-all reaction, the energy liberated is equivalent to the burning of about 10,000 tons of coal. Since the mass of the sun is so large and since it is mostly hydrogen, it would take a conversion of only 1 per cent of the sun's mass from hydrogen to helium to keep the sun shining at its present rate for another billion years.

Nuclear fusion, or thermonuclear reaction, as it is sometimes called, would seem impossible on the earth because of the high temperatures required. However, with new techniques, e.g., the release of energy by nuclear fission, temperatures have been produced on the earth high enough that thermonuclear reactions can occur. Hydrogen bombs are a spectacular illustration of the destructive violence that can be achieved when nuclear energy is rapidly released through nuclear fusion. The slow, controlled release of nuclear energy by nuclear fusion opens to man a source of energy that dwarfs any supply hitherto available.

QUESTIONS

29.1   *Radioactive decay.* Show how each of the following types of radioactivity changes the neutron-proton ratio and enables formation of a stable nucleus: K capture, alpha emission, beta decay, positron emission.

29.2   *Radioactive decay.* Write nuclear equations for each of the following processes: (*a*) K capture by $_4\mathrm{Be}^7$; (*b*) positron decay of $_{11}\mathrm{Na}^{22}$; (*c*) beta decay of $_{29}\mathrm{Cu}^{66}$; (*d*) alpha decay of $_{84}\mathrm{Po}^{208}$; (*e*) successive decay of $_{82}\mathrm{Pb}^{211}$ by beta, alpha, and beta emission.

29.3   *Half-life.* One gram of Mo^{99} decays by beta emission to ⅛ g. in 200 hr. What is the half-life?

29.4   *Fissionable material.* Describe two different methods for getting fissionable material from natural uranium.

29.5   *Nuclear energy.* Contrast nuclear fusion with nuclear fission.

29.6   *Belt of stability.* By reference to Fig. 29.1, show why fission fragments would be expected to be neutron emitters or beta emitters.

29.7   *C^{14} dating.* A piece of charcoal from the Lascaux Cave in France has been found to have a C^{14} to C^{12} ratio that is 13% that of the atmosphere. How old is the specimen?

29.8   *Binding energy.* The observed mass of $_{26}\mathrm{Fe}^{56}$ is 55.9375 a.m.u. (chemical scale). Using the proton and neutron masses given in Sec. 29.5, calculate the binding energy per nuclear particle. Compare with the binding energy per nuclear particle for $_2\mathrm{He}^4$.   *Ans.* 3.27×10^{-13} cal. for Fe^{56} and 2.7×10^{-13} cal. for He^4

29.9   *Radioactive series.* Make a graph using axes similar to those in Fig. 29.1, and plot each nucleus shown in the consecutive decay of $_{92}\mathrm{U}^{234}$ to $_{82}\mathrm{Pb}^{206}$ (Sec. 29.2). With arrows, indicate the path the decay follows.

29.10   *Solar energy.* In the fusion process, 27 million e.v. of energy is liberated per helium nucleus formed. The sun radiates 4.0×10^{33} ergs per sec. Calculate the tons of hydrogen that would be consumed per minute to account for the energy radiated.

Appendix 1   *Nomenclature of Inorganic Chemistry*

THE NAMES OF THE ELEMENTS are listed inside the back cover of the book. Some of the elements also have Latin names (argentum for silver, aurum for gold, cuprum for copper, ferrum for iron, plumbum for lead, and stannum for tin) which appear in the names of compounds of these elements.

Compounds composed of but two elements have names derived directly from the elements. Usually the more electropositive element is named first, and the other element is given an *-ide* ending. Thus, we have sodium chloride (NaCl), calcium oxide (CaO), and aluminum nitride (AlN). If more than one atom of an element is involved, prefixes such as *di-* (for 2), *tri-* (3), *tetra-* (4), *penta-* (5), and *sesqui-* (1½) are used. For example, AlF_3 is aluminum trifluoride, Na_3P is trisodium phosphide, and N_2O_4 is dinitrogen tetroxide. When the same two elements form more than one compound, the compounds can be distinguished as in the following example:

	$FeCl_2$	$FeCl_3$
(a)	Iron dichloride	Iron trichloride
(b)	Ferrous chloride	Ferric chloride
(c)	Iron(II) chloride	Iron(III) chloride

In (*a*), distinction is made through use of prefixes; in (*b*), the endings *-ous* and *-ic* denote the lower and higher oxidation states, respectively, of iron; in (*c*), the Roman numerals in parentheses indicate the oxidation states. In a given series of compounds, the suffixes *-ous* and *-ic* may not be sufficient for complete designation but may need to be supplemented by one of the other methods of nomenclature. For example, the oxides of nitrogen are usually named as follows:

N_2O	Nitrous oxide
NO	Nitric oxide
N_2O_3	Dinitrogen trioxide, or nitrogen sesquioxide
NO_2	Nitrogen dioxide
N_2O_4	Dinitrogen tetroxide, or nitrogen tetroxide
N_2O_5	Dinitrogen pentoxide, or nitrogen pentoxide

Compounds containing more than two elements are name differently depending on whether they are bases, acids, or salts. Since most bases contain hydroxide ion (OH^-), they are generally called hydroxides, e.g., sodium hydroxide ($NaOH$), calcium hydroxide [$Ca(OH)_2$], arsenic trihydroxide [$As(OH)_3$]. The naming of acids and of salts derived from them is more complicated, as can be seen from the following series:

Acid	**Sodium salt**
$HClO$, hypochlorous acid	$NaClO$, sodium hypochlorite
$HClO_2$, chlorous acid	$NaClO_2$, sodium chlorite
$HClO_3$, chloric acid	$NaClO_3$, sodium chlorate
$HClO_4$, perchloric acid	$NaClO_4$, sodium.perchlorate
H_2SO_3, sulfurous acid	Na_2SO_3, sodium sulfite
H_2SO_4, sulfuric acid	Na_2SO_4, sodium sulfate

When there are only two common oxyacids of a given element, the one corresponding to lower oxidation state is given the *-ous* ending, and the other the *-ic* ending. If there are more than two oxyacids, of different oxidation states, the prefixes *hypo-* and *per-* may also be used. As indicated in the above example, the prefix *hypo-* indicates an oxidation state lower than that of an *-ous* acid; the prefix *per-*, an oxidation state higher than that of an *-ic* acid. For salts derived from oxyacids, the names are formed by replacing the ending *-ous* by *-ite* and *-ic* by *-ate*. Salts derived from polyprotic acids (e.g., H_3PO_4) are best named so as to indicate the number of hydrogen atoms left unneutralized. For example, NaH_2PO_4 is monosodium dihydrogen phosphate, and Na_2HPO_4 is disodium monohydrogen phosphate. Frequently, the prefix *mono-* is left off. For monohydrogen salts of diprotic acids, such as $NaHSO_4$, the presence of hydrogen may also be indicated by the prefix *bi-*. Thus, $NaHSO_4$ is sometimes called sodium bisulfate, though the name sodium hydrogen sulfate is preferred.

Complex cations, such as $Cr(H_2O)_6^{+3}$, are named by giving the number and name of the groups attached to the central atom followed by the name of the central atom, with its oxidation number indicated by Roman numerals in parentheses. Thus, $Cr(H_2O)_6^{+3}$ is hexaaquochromium (III). Complex anions, such as $PtCl_6^{--}$, are named by giving the number and name of attached groups followed by the name of the element with an *-ate* ending and its oxidation number in parentheses. Thus, $PtCl_6^{--}$ is hexachloroplatinate(IV). Other examples of complex ions are:

$CrCl_2(H_2O)_4^+$	Dichlorotetraaquochromium(III)
$CrCl_4(H_2O)_2^-$	Tetrachlorodiaquochromate(III)
$Ni(NH_3)_6^{++}$	Hexaamminenickel(II)
$Ni(CN)_4^{--}$	Tetracyanonickelate(II)

It should be pointed out that in many cases systematic nomenclature is not followed, but common names are used instead, e.g., water for dihydrogen oxide and ammonia for trihydrogen nitride. Often names are not used at all, and compounds are referred to simply by their formulas.

(A more extensive treatment of inorganic nomenclature can be found in Chapter 18 of *Inorganic Reactions and Structure* by E. S. Gould (Holt, Rinehart and Winston, Inc.).

Appendix 2   **Exponential Numbers**

MULTIPLICATION BY A POSITIVE POWER OF 10 corresponds to moving the decimal point to the right; multiplication by a negative power of 10 corresponds to moving the decimal point to the left.

1.23×10^4 is $12,300$

1.23×10^{-4} is 0.000123

Numbers expressed with powers of 10 cannot be added or subtracted directly unless the powers of 10 are the same.

$$1.23 \times 10^4 + 1.23 \times 10^5 = 1.23 \times 10^4 + 12.3 \times 10^4$$

$$= 13.5 \times 10^4$$

$$1.23 \times 10^{-4} - 1.23 \times 10^{-5} = 1.23 \times 10^{-4} - 0.123 \times 10^{-4}$$

$$= 1.11 \times 10^{-4}$$

When powers of 10 are multiplied, exponents are added; when divided, exponents are subtracted.

$$(1.23 \times 10^4) \times (1.23 \times 10^5) = (1.23 \times 1.23) \times (10^4 \times 10^5)$$

$$= 1.51 \times 10^9$$

$$\frac{1.23 \times 10^{-4}}{1.23 \times 10^{-5}} = \frac{1.23}{1.23} \times \frac{10^{-4}}{10^{-5}} = 1.00 \times 10$$

In taking square roots of powers of 10, the exponent is divided by 2; in taking cube roots, by 3.

Square root of 9×10^4 is 3×10^2

Cube root of 8×10^{-12} is 2×10^{-4}

Appendix 3   ***Mathematical Operations***

3.1   PROPORTIONALITY

If one property A of a substance is related to, or depends on, another property B, then A is said to be proportional to B. The simplest kind of proportionality is the *direct proportionality*, in which any change in B produces an equal percentage change in A. (An example of a direct proportionality is the relation observed between mass and volume. Since the mass of a substance depends on the volume of it taken, we say that mass is directly proportional to volume.) Mathematically, direct proportionality is indicated as follows:

$$A \propto B$$

$$A = kB$$

The symbol $\propto$ is read "is directly proportional to" and is called a proportionality sign. In the second expression, the proportionality sign has been replaced by an equals sign and the proportionality constant k. The constant k represents the ratio of A to B and indicates that the ratio A/B is a constant. Thus, if B is doubled, A must also be doubled in order to maintain k

constant; if B is halved, A is halved, etc. For the direct proportionality between mass m and volume V, we can write

$$m \propto V$$
$$m = kV$$

where the proportionality constant k is the density (m/V) of the substance. Since the density of a substance does not depend on how much mass or volume of that substance we take, we can also write

$$\frac{m_1}{V_1} = \frac{m_2}{V_2} = \frac{m_3}{V_3}$$

where the subscripts 1, 2, and 3 refer to different samples of the same substance.

A more complicated proportionality is the *inverse proportionality* such as that found between volume and pressure of a gas. It is observed that doubling the pressure on a gas halves its volume. Mathematically, this inverse proportionality is expressed in any of the following ways:

$$V \propto \frac{1}{P} \quad \text{or} \quad V \propto P^{-1}$$
$$V = \frac{k}{P} \quad \text{or} \quad PV = k$$
$$P_1 V_1 = P_2 V_2 = P_3 V_3$$

The proportionality constant k has a fixed value so long as only P and V change. Its value does depend on the mass of the gas sample and its temperature. In other words, the inverse proportionality between P and V holds only for constant temperature and mass of sample.

In addition to direct and inverse proportionality, other proportionalities are possible. For example, the distance d traveled by a freely falling object is proportional to the square of the time of fall t.

$$d = kt^2$$

For a time twice as long, the object travels four times as far. Another example of a proportionality is the observation that the rate of diffusion R of a gas is inversely proportional to the square root of its molecular weight M. This can be written in several ways:

$$R = \frac{k}{\sqrt{M}}$$
$$R = \frac{k}{M^{1/2}}$$
$$R = kM^{-1/2}$$

3.2   GRAPHS

Often the best way to represent the dependence between two properties is to plot a graph in which the values of one property are shown along one axis, and values of the other property, along an axis perpendicular to the first. As shown in Fig. 1, each point represents the result of an observation. Distance along the horizontal axis (abscissa) is the value of B; distance along the vertical axis (ordinate) is the corresponding value of A. By convention, the abscissa represents the property that is independently varied (i.e., chosen at random), while the ordinate represents the dependent property that is observed as a result. For example, in Fig. 1, B might represent various values of the pressure placed on a gas, and A the values of the volume observed as a result.

The relation shown in Fig. 1 is an inverse proportionality, and the points lie on a curve whose equation is $A = k/B$. For a direct proportionality $(A = kB)$, the points would fall on a straight line, as shown in Fig. 2. The straight line goes through the origin (the point for which both A and B are zero), and its slope is determined by the numerical value of k. If, as in Fig. 3, the straight line does not pass through the origin, its equation is $A = kB + c$. The relation between A and B is still a linear one, but it is not a direct proportionality. The value of c is constant and is equal to the value of A when B is zero. Figure 3 is related to Fig. 2 by a

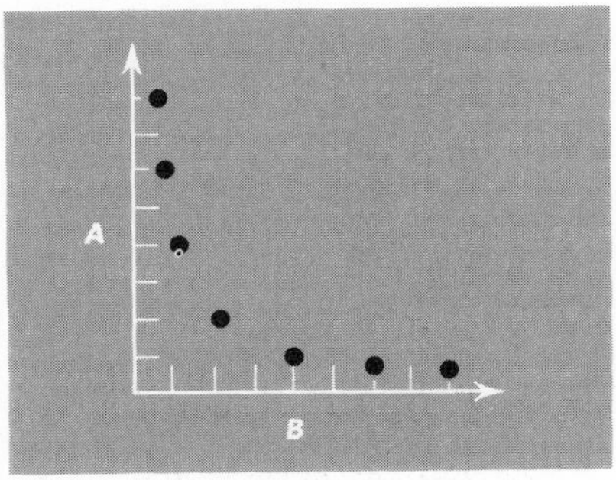

Fig. 1   *Graph of* **A** *vs.* **B.**

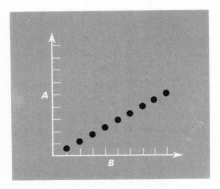

Fig. 2   *Graph of a direct proportionality.*

Table 1   Logarithms

	0.0	**0.1**	**0.2**	**0.3**	**0.4**	**0.5**	**0.6**	**0.7**	**0.8**	**0.9**
1	000	041	079	114	146	176	204	230	255	279
2	301	322	342	362	380	398	415	431	447	462
3	477	491	505	519	532	544	556	568	580	591
4	602	613	623	634	644	653	663	672	681	690
5	699	708	716	724	732	740	748	756	763	771
6	778	785	792	799	806	813	820	826	833	839
7	845	851	857	863	869	875	881	887	892	898
8	903	909	914	919	924	929	935	940	945	949
9	954	959	964	969	973	978	982	987	991	996

simple shift of origin. For gases, the linear relation between volume and centigrade temperature (Fig. 6.7) can be converted to a direct proportionality by changing the origin from $0°C.$ to $-273°C.$

3.3   LOGARITHMS

The logarithm of a number is the power to which the number 10 must be raised to equal that number. Thus, the log of 10,000 (or 10^4) is 4 and that of 0.01 (or 10^{-2}) is -2. Most numbers are not integer powers of 10, and therefore their logarithms are not immediately obvious. For such numbers, logs may be determined by use of log tables. A simple log table is given in Table 1.

To get the logarithm of the number 5.7, look for 5 in the first vertical column and then move across to the column headed by 0.7. The log of 5.7 is 0.756. To get the logarithm of any number not lying between 1.0 and 10, first write the number in exponential form (Appendix 2), so that it consists of a number between 1.0 and 10 multiplied by a power of 10. Thus, 570 becomes 5.7×10^2. Because the logarithm of a product $a \times b$ is the log of a plus the log of b, we can write

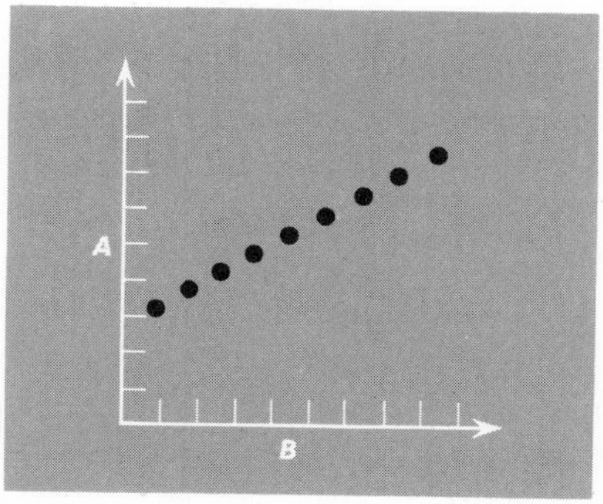

Fig. 3   Graph of $A = kB + c.$

$$\log (5.7 \times 10^2) = \log 5.7 + \log (10^2)$$
$$= 0.756 + 2$$
$$= 2.756$$

The principal use of logarithms in this text is in connection with pH, defined as the negative of the logarithm of the hydrogen-ion concentration. For a hydrogen-ion concentration of 0.00036 M, the pH is found as follows:

$$\log (0.00036) = \log (3.6 \times 10^{-4})$$
$$= \log 3.6 + \log (10^{-4})$$
$$= 0.556 - 4$$
$$= -3.444$$

$$pH = +3.444$$

Sometimes, the reverse procedure is required. For example, if a solution has a pH of 8.50, its hydrogen-ion concentration can be found as follows:

$$pH = 8.50$$
$$\log [H^+] = -8.50 = 0.50 - 9$$
$$[H^+] = 3.2 \times 10^{-9}$$

The number 3.2 is the antilog of 0.50 (the number whose log is 0.50). Antilogs are obtained by using Table 1 in reverse, i.e., by looking up the logarithm in the body of the table and then finding the number which corresponds to it.

3.4   QUADRATIC EQUATIONS

A quadratic equation is an algebraic equation in which a variable is raised to the second power but no higher and which can be written in the form

$$ax^2 + bx + c = 0$$

The solution of such an equation is

$$x = \frac{-b \pm \sqrt{b^2 - 4ac}}{2a}$$

where the $\pm$ sign indicates that there are two roots. Thus, the equation obtained in Example 2 of Sec. 17.2

$$1.8 \times 10^{-5} = \frac{(1.00 - y)(1.00 - y)}{y}$$

when rewritten gives

$$y^2 + (-2.00 - 1.8 \times 10^{-5})y + 1.00 = 0$$

for which the roots are

$$y = \frac{-(-2.000018) \pm \sqrt{(2.000018)^2 - (4)(1)(1.00)}}{(2)(1)}$$

$$= +1.004 \text{ or } 0.996$$

The first root ($y = 1.004$) is inadmissible from the nature of the problem (y cannot be greater than 1.00, which represents all the acid present). The second root ($y = 0.996$) must be the correct one. It might be noted that the usual rules for carrying through significant figures do not apply when we operate with the quadratic formula.

3.5   PROBLEM SOLVING

In solving problems, the obvious first step is to read the question carefully and decide what the question calls for. Let us take the following problem as a specific example: "A tank contains (*a*) a cube of iron 3.00 cm. on edge of density 7.86 g. per cc., (*b*) an aluminum sheet 0.500 cm. thick with an area of 96.0 sq. cm. and density of 2.70 g. per cc., and (*c*) 0.605 liter of water of density 0.998 g. per cc. What is the average density of matter in the tank?" The question calls for the average density, which is equal to the total mass divided by the total volume. The problem then is one of calculating these two quantities. In the calculation many find it helpful as a safeguard against errors to write down the dimensions (units) of each quantity.

$$\text{Density} \left(\frac{\text{g.}}{\text{cc.}}\right) = \frac{\text{total mass (g.)}}{\text{total volume (cc.)}}$$

Total mass (g.) = mass of iron (g.) + mass of aluminum (g.)

$$+ \text{ mass of water (g.)}$$

Mass of component (g.) = its volume (cc.) × its density $\left(\frac{\text{g.}}{\text{cc.}}\right)$

Total volume (cc.) = volume of iron (cc.)

$$+ \text{ volume of aluminum (cc.)} + \text{ volume of water (cc.)}$$

Volume of iron (cc.) = $(3.00 \text{ cm.})^3 = 27.0$ cc.

Volume of aluminum (cc.) = 0.500 cm. × 96.0 cm.² = 48.0 cc.

Volume of water (cc.) = 0.605 liter × 1,000 $\frac{\text{cc.}}{\text{liter}}$ = 605 cc.

Total volume (cc.) = 27.0 cc. + 48.0 cc. + 605 cc. = 680 cc.

Mass of iron (g.) = 27.0 c̶c̶. × 7.86 $\frac{\text{g.}}{\text{c̶c̶.}}$ = 212 g.

Mass of aluminum (g.) = 48.0 c̶c̶. × 2.70 $\frac{\text{g.}}{\text{c̶c̶.}}$ = 130 g.

Mass of water (g.) = 605 c̶c̶. × 0.998 $\frac{\text{g.}}{\text{c̶c̶.}}$ = 604 g.

Total mass (g.) = 212 g. + 130 g. + 604 g. = 946 g.

Average density $\left(\frac{\text{g.}}{\text{cc.}}\right)$ = $\dfrac{946 \text{ g.}}{680 \text{ cc.}}$ = 1.39 $\frac{\text{g.}}{\text{cc.}}$

Appendix 4   *Definitions from Physics*

4.1   VELOCITY AND ACCELERATION

When an object changes its position, it is said to undergo a *displacement*. The rate at which displacement changes with time is called the *velocity* and has the dimensions of distance divided by time (e.g., miles per hour, centimeters per second). *Acceleration* is the rate at which velocity changes with time and has the dimensions of velocity divided by time (e.g., centimeters per second per second, or cm per sec.^{2}).

4.2   FORCE AND MASS

Force can be thought of as a push or pull on an object which tends to change its motion, to speed it up or slow it down or to cause it to deviate from its path. Mass is a quantitative measure of the inertia of an object to having its motion changed. Thus, mass determines how difficult it is to accelerate an object. Quantitatively, force and mass are related by the equation

$$F = ma$$

where F is the force which produces acceleration a in mass m. If m is in grams and a is in centimeters per second per second, then F is in gram-centimeters per second per second, or dynes. Weight is an expression of force and arises because every object has mass and is being accelerated by gravity. Pounds weight is therefore a measure of force.

4.3 MOMENTUM AND IMPULSE

In dealing with collision problems it is useful to have terms for describing the combined effect of mass and velocity and its change with time. *Mass times velocity*, mv, is called the *momentum* and determines the length of time required to bring a moving body to rest when decelerated by a constant force. Thus, for a particle of momentum mv to be stopped by a constant force F, the time required t is mv/F.

The *impulse* is defined for the case of a constant force as Ft, where t is the time during which the force F acts. Thus, for the stopping of a particle originally of momentum mv by force F in time t, the impulse is just

$$Ft = F\frac{mv}{F} = mv$$

This is true if the particle comes to a complete rest. If, however, the particle bounces back, as it would on collision with a rigid wall, the particle is reflected from the wall with momentum $-mv$ (the minus sign indicating that the velocity is now in the opposite direction). The total impulse, counting the time for deceleration to zero and acceleration to $-mv$, is twice what it was before, or $2mv$.

In considering the pressure exerted by a gas, impulse comes in as follows. The pressure, or force per unit area, is the rate of collision per unit area times the effect of each collision.

$$\text{Pressure} = \frac{\text{force}}{\text{area}} = \frac{\text{number of collisions}}{(\text{time})(\text{area})} \times \text{?}$$

$$\text{?} = \frac{(\text{force})(\text{time})}{\text{number of collisions}} = \text{impulse per collision}$$

4.4 WORK AND ENERGY

When a force F operates on (e.g., pushes) an object through a distance d, work W is done.

$$W = Fd$$

If force is expressed in dynes (gram-centimeters per second per second) and distance in centimeters, then work has the dimensions dyne-centimeters (gm.-cm.^{2} per sec.^{2}), or ergs. One erg is thus the work done in moving one gram through one centimeter so as to increase its velocity by one centimeter per second all in one second. (For reference, 1 erg is approximately the work a fly does in one push-up.)

Energy is the ability to do work, and the dimensions of energy are the same as those of work. Kinetic energy is the energy a body possesses because of its motion and mass. It is equal to one-half the mass times the square of its velocity. Potential energy is the energy a body possesses because of its position or arrangement with respect to other bodies. For example, the potential energy of a rock depends on its distance from the earth. As the rock falls toward the earth, its kinetic energy increases, and its potential energy decreases.

4.5   ELECTRIC CHARGE AND ELECTRIC FIELD

Electric charge is a property assigned to objects to account for certain observed attractions or repulsions which cannot be explained in terms of gravitational attraction between masses. Electric charge can be of two types, positive and negative. Objects which have the same type of electric charge repel each other; objects with opposite charges attract each other. A unit of charge can be defined as the quantity of electric charge which at a distance of one centimeter from another identical charge produces a repulsive force of one dyne in a vacuum. This unit of charge is called the electrostatic unit (e.s.u.). An electron has a negative charge of 4.80×10^{-10} e.s.u. The practical unit of electric charge is the coulomb, which is almost exactly 3×10^9 e.s.u. In coulombs, the charge of an electron is 1.60×10^{-19} coulomb.

An electric field is said to exist at a point if a force of electrical origin is exerted on any charged body placed at that point. The intensity of an electric field is defined as the magnitude of the electric force exerted on a unit charge. Any electrically charged body placed in an electric field moves unless otherwise constrained. The direction of a field is usually defined as the direction in which a positive charge would move.

4.6   VOLTAGE AND CAPACITY

An electric condenser is a device for storing electric charge. In its simplest form a condenser consists of two parallel, electrically conducting plates separated by some distance. The condenser can be charged by making one plate positive and the other plate negative. In order to transfer a unit positive charge from the negative plate to the positive plate, work must be done against the electric field which exists between the charged plates. Therefore, the potential energy of the unit charge is increased in the process. In other words, there is a change in potential energy in going from one plate to the other. This difference in potential energy for a unit charge moved from one plate to the other is called the potential difference, or the voltage, of the condenser. Voltage, or potential difference, is not restricted to condensers but may exist between any two points so long as work must be done in transferring an electric charge from one point to the other. The potential difference between two points is said to be one volt if it requires 10^7 ergs to move one coulomb of charge from one point to the other. To move an electron through a potential difference of one volt requires an amount of energy, called the electron volt, equal to 1.6×10^{-12} erg.

Capacity is the term used to describe quantitatively the amount of charge that can be stored on a condenser. It is equal to the amount of charge that can be stored on the plates when the voltage difference between the plates is one volt. In general, the amount of charge a condenser can hold is directly proportional to the voltage; the capacity is simply the proportionality constant.

$$Q = CV$$

If Q, the charge, is one coulomb and if V, the voltage, is one volt, then C, the capacity, is one farad. The capacity of a condenser depends on its design (area of the plates, distance between them) and on the nature of the material between the plates. For a parallel-plate condenser, the capacity is given approximately by the following equation:

$$C = \frac{KA}{4\pi d}$$

A is the area of the plates, d is the distance between the plates, and K is the dielectric constant of the material between the plates. For a vacuum, the dielectric constant K is exactly equal to 1; for all other substances, K is greater than 1. Some typical dielectric constants are: 1.00059 for air at STP, 1.00026 for hydrogen gas at STP, 1.0046 for HCl gas at STP, 80 for liquid water at 20°C., 28.4 for ethyl alcohol at 0°C., 2 for petroleum, 4 for solid sulfur.

4.7   ELECTRIC CURRENT

A collection of moving charges is called an electric current. The unit of current is the ampere, which corresponds to a flow of one coulomb of charge past a point in one second. Since current specifies the rate at which charge is transferred, the product of current multiplied by time gives the total amount of charge transferred.

$$Q = It$$

If the current I is in amperes (coulombs per second) and the time t is in seconds, the charge Q is in coulombs.

The current that a wire carries is directly proportional to the voltage difference between the ends of the wire. The proportionality constant is called the conductance of the wire and is equal to the reciprocal of the resistance of the wire.

$$I = \frac{1}{R} V \qquad \text{or} \qquad V = IR$$

If V is the potential difference in volts and I is the current in amperes, R is the resistance in ohms.

There are two important kinds of current, direct and alternating. Direct current (d.c.) implies that the charge is constantly moving in the same direction along the wire. Alternating current (a.c.) implies that the current reverses its direction at regular intervals of time. The usual house current is 60-cycle alternating current, i.e., it goes through 60 complete back-and-forth oscillations per second.

Appendix 5   *Units*

kilo- means one thousand
centi- means one-hundredth
milli- means one-thousandth
micro- means one-millionth

1 kilometer (km.) = 1,000 meters = 0.621 mile
1 meter (m.) = 100 centimeters = 39.4 inches
1 centimeter (cm.) = 10 millimeters (mm.) = 0.394 inch

1 kilogram (kg.) = 1,000 grams = 2.20 pounds
1 gram (g.) = 1,000 milligrams (mg.) = 0.0353 ounce

1 liter (l.) = 1,000 milliliters = 1.06 quarts
1 milliliter (ml.) = 1.000027 cubic centimeters (cc.)

1 atomic mass unit (a.m.u.) = 1.66×10^{-24} g.
1 angstrom (A.) = 1×10^{-8} cm.
1 faraday = 96,500 coulombs
1 electron volt (e.v.) = 1.60×10^{-12} erg = 23.07 kcal./mole
1 erg = 2.39×10^{-11} kilocalorie
Avogadro number = 6.0235×10^{23}

Appendix 6   *Vapor Pressure of Water*

Temp., °C.	Pressure, mm. Hg	Temp., °C.	Pressure, mm. Hg
0	4.6	23	21.1
1	4.9	24	22.4
2	5.3	25	23.8
3	5.7	26	25.2
4	6.1	27	26.7
5	6.5	28	28.3
6	7.0	29	30.0
7	7.5	30	31.8
8	8.0	35	42.2
9	8.6	40	55.3
10	9.2	45	71.9
11	9.8	50	92.5
12	10.5	55	118.0
13	11.2	60	149.4
14	12.0	65	187.5
15	12.8	70	233.7
16	13.6	75	289.1
17	14.5	80	355.1
18	15.5	85	433.6
19	16.5	90	525.8
20	17.5	95	633.9
21	18.7	100	760.0
22	19.8	105	906.1

Appendix 7   **Oxidation Potentials**

Half-reaction	Voltage*
$Li(s) \rightleftharpoons Li^+ + e^-$	$+3.05$
$K(s) \rightleftharpoons K^+ + e^-$	$+2.93$
$Rb(s) \rightleftharpoons Rb^+ + e^-$	$+2.93$
$Cs(s) \rightleftharpoons Cs^+ + e^-$	$+2.92$
$Ra(s) \rightleftharpoons Ra^{++} + 2e^-$	$+2.92$
$Ba(s) \rightleftharpoons Ba^{++} + 2e^-$	$+2.90$
$Sr(s) \rightleftharpoons Sr^{++} + 2e^-$	$+2.89$
$Ca(s) \rightleftharpoons Ca^{++} + 2e^-$	$+2.87$
$Na(s) \rightleftharpoons Na^+ + e^-$	$+2.71$
$Mg(s) \rightleftharpoons Mg^{++} + 2e^-$	$+2.37$
$H^- \rightleftharpoons \frac{1}{2}H_2(g) + e^-$	$+2.25$
$Al(s) \rightleftharpoons Al^{+3} + 3e^-$	$+1.66$
$Mn(s) \rightleftharpoons Mn^{++} + 2e^-$	$+1.18$
$Zn(s) \rightleftharpoons Zn^{++} + 2e^-$	$+0.76$
$Cr(s) \rightleftharpoons Cr^{+3} + 3e^-$	$+0.74$
$Fe(s) \rightleftharpoons Fe^{++} + 2e^-$	$+0.44$
$Cr^{++} \rightleftharpoons Cr^{+3} + e^-$	$+0.41$
$Co(s) \rightleftharpoons Co^{++} + 2e^-$	$+0.28$
$H_2O + H_3PO_3 \rightleftharpoons H_3PO_4 + 2H^+ + 2e^-$	$+0.28$
$Ni(s) \rightleftharpoons Ni^{++} + 2e^-$	$+0.25$
$Sn(s) \rightleftharpoons Sn^{++} + 2e^-$	$+0.14$

* After W. M. Latimer, *Oxidation Potentials*, 2d ed., Prentice-Hall, Inc., Englewood Cliffs, New Jersey, 1952.

Half-reaction	Voltage*
$Pb(s) \rightleftharpoons Pb^{++} + 2e^-$	+0.13
$H_2(g) \rightleftharpoons 2H^+ + 2e^-$	0.00
$H_2O + H_2SO_3 \rightleftharpoons HSO_4^- + 3H^+ + 2e^-$	−0.11
$H_2S(g) \rightleftharpoons S(s) + 2H^+ + 2e^-$	−0.14
$Sn^{++} \rightleftharpoons Sn^{+4} + 2e^-$	−0.15
$Cu^+ \rightleftharpoons Cu^{++} + e^-$	−0.15
$Cu(s) \rightleftharpoons Cu^{++} + 2e^-$	−0.34
$Cu(s) \rightleftharpoons Cu^+ + e^-$	−0.52
$2I^- \rightleftharpoons I_2 + 2e^-$	−0.54
$2H_2O + HAsO_2 \rightleftharpoons H_3AsO_4 + 2H^+ + 2e^-$	−0.56
$H_2O_2 \rightleftharpoons O_2(g) + 2H^+ + 2e^-$	−0.68
$Fe^{++} \rightleftharpoons Fe^{+3} + e^-$	−0.77
$2Hg(l) \rightleftharpoons Hg_2^{++} + 2e^-$	−0.79
$H_2O + NO_2(g) \rightleftharpoons NO_3^- + 2H^+ + e^-$	−0.79
$Ag(s) \rightleftharpoons Ag^+ + e^-$	−0.80
$Hg(l) \rightleftharpoons Hg^{++} + 2e^-$	−0.85
$2H_2O + NO(g) \rightleftharpoons NO_3^- + 4H^+ + 3e^-$	−0.96
$2Br^- \rightleftharpoons Br_2 + 2e^-$	−1.09
$2H_2O \rightleftharpoons O_2(g) + 4H^+ + 4e^-$	−1.23
$2H_2O + Mn^{++} \rightleftharpoons MnO_2(s) + 4H^+ + 2e^-$	−1.23
$7H_2O + 2Cr^{+3} \rightleftharpoons Cr_2O_7^{--} + 14H^+ + 6e^-$	−1.33
$2Cl^- \rightleftharpoons Cl_2(g) + 2e^-$	−1.36
$4H_2O + Mn^{++} \rightleftharpoons MnO_4^- + 8H^+ + 5e^-$	−1.51
$2H_2O \rightleftharpoons H_2O_2 + 2H^+ + 2e^-$	−1.77
$Co^{++} \rightleftharpoons Co^{+3} + e^-$	−1.84
$H_2O + O_2(g) \rightleftharpoons O_3(g) + 2H^+ + 2e^-$	−2.07
$2F^- \rightleftharpoons F_2(g) + 2e^-$	−2.87

Appendix 8   ***Equilibrium Constants***

Dissociation constants (first step only):

$CrOH^{++}$	5×10^{-11}	$H_2AsO_4^-$	5.6×10^{-8}
$CuOH^+$	1×10^{-8}	$HAsO_4^{--}$	3×10^{-13}
$ZnOH^+$	4×10^{-5}	H_2O	1.0×10^{-14}
H_3BO_3	6.0×10^{-10}	H_2S	1.1×10^{-7}
$CO_2 + H_2O$	4.2×10^{-7}	HS^-	1×10^{-14}
HCO_3^-	4.8×10^{-11}	H_2SO_3	1.3×10^{-2}
$HC_2H_3O_2$	1.8×10^{-5}	HSO_3^-	5.6×10^{-8}
HCN	4.0×10^{-10}	HSO_4^-	1.3×10^{-2}
NH_4OH	1.8×10^{-5}	H_2Se	1.9×10^{-4}
HNO_2	4.5×10^{-4}	H_2SeO_3	2.7×10^{-3}
H_3PO_3	1.6×10^{-2}	$HSeO_3^-$	2.5×10^{-7}
$H_2PO_3^-$	7×10^{-7}	H_2Te	2.3×10^{-3}
H_3PO_4	7.5×10^{-3}	HF	6.7×10^{-4}
$H_2PO_4^-$	6.2×10^{-8}	$HOCl$	3.2×10^{-8}
HPO_4^{--}	10^{-12}	$HClO_2$	1.1×10^{-2}
H_3AsO_4	2.5×10^{-4}		

Solubility products:

$Mg(OH)_2$	8.9×10^{-12}	NiS	3×10^{-21}
MgF_2	8×10^{-8}	PtS	8×10^{-73}
MgC_2O_4	8.6×10^{-5}	$Cu(OH)_2$	1.6×10^{-19}
$Ca(OH)_2$	1.3×10^{-6}	CuS	8×10^{-37}
CaF_2	1.7×10^{-10}	$AgCl$	1.7×10^{-10}

$CaCO_3$	4.7×10^{-9}	AgBr	5.0×10^{-13}
$CaSO_4$	2.4×10^{-5}	AgI	8.5×10^{-17}
CaC_2O_4	1.3×10^{-9}	AgCN	1.6×10^{-14}
$Sr(OH)_2$	3.2×10^{-4}	Ag_2S	5.5×10^{-51}
$SrSO_4$	7.6×10^{-7}	ZnS	1×10^{-22}
$SrCrO_4$	3.6×10^{-5}	CdS	1.0×10^{-28}
$Ba(OH)_2$	5.0×10^{-3}	Hg_2Cl_2	1.1×10^{-18}
$BaSO_4$	1.5×10^{-9}	Hg_2Br_2	1.3×10^{-22}
$BaCrO_4$	8.5×10^{-11}	Hg_2I_2	4.5×10^{-29}
$Cr(OH)_3$	6.7×10^{-31}	HgS	1.6×10^{-54}
$Mn(OH)_2$	2×10^{-13}	$Al(OH)_3$	5×10^{-33}
MnS	7×10^{-16}	SnS	1×10^{-26}
FeS	4×10^{-19}	$Pb(OH)_2$	4.2×10^{-15}
$Fe(OH)_3$	6×10^{-38}	$PbCl_2$	1.6×10^{-5}
CoS	5×10^{-22}	PbS	7×10^{-29}

Appendix 9   *References*

ADDITIONAL INFORMATION AND BACKGROUND MATERIAL for subjects discussed in this text can be found in the following books:

A Source Book in Chemistry, 1400–1900 by Leicester and Klickstein (McGraw-Hill) contains extracts from the original papers that describe major advances in chemical science. It is particularly useful for supplying historical background for some of our early chapters.

Nature of the Chemical Bond by L. Pauling (Cornell University Press), *Electronic Structure and Chemical Binding* by O. K. Rice (McGraw-Hill), *Valence* by C. A. Coulson (Oxford), and *The Structure of Matter* by Rice and Teller (Wiley) contain extensive discussion of the problems of chemical binding.

A good treatment of states of matter, chemical kinetics, and chemical equilibrium is found in *Physical Chemistry* by W. J. Moore (Prentice-Hall).

Background material for much of Part I can be got from *Inorganic Reactions and Structure* by E. S. Gould (Holt). This latter book also contains selected descriptive material that can be used to supplement Part II.

More extended treatment of descriptive chemistry is found in *Inorganic Chemistry* by Kleinberg, Argersinger, and Griswold (Heath), *Reference Book of Inorganic Chemistry* by Latimer and Hildebrand (Macmillan),

Inorganic Chemistry by T. Moeller (Wiley), *Oxidation Potentials* by W. M. Latimer (Prentice-Hall), and *Structural Inorganic Chemistry* by A. F. Wells (Oxford).

Excellent discussions of organic chemistry are given in *Organic Chemistry* by Fieser and Fieser (Reinhold) and *Principles of Organic Chemistry* by Cram and Hammond (McGraw-Hill).

Radiochemistry is well presented in *Nuclear and Radiochemistry* by Friedlander and Kennedy (Wiley).

Index